Speech Correction

Speech Correction

Principles and Methods

THIRD EDITION

Charles Van Riper

Director of the Speech Clinic
Western Michigan College
of Education

1954

NEW YORK   PRENTICE-HALL, INC.

*This book is dedicated to my wife
who refuses to allow her name
to appear as co-author*

Preface to the Third Edition

The revision of a book always presents several dangers. First of all, the author must be able to be self-critical enough to discover the faults of a former edition and ruthless enough to do the necessary surgery.

Secondly, the author must try to discern the developing trends in his field and to provide new material to satisfy them. Finally, he must be careful not to throw out the baby with the bathwater, but to preserve and retain those parts that had proved valuable. How well these three criteria have been fulfilled only the reader can judge.

The book, as now constituted, has as its basic purpose providing the essential information concerning the nature, causes, and treatment of the various speech disorders and defects. It is not aimed at any one group of prospective readers. It does not confine itself to supplying information for the prospective speech therapist alone, or for the elementary teacher, or for the graduate student. Its focus is upon the case, upon the child or adult who cannot speak normally enough to avoid penalty, emotional upset, or frustration. It tries to answer the questions: "What is wrong?" and "What should be done?"

Many portions of the second edition have been entirely re-written. New points of view and new techniques have been added. Research findings have been brought up to date. Illustrations from the practice of public school speech therapy will be found in greater abundance. It should be a much more useful book.

C. Van Riper

Contents

⊔⊓

7. ARTICULATION DISORDERS (*Cont.*)

8. VOICE DISORDERS

9. STUTTERING

Illustrations

LՈՈՈՈՈՈՈՈՈՈՈՈՈՈՈՈՈՈՈՈՈՈՈr

Speech Correction

1. Speech Defects as Handicaps

One of the most vivid characteristics of the American is his extreme concern for the unfortunate. No other culture has ever shown such a wealth of agencies, campaigns, foundations, and private charities focusing their effort and wealth in the attempt to aid the crippled in mind and body to rejoin society. One drive for funds follows another. All causes compete with each other, and all seem worthy. To list but a very few, we have the Red Cross, the National Society for Crippled Children and Adults, The March of Dimes, The Seeing Eye Foundation, the United Cerebral Palsy Association, The American Society for the Hard of Hearing. There are literally hundreds of others, most of them highly organized and well staffed.

Cultural anthropologists have regarded this altruism with more than academic interest. They point out that our culture is one that features the setting up of a constant series of material goals and possessions which are highly advertised. Prestige and status seem often to be based upon winning these possessions and positions in a highly competitive struggle. We fight for security and approval, but in the process we trample underfoot the security of others. Some psychologists have felt

1

that our need to help the handicapped is a product of the guilt-feelings we possess from this trampling. Others attribute our concern for the underprivileged to fear lest someday we too will be the losers in the battle for life. They claim that we tend to say to ourselves, "There, but for grace of God, go I," when we meet someone who has failed to find a place for himself in our world for reasons beyond his control. For this reason, we truly hunger to help those who have "never had a chance."

We Americans are also great joiners. We have innumerable clubs, societies, trade associations, recreational groups. We feel a strong need to belong. We feel uneasy when we are unable to become part of a group functioning near us. We find great security and strength from the mere fact of membership.

The person who is different—the deviant individual—is of course faced with great difficulties when he attempts to enter the normal groups, since much of their functioning depends upon communication. The speech defective cannot talk his way in; the crippled cannot join a ski club; the deafened find, even the usual church services of little satisfaction; the blind find many restrictions. Such handicapped individuals usually form groups of their own. Those who have lost their larynxes form a Lost Chord Club, and speak to each other belchingly. A group of paraplegic veterans have a wheel chair basketball team. Stutterers have a Demosthenator Organization. But, at best, these are poor substitutes. Those who are different want to belong to the same groups to which normal individuals belong. And so they seek and are given the opportunities for special education and rehabilitation that may help them to rejoin the culture as a whole. We help our unfortunate now. But this was not always the case.

History of the handicapped. No one can understand the problem of the handicapped except in terms of the penalties which their infirmity provokes. Every handicap has an emotional fraction of shame, fear, or frustration, the heritage of centuries of cruelty and neglect. Cultural history demonstrates that the stupid, the blind, the deaf, the crippled, and those who could not talk have been treated progressively as a nuisance, a disgrace, an object of mirth, a problem, and a challenge. These attitudes are still in evidence.

Rejection. Primitive society tolerated no weakness. Tribes struggled hard for survival, and those members who could not aid materially were quickly rejected. The leaders were killed by the younger men after the former had lost their teeth or their energies had abated. The inhabitants of ancient India cast their cripples into the Ganges; the Spartans hurled theirs from a precipice. The Aztecs regularly sacrificed deformed persons in times of famine or when one of their leaders died. The Melanesians had a simple solution for the problem of the handicapped; they buried them alive. Among the earlier Romans, twins were considered so abnormal that one of them was always put to death, and frequently both were killed. They left their malformed children on the highways or in the forests. If the children survived, they were often picked up by those who always prey upon the handicapped and were carried to the market place to be trained as beggars. They were not valuable enough to be slaves.

The Bible clearly reflects these early rejection attitudes. Remember Job? The prevailing belief in Old Testament times was that man's physical state was determined by his good or bad relationship with his deity. Disabilities were regarded as divine punishment for sin. A normal person could invoke similar punishment merely by associating with those who had thus incurred the wrath of God. Consequently, the blind and the crippled wailed with the lepers—outside the city wall.

During the Middle Ages the physically disabled were frequently considered to be possessed of evil spirits. They were confined to their own homes. They dared not walk to the market place lest they be stoned. Even in this century, elimination of the handicapped has been practiced. The Kaffir tribes in South Africa clubbed sickly or deformed children. The Nazis kept only the best of their civilian prisoners for slaves. The others died in the gas chamber, in the crematorium.

In this country we would hang the man who killed his crippled son. We have come far in our journey toward civilization, but perhaps not far enough. Rejection takes many other forms. Spirits, too, can be killed. This is what one handicapped person has to say:

We think the inhabitants of old Sparta cruel for putting to death the weak, those who would be unable to compete, or to contribute much to their society; but were they after all much more inhuman than we, who nurse the weakling, keep it alive, yet as much as possible keep it from normal persons, especially the children, for fear its contact will contaminate them; then throw it out to compete with normal adults? [1]

How many of those reading this book would unhesitatingly accept an invitation to a dance if it were tendered by a hunchback?

Humor. It did not take the promoters long to discover that the handicapped provided a rewarding source of humor. One history of the subject states that before 1000 B.C. the fool or buffoon became a necessary part of feast making and "won the laughter of the guests by his idiocy or his deformity." In Homer's *Odyssey* comic relief from tragedy was illustrated by the vain efforts of the one-eyed Polyphemus to pursue his tormentors after they had blinded him. For a thousand years thereafter every court had its crippled buffoons, its dwarf jesters, its stuttering fools. Attila the Hun held banquets at which "a Moorish and Scythian buffoon successively excited the mirth of the rude spectators by their deformed figures, ridiculous dress, antic gestures, and absurd speech." Cages along the Appian Way held various grotesque human disabilities including "Balbus Blaesus" the stutterer, who would attempt to talk when a coin was flung through the bars. In Shakespeare's *Timon of Athens* Caphis says, "Here comes the fool; let's ha' some sport with 'im." Often this sport consisted of physical abuse or exposure of the twisted limb. These handicapped fools

---

[1] McKnight, R. V., "A Self-analysis of a Case of Reading, Writing, and Speaking Disability," *Archives of Speech,* 1936, Volume 1, page 43.

accepted and expected ridicule. At least it provided a means of
survival, a livelihood, and it represented an advance in civilized
living.

Gradually, the use of the handicapped to provoke mirth became less popular in continental Europe, and the more enter-
prising had to migrate to less culturally advanced areas to make
a living. At one time Peter the Great had so many fools that
he found it necessary to classify them for different occasions.
In this country today we have a much higher regard for the
handicapped than Cortez found when he conquered Mexico
and discovered deformed creatures of all kinds at the Court of
Montezuma. Now you may find them used to provoke laughter
only in the circus side shows, in the movies, on the radio, and
in every schoolyard.

Pity. Religion is doubtless responsible for the development
of true pity as a cultural reaction to the handicapped. James
Joyce says that pity is the feeling which arrests the mind in the
presence of whatsoever is grave and constant in human suffering and unites it with the human sufferer. It was this spontaneous feeling that prompted religious leaders to give the
handicapped shelter and protection. Before 200 B.C. Asoka, a
Buddhist, created a ministry for the care of unfortunates and
appointed officers to supervise charitable works. Confucius said,
"With whom should I associate but with suffering men?" Jesus
preached compassion for all the disabled and made all men their
brothers' keepers. In the seventh century after Jesus' death the
Mohammedan religion proposed a society free from cruelty and
social oppression, and insisted on kindliness and consideration
for all men. A few hundred years later St. Francis of Assisi
devoted his life to the care of the sick and the disabled. Following this, the "Mad Priest of Kent," John Ball, was so aroused
by the plight of the crippled and needy left in the wake of the
Black Death that he pled publicly for their cause, often at the
risk of his own life. With the rise of the middle class, true pity
for the handicapped became much more commonplace. The
oppression which the merchants and serfs had suffered left them

more sympathetic to others who were ill used. The doctrine of the equality of man did much for the handicapped as well as for the economically downtrodden.

However, many crimes have been committed in the name of charity. The halt and the blind began to acquire commercial value as beggars. Legs and backs of little children were broken and twisted by their exploiters. Soon the commercialization of pity became so universal that it became a community nuisance. Alms became a conventional gesture to buy relief from the piteous whining that dominated every public place. True pity was lost in revulsion. Recognizing this unhappy trend, Hyperius of Ypres advocated that beggars should be classified so that work could be provided according to their capacities. His own motives were humanitarian, but he cleverly won support for his cause by pointing out that other citizens "would be freed of clamor, of fear of outrage, of the sight of ugly bodies." His appeal was successful, and asylums and homes for the handicapped began to appear, if only to isolate the occupants so the public need not be reminded of their distress. Another motive which improved the position of the handicapped was the belief that one could purchase his way into heaven or out of hell by charity. The coin thrown to the cripple has been impelled by many motives. The longing for religious security, the heightening of one's own superiority by comparison with the unfortunate, the social prestige of philanthropy, and the desire to be freed from embarrassment have all contributed to the welfare of the handicapped. Pseudo pity has accomplished much, but true compassion would have ended the tragedy.

Use. As the problem of the handicapped kept irritating the consciences of civilized men everywhere, the true solution began to present itself. Somehow the person who is different must be given a specialized type of education to enable him to attain self-sufficiency or at least to contribute to the group welfare. If he cannot be ornamental, at least he can be useful. In the seventeenth century the Sisters of Charity, realizing that the handicapped needed work as well as food, endeavored to find manual jobs commensurate with their individual ability. By 1560 a college for the blind had been established at Bruges where the pupils were taught to play the organ and other musical instruments, to make brooms and baskets, and to manipulate wine presses and hand mills. The implication of this occupational therapy in decreasing the total handicap gradually found acceptance. Much of this first activity was mere busy work to facilitate contentment in their isolation. Then in 1832 a philanthropist in Munich founded the first comprehensive institution for the care and education of cripples. In this country, the Boston Industrial School for the Crippled and Deformed, the first true training school that recognized the handicapped person's need for usefulness, was founded as recently as 1893. Both World Wars have given tremendous impetus to the vocational and social rehabilitation of the handicapped, and the future is bright.

Because our cultural attitudes toward the handicapped have progressed from the cruel to the humane, we must not think that the older reactions have entirely vanished. Children and uneducated adults often react in the old, primitive ways. Every handicapped person has experienced degrees of rejection, mockery, and pity. The old attitudes are there to salt his wounds. They multiply his insecurities, decrease his courage, and destroy his hope. The defective in speech know them well.

Why should we do so much for our deviant and defective children? Some people feel that it is only the normal child who is neglected:

> Johnny Jones has lost a leg
> Fanny's deaf and dumb.
> Marie has epileptic fits;
> Tom's eyes are on the bum.
> Sadie stutters when she talks;
> Mabel has T.B.
> Morris is a splendid case
> Of imbecility.
> Gwendolin's a millionaire;
> Gerald is a fool;

So every one of these darned kids
Goes to a special school.
They've specially nice teachers,
And special things to wear,
And special things to play in,
And a special kind of air.
They've special lunches right in school,
While I—it makes me wild!
I haven't any specialties;
I'm just a normal child.[2]

If such a rhyme brings a wry grin to our faces, it should also remind us that such a condition was not always present and that it is still more rare than commonplace. Centuries of neglect and penalty have perpetrated an unpardonable waste of handicapped human energy. A civilization that does not accept its responsibility for helping the unfortunate scarcely merits the name.

Morally, we cannot deny the right of the handicapped child to his place in the scheme of civilized living. The philosopher and the priest, in every age and country, have generally recognized this moral obligation. Economically, we have wasted a great deal of man and brain power by failing to develop those abilities which the handicapped possess. In times of emergency, as during World War II, the halt and deaf and blind were rushed into service. Their records were admirable. Of all their desires, the desire to support themselves and thereby to free society from their burden has always been a vital one. It is to the everlasting credit of thousands of handicapped persons that, despite prejudice and penalty, they have conquered almost insurmountable obstacles in their struggle to attain self-sufficiency and self-respect.

Modern society needs no justification for removing a few of the obstacles which every handicapped person finds in his path. The illustrious names of those who have given great things to civilization despite their handicaps are proof enough of such a

---

[2] From the *School Board Journal*, quoted by Scheideman, N. V., *The Psychology of Exceptional Children*, Boston, Houghton Mifflin, 1931.

policy. Music? Gounod, Handel, Mozart were crippled; Mendelssohn had a speech defect; Beethoven was deaf; Templeton is blind. Literature? Byron, Poe, Scott, Balzac were physically handicapped; Milton and Homer were blind; Somerset Maugham stutters. Science? Steinmetz, Edison, Darwin are a few of the legion. Philosophy? Socrates, Spinoza, Erasmus, and Schopenhauer left a considerable legacy. If these giants could arise in spite of the penalties of society, the cause of the handicapped is the duty of every civilized human being.

Present treatment of the speech handicapped. We have sketched the treatment accorded the handicapped at some length because the speech-defective person is diagnosed immediately as belonging to that unfortunate group. The moment the cleft-palate child or stutterer speaks he joins his brethren, the crippled, the deaf, the spastic, the blind, and, perhaps, the fool. He is different. He possesses an abnormality. A little child hesitates in his speech; his parents diagnose him as a stammerer; he reacts to his hesitations as though they were revoltingly unpleasant; his playmates accept his evaluation, or his parents' evaluation, and reject, laugh at, or pity him; and so he joins the unhappy tribe of the million stammerers who exist in this country today.

It may seem strange to learn that the primitive attitudes of rejection, humor and pity, are still very common reactions to the perception of speech defects today. Listen to these:

They got me inside a circle of them and every time I tried to break out and go home, they pushed me back. "Make a speech. Make a speech." I tried to tell them I had to get my groceries home. My mother had to have them for supper, but the men would just laugh all the harder and push me back. They told me to say different things if I wanted to get out, things like "She sells sea shells" and dirty words. I was crying and I got mad and swore at them and then they let me go but I can hear them yet.

I asked the girl for a dance and had a hard time getting it out. She flushed, then blurted out, "Well, I'm not that hard up yet."

I can take almost anything but that pitying glance. It's sort of as if I have a cup in my hand every time I talk and people feel they ought to put some pennies in it. I can't explain it but when they look away or down at their feet, I feel like something unclean. I can't help it that my operation tore loose, and I talk through my nose, but I can't even explain it to them.

We no longer keep our "Balbus Blaesuses" in cages, but a current radio program features a "comedian" whose main humorous appeal is based upon his substitution of w for l and r. The song about "K-K-K-Katy" is still being sung although "Stuttering in the Starlight" and "You-you-you tell 'em that I-I-I stutter" have been forgotten. Cartoons and comic strips do not fail to exploit the impediments of speech.

Many of these primitive reactions to speech handicaps exist because of a lack of understanding. Abnormal speech has been attributed to everything from feeble-mindedness to a lack of will power. Few people know anything of the causes or development of the various speech disorders. Then, too, the general public is unaware of the great number of speech defectives in our population. All of us meet an occasional person with faulty speech, but few of us realize that there are more speech cripples than there are crippled, deaf, and blind combined. The report of the White House Conference (1931) on Special Education, still the most comprehensive survey of speech defects, cited an average incidence of 5 per cent (13).[3] One of the more intensive surveys of a city school system[4] showed over 10 per cent to have speech defects. At any rate, two or three million persons are handicapped in speech, and they deserve more understanding and better treatment than they have been receiving. Finally, few normally speaking individuals realize that communication is the lifeblood of modern existence and that a person who cannot communicate effectively is severely handicapped. In procuring an education, in winning a mate, in holding a job, effective speech is vital. Without it, the normal activities of a highly communicative society become very difficult. The

---

[3] Numbers in parentheses will refer to the sources listed at the end of the chapter.

[4] Mills, A., and Streit, H., "Report of a Speech Survey, Holyoke, Massachusetts," *Journal of Speech Disorders*, 1942, Volume 7, pages 161–169.

frustration and anxiety which result from a speech defect often build an additional emotional handicap which doubles the speech defective's burden. Only those normal speakers who have lived in close relationship to some speech cripple understand this. As society comes to understand the problem of the speech handicapped, the old attitudes will be replaced. Meanwhile, there is much work to be done.

The responsibility for speech correction. Some agency of society must accept the responsibility for seeing that these millions of speech-handicapped individuals receive the rehabilitation they so urgently need. In this country the medical profession, which in Europe treated or supervised the treatment of speech defects, has seemed uninterested in the problem. Parents do not have the information or the teaching ability that is required. Our public-school system is about the only organization large enough to do the job. It can employ trained teachers and it has the child during those years when speech correction can be most effective. It has already accepted responsibility for training other types of handicapped persons. It has the contact with the colleges and universities whose research and teacher-training facilities are so vital to adequate therapy. The basic philosophy of our public schools is education according to the student's need. The average speech defective is retarded one year in school because of his handicap, and the over-all educational expenditure is, because of the retardation, greater. In terms of dollars and cents alone, it would be economical to provide speech-correction services in the public schools. Many of the larger school systems have recognized this practical economy by hiring speech correctionists. Despite the great expense involved in educating the physically handicapped, the majority of them are receiving this help. The feeble-minded child, however, receives far more special education than does the speech handicapped. We hold no brief for decreasing educational expenditures for the physically handicapped. We only wish to point out that the future economic gain in turning the speech handicapped from economic misfits into productive, self-sufficient individuals far outweighs the trifling expense. We teach our children to read and write. Some day we shall be teaching our children to talk as well. The elementary school-teacher will be trained in the daily program, and speech-improvement classes will be a part of elementary speech correction. Special speech-correction departments in the teachers colleges and universities will organize programs of parent education and teacher training and provide clinics where adults may receive treatment. When that day comes, and it is fast approaching, the speech-handicapped child will no longer be laughed at, rejected, or pitied. He will be helped.

This discussion of the development of speech therapy should not allow us to be complacent. There are many children and adults with speech defects who are not receiving help. Their numbers far exceed the numbers of those who do. According to one survey more than 15,000 speech therapists are needed in the United States alone. The colleges and university training centers have never been able to meet the demand for public school speech correction teachers. Students hunting for a career in which they can be of service to their fellow man seldom hear about this new profession, or they hear about it too late in their college years.

Meanwhile the lisper, the cleft-palate child, the child who has never learned to speak, the boy with the hearing loss, and the girl with cerebral palsy find it hard to join the human race because they cannot speak its language. The old reactions of rejection, amusement and pity reveal themselves in every medium of communication. The movie comedian distorts his r's and drops his l's. The comic books portray P-P-Porky the St-st-stuttering P-P-P-Pig. On the radio we hear the honking of cleft-palate speech used to represent feeble-mindedness. The television clown affects an adenoidal voice for belly laughs and a man without a larynx is chosen as a contestant on a maudlin giveaway program.

One of our cleft-palate cases, a skilled accountant, applied for employment at eighty-six places before he got past the reception clerk. Another, a stutterer with a master's degree was fired from his job as cookee (scullery helper) in a lumber-camp when he had to take an oral message to the foreman. A girl with a severe lateral lisp and a college education found herself unemployable as a librarian, dime-store clerk, medical receptionist, waitress, and baby-sitter. She tried each in turn, then attempted to get a factory job. The employment manager turned her down as soon as he heard her talk, saying, "We don't hire women who drink."

The list of occupations open to the person severely handi-capped in speech is very restricted. Teaching is out. Law and medical schools usually exclude such applicants. Business re-quires efficient communication. One of our cases was fired from a night watchman's job because he "might not be able to call the police when needed." There are noticeable exceptions to these observations, of course. One of the best salesmen on the force of a big agricultural implement company was a severe stutterer, whose good nature and personality compensated for his speech infirmity. "They nnnnnnn---e-e-ever for-g-g-get me," he said, and he used a hundred jokes about stuttering to get acceptance through humor, even as did the professional fools of the Middle Ages. Many speech defectives battle their way to the top, fighting rejection, laughter and pity all the way, so that they can get the money, power or prestige to permit them to ignore the uncivilized penalties of our modern civilization. The person with a speech defect has a tough time in a society which insists on the satisfaction of so many desires and de-mands that the competition is ruthless.

The "need to belong to a group" is a need felt by every per-son with a speech defect and it is felt with an intensity that few normal speakers can fathom. The anxieties of parents, the re-jections and laughter of the child's playmates, the teacher's policies of excluding speech defective children from recitation, the savage social penalties of adolescents on the boy or girl who is different, the painful silence that interrupts the small talk of an adult group when someone stutters, the uneasy pity that spoils good fellowship, all these and many other reactions put an almost unbearable pressure on the speech defective who tries to belong. He who has a speech defect must have a good many other vivid assets if he is to find membership in most of the groups that comprise our society.

It is only recently that the crippled in speech have been able to hope. The special training which will permit them to contribute their share to the productiveness of our nation is now available somewhere near to them. It is true we need many more speech therapists and speech clinics and much more public information concerning speech defects, their prevention and relief. The student who reads this may or may not become a speech therapist, but he can help to spread his new knowledge, encourage the establishment of centers of speech therapy, and above all he can show the speech defectives whom he meets the path to rehabilitation.

References

1. Anderson, V. A., *Improving the Child's Speech*, New York, Oxford University Press, 1953.

In the first chapter the author describes the problem of the speech handicapped as an obligation of special education. Data on the needs of the speech handicapped and the services provided for them are given.

2. Doll, E. A., "Understanding the Handicapped Child," *Crippled Child*, 1950, Volume 28, pages 10–12.

T-F: The handicapped child needs more understanding and less technique.

T-F: The special teacher needs training in handling emotional problems.

Essay: What does the author mean by "the educated heart?"

3. Greenberg, H. A., "Problem Parents of Handicapped Children," *Journal of Exceptional Children*, 1950, Volume 17, pages 1–7, 23–24.

The effects of cultural and social changes upon the parents of a handicapped child when he joins the family are made clear as are the effects of parental maladjustment and anxiety.

4. Linck, L. J., "Mobilizing Our Nationwide Resources for Service

to the Handicapped," *Journal of Speech Disorders*, 1947, Volume 12, pages 11–16.

A plea for better public understanding and for more help for the handicapped.

5. McKibben, S., "The Spastic Situation," *Journal of Speech Disorders*, 1943, Volume 8, pages 147–153.

T-F: A cerebral palsied person can decrease his handicap by controlling his emotions.

T-F: Cerebral palsied children should not compete with normal children in the classroom.

Essay: What does the author mean by the "spastic situation?"

6. Meyerson, L. (editor), "The Social Psychology of Physical Disability," *Journal of Social Issues*, 1948, Volume 4.

This entire volume is devoted to the social and psychological problems of those with physical disability—their acceptance, personality distortions, rigidity, and chances for employment.

7. Morley, D., "The Speech Handicapped Adult," *Journal of Rehabilitation*, 1952, Volume 18, pages 16–18, 26–27.

A description of different types of speech defective individuals in terms of their prognosis and employment outlook.

8. *Physically Handicapped Children in New York City*, New York, Board of Education of the City of New York, 1941, pages 1–155.

The program for the education and rehabilitation of the various types of handicapped children in New York City is described in terms of organization, administration, and costs. The general philosophy underlying the provision of education especially suited to the needs of handicapped children is discussed.

9. Pintner, R., Eisenson, J., and Stanton, M., *The Psychology of the Physically Handicapped*, New York, Crofts, 1941.

The blind, deaf, crippled, and speech-defective child's problem is discussed in terms of the following factors: intelligence, educational achievement, personality and special abilities. Chapters on personality development and mental hygiene of the handicapped will be of interest to the speech correctionist.

10. Shortley, M. J., "Helping the Disabled to Help Themselves," *Journal of Exceptional Children*, November, 1944, pages 34–41.

A discussion of modern attitudes toward the handicapped with special emphasis on vocational placement.

11. Tinney, J. W., "The Minority Status of the Handicapped," *Journal of Exceptional Children*, 1953, Volume 20, pages 260–264.

T-F: Our society has preserved but limited the handicapped person.

T-F: We are spending too much on treating and not enough on preventing handicaps.

Essay: What benefits does society receive from helping the handicapped?

12. White, Helen C., *Social Criticism in Popular Religious Literature of the Sixteenth Century*, New York, Macmillan, 1944.

Medieval attitudes toward the handicapped are vividly described with many illustrations from the literature of the time. The beginnings of modern practices in the treatment of the unfortunate are clearly sketched.

13. *White House Conference on Child Health and Protection, Special Education,* Chapter on "The Child Defective in Speech," New York, D. Appleton-Century, 1931.

A report from questionnaires issued to cities with populations of over 10,000, showing incidence of speech defectives to range from 1.0 to 21.4 per cent, with an average from the totals of 5 per cent.

14. White House Conference Report, 1950, "Speech Disorders and Speech Correction," *Journal of Speech and Hearing Disorders,* 1952, Volume 17, pages 129–137.

T-F: There are 2,000,000 speech-defective children in the U.S.

T-F: Of all the handicapping conditions, speech disorders are among the most prevalent.

Essay: How well are these children being taken care of?

2. The Disorders of Speech

Perhaps you have wondered what goes on in the physician's mind as he listens to the patient's description of some physical distress. The training he has received compels him first to listen until he clearly understands what is called the "complaint." "Just what does this patient feel is unusual and unpleasantly different in his sense of well-being?" he is thinking. He is trained to withhold judgement until he is sure he understands what the patient feels is wrong. He wants to know a good deal about the history of your illness. He asks questions to probe the matter further until a certain set of symptoms emerges. He then makes certain tests, takes temperature and pulse, observes your general appearance, checks the white-cell count in a drop of blood and perhaps many other items.

While the complaint is an important beginning in the problem of diagnosis, few doctors will accept it as valid. They have an old professional saying: "The doctor who diagnoses himself has a fool for a physician." It is difficult for one who is sick to be objective enough about his ailment to examine it unemotionally. What the physician has to do is to evaluate all of his information through a process known as a _differential diagnosis_. Most diseases have a pattern of symptoms, but many diseases have several symptoms in common with each other. What the doctor has to do is first to rule out the impossible diseases which obviously do not fit the pattern of symptoms shown, then the improbable diseases, and finally he makes his decision in terms of the disease which best fits all the symptoms and test results. Only after such a differential diagnosis is he able to prescribe treatment and estimate a prognosis or outcome.

In speech therapy we face the same problems and must go through the same procedures. Here are a few of the complaints as stated in letters to a speech clinic:

Dear Sir: I am a country schoolteacher in a two-room school. In my room there is a little boy in the third grade with a kind of funny voice. I mean he doesn't talk like other children. He can't say some of the words right that he knows just as well as I do. I have tried to correct him on the word "scissors" which is hard for him but he just can't get it out right. Is this stammering or just baby talk and how can I cure him? Please send me some tongue exercises or something. He is a sweet little child and needs some help.

Here is another:

I want you should help me. My boy he dont talk right. He gets tangeled up in his nose and it sounds funny. When can I bring him.

And another:

I have a bad habit in talking that makes my talk so other people cant understand me although I know what I'm saying. They yell at me as if I'm deaf and dumb but I can hear good. I just can't talk good.

One more:

I have an impediment or something in my mouth. Sometimes I talk all right but not always. I open my mouth and the words won't come out right.

These examples should demonstrate not only the necessity for further investigation and analysis but also the need for information as to the common patterns of abnormal speech. In this chapter we present the symptom pictures of the various speech disorders. Once we know these we can hope to begin our differential diagnosis.

But first we must face another problem well known to the physician too: "Does this person actually have anything wrong with him?" There are thousands upon thousands of variations in normal speech. If there were not, we could never recognize our friends by their voices. Even the same person seldom says the same word twice in identical fashion. When is a speech difference a speech defect? How do we judge?

These questions are not academic. Misdiagnosis has caused untold misery. A mother who did not know that few children master their *str* and *spl* blends before the age of five, grew anxious about her three-year-old's mistakes on those sounds, and then she corrected him so frequently, made so many visits to elocution teachers, faith healers and physicians, and punished him so severely that finally the child stopped talking altogether and remained mute for three years. Another child with delayed speech was misdiagnosed as being deaf and feeble-minded. We found her at sixteen, using sign language, and unable to understand except when she lip-read, this despite the fact that her audiogram revealed normal hearing, and a performance test a normal IQ. Many a normal child has been turned into a severe stutterer by having the normal hesitations and repetitions of early speech labeled and penalized as stuttering until finally he came to accept the label and began to avoid speech or to struggle with his utterance. Many a child has been treated as a lisper when the *s* and *z* sounds were well within the limits tolerated by anyone except the hypercritical parent or teacher who committed the crime.

So let us define a speech defect.

Speech is defective when it deviates so far from the speech of other people that it calls attention to itself, interferes with communication or causes its possessor to be maladjusted.

We can condense this definition into three adjectives. Speech is defective when it is *conspicuous, unintelligible* or *unpleasant.* The first adjective refers to the fact that abnormal speech is different enough to be noted. It varies too far from the norm. A child of three who says "wabbit" for "rabbit" has no speech defect, but the adult of fifty who uses that pronunciation would have one because it would be a real deviation from the pronunciation of other adults. If you said *deze, doze* and *dem* for *these, those* and *them* in a hobo jungle, none of the other vagrants would notice. If you used the same sounds in a talk to a P.T.A. meeting a good many ears would prickle. Many of us force the airstream down too broad a tongue groove to produce the high-pitched *s* sound characteristic of our English speech. Because we do so does not necessarily mean that we have lateral lisps. Only when our *s* is so slushy and low in pitch that it calls attention to itself can we be said to have that type of speech defect.

How wide a variation is required before we should be concerned about a speech difference? Only the cultural norms can answer this question. Among the Pilagra Indians no attention is ever paid to baby-talk or peculiar speech until the child is at least seven years of age. Many Indian tribes do not even have a word for stuttering although many of their membership no doubt have hesitant speech. According to the famous anthropologist, Sapir, among the Nootka, repetitive and hesitant speech seems to be more common than fluent rhythmic speech. One would have to stutter badly indeed to have a speech defect in such a culture. In England the dropping of an *h* or the flatting of a vowel would cause instant social penalty in upper class society where the same behavior would be quite unnoticeable in Australia. Excessive assimilation nasality would not be noticed by a Tennessee mountaineer when the same voice quality in an Eastern girls' school would send its owner to the speech clinic. A speech defect, then, is one which is so different from the normal speech of the social group that it is highly conspicuous. The individual who refers a case to the speech therapist should evaluate its context accordingly.

The second part of the definition refers to intelligibility. When a speech difference interferes with communication it tends to be labeled as defective.

When you listen, not to what a stranger says, but to his peculiar voice or hesitations or distorted consonants, communication is broken. If his face suddenly jumps around as he struggles to utter an ordinary word, all communicative content is lost in amusement or amazement. Many stutterers habitually lower their eyes to escape the shock of observing the expression of incredulity and surprise on the faces of their auditors. Cleft-palate adults have been known to pretend to be deaf and dumb and to beg for a pencil so that their communication could be accomplished without interruption.

A recent study has shown that the intelligibility (the ability to utter words understandably) of speech is markedly reduced by the presence of articulation errors[1] and anyone who has ever listened to a severe articulation case would quite agree. Here is the phonetic transcription of the first few lines of Lincoln's Gettysburg Address as spoken by an eighteen-year-old boy with an IQ of 123:

> po koɪ æ tɛbə jiː ədo ɑu popadə bɔ po əpɔ dɪ kanəɪ
> ə nu netə. . . .

That communication is impaired when a person loses his voice (aphonia) is obvious. The person whose larynx has been removed is pretty helpless until he learns to swallow air and speak on the expelled burp. But even then, the monotone is difficult to listen to or to understand. The cleft-palate child's teacher finds great difficulty in fathoming what he is trying to recite. A falsetto voice distracts attention from what is being said. The more conspicuous the vocal abnormality the more unintelligible the speech becomes.

Many a stutterer has had to ask for a paper and pencil in order to make his simplest wants known. The words emerge from such contortions and broken garblings of utterance that frequently both the stutterer and the listener give up.

A speech defect, then, is one which calls attention to itself and interferes with communication.

The final part of our definition deals with the maladjustment and emotional handicap which the speech defective adds to his disability. Sometimes this maladjustment is the dominant fea-

---

[1] Penninggroth, Ann, "A Study of the Relative Intelligibility of Selected Speakers," Unpublished M. A. Thesis, Ohio State Univ., 1951.

ture of the disorder. We worked with a woman who claimed to have stuttered actually only once in her life—during a high-school graduation speech. Her speech was certainly not fluent since it was marked by numerous hesitations, pauses, and avoidances of certain words. She was badly handicapped socially and vocationally. Her listeners were constantly puzzled and confused by her peculiar speech behavior. And yet she had actually "stuttered" only once. This case, of course, is an extreme instance of the importance of maladjustment in producing a speech defect. Usually, the abnormality of rhythm, voice, or articulation is sufficiently bizarre to provoke so many social penalties that maladjustment is almost inevitable.

One of the specific types of aphonia with which speech therapists must deal is that possessed by an individual whose larynx has been removed. Since these persons inhale and exhale through a hole in their neck, they are unable to produce any voice in the normal way. Some of them use an artificial larynx with a tube which they insert into the corner of their mouths. Others learn to speak on esophageal air. They all suffer.

Classification of speech disorders. It should be obvious that before anyone can treat a speech-defective child he must be able to recognize the type of disorder present. Yet so deep is the ignorance surrounding speech disorders that the following letter is not unusual.

Dear Sir: I am a country schoolteacher in a two-room school. In my room there is a little boy in the third grade with a kind of funny voice. I mean he doesn't talk like other children. He can't say some of the words right that he knows just as well as I do. I have tried to correct him on the word "scissors" which is hard for him but he just can't get it out right. Is this stammering or just baby talk and how can I cure him? Please send me some tongue exercises or something. He is a sweet little child and needs some help.

In terms of our definition, we find that speech defects or speech disorders divide themselves into four large categories: disorders of rhythm, articulation, phonation, and symbolization, according to the types of symptoms shown. Many other

classifications, of course, may be used, and many other terminologies are common. However, in our presentation we shall
use the most common classification, that of the symptoms.

Under disorders of rhythm we include *stuttering* (stammering)
and *cluttering*. It is difficult to define or describe stuttering. The
flow of speech is broken by hesitations, stoppages, or repetitions and prolongations of the speech sounds. Fluency is interrupted by spasms, contortions, tremors, or abnormalities of
phonation and respiration. It consists of moments of speech
interruption of such frequency and abnormality as to attract
attention, interfere with communication, and produce maladjustment. It is the speech behavior that has been labeled by
others and accepted by its possessor as "stuttering." This label
is usually first bestowed when the child's speech is "marked by
effortless repetition of words, phrases, or the first sounds or syllables of words" without any awareness on his part "either that
he was repeating or that the repetitions constituted a difficulty
or abnormality."[2] This phase of the disorder is termed *primary
stuttering*. The child does not struggle or consciously withdraw
from speaking. He just bubbles along, doing his best to communicate. An excerpt from a parent's letter may illustrate this
primary stuttering.

I would appreciate some advice about my daughter. She is almost
three years old, and has always been precocious in speech. Four weeks
ago she recovered from a severe attack of whooping cough and it was
immediately after that when she began to show some trouble with her
speech. One morning she came downstairs and asked for orange juice,
and it sounded like this: "Wh-wh-wh-wh-where's my orange juice?"
Since then she has repeated one or two words in almost every sentence, sometimes repeating twice, and sometimes eight or nine times.
It doesn't seem to bother her but I'm worried about it as it gets a lot
worse when she asks questions or when she is tired, and I'm afraid
other children will start laughing at her. One of her playmates has
already imitated her several times. No one else in our family has any
trouble talking. What do you think we should do? Up to now we have
just been ignoring it and hoping it will go away.

---

[2] These quotations are from Johnson, W., "Stuttering in the Pre-school Child,"
University of Iowa Studies in Child Welfare, No. 37, 1934.

Unfortunately, stuttering does not always remain primary. It changes its symptoms as the child reacts to the penalties and evaluations of his parents, associates, or strangers. He begins to avoid and disguise his speech interruptions. Struggle behavior develops. The repetitions change to prolonged fixations of the tongue, lips, jaws, or vocal cords. Breathing abnormalities of the most grotesque variety are adopted. Contortions of the face or body occur. All of these symptoms are lumped together under the term *secondary stuttering*.

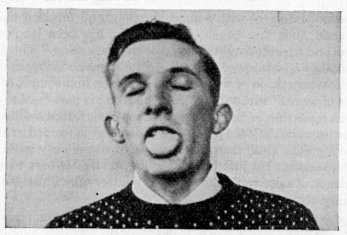

Fig. 1. Stuttering. It interferes with communication, calls attention to itself, and makes its victim maladjusted.

Secondary stuttering occurs in many forms, since different individuals react to their speech interruptions in different ways. One German authority carefully described ninety-two different varieties of stuttering (each christened with beautiful Greek and Latin verbiage), and we are sure that there must be many more. Stutterers have been known to grunt or spit or pound themselves or protrude their tongues or speak on inhalation or waltz or jump or merely stare glassily when in the throes of what they call a "spasm" or a "block." The late Irvin S. Cobb described a certain Captain Joe Fowler who manifested his stuttering through the use of profanity. Captain Joe was able to speak very well under ordinary circumstances, but when he got angry or excited, his speech stopped entirely, and he was only able to get started again through the use of a stereotyped bit of cursing. Some of the imitations of stuttering heard in the movies and on the radio may seem grotesque, yet the reality may be even more unusual.

Some stutterers develop an almost complete inability to make a direct speech attempt upon a feared word. They approach it, back away, say "a-a-a-a" or "um-um-um," go back to the beginning of the sentence and try again and again, until finally they give up communication altogether. Many stutterers become so adept at substituting synonyms for their difficult words, and disguising the interruptions which do occur, that they are able to pose as normal speakers. We have known seven severe stutterers whose spouses first discovered their speech impediments after the wedding ceremony. Stutterers have preached and taught school and become successful traveling salesmen without ever betraying their infirmity, but they are not happy individuals. The nervous strain and vigilance necessary to avoid and disguise their symptoms often create stresses so severe as to produce profound emotional breakdowns.

Cluttering. Another disorder of rhythm is cluttering. It is characterized by slurred and omitted syllables, by improper phrasing and pauses due to excessive speed. Clutterers speak by spurts and their speech organs pile up like keys on a typewriter when a novice stenographer tries for more speed than her skill permits. An old text in speech correction has this description: ". . . a torrent of half articulated words, following each other like peas running out of a spout"; but the torrent is also irregularly interrupted in its flow. People constantly ask the clutterer to repeat. They are emphatically irritated by his uneven volleys of hasty syllables. They find themselves interrupting during his panting pauses and then in turn being interrupted by a new overwhelming rush of jumbled words.

Spastic speech frequently involves a disorder of rhythm. It is difficult for the victims of cerebral palsy to make smooth transitions or to marshal an air flow constant enough to produce a polysyllabic word or a phrase without a break. Even when their articulation and voice quality is fairly normal, these interruptions in the fluency are noticeable enough to interfere with communication.

Articulation. Under disorders of articulation we include all those disorders characterized by the substitution, omission, addition, and distortion of the speech sounds. There are many somewhat synonymous and overlapping terms in common use for these disorders, among which we can name *baby talk* (infantile perseveration), a disorder with no organic basis but characterized by stereotyped substitutions similar to those used by the normal child in the early stages of speech development; *lalling*, characterized by defective *r*, *l*, *t*, *d*, or *s* sounds, and largely due to inactivity or sluggishness of the tongue tip; *lisping*, a disorder of the sibilant sounds, especially *s* and *z*, characterized by the substitution of the *th* (*θ*; *ð*) consonants (a lingual or frontal lisp), a mushy *sh* (ʃ) or *zh* (ʒ) sound (a lateral lisp), *t* or *d* (occluded lisp), or the nasal snort resulting from the attempt to make an *s* or *z* through the nose (nasal lisp); *delayed speech*, characterized by a narrow repertoire of consonants and unintelligibility; and *oral inaccuracy*, which is a wastebasket term for any mild articulatory defect.

Actually these names do not denote different types of disorders. They are not mutually exclusive. Lallers often lisp, and lispers talk baby talk, and all of them show oral inaccuracy. The important features of all articulatory disorders are the presence of defective and incorrect sounds. The forty-year-old farmer who wept when he heard his voice on a recording of a children's rhyme did so because of the defective and incorrect sounds he had produced. A six year old said this:

> Tinko Tinko itto tah,
> How I wondah wheh you ah,
> Up abuh duh woh soh high
> Yike a diamon' in duh kye.

As the above selection indicates, most articulatory cases have more than one error and are not always consistent in their substitutions, omissions, insertions, or distortions. This is not always the case, however. Thum lingual lithperth merely thubthitute a *th* for the *eth* thound. Otherzh shkwirt the air shtream over the shide of the tongue and are shed to have a lateral lishp. Others thnort the thnound (nasal lisp). Many children have been known to buy an "ite tream toda" or an all day "tucker."

It would be impossible to portray the acoustic characteristics of some of the distortions used by articulatory cases even if we used the phonetic alphabet. Seldom does an adult substitute a true *w* for the *r* as he attempts such a phrase as "around the rock." He usually produces a sound "something like a *w* and something like the velar *r* made with the back of the tongue elevated and the tip depressed" (13). In some lateral lisping, the sound produced is more of a salivary unvoiced *l* instead of the *s*, a sloppy slurping sound which not only disgusts its hearers but its speaker too.

Many of the omissions heard in articulation cases are merely weakly stressed consonants. When in a noisy room, an eighteen-year-old boy in describing a winter scene would seem to say, "The 'ky and 'no in wintuh." The missing sounds, however, were evident in quiet surroundings and were perfectly formed, but their duration was so brief that any noise seemed to mask their presence. Many cases, however, do entirely omit sounds they cannot produce.

Additions of linking sounds are frequently found in blends ("the buhlue-guhreen color of spuhruce trees"), and when a child adds *ee* to every final *r* sound, as one of our cases did, the peculiarity is very noticeable.

To many persons, articulatory defects seem relatively unimportant. But severe articulation cases find the demands of modern life very difficult. We knew a woman who could not produce the *s*, *l*, and *r* sounds and yet who had to buy a railroad ticket to Robeline, Louisiana. She did it with pencil and paper. Another man with the same difficulty became a farmer's hired hand after he graduated from college rather than suffer the penalties of a more verbal existence. Many children are said to outgrow their defective consonant sounds. Actually, they overcome them through blundering methods of self-help, and far too many of them never manage the feat. One man, aged 65, asked us bitterly when we thought he would outgrow his baby talk.

In severe cases, communication is almost impossible. Mothers cannot understand their own children. The delayed-speech case, deprived of normal verbal outlets for his emotion, becomes a behavior problem. Try, for instance, to translate the following nursery rhymes as transcribed from phonograph recordings:

> Ha ta buh, Hah ta buh,
> Wuhnuh peh, two uh peh,
> Ha ta buh.

> Tippo Tymuh meh a pyemuh,
> Doh too peh,
> Ted Tippo Tymuh to duh pyemuh
> Yeh me tee oo weh.

> ə dɪjə, ə dɑjə, ə tɛnə ta tɑjə,
> Wɑ meɪ ju tʌm toʊ tun,
> ju juːt tə tʌm æ tɛn əta,
> bʌt naʊ ju tʌm æ nun.

Voice disorders. Under disorders of phonation (voice) we have three major divisions: disorders of pitch, of intensity, and of timbre (voice quality). Typical pitch disorders are the *monotone*, the *too high pitched* or *too low pitched* voice, and the voice that is characterized by *stereotyped inflections*. Typical disorders of intensity are *aphonia*, the lack of any voice, often characterized by strained whispering; and the *too loud* or *too weak* voice. Under disorders of voice quality we find two frequent types, *hypernasality* (including cleft palate) and *hyponasality*, and a multitude of other types which have been described in the literature by as many names as there are appropriate adjectives. Among these we shall mention the *pectoral*, the *guttural*, the *harsh* or *strident*, the *husky*, and the *hoarse* voice. Certain voice disorders such as the *falsetto* voice involve both pitch and timbre abnormalities.

The following description was uttered by a two-hundred-pound football player in his high, piping, shrill child's voice:

> Yes, I was one of those boy sopranos and my music teacher loved me. I soloed in all the cantatas and programs and sang in the choir and glee clubs and they never let my voice change. I socked a guy the other day who wise-cracked about it, but I'm still a boy soprano at twenty-two. I'm getting so I'm afraid to open my mouth. Strangers start looking for a Charlie McCarthy somewhere. I got to get over it, and quick. Why, I can't even swear but some guy who's been saying the same words looks shocked.

A high-pitched voice in a male is definitely a handicap, communicative, economic, and social.

When a woman's voice is pitched very low and carries a certain type of male inflection, it certainly calls attention to itself and causes maladjustment. The following sentence, spoken by a casual acquaintance and overheard by the girl to whom it referred, practically wrecked her entire security: "Every time I hear her talk I look around to see if it's the bearded lady of the circus."

On every campus some professor possesses that enemy of education, a monotonous voice. A true monotone is comparatively rare, yet it dominates any conversation by its difference. To hear a person laugh on a single note is enough to stir the scalp. Questions asked in a true monotone seem curiously devoid of life. Fortunately most cases of monotonous voice are not so extreme. Many of them could be described as the "poker voice"—even as a face without expression is termed a "poker face." Inflections are present, but for fear of revealing insecurity or inadequacy they are reduced to a minimum.

By stereotyped inflections we refer to the voice which calls attention to itself through its pitch patterning. The sing-song voice, the voice that ends every phrase or sentence with a falling inflection, the "schoolmaam's voice" with its emphatic dogmatic inflections, are all types of variation which, *when extreme*, may be considered speech defects.

The intensity disorders need little illustration. Many of us have experienced *aphonia*, after prolonged abuse of voice through screaming or when laryngitis has caused us to "lose" our voice. People who earn their living by their mouths— among them, singers, train announcers, clergymen, and school-teachers—are subject to aphonia, hysterical or otherwise. Most very soft or weak voices are due to insecurity or hearing loss. The extremely loud—to the point of irritation—voices are often due to personality problems or defective hearing. The *strident* voice combines excessive intensity with a harsh voice quality to pierce the ears and rasp the sensibilities of its victims. One of the most difficult voices to correct is that which is marked by sudden bursts of loudness or by the "trailing off into nothingness" at the end of each phrase. Both irritate their listeners.

That the disorders of voice quality are difficult to describe is indicated not only by the names which we listed earlier in our classification but also by the names we omitted. Voices have been called *thick*, *thin*, *heavy*, *sweet*, *round*, *brilliant*, *hard*, *metallic*, and *rich* as well as *poor*. The terms we have used are not much better, but at least they do not confuse auditory perceptions with those of taste or touch. The science of experimental phonetics has not yet been able to provide a better classification for variations in timbre.

The quality of *excessive nasality* (hypernasality, rhinolalia aperta) is easily recognized. Its possessor not only seems to speak his *m*, *n*, and ŋ sounds through his nose, but also many of the vowels and voiced continuants such as *r*, *v*, and *z*. When combined with certain inflection patterns it has been described as a "whining" voice. In certain sections of the country a variety of hypernasality is dialectal and of course in this setting it would not be a speech defect. In *assimilation nasality* only the sounds preceding or following the *m*, *n* and ŋ sounds are excessively nasalized, but these can occur frequently enough to provoke audience irritation.

In *hyponasality* (denasality, adenoidal voice, rhinolalia clausa) the speaker does not or cannot utter the nasal sounds through the nose. The voice quality is deadened and muffled, as though its owner had a perpetual cold or post-nasal drip. The *m* resembles a blend of *m* and *b* spoken simultaneously, and the other nasals have similar cognates. Often habituated during the presence of adenoidal growths in early life, it persists long after the adenoids have been removed. People listening to denasal voices find themselves swallowing and clearing their throats and consumed by the urge to get out of range.

Other voice-quality disorders are occasionally noted by the teacher doing speech correction in the public school. Many boys' voices become husky and hoarse during the two or three years prior to voice change and become clear again after that event. Overstrain due to prolonged yelling, screeching, or shouting can cause this quality in any of us. Perhaps the *strident*, *hoarse*, *husky*, and *breathy* qualities of voice indicate a two-factor continuum involving (1) breath expenditure and (2) muscular strain. The strident voice shows a preponderance of tension in the muscles that squeeze the pharynx while the breathy voice represents a minimum of strain and a maximum of breath expenditure.

The words *throaty* and *pectoral* as adjectives to describe voice quality are probably identical save for the sex of the persons concerned. Throaty voices in the female are paralleled by the voice of hollow booming pectoral timbre in the male. Both involve lower pitch levels, rounded mouth openings, and retracted chins. Pectoral voice has been called the "rain-barrel voice." There are echoes in it. It reverberates like song in the bathtub. It was formerly much used by preachers and politicians and by undertakers and insecure high-school teachers.

The *falsetto* voice is a grievous burden to its owner unless he yodels for a living. A complicated arrangement of the laryngeal cartilages and muscles causes only a portion of the vocal cords to vibrate, and the high-pitched tones thereby produced are amplified by constricted resonating cavities in the mouth and throat. It is almost impossible to produce the falsetto with the head pulled backward as far as possible.

Cleft-palate speech involves both a voice and articulation defect. Not only are the consonants nasally emitted, but many of those which are not so emitted are slurred and distorted. The voice quality is hypernasal. Cleft-palate speakers honk their speech sounds in a manner which, once heard, is never thereafter mistaken.

Foreign accent is another disorder which involves both articulation and voice. Speakers of a foreign tongue use sound substitutions and distortions, and they also use inflection patterns unfamiliar to our ears. The rising inflection at the conclusion of the phrase as spoken by a Scandinavian speaking English may serve as an illustration. In treating such a disorder we organize our therapy so as to attack both phases of the problem.

Symbolization disorders. The problem of _dysphasia_ (the general term for all disorders of symbolic formulation and expression) is rarely met in public-school speech correction. Occasionally it occurs in mild form as a pronounced reading, writing, and speaking disability. In the speech clinic we often are required to help aphasics, and the end of World War II required the services of a good many speech correctionists to teach those who had received head and brain injuries. Children who have had meningitis or jaundice, and some adults who have suffered a paralytic stroke, often demonstrate the symptoms of aphasia. Such persons find it difficult to use or comprehend linguistic symbols, whether they be written or spoken. In the moto-expressive type of aphasia, the case may say "bum-bum-bum" for "cigarette," and "bum" for "shoe." Another aphasic may grope for words in attempting to say "pencil" but say "eraser" or "pen" or "stick" instead. Yet he knows his errors the instant they are spoken. In the receptive type of aphasia the difficulty lies in the perception. R. V. McKnight describes her own aphasic reaction to the word "your" as follows:

I mentally heard it but it had no meaning. I felt that it was related to the word "you" but I could not figure out the relationship between the two. I continued to puzzle over this until the speaker had finished his lecture and sat down. . . . More generally when I do not recognize the meaning I do not recognize the sound. The word is a jumble of letters.

Children who have such difficulties are often mistakenly diagnosed as hard of hearing or feeble-minded. Some cases of delayed onset or slow development of speech are probably due to aphasia.

The child with *delayed speech* may, or may not, belong in the category of symbolization disorders. Injuries to the brain have often, in young children, interrupted speech development or retarded it. The differential diagnosis of "congenital aphasia" is always difficult, as we shall see in later chapters. It is also certain that many children who are mute or speak in an unintelligible jargon or gibberish have been called "brain-injured" when they were entirely normal individuals who just had not been taught to talk. Some parents learn their child's language instead of teaching them the adult tongue. Delayed speech often approximates the pattern of a very severe articulation disorder and some cases, so diagnosed, probably belong in this category.

Frequency of occurrence. The relative frequency of the different speech defects is difficult to determine with accuracy. There have been hundreds of surveys, each yielding percentages, but we can be sure that the defects of articulation are in the great majority. Every survey has demonstrated this fact. One of the most thorough of all the surveys, that by Mills and Streit[3] in which each child in the elementary grades was examined individually, and all those diagnosed were doubly and triply checked, found that 10% of the school population had some speech defect. Of these speech defective children, 45% were seriously handicapped. Articulation disorders characterized 7% of all school children, voice disorders 1.5% and rhythm disorders 1.5%. This coincides roughly with the results of the White House Conference report of 1931.

---

[3] Mills, A. W., and Streit, H., "Report of a Speech Survey, Holyoke, Massachusetts," *Journal of Speech Disorders*, 1942. Volume 7, page 161–167.

A more recent survey of 87,288 children in New England[4] showed that 7.8% were handicapped in speech. The proportions of speech and hearing children were as follows: articulation, 50%; voice, 6.6%; stuttering, 10.9%; hard of hearing, 15.4%; deaf, 8.4%; delayed speech, 4.4%; cleft palate, 1.2%; cerebral palsy, 1.2%; aphasia, 0.5%; and miscellaneous, 1.6%.

Using the *estimates* given in the report submitted by the American Speech and Hearing Association Committee for the 1950 White House Conference we have the following figures which the report states, "are the lowest estimates which can be scientifically defended." Six per cent of the total population has some variety of speech defect. Four per cent of the total population has an articulation disorder. Seven individuals in each thousand are stutterers. Five out of every thousand have a voice disorder; five more have delayed speech; two more have speech disorders due to brain injuries; and one in each thousand has a cleft palate speech problem.

When these percentages are applied to the 1951 population, we have the following numbers of individuals handicapped in speech:

ESTIMATES OF NUMBER OF SPEECH DEFECTS[5]

Type of Disorder	In the Total Population	In School Population
Functional Articulation	6,139,600	1,324,840
Stuttering	1,074,430	231,847
Voice Disorders	767,450	165,605
Retarded Speech Development	767,450	165,605
Cerebral Speech Disorders	306,930	66,242
Cleft-Palate Speech	153,490	33,121

The frequency of occurrence is, however, not the true measure of the seriousness of the problem. Although their relative

---

[4] Pronovost, Wilbert, "A Survey of Services for the Speech and Hearing Handicapped in New England," *Journal of Speech Disorders*, 1951, Volume 16, pages 148–156.

[5] Spilka, Bernard, and Steer, M. D., "Incidence of Speech and Hearing Deficiency in the General Population and Schools of the U.S., 1951," Purdue Speech and Hearing Clinic *Research Staff Report No. 2.*

numbers are small, cases of stuttering, cleft palate, cerebral palsy and hearing disabilities present great difficulties in treatment. Recently in the State of Michigan, where the minimum case load for public school speech therapists was 125, the requirement has been reduced proportionally to the number of severely handicapped children enrolled. Generally speaking, the articulatory cases respond most easily and quickly to therapy, but there are many exceptions to this rule. Our culture tends to judge articulation and voice defects as being less handicapping than the other speech disorders, but in the final analysis the speech defective individual himself is the only one who can make this evaluation. A tiny lisp may become invested with so much emotion that it may dominate an entire lifetime. The third part of our definition of a speech defect must always be considered.

References

1. Beebe, H. H., "Sigmatismus Nasalis," *Journal of Speech Disorders*, 1946, Volume 11, pages 35–37.
T-F: The title means an excessively nasal voice quality.
T-F: The disorder is organically caused.
Essay: What has snoring to do with *sigmatismus nasalis?*
2. Belgum, D., "Stuttering," *Hygeia*, 1944, Volume 22, pages 346–347.
T-F: The peculiar contortions of stuttering are due to disordered nervous impulses.
T-F: It is wise to use synonyms for the difficult words.
Essay: How do stutterers avoid feared speech situations?
3. Dalrymple, L. H., "Our Child Had a Cleft Palate," *Hygeia*, 1949, Volume 27, pages 186–187, 199–200.
The story of the child, her palatal abnormality and hare lip, the operations required, the speech therapy and the mental hygiene are all presented readably.
4. Despert, J. L., "Psychopathology of Stuttering," *American Journal of Psychiatry*, 1943, Volume 99, pages 881–885.
A discussion of the theories and symptoms of stuttering. One typical case history with an account of the treatment is given.
5. Huber, M. W., *The Practice of Speech Correction in the Medical*

Clinic, together with Kopp, A. E., *Speech Correction from a Dental Viewpoint,* Boston, Expression Company, 1942.

This little book is especially valuable in providing the student with descriptions of the voice defects of organic causation. Cleft palate and aphonic, hoarse, and denasal voices are presented.

6. Johnson, W., Brown, S. F., Curtis, J. F., Edney, C., and Keaster, J., *Speech Handicapped School Children,* New York, Harper & Brothers, 1948.

Chapter 1 treats the various types of disorders from a diagnostic point of view and introduces the student to speech therapy as it applies to public school speech correction.

7. Ogilvie, M., *Terminology and Definitions of Speech Defects,* New York, Columbia University Teachers College Contributions to Education, Number 859, 1942.

T-F: Functional Aphonia means a loss of voice due to growths on the vocal folds.

Essay: List thirty names for articulation defects of various kinds.

Essay: What does the author say about lambdacism as a label?

8. Platt, J. H., *"Myasthenia Laryngis:* A Case Report," *Journal of Speech Disorders,* 1946, Volume 11, pages 187–188.

T-F: This voice problem is caused by inflammation.

T-F: The aphonia disappeared after treatment with pharyngeal relaxation.

9. Porter, F., "Speech Correction in an Orphanage," *Journal of Speech Disorders,* 1945, Volume 10, pages 241–248.

Essay: Describe all the articulatory disorders.

10. Robbins, S., "Dyslalia," Chapter 10 in Froeschels, E., *Twentieth Century Speech Correction,* New York, Philosophical Library, 1948.

Essay: Define: metalalia, barbaralalia, rhotacism, asapholalia.

11. Shryock, H., "Speech without a Larynx," *Hygeia,* 1947, Volume 25, pages 752–753.

T-F: The patient learned to speak on a belch not on a burp.

T-F: One must hold one's breath while using esophageal speech.

Essay: How skillful can one become in speaking without a larynx?

12. Werner, L. S., "Treatment of a Child with Delayed Speech," *Journal of Speech Disorders,* 1945, Volume 10, pages 329–334.

The story of a five-year-old girl who had never uttered a sound with a description of the therapy.

13. West, R., "Rehabilitation of Speech," *Journal of Exceptional Children,* 1950, Volume 16, pages 165–172.

A review of the types of speech problems and the need for cooperation on the part of all those dealing with the child.

3. Understanding
the Speech Defective

Why we must know our cases. The speech therapist works with human beings, not disembodied voices. So do all teachers, all psychologists, psychiatrists and physicians. It is difficult to straighten a nose without altering the shape of the patient's personality. Every parent has a molding effect upon a child. Each person alters every other individual with whom he makes contact. This point is stressed because from infancy our culture teaches us to protect our own privacy and respect the privacy of others. Many students feel a natural hesitancy when confronted with the task of having to explore another human mind. On the one hand they fear the attack which normally comes when one individual begins to pry or probe too deeply. And on the other hand, those who have many unpleasant secrets of their own to protect are naturally reluctant to approve such a procedure. They know that it is difficult to pull a pig out of the mud without getting a little dirty. This, then, is a very common and a very natural reaction which must be understood and accepted.

Two questions immediately present themselves. How deeply must we explore our cases and is such exploration really necessary? The answer to the first is simply this: don't fish for sharks with a two ounce line. Few speech therapists are trained or competent enough to deal with those profound emotional conflicts which fill our mental institutions. We do not fish for the monsters of the deep. We stay pretty close to shore. If we sense the threat of abnormality beyond our ability to understand or cope, we call in the professional—the psychiatrist. But every one of us, whatever our trade or profession, comes into daily contact with people in trouble, and, so far as we are able, we do our best to help. The speech therapist has a close relationship with his cases and so his power to help is greater. His power to hurt is also greater. If we are to keep from making these mistakes we will have to know our cases well. We must remove the obstacles in the path to normal speech, not insert them.

The essential task of the speech correctionist is to help his articulatory, voice, or stuttering cases to overcome their speech handicaps. He is often asked for exercises or drills which will accomplish this, but the mere fact that no ethical worker in the field will ever guarantee a cure should indicate that the problem is not simple. First, the techniques used in speech correction all involve learning and unlearning. New habits must be taught and old ones broken. People differ in their modifiability. Motivation can vary all the way from:

I've burned my bridges behind me. I've told everybody I know that I'm not coming back until I can talk right. I told my girl our marriage was off unless I licked this speech impediment. I'll do anything, even if it takes three years of my life. This is it. Tell me what to do first.

to:

My vacation starts in June but I want to go up to the cottage for a few weeks first, to rest up and play a bit. I would prefer to come the last two weeks of July if you find you cannot help me by correspondence. My stuttering is not very severe and many times I do not stutter at all. I am sure it would not take long if you could just help me get confidence in myself.

Besides motivation, we must always take into account the presence of emotional factors which might prevent the person from facing his speech defect as a problem in re-education. A lisper who has been severely penalized for his sibilant errors finds it very difficult to accept the temporary partial failures which always accompany the type of learning process involved in speech correction. The stutterer who has always tried to hide or disguise his disorder will be tempted to escape any therapy which necessitates the exposure, manipulation, and control of his stuttering spasms. Therapy must always be tailored to fit the person we are trying to help. Some methods just will not work with a given individual. For example:

Ordinarily, we use phonograph recordings of the speech of our foreign accent cases for purposes of phonetic analysis and ear training. While there is often a first shock on hearing one's own errors, it usually passes quickly and the case soon looks forward to the convenience the recording provides in recognizing and eliminating errors. In one of our cases, an American-born woman who had learned three languages simultaneously before the age of five—(her parents had planned a ballet career for her), each recording provoked an emotional outburst and retarded her progress. We attributed her reactions to her hatred of the speech defect but she told us later that she went into a frenzy whenever she heard any phonograph record since it reminded her of all the wasted hours of her youth, spent in the rigid discipline of the classic dance.

Most of our failures in speech correction are due to ignorance, and most of that ignorance concerns the person whom we are treating. Every worker in our field makes mistakes in helping any child or adult to overcome his speech handicap. Most of these mistakes are minute. They may concern timing, for instance. If a lisper has finally learned a good *s* in isolation, how soon should we require him to start using it in familiar words? When dare we ask him to alternate syllables such as *see* and *thee* at fast speeds? Other mistakes are more vital and if he loses confidence over this one we may lose our opportunity to help the person who has come to us. These mistakes are the ones that haunt us and keep us humble in the profession of speech correction. Most of them could be avoided, if only we could get to know our speech defective more thoroughly.

If we neglect our study of the person we are treating, we may work in vain. Emotional conflicts of which we may be entirely ignorant may cause relapse. This is well known in such psychosomatic disorders as asthma, ulcerative colitis, and peptic ulcer. In speech correction, relapses in stutterers have been so common that attitudes of pessimism are held by every esteemed authority in the field. Even simple articulatory defects, such as the substitution of *w* for *l*, may return years after the errors have been eliminated from all ordinary speech, and we remember very well that case of ours who lost her voice on the first of every month. Her husband disliked paying her bills and was very verbal about it. A few of these unfortunate episodes soon teach the speech correctionist to study his cases.

A good share of the total handicap which most adult speech defectives possess is emotional in nature. They suffer from fears, shames, and embarrassment, and their reactions to these penalties interfere with communication. Many a stutterer could talk undetected were it not for the marked fear and embarrassment which themselves attract attention.

A girl of fourteen was referred by her classroom teacher to the speech therapist as a stutterer because of her marked hesitations and her prolongations. However, her speech was very broken and nonfluent. She avoided recitation, speaking to strangers, and most situations involving any quick communication. Investigation showed that the girl was a post-operative cleft palate case, very sensitive about it, and desirous of hiding any evidence that such an abnormality had occurred. These reactions were also those of her parents. The girl's speech was excellent except that occasionally a slight nasal lisp was evident. If she watched herself carefully and monitored her speech, she could either avoid all *s* and *z* sounds or say them slowly and carefully enough to avoid detection. The result of all this vigilance was a very marked non-fluency and another very conspicuous handicap.

But more handicapping still are those inner emotional reactions which no listener ever sees but which govern the speech defective's life and shape his personality. So closely linked is the inner emotional burden with the outer speech handicap that the one can seldom be treated without doing something about the other. Travis (18) has said:

The primary concern of speech correction is the person. . . . It is not enough to know what sort of a speech defect a person has. In addition, one should know what kind of a person has a speech defect. The speech defect has no particular meaning apart from the person who presents the defect. We are not interested in speech defects, but in speech defectives.

In these words, Travis expresses the reason for this chapter. Speech correction is but one small area in the field of clinical psychology, and the speech correctionist who thinks that he deals with lisping rather than lispers, and with stuttering rather than stutterers, will find discouragement at every turn.

Emotional conflicts may also serve as predisposing, precipitating, and maintaining causes of speech disorders. The literature is thronged with case studies showing the influence of personality and behavior problems in producing speech disorders, but we cite two that are more clear cut than those usually found.

Just before school opened after the holidays, C. K., a Junior High School teacher, age 38, was jilted by her fiancé. She had never been able to maintain discipline among her students and had not enjoyed teaching, according to the report of her principal. A slight cold caused her to lose her voice completely. Two months later, she was still unable to speak above a whisper, although the physician's report stated that no inflammation or other pathology existed. He diagnosed her disorder as hysterical aphonia.

A. T., a girl of 15, suddenly began to lisp and substitute *w* for *r*. She had previously spoken without any articulatory defect for at least six years, although her first-grade teacher declared she had some kind of speech disorder when she was seven years old. Three months later the disorder disappeared as suddenly as it had appeared. The only explanation which seemed to have any evidence to support it was that the girl knew of her parents' plan to get a divorce and adopted the symptoms of an earlier age level when no family conflict was threatening to disrupt her security. At any rate, the disorder disappeared as soon as a parental reconciliation was effected.

It is easily seen from these cases that a thorough knowledge of the speech defective's personality and history is vital to successful treatment.

Speech defects are so conspicuously different that they themselves can serve as the cause or the nucleus of personality problems. A stutterer who reacts to rejection, pity, or humor by attacking will be likely to have antagonistic responses toward the speech correctionist. The lisper who withdraws when penalties are threatened is prone to avoid and postpone those very measures that may solve his basic problem.

A public school speech therapist had an eight-year-old boy who steadfastly refused to attempt any sound that she presented, even sounds which he could utter perfectly. He would always respond, "I can't, I can't." This response had become conditioned to any request for speech so that it occurred almost automatically. The problem was finally solved by having him blow a horn as soon as a request for speech was made, then follow the horn blowing with a familiar song. Gradually, the speech therapy was introduced first through song, then through humming and finally by prolonging the sounds to be taught. Along with this went a lot of release therapy and some conferences with the parents who changed their home policies of mockery when errors occurred.

Often these aggressive and retreat reactions are disguised so cleverly that only careful study will disclose them. In any event, these personality problems can interfere or entirely frustrate our corrective efforts unless we understand them well enough to fit them into our remedial program. We should solve them if we can. We dare not ignore them.

How to study your cases. Since it is vitally important for us to know the people with whom we work, we should also know the methods commonly used. In speech correction we always take a case history; we sometimes require a verbal or written autobiography; we employ psychological tests of intelligence, vocational aptitude, personality, and school achievement; we collect as much information as we can from the speech defective's associates; we interview the case himself, sometimes at great length; and we observe his behavior in both ordinary and controlled situations.

The extent of this exploration usually depends on the severity of the speech defective's emotional handicap. Many of the younger children, especially those with mild articulatory defects, require no great amount of detailed investigation. The following report by a public school speech correctionist will illustrate about how much information may be gathered on one of the milder cases.

I am writing this brief summary of what I know about J. S. at the request of his mother, who has informed me you are planning to work with him this summer. He has a simple frontal lisp substituting the *th* sounds for the *s* and *z*. All other sounds are good, and he can make these sounds when he is careful, but only at slow speeds. All of the *s* blends are bad. His mother tells me that formerly he had difficulty with other sounds but outgrew these errors. No one else in the family li-ped. His hearing is adequate but he has been slow to recognize errors except in isolated sounds. No one seems to tease him about it, and he is not at all self-conscious. He has always enjoyed coming to speech class. He has been very cooperative, but I only see him once a week for a fifteen-minute period and then only as a member of a group of six. He is bright and doing excellent school work. His reading is superior for a third grader. No dental abnormality, though his mother thinks a former thumb-sucking habit caused the lisp. Never has been a behavior problem at home or school. All he needs is a more thorough retraining than we can give here and I am glad you are going to help this summer. I'm sorry I cannot tell you more about him but I have over 150 other children and I've only seen the mother once. His third-grade teacher says that he is no problem to her. He will probably come out of it anyway, but I think perhaps the mother is overanxious because she said an aunt of hers still lisps.

At the other extreme are the very difficult cases, some of whose folders in the clinic files are several inches thick.

The case history. Although the case history as an instrument for exploring another human being is incomplete, unsatisfactory, and unreliable in many ways, no convenient substitute for it has ever been found. Its function is to serve as an outline of questioning and prompting, as a system of signposts pointing out pathways that should be followed, as a land-marked map of unexplored territory. It tends to prevent superficiality and snap judgment during diagnosis. It conserves time and energy. When used by a trained examiner who appreciates its weaknesses and limitations and who is alert to follow up any significant leads that appear, it gives us a picture of the individual which is of inestimable value. When used by a poor examiner who merely asks the questions and records the answers, or who loses himself in a mass of irrelevant information, it is practically worthless. A sample outline of the general case history and the special case histories for articulation, voice, and stuttering disorders will be found in the Appendix at the end of this book.

A typical general case history summary is now given, not so much as a model of what a case history should be but as a practical illustration of the information usually procured by this means.

CASE HISTORY SUMMARY

Informant: Mother.

Family: Paternal grandfather stuttered; paternal uncle left-handed.

Economic status: Isolated farm; very poor; insufficient food at times. Insufficient clothing.

Home conditions: Father very brutal to members of family; beats mother and children, including case; "terrible temper," almost killed son-in-law by kicking in head; taunts mother with inability to get divorce or to live afterward; boasts of extramarital relations; eldest two daughters left home "to get away from him"; "chased daughters out in middle of winter"; shames and beats boy for lack of speech; "very smooth talker when authorities come" and declares wife is crazy; (*Note.* We found no evidence of paranoia in informant); angry when each new baby comes (nine children, seven living; two miscarriages), but no sexual control. Mother works in fields and woods; in great fear of being hurt or possibly killed; once "loved the very ground he walked on but not now"; interested in helping child; child is very fond of mother and cooperates with her; will speak a few words when she coaxes him; mother wants a divorce but is afraid. Child is very much afraid of father but identifies himself somewhat with the man; child has always been forced to do things by father; father beats child for not repeating correctly; the other children adopt the father's attitude and tease, shame, and brutalize the boy; boy seems much more afraid of men strangers than of women.

Development: The child's physical development was normal; no birth injuries or accidents; no serious illnesses; had bad temper tantrums, beating head on floor; some of these still continue; speech development fairly normal; lalling, vocal play, and inflection practice coming at the proper time; said "mama" and "papa" at 18 months; made peculiar sucking and throat noises; breathes very heavily; has had tonsillectomy and adenectomy (July, 1936), but still shows some nasal stoppage and mouth breathing; thyroid disturbance suspected; hearing was tested and seemed adequate, although attention lapses occurred (we could not test for auditory aphasia, and it may be a possible explanation); at certain times does not seem able to understand, but does so under adequate motivation; the child uttered the words "Oh boy" under strong emotion, but has never said them before or since; he does not seem to be using silence as an attention-gaining device; mother said that child first refused to make any speech attempt and showed the negativism when he put "watermelon seeds up his nose at the age of three or a little earlier." I.Q. could not be determined, but went above the 5-year level on the Grace Arthur tests; seems ambidextrous.

Speech: The boy has said the following words: "Junior, Wright, Oh boy, Spot (dog's name), here, Maud and Molly (horses' names), pig, chicken, automobile." The child will repeat words after mother by watching her mouth, but only at certain times. Learned "one-two-three; a-b-c" at school the first day (when substitute teacher taught) but refused and was rejected when regular teacher came back. Said "No" to examiner. We could not make examination for organic defects, because of child's fears. We were able to get him to say a few words when mother was present.

The autobiography. Adults are often asked to write or give orally an autobiography. Instructions for such an autobiography might run as follows:

The purpose in our asking you to write an autobiography is to become well enough acquainted with you to fit our treatment to your needs. We must know as much as possible about:

    your parents and brothers and sisters
    your friends and enemies

your teachers
your employers or fellow workers
strangers who have played an important part in your life.

achievements you have been proud of, or praised for
talents you possess (your good points)

your bad points
things you have done for which others have punished or re-
    jected you
unpleasant experiences
things which made you unhappy

how you react when you are praised or appreciated
how you react when you are punished

Note. Write down your character sketches and your memories as they come to you. Put them on cards or individual sheets of scratch paper. Then organize later into three chapters: Chapter I. My pre-school period; Chapter II. School days; Chapter III. Since. The autobiography should run about ten pages or more. Give us a good picture of the people who were important in your life and why. What have been your assets and liabilities? How have others reacted to them? What kind of a person were you during each period?

Here are a few excerpts from actual autobiographies to illustrate the kind of information which they can contribute to our understanding of the speech defective:

My family life at home was very unsatisfactory. I felt that Mother and Dad hated my stuttering intensely, that they thought it unfair that a daughter of theirs should be so afflicted. I felt that I was a disappointment to them. I was impulsive, nervous and "bull-headed" in their eyes. I quarreled with my sisters. I was indeed a problem.

When I was in the second grade, "spit-balling" was all the rage. I never threw any but the boy behind me sure did. One day when he was caught he laid the blame on me so artfully that I was kept after school and quizzed by my teacher. She was an old witch anyway and couldn't understand what I was trying to say. But then when I got excited nobody could understand me. She then said that as a result of my throwing the spit balls she was considering putting me back in the first grade. All I could do was cry.   .

Observation of behavior. Probably the most valid of all the methods for getting to know and understand another human being is that of careful observation. Every worker in the field of speech correction relies upon this method of checking his interpretations and his information. One of the statements in the code of ethics prescribed by the American Speech Correction Association states that no treatment shall ever be administered entirely through correspondence. The reason for this statement is obvious. We cannot truly know an individual except through observing his behavior. The student of speech correction should train himself in this method for studying his cases. He should avail himself of every opportunity to predict human behavior. He must learn to observe and appreciate the little human dramas which roll up their curtains in the most unexpected places. He should make an intensive and systematic study of a few of his acquaintances, writing down his findings in a notebook with examples of correct and incorrect predictions of their behavior. Here is one of the examples from a student's notebook:

My batting average in predicting the behavior was pretty poor today, though I had one good success. Into the lunchroom where I eat my breakfast came a man. I told my companion that I would wager a nickel that he would stir his coffee with the spoon in his left hand. I had based my prediction on the following observations. His hat was tipped slightly to the left on his head, and although he removed it with his right hand, he put it into the rack with his left. He took off the right sleeve of his coat first and I have previously observed that most people take off the sleeve of the nonpreferred arm before the other. Then, too, he rubbed his chin with his left hand as he contemplated the menu on the wall. I won the nickel.

It is always important to separate observation from interpretation. The following passage is entirely free from the latter:

When his mother carried him into the room, his chin quivered and then he began to cry. She shook her head and he stopped momentarily, then began to cry more loudly. She shook him and covered his mouth with her hand, saying, "Don't cry like that! The doctor will spank you. See the pretty chair. Do you want to sit in it?" The child yelled more loudly. She shook him again. "Tell the doctor your name. Bobby! Say, 'Bobby.' " She sat him down forcibly in the chair and turned to the examiner. "He won't ever do what I say. He's bull-headed just like his no-account father." She got up and looked out of the window, then returned to the child. "Now look here," she said, "I brought you thirty miles to talk to this man and you better do it, dummy. You won't get any ice-cream cone either."

The following excerpt will represent the same experience but with interpretations, some of which are not justified:

The child was forcibly carried into the room by the mother who scolded him for not talking. She threatened and reproached him for not cooperating. She was disgusted with the child's behavior and told him she would punish him for his obstinacy. She could not control him at all. The child knew that he could refuse to talk and get away with his refusal. He cried bitterly during most of the period. The boy's delayed speech is probably due to negativism.

Interpretations are inescapable in any study of another human being, but most of our clinical errors result from mistaking them for factual observations.

It is often possible to learn a lot about a person by introducing him into situations that have been designed especially to bring out hidden conflicts. For instance, we have used psychodrama to demonstrate the existence of family frictions of which we had no previous knowledge. We have sent stutterers into situations where we knew they would be laughed at for their disorder, so that we could observe their reactions to this penalty. We have watched their response to praise which had been prearranged. We have given small children clay images of their fathers, mothers, and brothers, and have seen their play reveal hostilities which were never revealed in any other way. The use of fist puppets with appropriate dialogue between the puppet and the child has often yielded material that was very important to treatment. For instance:

The parents of the six-year-old girl, a lisper, had been divorced a year before the child was brought to the clinic. Our problem was to determine who should carry on the remedial speech work which we had started. Neither the mother nor the father was available. The first-grade teacher had forty-two children in her room and was reluctant. The father's sister, who lived with him and the child, was very intelligent and pleasant. She had taught school successfully and was eager to help. The child seemed to be very fond of her. However, a puppet named "Aunty" and another named "Teacher" first held a pleasant dialogue with each other, then with the child. The child enjoyed the drama very much and took part in it freely. She refused to speak to the aunty puppet except briefly. She told her to go away and fall down and get run over by a car. She told the teacher puppet to spank Aunty and make her go home. When this was carried out in pantomime, she laughed and clapped her hands. She also accepted a correction of her speech when the teacher puppet asked her to say an *s* word correctly. When Aunty tried the same correction later, she told her to shut up and "go home and be dead."

Needless to say, the girl's aunt was not chosen to do the speech correction.

Interviewing. The art of interviewing, both as a diagnostic and a therapeutic device, is receiving the increasing emphasis in clinical psychology which it richly deserves. We feel that all teachers or clinicians who deal with problem children or adults should be trained in methods of interviewing. The moment a person begins to discuss his difficulties, he opens the shell that protects his hidden insecurities. Speech is always revelation, and never more so than when it is free and uninhibited. Much of the art of interviewing centers about the creation of attitudes which encourage free spontaneous expression.

Directive interviewing is used mainly in procuring an adequate case history, in getting factual reports of the case's self-therapy, in provoking spontaneous speech, in getting information from many informants. In such interviews, it is usually wise to state the purpose of the interview and to define your own role, your trustworthiness, and the reasons for your interest in the information sought. As you begin, you should do most of the talking, so as to reveal your adequacy as an interviewer. The first responses required of the informant should be fairly unimportant and casual and designed mainly to encourage further response.

Then general questions should be asked, not the *yes* or *no* variety: "Could you give me some idea about how Sally gets along in school?" instead of "Does Sally like school?" The more specific questions can come later, as the flow of spontaneous speech begins to dwindle. Learn to ask a clean-cut question without revising it as you go— Not: "And is John beginning . . . that is to say . . . . does he show any signs . . . . . of growing up, of being adolescent?" but: "What behavior, if any, indicates that John is getting interested in girls?" Be careful that your questions do not suggest or imply any given answer— Not: "Does your boy get teased a lot about his stuttering by his schoolmates?" but "How do the other children react to your boy when he stutters?" Delicate questions, or those that tend to provoke anxiety or guilt feelings, must be led up to gradually, but asked very matter-of-factly. Ask for examples of behavior which will illustrate the point made by the informant. These anecdotes are often some of the most revealing sources of information. Maintain a mastery of the situation. Do not let the interviewee run away with the interview and cause you to lose the opportunity, but exert your control gracefully and unobtrusively.

The nondirective method of interviewing might be termed dynamic listening. The speech correctionist gets his case to talking about his problems, places most of the responsibility for this discussion on the case, and when pauses or requests for comment occur, he merely tries to repeat in his own words the emotional attitudes which the case has been expressing. He must be the perfect listener, always in tune with the speaker's thoughts. When he responds, he should respond primarily to the feelings expressed by the speech defective rather than to the intellectual content of his disclosure. The speech correctionist neither approves nor disapproves of what is told him. He does not judge. He merely keeps trying to understand. If the case is kept talking freely and feels that he is understood, he can hardly fail to verbalize his basic conflicts.

It might seem to the uninitiated that the nondirective method of interviewing is easily mastered. We have not found it so. There are many pitfalls for the unwary dynamic listener.

He finds himself listening intellectually rather than emotionally. He finds himself talking too much, interpreting, directing, and pointing out implications. No, the nondirective method of interviewing is not easy, but it is extremely productive of insight, not only for the speech correctionist but also for the speech defective himself. We heartily recommend the book *Counselling and Psychotherapy* by Rogers (16), from which the following partial transcription of a phonographically recorded interview is taken:

Subject. When I wax enthusiastic philosophically, I oftentimes have quite a blocking in my speech—maybe you notice how I hesitate. Now, my hesitation is not a groping for words, although that's a sort of a—well, I want to make it seem so, for what you might call protective coloration.

Counsellor. Defend yourself a little bit that way?

S. Yeah. I like to make people think that I'm groping for just the exact word—that I'm a careful thinker, but actually I know right off what I want to say, and when I am fluent, I get very exact and nice diction without having to grope for a word.

C. So that in that particular situation your blocking keeps you from being your best and fluent self. And in that situation, it's speech blocking that is primarily . . .

S. Well, yes. I mean it seems like—well, there wouldn't be any other blocking. No other form of activity than speech is going on, and that's the thing, of course, which I notice—that is, of course the thought—my thought is also to a certain extent blocked—that is they sort of go hand in hand. When I'm able to speak more fluently, I'm able to think more fluently.

C. M-hm.[1]

Intelligence tests. Since learning and unlearning depend greatly upon intelligence, some estimate of this factor must always be made.

The part played by low intelligence in producing articulatory and voice disorders is well known. Not only are children of low intelligence slow to learn to talk, but their speech patterns are

---

[1] Rogers, C. W., *Counselling and Psychotherapy*, Boston, Houghton-Mifflin, 1942, pp. 281–282.

frequently slurred, confused with sound substitutions, and complicated by peculiar intonations. Motor skills are retarded, and speech, the most complicated of all motor skills, certainly demonstrates the effect of this retardation. The feeble-minded child's lack of discrimination, his distractibility, and his lack of response to social stimulation—all contribute to inaccurate and defective speech. Moreover, the same factors make rapid remedial work impossible and necessitate techniques other than those ordinarily employed.

On the other hand, the child of average and superior intelligence can be expected to respond to adequate therapy if his emotional reactions do not interfere. The brilliant child especially can be relied on to take charge of his own case to a large extent, and such self-reliance should be encouraged. These and other equally obvious observations point out the great necessity for a valid estimate of the child's intelligence.

An excellent paper-and-pencil test which does not stress language skills is the California Test of Mental Maturity. We must always remember, however, that defective speech may interfere with expression. Stutterers may prefer to remain silent rather than suffer exposure of their difficulty. Delayed-speech cases are so deficient in vocabulary that they are penalized by any verbal test. Articulation cases are often retarded in reading skills.

Personality tests. Although personality tests can never serve as an adequate substitute for the intensive personality study which much of speech re-education demands, they can often give us a quick picture of general tendencies toward maladjustment. Analysis of the items of such paper-and-pencil tests as the Mooney Problem Check List, the Haggerty-Olson-Wickman Behavior Rating Scale, or the Bell Adjustment Inventory can often open up avenues of exploration that might otherwise be overlooked. In our own clinical practice we have found the Minnesota Multiphasic Personality Inventory, the Murray Thematic Apperception Test, and the Rorschach Ink-Blot

Test to be especially valuable in detecting infantile emotional reactions or hidden anxieties and frustrations.

Achievement tests. These tests are used in speech correction primarily for discovering whether or not a child's educational retardation is due to the influence of his speech defect on reading skills. Articulatory disorders commonly reflect themselves in reading, producing similar errors there, and stuttering and voice cases frequently dislike oral reading so much that it affects their silent skills. Remedial reading can easily be combined with remedial speech work, and improvement in both will frequently solve the child's other scholastic problems. Two excellent batteries are the Stanford Achievement Tests and the Unit Scales of Attainment, but these should be supplemented by the diagnostic reading tests of Gates and Monroe.

Aptitude tests. Since severe speech defectives are often unemployed or are situated in occupations ill-suited to their abilities, they generally need some vocational counseling. We have found the Kuder Preference Record and the Cleeton Vocational Interest Inventory to be valuable aids in this counseling.

Integrating the information. The techniques described above will produce a great deal of information, much of which may have little meaning for speech correction. Even the significant facts obtained by such methods will be worthless unless they can be interrelated so as to give an organized picture of the person we are studying. A mass of disorganized historical facts is not a history, nor is a scattering of environmental data a geography. Some form of organization is likewise necessary in the study of personality. Despite the risk of creating certain artifacts, we have found it clinically convenient to organize and orient our personality information with respect to the following three questions:

1. What marked differences of physical appearance, behavior, or environment distinguished this person from his associates?

2. Which of these differences were approved, which were penalized, and by whom?

3. How did this person react to this approval or penalty?

If our information is sufficient to give an adequate answer to all three questions (at each of the various age levels or stages of social interaction), we shall have gained an excellently integrated picture of the person possessing the speech defect. Although the preceding method for integrating personal data is the result of clinical technique, theoretical justification may be found in its defense. There are almost as many definitions of personality as there are authors who have written about it, yet the majority of them concern themselves with "traits," "reaction tendencies," and "adjustment." These terms indicate that clinical psychologists and psychiatrists, however they may phrase their common problem, are concerned with: (1) physical, environmental, and behavioral differences; (2) social approvals and penalties; and (3) reactions on the part of the individual to these penalties or approvals. In other words, personality is based on *evaluated individuality*.

The importance of physical, environmental, and behavioral differences. Individuality itself is based on the ways in which a person differs from his associates. Those characteristics which he possesses in common with all other members of his group contribute little to his personality. A white skin will not affect his personality development unless he numbers among his associates someone who is not Caucasian. Surpassing beauty, low intelligence, a long nose, pronounced athletic ability, a hearing defect, an ability to use picturesque language, extreme shyness, a speech defect, and many other differences can affect personality development if they set the person apart from his fellows.

I hate my hair. I even hate to touch it. Hair brushes disgust me. I like to throw them when I get mad. And that's funny, because my hair is probably my best feature. Everybody has praised it since I was tiny. Such beautiful blonde hair, so silky, so smooth! I get furious just writing these words, but I've heard those words over and over for years and years. My mother, my sister, my friends (so-called) all were always fussing with it, fixing it, putting it up. My hair was always mentioned . . . but never my hare-lip.

Twenty severe stutterers undergoing treatment by the author were studied very intensively through interviews, autobiographies, conferences with parents and associates, and other devices. Among other results, it was found that many differences in addition to their speech defect had influenced the development of their personalities. Some of the differences that seemed most determinative of their insecurities were: protruding teeth, effeminacy due to the influence of seven older sisters, lack of sufficient spending money to maintain position in exclusive girls' school, a habitual facial grimace (tic), extremely short stature, illegitimacy, a father in an institution for the insane, red hair, and a reading disability. On the other hand, certain differences were viewed as securities, and among those that seemed most significant were: athletic ability, personal beauty, ownership of a pony and many playthings, pronounced musical talent, prestige of having traveled widely, younger playmates, a brother who was a prize fighter, and high intelligence. It may be pointed out that, in each case, the difference in itself was not so important as its interpretation by the speech defective's associates. In some instances, the same difference was interpreted by one speech defective as an asset and by another as a liability.

Since individuality depends upon the persons who are the speech defective's associates, we must know something about his companions at the various age levels. At the preschool level, these are largely confined to the father, mother, brothers and sisters, servants, relatives or friends of the family, and a few playmates. When the child enters school, the teacher and schoolmates may entirely alter the pattern of his differences. Later on, other new associates will enter the person's sphere of social, educational, sexual, or economic contacts, and these will either create new or accentuate old differences. Each of us recognizes that our personalities vary somewhat with the group we join.

My folks never knew what a rat I was, and fortunately they died before they found out. Maybe it would have been better for me if they had. It's tough when both your parents die when you're only fifteen. But I was the perfect little gentleman at home. Fine manners. You know, courteous to old ladies, run and get my Dad's slippers, help my mother, say sir to everyone, be quiet in church, read a lot at home. I sure looked good, but was I rotten inside. I learned to smoke and curse and fight and steal before I was five. I ran the gang and no one squealed if any of them who did the dirty work got caught. My folks thought I was wonderful, and I was when I was with them. When they died though it tore me apart. I lost half of myself and the other half didn't belong either. I was a good twin and a bad twin, and if one twin dies you aren't a twin any longer. I didn't know what to do. Raising hell didn't seem to be any fun any more.

We are not the same persons to our parents that we are to our students. In studying the speech defective, then, we must know his associates if we would recognize the differences about which his personality was built.

A speech defect is naturally an outstanding difference. Most of us speak without breaks in rhythm, peculiar speech sounds, or inadequate tones. Although small children do not tend to perceive a speech defect as quickly as adults, their games and activities depend upon communication, and the speech defect is usually discovered sooner or later. Occasionally we meet a child from a family in which most of the other members have a similar speech defect. Again, we find cases in which the parents have grown accustomed so gradually to a child's defective speech that they fail to recognize it. Children from these families will be likely to develop personality and behavior problems when they first enter school.

Penalties and approvals. The second of the three questions previously mentioned in this chapter asked what penalties or approvals by the person's associates contributed to his personality problem. This question is necessary because personality is not merely individuality but *evaluated* individuality. Differences in themselves are not of vital importance to their possessor. They assume their significance because they are judged or evaluated by his associates. They may be judged as assets, as liabilities, or as neither one. If they are evaluated as assets—as helping to fulfill the desires of his associates—the group will tend to welcome him. If they are judged to be liabilities, the group will tend to reject him. Thus approval and penalty are the results of the group's evaluation of the differences the individual possesses. Fortunately, most groups base their final rejection or acceptance of an individual bidding for inclusion upon more than one difference. They note all of his liabilities and all of his assets, and if the latter outweigh the former, he probably will be accepted. Thus it is possible for a severe speech defective to go through life with a minimum of rejection, even though he never overcomes his liability.

Moreover, different groups will evaluate a speech defect in different ways. A debating society would evaluate it as a much greater liability than would a baseball team. The group will accept the speech defective's difference if its members feel that it is not conspicuous enough to penalize them socially, thwart their free communication, or cause them uncomfortable emotional reactions. If it is overshadowed by other differences, such as a good sense of humor or an ability to listen effectively, it will be tolerated and its possessor accepted. Rejection, acceptance, and toleration are the three possible resultants of evaluating a difference. If we are to understand the speech defective's problem, we must know what rejections, tolerances, and acceptances he has met, and in what groups or through what individuals they have occurred. Many types of penalties are used by society to ensure conformity and to prevent the liabilities of any one individual from handicapping the other members of the group. Some illustrative penalties from stutterers' autobiographies follow:

Most clerks always look away when I get stuck and begin to force. It always infuriates me that they don't even have the decency to look at me. Once I even went to the manager of a store about it and he looked away too.

My father wouldn't ever listen to me when I stuttered. He always walked off. I finally got so I'd say everything to him by having mother give him the message.

People do not usually laugh at my other kinds of stuttering, but when I begin to go up in pitch, they always smile or laugh right out loud. I was phoning a girl today and hung up when I heard her snickering.

My mother always hurried to say the word for me whenever company was in the house. I often asked her not to but she couldn't help herself. It used to shame me so, I'd go up in my room and cry and I never went visiting with them. Sometimes I'd eat in the kitchen when we had strangers come for dinner.

The other boys in the school used to call me "stuttercat" and imitate me whenever I came to school. At first I always managed to be tardy and stay after school to avoid them, but my folks got after me and then I began to fight with them. I got to be a pretty good fighter, but the bigger boys always licked me and the teacher punished me when I hit the girls. I still hate girls.

After I came to high school from the country, everybody laughed at me whenever I tried to recite. After that I pretended to be dumb and always said "I don't know" when the teacher called on me. That's why I quit school.

Every time I'd ask for a job a funny look would come over their face and some of them would say no right away even before I finished what I was going to say. Some of the others, and one of them was a stutterer too, just waited till I finally got it out and then they'd shake their heads. One storekeeper was so sympathetic I could hardly get out of there fast enough.

The worst time I ever had was when a hotel clerk saw me jumping around and called a doctor. He thought I was having a fit.

These are but a few of the many penalties and rejections which any speech defective or any other individual with an unpleasant difference is likely to experience. Imitative behavior, curiosity, nicknaming, humorous response, embarrassed withdrawal, brutal attack, impatience, quick rejection or exclusion, overprotection, pity, misinterpretation, and condescension are some of the other common penalties.

The amount and kind of penalty inflicted on a speech defective are dependent on four factors: (1) the vividness or peculiarity of the speech difference; (2) the speech defective's attitude toward his own difference; (3) the sensitivities, maladjustments, or preconceived attitudes of the people who penalize him; and (4) the presence of other personality assets.

First of all, in general, the more frequent or bizarre the speech peculiarity, the more frequently and strongly it is penalized. Thus a child with only one sound substitution or one that occurs only intermittently will be penalized less than one with almost unintelligible speech, and a mild stutterer will be penalized less than a severe one. *Second,* as Bryngelson[2] has so clearly pointed out, the speech defective's own attitude toward his defect often determines what the attitude of the auditor will be. If the speech defective considers it a shameful abnormality, his listeners can hardly be expected to contradict him. Empathic response is a powerful agent in the creation of attitudes. Third, the worst penalties will come from those individuals who are sensitive about some difference of their own. Since many speech defectives have parents or siblings with similar speech differences, they are often penalized very early in life by those persons.

You ask why I slap Jerry every time he stutters? I do it for his own good. If my mother had slapped me every time I did it I could have broken myself of this habit. It's horrible going through life stuttering every time you open your mouth and my boy isn't going to have to do it even if I have to knock his head off.

Moreover, many individuals have such preconceived notions or attitudes concerning the causes or the unpleasantness of speech handicaps that they react in a more or less stereotyped fashion to such differences, no matter how well adjusted the speech defective himself may be. Finally, as we have pointed out, the speech defective may possess other abilities or personal assets which so overshadow his speech difference that the latter is penalized very little.

After the first week of intensive speech therapy, June, a very pretty twenty-year-old girl asked for a special conference. "I don't want to be a quitter," she said, "and I've never before quit anything I started.

[2] Bryngelson, Bryng, "The Reëducation of Speech Failures," *Quarterly Journal of Speech*, April, 1933, pages 227–229.

But I don't think I can take this. It makes me feel too abnormal. I've stuttered all my life but it really hasn't been anything but a minor nuisance. These other people have suffered so much they've become morbid and strange. I don't think like they do. They're ashamed and afraid. I'm not. I've always talked everywhere and all the time. I've always been popular, had lots of friends and dates. I've never had anyone make fun of my speech or get upset because I hesitated. My stuttering isn't ugly; it just bounces my words around and slows me up, but people always wait and I talk pretty fast anyway. So I don't want to be around those . . . those . . . well, the only word I think of is 'creeps.' I don't want to have my speech so important in my life. I don't want to catch the way they feel. I want to leave here right away."

In considering the effects of these penalties on the personality, we must remember that penalty need not be overt to produce a reaction. Insecurity, a common term in this clinical field, refers to the fear of penalty rather than to its actual presence, and insecurity alone can warp a personality. Speech defectives often become very suspicious and paranoid. They vividly remember the penalties which were inflicted by a few individuals and imagine that all other people have the same attitudes but are too polite to express them. These imaginary or expected penalties can affect an individual as well as the real ones can.

One of our cerebral palsy cases had a bitter and suspicious attitude toward strangers which resulted always in so great an increase in bodily tension that his trembling and spasmodic body movements became much more conspicuous. He was convinced that, except a few intimate friends whom he could trust, all other individuals found his disorder grotesquely amusing. Here is one quotation from a daily report: "Among the people I hated today which you asked me to collect is Joe Zins. He's always cracking wise or telling jokes when I'm around. The other guys think he's good company but I'm on to him. He wants to laugh at me when I begin shaking or talking funny and doesn't dare to, and so he tells a joke so he can laugh then. But he's really laughing at me and I know it."

Reaction to penalty or approval. We have now considered two of the three major factors contributing to the development of the personality: the differences themselves, and the accompanying approvals or penalties. The third factor is the person's reaction to these approvals or penalties. The penalties themselves would have little effect on the speech defective's personality were he, for example, to ignore them. But his reaction to the penalty is probably the most important of all these factors.

A speech defective or any other individual can react to the penalties inflicted by his associates upon his difference in three main ways: (1) by regressive or withdrawal behavior, (2) by aggressive or protest behavior, or (3) by understanding, unemotional acceptance. These reactions themselves may be considered as differences.

Regressive or withdrawal behavior as a reaction to penalty. When a difference such as that of a speech defect is so conspicuous that a group will not accept its possessor, that person may retreat from further attempts in group activity. He may isolate himself as much as possible from others and lead a sedentary life. He may refuse to attempt to cope with reality, and indulge in daydreaming and fantasy. He may retreat completely from the problem of his difference and develop an interest in other things. These other interests may be developed so highly that he will overcompensate for his weakness.

At thirty-two, a very talented singer developed cancer of the larynx, and it was removed surgically. She reacted to the challenge with courage, mastered esophageal speech and began to specialize in the history of musical instruments, playing the lute, the Irish harp and many other of the ancient strings. She said, "I would have been only a second best vocalist and I should have spent my life in self-love, self-exhibition, and frustration. Now I have many more friends and acquaintances. I have things to give. I hardly ever think of myself. It's a good thing I lost my voice."

Compensation in a small degree does not harm a person. It may develop talents and skills which will add to his personality assets. But if all attention is focused upon the compensation, and the difference is completely disregarded, other serious personality problems will arise. The overcompensation itself may be evaluated as a weakness by the group. Finally, an individual may regress to a former stage of life and revel in his past achievements. He may deny that he has any such difference. He may overemphasize his former acceptances by groups and dwell in the remembrance of the days when he made satisfactory adjustments and had his parents and teachers to reinforce his strength if those adjustments failed. All of these mechanisms denote a retreat from reality, a refusal to struggle further with the problem caused by his rejection.

Some speech defectives react in the ways just described. They are especially prone to indulge in such substitute satisfactions as creative writing, music, or reading. They hunt for havens wherein they can avoid the penalties that communication usually provokes.

In a hut by a wilderness in Northern Michigan lives a poet with a cleft palate and harelip who is convinced that the world is not ready for his genius. He has a large folio of rejection slips. He writes constantly, and this is his masterpiece:

> Man Speaks to Man
>
> No?
>
> . . . .
>
> No!

He is quite rational and quite objective. "My parents were very fond of me, their only child. They could not bear to have my palate and lip operated on. Instead they decided to train me to be a genius. Everything I ever wrote they saved and praised. I used to hide the bad poetry but I was never quite sure what was bad. They trained me well, but only in one direction. All I can do is write poetry, advanced poetry. I'm pretty sure it's too advanced. But poets have a hard time living in this society and so do cleft palate people. So I live by myself. Even if I could talk like other people. I wouldn't know what to say to them. Such a course would give me more problems than I could possibly cope with. This is better. Among the things I write should be a few that will be great. . . ."

Sometimes the speech clinic itself becomes such a haven. Withdrawal behavior is often fostered by misinformed parents and teachers, but it never solves the speech defective's problem.

Indeed, it frequently causes him to avoid the speech correctionist who could help him. Moreover, when the associates of a withdrawing speech defective are constantly confronted by his attitude of avoidance, they respond in the same way, and so reinforce the total maladjustment.

Aggressive or protest behavior as a reaction to penalty. Penalty and rejection by his associates may lead an individual to react aggressively by attack, protest, or some form of rebellion. He may employ the mechanism of projection and blame his parents, teachers, or playmates for his objectionable difference. He may display toward the weaknesses of those in the group the same intolerant attitude which they have manifested toward his own. In this way he not only temporarily minimizes the importance of his own handicap, but also enjoys the revenge of recognizing weaknesses in others. He may attempt to shift the blame for rejection. He will say, "They didn't keep me out because I stuttered—they just didn't think I had as nice clothes as the rest of them wore." In this way he will exaggerate the unfairness of the group evaluation and ignore the actual cause. Another attack reaction may be that of focusing all attention upon himself. He can refuse to co-operate with the group in any way, can belittle its importance openly, and can refuse to consider it in his scheme of existence. Finally, he may react by a direct outward attack. A child, or an adult with an easily provoked temper, may indulge in actual physical conflict with members of the group which has not accepted him.

The Case of the Grandmother's Nose

Ivan, whom we straightway named The Terrible, was a very agile little boy of six with completely unintelligible speech. He was a holy terror. Other mothers would sweep their children back into the house when Ivan came tricycling up the sidewalk. No baby-sitter ever sat twice at his house. His mother worked days, probably in self defence, and the boy was cared for by his grandfather and grandmother who lived upstairs. Only the grandfather could control Ivan and when he left the house to go to the store the grandmother would flee to her bedroom and lock the door, because Ivan would occasionally swarm up her and bite her, preferably on the nose. She was hard of hearing and found Ivan's garbled jargon quite impossible to comprehend. Ivan demanded that people understand him. If they did, he was well behaved and cooperative. But when they didn't, he went berserk; he scratched, bit and attacked the object of his hatred. It took two years before Ivan was tamed and talking and our speech clinic still bears certain scars as an enduring memorial to Ivan. So does this therapist's hands.

A rejected individual may spread pointed criticism of the group in a resentful manner. In any of these methods, the object of the rejection does not retreat from reality—he reacts antagonistically and attacks those who made his reality unpleasant.

Among the speech defectives the author has examined, the behavior problems that seemed due to a protest reaction against the group's penalty include: lying, enuresis, constipation, temper tantrums, stealing, arson, suicide, use of obscene language, cruelty to pets, truancy, fighting, destruction of property, disobedience, attempted suicide, sexual promiscuity, and feeding difficulties.

Some speech defectives show few outward signs of these reactions except attitudes of sullenness or non-co-operation; in others, the protest is unmistakable. Unfortunately, these protest reactions do not solve the problem. They merely increase its unpleasantness.

The more the speech defective attacks the group, the more it penalizes him. Often such reactions interfere with treatment, for many of these speech defectives resent any proffered aid. They attack the speech correctionist and sabotage his assignments. The inevitable result of these attack reactions is to push the speech defective even further from normal speech and adequate adjustment.

Intelligent unemotional acceptance as a reaction to penalty. The two reactions previously discussed ignored reality. This third type of reaction involves an admission of reality. A person may honestly state the reason for the group's rejection of him. He may even tell why his difference would be a weakness to that group. There are two kinds of admission: (1) the individual accepts the rejection in an emotional and pessimistic manner; (2) he admits the basis for the group action, but regrets it, and accepts the inevitability of future similar defeats. The second method of admission is an unemotional one in which the person realizes the validity of the group's action. He accepts the rejection wholesomely and takes an objective attitude toward both the group's action and his handicap. The basis of his reactions is the short sentence uttered by the greatest of all mental hygienists, the cartoon character Popeye, who says, "I yam what I yam." The individual with such an attitude says, "Of course I have a difference. I stutter (or have red hair, or weigh two hundred and fifty pounds, or have a big nose), but what of it? That's just the way I am." This type of reaction destroys much of the emotionality and abnormal behavior usually built around a difference. It provides no necessity for using the tricks and subterfuges which always accompany attempts to hide or to minimize a defect. It furnishes the essential basis for subsequent remedial speech work as it brings the defect into the open and allows its possessor to study it thoroughly and to work on overcoming it. No speech defect can be eradicated when it is hidden. It must be seen as a problem to be solved before its possessor can solve it. Johnson[3] gives some excellent examples of this reaction in his monograph on the personality of stutterers, and Bryngelson[4] has discussed the theory of the "objective attitude" in several publications. The student is urged to master these concepts, since they serve as a basis for much speech-correction therapy.

If a speech defective honestly admits his difference, the group will accept it unemotionally. If he states his determination to work on his speech problem, the group's support will reinforce his determination. The group will criticize and encourage him, and, realizing that the disappearance of the handicap will ultimately strengthen its own power, will refuse to penalize him

[3] Johnson, Wendell, "The Influence of Stuttering on the Personality," *University of Iowa Studies in Child Welfare*, 1932, Volume 5.

[4] Bryngelson, Bryng, "Psychological Problems in Stuttering," *Mental Hygiene*, 1937, Volume 21, pages 631–639.

during the remedial process. It not only will enable the defective to enjoy group association devoid of deceit and its accompanying nervous strain, but also will give him a more normal personality and increase his motivation during the period of speech retraining.

The author, in his effort to improve himself as a speech therapist, has religiously kept a file entitled "Clinical Mistakes," which he opens to those student therapists who have become emotional over their own grievous errors in therapy. Almost all of these mistakes are errors of ignorance. Certain facts or traits or patterns of behavior had not been understood. Here is one selection from the file:

G. H., a severe lateral lisper, had been very slow in achieving a good *s* sound. Time after time he would make one but before he could feel it and hear it clearly he would lose it. Three hourly sessions a week for two months showed no improvement. Then one day by putting headphones on him, and introducing a masking noise which would prevent him from hearing himself, we achieved (through placement of the tongue and teeth) a series of prolonged *s* sounds which were perfect. Shutting off the masking noise suddenly and feeding his own *s* through the phones, we enabled him to hear it vividly. "You mean that you want me to make, that high-pitched *sssss?*" he asked? "Sure, that's the very sound you've been trying to make," we replied. "Hell," he exclaimed angrily, "I could have made that the very first day, but if you think I want to sound like Aunt Emma, you're crazy." And he put on his hat and left and refused to return for further therapy.

We found out later that this aunt who lived with the family had been thoroughly hated by G. H. Furthermore, Aunt Emma had an ill-fitting denture which produced a very strident high-pitched whistling *s*. Although his auditory acuity was perfect he had equated the acoustic pattern of the normal *s* with the whistle of his aunt's.

Memo to CVR: Hereafter remember to ask your lispers if any associate has had a peculiar *s* sound. Also: have the case try to make as many different *s* sounds as possible when you examine him. And study your cases better.

References

1. Anderson, V. A., *Improving the Child's Speech*, New York, Oxford University Press, 1953, Chapter 4.

T-F: All other possible causes should be discarded before we accept one of psychogenic origin.

T-F: Regression refers to the occasional errors shown by an articulation case while mastering his new sound.

Essay: What can the therapist do to help a child solve his personal emotional problems?

2. Bender, L., and Woltmann, A. G., "The Use of Plastic Materials as a Psychiatric Approach to Emotional Problems in Children," *American Journal of Orthopsychiatry*, July, 1937, Volume 7, pages 283–300.

Children's activities in playing with modeling clay are observed and interpreted in the light of their emotional conflicts.

3. Bingham, W. V. D., and Moore, B. V., *How to Interview* (third revised edition), New York, Harper & Brothers, 1941.

This is probably the best book on interviewing techniques in all fields. It provides an outline for the training of interviewers which any student could follow.

4. Chapin, A. B., "When a School Child Stutters," *National Parent Teacher*, 1949, Volume 43, pages 14–16.

An example of information to be provided parents and teachers so that they can understand the child's difficulty.

5. Dub, A., "Great Psychological Effects of a Minor Speech Defect," *Journal of Speech and Hearing Disorders*, 1948, Volume 13, pages 251–255.

A case study showing how a defective *l* sound caused a profound emotional handicap.

6. Garrett, A., *Interviewing: Its Principles and Methods*, New York, Family Service Association of America, 1942.

A small book with important contributions from the field of social case work in terms of interviewing skills. An actual interview with comments is provided.

7. Glauber, I. P., "Speech Characteristics of Psychoneurotic Patients," *Journal of Speech Disorders*, March, 1944, Volume 9, pages 18–30.

Ten brief case histories of neurotic patients are given to illustrate the point that emotional conflicts reflect themselves in the speech of these individuals.

8. Hunt, W. A., and Stevenson, C., "I. Psychological Testing in Military Clinical Psychology: II. Personality Testing," *Psychological Review*, 1946, Volume 53, pages 107–115.

A good description of various personality tests and their application to psychotherapy.

9. Irwin, R. B., *Speech and Hearing Therapy*, New York, Prentice-Hall, Inc., 1953. Chapter 5.

T-F: Travis claims we should not be interested in speech defects.

T-F: Irwin recommends the use of the Thematic Apperception Test.

Essay: What personality and intelligence tests are recommended?

10. Johnson, W., Darley, F. L., and Spriestersbach, D. C., *Diagnostic Manual of Speech Correction*, New York, Harper & Brothers, 1952.

Essay: What materials contained in this diagnostic manual could be used to get a picture of the individual's personality?

11. Louttit, G. M., *Clinical Psychology*, New York, Harper & Brothers, 1936.

Contains a complete chapter on speech defects (Chapter 11), and also considers school retardation, specific disabilities in school subjects, superiority, behavior and conduct problems, personality problems, juvenile delinquency, sensory defects, psychoneuroses and psychoses, and neurological and physical disabilities.

12. MacKenzie, C. M., "Facial Deformity and Changes in Personality Following Corrective Surgery," *Northwest Medicine*, August, 1944, Volume 43, pages 230–231.

Patients with facial deformities usually withdraw from society. Remarkable changes in personality may result from corrective surgery.

13. Marquit, S. and Berman, A. B., "Psychological Techniques and Mechanisms in Guidance," *Journal of General Psychology*, 1942, Volume 27, pages 231–240.

Seven case summaries are presented to show the types of psychological tests and methods used in guidance.

14. Peterson, H. A., *Educational Psychology*, New York, Macmillan, 1948.

He stresses the need for learning to handle situations as part of the basic process of education. School problems from the point of view of adjustment are clearly described.

15. Richardson, L. H., "A Personality Study of Stutterers and Non-stutterers," *Journal of Speech Disorders*, June, 1944, Volume 9, pages 152–160.

This reference illustrates the use of various personality tests in speech correction. The author discusses the value of the Rorschach, the Thematic-Apperception test, the Personality Inventory, and other diagnostic aids.

16. Rogers, C. W., *Counselling and Psychotherapy*, Boston, Houghton Mifflin, 1942.

This text has already become a classic in its field: the indirect interview as a device for conflict diagnosis and psychotherapy. Every speech clinician should not only read this book but also train himself in the techniques so clearly illustrated therein.

17. Thorn, K. F., and Bryngelson, B., "An Analytical Study of the Social and Speech Adjustment of Good and Poor Speakers by Means of the Autobiographic Method," *Speech Monographs*, 1945, Volume 12, pages 61–73.

18. Travis, L. E., "A Point of View in Speech Correction," *Quarterly Journal of Speech*, 1936, Volume 22, pages 57–61.

A statement of the basic principles which should underlie speech correction, with especial emphasis on treating the speech defective rather than the speech defect.

4. Psychotherapy

In our definition of a speech defect we included the phrase "or causes its possessor to be maladjusted." In our last chapter we stressed the need for understanding the person crippled in speech and implied that the penalties inflicted by society provoked reactions which did not help the speech defective to live a normal emotional life. Do these presentations mean that all speech defectives are abnormal and need psychotherapy? How much psychotherapy will the speech therapist have to use? How deeply will he need to become involved in this ticklish business? How much training will he need?

Speech defectives need psychotherapy when their reaction to the speech defect is abnormal. But how can we tell? First of all, the concept of *normality* always implies a range of behavior. All of us get angry at certain times and under certain conditions of stress. This is normal. But when a person stays angry most of the time and gets insanely furious because the weather is rainy or the sugar is lumpy or a rubber is hard to put on, he shows himself to be beyond the normal range of irritability. If he starts cutting himself with a knife or in a rage attacks complete strangers, our society arrests him and puts him away for safekeeping and for treatment.

Gene, a boy of seven, in the first grade, was corrected by his teacher three times in one arithmetic lesson for saying "theven" and "thickth." He stopped talking completely both in school, on the playground and at home. Few child lispers would have shown this reaction or maintained it for the three years elapsing until he came to the speech clinic and received psychotherapy. Many such children might have stopped reciting for that day. Many others would have accepted the correction without emotion, but Gene's behavior was definitely abnormal.

Normality, however, depends upon other things also, upon age, sex, social status, the cultural pattern and many other factors. A child of three who banged his head on the floor in a temper tantrum would not be as abnormal as a man of sixty who did the same thing. The man who compulsively insisted on powdering his nose in public would be considered queer unless he happened to be getting made-up for a television camera. A Zuni Indian who devoted his life to acquiring a wealth of blankets, horses, sheep and money would be considered crazy by that culture. The Kalingas, a murder-loving tribe on Luzon, in the Philippines, would be certain of the insanity of any Zuni who showed the dominant traits of the latters' culture: co-operation, non-competition, no physical attack, emotional display, or ambition to dominate. This point has application in speech therapy. If we are to understand the amount of abnormal behavior we must comprehend it not only in terms of its deviation from our own common ways of behaving, but also in terms of the cultural group from which the person came.

We once worked with an Indian from Oklahoma who stuttered. He was a very difficult case, primarily because he was completely unable to get prepared for any word on which he might stutter. It was quite apparent that he did fear certain sounds and certain words because he would pause and hesitate for a long time before attempting them. However, during these preparatory pauses he just seemed to "blank out." He became detached from the situation and from his utterance. During these pauses he was quite relaxed and passive, but he did not seem to hear anything said to him. These were not *petit mal* epileptic seizures. Finally, we found out. "My old grandmother, a wise woman, told me when I was a little boy that if my spirit went to the mountains I would never be afraid. So when I see hard word coming I go to mountains."

Another stutterer, a girl of twenty, came from the highest strata of society in the British set in Montreal, Canada. Her eye contact was perfect, her composure completely unruffled, but her face and mouth went through some of the worst contortions we had ever seen. As soon as one of these contortions had subsided and the word was said she continued as though nothing at all had happened. She too found it very difficult to modify her stuttering. She had been trained to ignore it. This is what she said, "In my set we always ignore the unpleasant, the ugly and the uncomfortable. No one in my whole life ever raised an eyebrow or said a word about my stuttering. They always acted as though I spoke as well as they. *Noblesse oblige*, you know."

Still another stutterer, a Negro, proved completely resistant to any therapy until he had moved North, got a college education, succeeded in business and attained a respected position in the community. "Every time I stuttered to a white man I shamed my race," he said later, "and until I proved myself I could never afford to do anything but hide it. Now I don't care and so I can conquer it."

There are a few speech therapists who tend to look upon all speech defects as though they were, of themselves, symptoms of an underlying emotional conflict. These therapists insist on psychotherapy for every case, a prescription which probably does no great harm if the psychotherapy is well done. Every so called normal individual has enough abnormality within him to profit from some psychotherapy. None of us is always and entirely adequate.

However, there are dangers inherent in such a blanket diagnosis and treatment. The aphasic, the laryngectomy, the foreign dialect case, the cerebral palsied, the deaf child, all these obviously have additional reasons for their speech handicap. To claim that all articulation cases are neurotic baby-talkers refusing to grow up, is to over-simplify the problem. Speech is taught and learned; it isn't instinctively acquired. There are poor teachers and poor learners. To be convinced that *all* stutterers, merely because they stutter, are thereby symbolically biting their listeners, orally masturbating, or refusing the responsibilities of maturity is to show oneself theoretically biased and prejudiced. The child whose voice is overly nasal may not be compulsively identifying herself with her nasal-voiced mother. She may have too short or sluggish a soft palate.

A public school speech therapist was asked to study his 132 cases for two months and then to report on all those who needed psychotherapy. This is his report:

I am not sure, not at all certain of my findings. The more I studied and probed the children, the more emotional difficulties I discovered. In terms of obviously abnormal behavior patterns, there were only sixteen children whom I would refer to a child-guidance center for study and therapy and only two that I would refer to a psychiatrist.

Ninety-two of the children seemed entirely within the normal range. They appeared secure with adequate self-esteem; they were spontaneous in speaking and emoting; little day-dreaming, withdrawal behavior or excessive aggressiveness; they could subordinate themselves to the group activities and also accept leadership in the group; they can learn; they are flexible; they can have fun. They didn't seem too much concerned about their speech problems. Their teachers did not report any of them as problem children.

The other twenty-two children were borderline cases. They intermittently had other problems; truancy, lying, stealing, fighting, mischief, school failures, sick-headaches, crying spells and so on. Most of the children in this group had only one or two of the above patterns of abnormal behavior, and except for this they were just like the ninety-two normal children. They were occasionally in trouble, yet by and large they were getting along. I don't feel that I should refer them for psychotherapy, but I feel that I should be helping them a little, studying them, conferring with teachers and parents, and giving them some release therapy.

The two that I feel should have psychiatric help are these: D. B., a thirteen year old stutterer, occasionally comes to school intoxicated; constantly curses to get speech under way; often truant; has hit several teachers; thrice expelled; parents both work; stormy scenes at home; very belligerent in speech class.

My other case is R. S., a girl with a severe articulation disorder which many people cannot understand. She just sits and looks out of the window in her fourth grade class; is becoming more and more detached daily; does not respond to questioning; seems uninterested in what the other children are doing. Keeps putting the end of her pencil under her finger-nails until they bleed. She too needs immediate psychiatric treatment.

The sixteen cases who I definitely feel need some psychotherapy (but not psychiatric help) are children usually with severe speech defects. One girl has become my silent shadow, following me everywhere, mutely begging for a kind word or glance. Another comes in regularly to speech class crying that all the other kids hate her, that she has no friends and her teacher has it in for her. A boy stutterer never speaks except in a very low voice, never looks at his listener, and constantly hangs his head. A little Latvian boy of ten is still terrified of life and trusts no one, least of all strange men. A lateral lisper of thirteen cannot stop talking, but keeps a finger always in the corner of his mouth. These, and others like them, comprise the group which I would like to work with myself, if only I had time to do some decent psychotherapy. Since I don't, I hope that the child guidance center can accept them.

This report brings us back to the problem of who should do the psychotherapy. The answer is, as we mentioned in an earlier chapter, the person who is qualified. When the case is seriously disturbed we must always refer him to the psychiatrist. With less serious problems, the referral can be made to trained clinical psychologists, or psychiatric social workers. But many of the problems can be solved by the speech therapist. We must remember that there are various levels of emotional difficulty, of anxiety, of compulsiveness, of neuroticism. Whether or not we wish to do psychotherapy, we are compelled to use it, but let us always know our limitations.

A certain amount of psychotherapy is employed by every speech correctionist with every case. When a teacher says to a little child who has finally been able to produce a correct *r* sound, "That's fine, Dorothy; now let's practice it so you can show your mother that you can say the word 'radio' just like big people say it," she is using psychotherapy. When the speech correctionist attempts to persuade the schoolteacher to give the young cleft-palate child a position of some responsibility in the classroom (even if it is only to take care of the chalk supply), we are witnessing a form of psychotherapy. Speech correction is much more than the making and breaking of speech habits. Many of the cases seen by the speech correctionist can only be helped by preliminary or concurrent psychotherapy. Some need psychotherapy and nothing else.

The amount of psychotherapy used with any given case can only be determined by studying his history and behavior. Generally speaking, it is wise to plan a careful program of psychotherapy when the speech defective (1) shows very obvious peculiarities of physique, speech, or behavior; (2) has a history of frequent rejection or other social penalty; (3) reacts by marked aggressiveness or withdrawal tendencies to the normal challenges of life; (4) shows great tension or stress in ordinary situations; (5) rejects or sabotages the efforts of the speech correctionist to improve his speech. The last three of these items can also be used to measure the progress of psychotherapy. When the antagonistic stutterer becomes more friendly, when the tense falsetto-speaking girl becomes more calm and relaxed, when the speech defective approaches his conferences with eagerness and co-operation, the treatment is progressing satisfactorily. When the opposite reactions are in evidence, the speech correctionist should revaluate his methods and diagnoses.

The methods of psychotherapy vary from simple suggestion to profound psychoanalysis. Yet they all seem to be focused on the attainment of the following goals: (1) *to help the speech defective understand his problem;* (2) *to let him get the emotional poison out of his system by freely expressing his true feelings;* (3) *to help him organize and carry out a campaign which will (a) increase his social assets and eliminate or minimize his abnormalities; (b) eliminate or minimize the penalties inflicted upon him; (c) develop attitudes toward his speech defect and other social liabilities which will not handicap him.* We italicize these goals because far too many speech correctionists perform their psychotherapy in a hit-or-miss fashion. Through lack of planning and integration, the result is often so sketchy and incomplete that basic conflicts are untouched. When this happens, progress in speech rehabilitation is slow or entirely blocked.

Fluency for the stutterer or satisfactory *s* sounds for the lisper may be temporarily attained but later lost in a mysterious relapse. If we are to do our work thoroughly and well, we must plan and carry out a systematic program of psychotherapy for the person who needs it.

Helping the speech defective to understand his problems. We once asked a small child who had received some speech-correction help in the public schools to tell us what his speech difficulty was. Although he had a very bad lateral lisp, he finally said, "I don't know. I guess I don't talk slow enough." There is no excuse for such blind treatment. The speech defective should always know what his problems are, and this holds true whether they deal with pronunciation errors or profound emotional conflicts.

A far too common practice in speech correction is the imposition of the problem by the speech correctionist. The latter makes his diagnosis and then forces it upon his victim. He tells the adolescent girl, "You still talk baby talk because you don't want to grow up or accept the responsibilities of maturity. You are afraid of rejection by others of your own age. You still wish to be the child that you once were, protected and loved by your parents and playmates." Even when such a diagnosis is correct, it is unwise to try to foist it upon the case. She will probably reject it anyway, and even when she accepts it as the intellectual truth, she will be unable to change her basic emotional attitudes. It is always wise to let the person with a problem find it himself. The task in psychotherapy is to provide the means whereby this insight can be achieved.

The best method for getting a person to locate and define his problems is free, uninhibited talking. If anyone talks long enough and freely enough he will reveal his basic maladjustment not only to others but also to himself. The art of the speech correctionist comes in creating a situation where the person can feel this freedom of expression. It is not wise to give this assurance directly ("You may feel free to talk to me frankly about anything"). Instead, the speech correctionist should endeavor, by his responses to what the case tells him, to make clear that he is fundamentally interested only in trying to understand. He does not judge. When he does speak, he merely restates the attitudes which have been expressed by the speech defective. He may clarify them, but he never tries to modify them in the direction of better adjustment. The case will do that himself, if permitted to. The speech correctionist never tries to reassure the case that expresses pessimism or hopelessness. He is merely interested. He does not try to convince his case that the latter's fears, hostility, or guilt feelings are exaggerated or unreasonable. If they exist, they are important enough to merit the dynamic listening described in the previous chapter.

There are instances in which the verbalization of insight cannot be achieved. There are cases in which it is not necessary. Here is one from the excellent book by Travis and Baruch.[1]

Speech retardation is merely one aspect of the whole problem of withdrawal. Speech is in great part a means for contact. When contact brings eventual inner pain, why go after it? Speech is in itself a reaching out toward other people. It is a matter of touching. When counter-touch results in inner writhing, why attempt to get it? Why talk?

Jerry apparently had built up this complex. His lack of spontaneity, his shyness, his imperviousness, his lack of initiative, his doless-ness, his lack of speech, were all a part and parcel of the same pattern. His parents were desperate. To disprove feeble-mindedness in their family, they would do *anything*. And so they started on treatment which took Spartan courage.

First, they said, "Hands off," to the older brothers. All teasings and naggings were stopped. Second, the mother began to examine her own attitudes. Gradually she came to see the part her rejection of Jerry had played. She came to recognize too some of the elements

[1] Travis, Lee Edward, and Baruch, Dorothy Walter, *Personal Problems of Everyday Life*, D. Appleton Century Co., New York, 1941, pages 178–79, by permission of the publishers.

which had gone into creating this attitude of rejection in her. She became freer within herself to accept Jerry and to give him some belated loving. Third, to afford Jerry release for the hostility which the parents were willing to grant might possibly e present, all rules and regulations were waived. Jerry went to town. He aggra ated at will. He soiled his bed. He sucked his thumb with vigorous pulls—his first signs of vigorous action of any sort. Slowly these two modes of behavior dwindled. Others took their place. Jerry became destructive. He broke his toys. He broke a window. The crowning glory came on a day when the mother disc vered that he had lined up his father's shoes, her shoes, and the shoes of his four brothers and was throwing them blithely off an upstairs balcony at a man cleaning the street below. Several times the family thought they could stand no more. But stand it they did valiantly. And at last they had their reward.

In about a year's time, Jerry was a new person. He laughed. He ran. He carried out many play projects. He talked and talked well. He was a spontaneous and normal, happy small boy. His semblance of feeble-mindedness had completely vanished. He was, at last, able to use the good intelligence he possessed. He went sailing ahead.

Fortunately, few of our cases require such drastic treatment. But here was a case in which verbal insight was not achieved, and yet the child was able to solve his problem. The important thing in each instance is to break down the old barriers, build a new foundation upon which normal behavior can be built.

Letting the speech defective express his repressed feelings. Speech defective children have all the emotions and repressions common to children in our culture, but they have one special problem in magnified proportions. They meet *frustration* much more frequently than do normal children, who certainly meet it often enough. Among the Pilagra Indians, among the Eskimos, among the Arapesh, the children can do just about anything they please. They are not nursed on a four hour schedule, but fed when they cry. They are close to their mothers constantly. Toilet training is not hurried. Emotional displays are accepted. Our own culture makes it tough on small children and babies. We meet frustration almost from the time we are born. Many of the emotional ills that plague adults can be traced to the frustrations of early childhood.

If we are to understand how great a need the speech defective has for expressing his emotions, we should try to sense the amount of frustrations he has experienced. Here are some reports from adults: The first is from an aphasic veteran shot through the head:

The worst feature of my brain injury was the frustration. I would know exactly what I wanted to say but it would come out of my mouth differently. If I wanted to say "Please pass the cake" my mouth might say "Please part the ice" which didn't make sense to anyone else or even to my own ears. A hundred times a day this would happen. I'd find myself crying or cursing or frozen into some stiff posture or making meaningless movements with my leg and I knew that these were just my ways of trying to handle the complete feeling of inability that characterized my life.

The experience of being misunderstood, of having your listeners ask you to repeat your utterance is the usual state of affairs for most speech defectives.

A severe articulation case, aged 18, said the following:

The most wonderful thing about being able to pronounce my sounds now is that people aren't always saying "What? What's that?" I bet I've heard that fifty thousand times. Often they'd shout at me as though I were deaf and that usually made me talk worse. Or they'd answer "Yes" when that just didn't make sense. I still occasionally find myself getting set for these reactions and steeling myself against them and being surprised when other people just listen.

A cleft-palate child was crying:

I can't talk. I can't talk. . . . I know all the words but Dad doesn't listen right . . . I try and try again and it's important but he can't understand. . . .

A stutterer speaks:

I must be pretty tough because I'm not in the bug house. The constant experience of starting to say something and never having it come out when I want it to should have driven me crazy long ago. I can't even say my own name. Once in a while I get a little streak of easy speech and then wham, I'm plugged, tripped up, helpless, making silent mouth openings like a goldfish. It's like trying to play the piano with half the keys sticking. I can't even get used to it because sometimes I can fear a word and out it pops; then again when I am expecting smooth speech and everything's going all right, boom I'm stuck. It sure's exasperating.

The most common response to frustration is aggression. The golfer breaks his club against the tree. The little boy, deprived of a chance to play ball, attacks the piano with a mallet instead of with his fingers. An adolescent girl who is unable to have dates becomes bitter and sarcastic, verbally attacking both her girl and boy acquaintances. Privation and deprivation are well known to speech defectives. The barriers which block them from achieving their goals are, however, not outside but inside. It is difficult to hate your mouth without hating yourself. Normal speech is pretty effortless, and when one struggles with one's speech organs, the resulting tension makes good speech even more impossible. The lisper who viciously hates his lisp presents a difficult case.

But there are other types of reaction to frustration than that shown by Ivan the Terrible. Some speech defectives persist in attacking anyone connected with the frustrating situation. Others hate and punish themselves by behavior which invites penalty. It is a frequent observation among speech therapists that behavior problems often clear up as soon as the speech problem is solved. The converse can also be true. Other speech defectives, when subjected to the constant frustration of having their communications impeded, "escape from the field." They go into fantasy, day dreaming, unrealistic goal activities.

One of our most severe stutterers, a college student, used to spend three and four hours daily listening to symphonic records up in his dormitory room with the door locked. He would play each recording several times, conducting the invisible orchestra with a baton, stopping the record player every so often to scold the bassoon player or to demand another playing of the previous passage. Said he, "I know it sounds silly, but after a lot of wretched talking it's the only thing that gives me a little peace."

When an individual is constantly frustrated and at the same time deprived of any chance to express his hostility, to find a substitute reward or to escape from the situation, a good deal of anxiety is aroused. This is painful, and the person tries in many ways to reduce the discomfort. He may begin to worry about his health, about his job, about school marks, and actually create difficulties in each of these areas so that they, instead of the speech problem, can be considered the true difficulty.

A seventh grade girl who lalled (distorted most of the tongue-tip sounds) and found it difficult to be understood showed no interest in her speech and refused to come to the public school speech therapist for help. She had frequent attacks of asthma and a poor academic record despite an average I.Q. Finally she was persuaded to come, and after some initial difficulty, she made rapid progress in correcting her articulation. At the end of two months her speech was almost normal, the asthmatic attacks which had absented her from school almost once each week had disappeared, and she was making good grades.

A high school boy, whose control of pitch was very uncertain and whose voice had been "changing" for three years was finally referred to the public school speech therapist. He claimed to have no concern at all about his voice, became angry when it was mentioned, and refused to have a recording made. He insisted his only difficulty was with his school work. He worried constantly before tests, was unable to eat and sleep, always took his books home at night and studied constantly, all this despite the fact that he always did well and made good grades. On the pretext of helping him learn how to study, a series of counselling interviews enabled the boy to understand his anxiety, accept his voice problem and then undergo enough therapy to produce a stable mature male voice. His excessive concern over his studies decreased and he was able to try out for the basketball team.

To summarize, then, we can say that psychotherapy in speech correction always involves some kind of release therapy. If the speech disorder is itself a neurotic symptom, as when a fourteen year old girl suddenly begins to talk baby talk compulsively, or when, without organic cause, a child loses his voice completely, we must provide some opportunity for the expression of hidden emotion. But we must also realize that a speech defect is in itself a very frustrating experience. When the speech itself is defective, a normal avenue for blowing off steam has been blocked. Every speech therapist should learn how to open up the channels and help the speech defective to express and understand his feelings.

Types of release therapy. We have already briefly described the methods of non-directive counselling. More thorough presentations of the technique are given in the references at the end of this chapter. Only a relatively few speech therapists are qualified to do deep psychiatry or psychoanalysis and these types of therapy are for such specialists. The person who works with most speech problems will find plenty to do without having to train himself in these disciplines. Most of our cases merely need a kindly, sensitive and understanding ear. If we can get them to trust us enough to pour out their troubles, fears and unpleasant memories, they will find great relief and new sources of energy with which to conquer their speech difficulties. Often all they need is some adult to support them, to have faith in their ability to solve their own problems. The speech therapist does not judge, nor condemn, but he tries mightily to understand. He becomes so far as possible an undistorted mirror in which the speech defective can see himself objectively and come to tolerate what he sees. In the majority of our cases the anxieties are seldom so strong or the repressions so deep that we must confess ourselves helpless. We do what we can, and only what we can.

Solving personality problems. Release therapy is only a part of the therapeutic process. It does remove many of the emotional blocks and barriers. It permits the person to mobilize his energies and use them constructively. But often there remain handicapping physical differences, lisps to unlearn, poor voice habits to break, or environmental situations which present constant threat. No matter how much repressed hostility is released in play therapy with the speech therapist, if the father still reacts to the boy's stuttering by slapping him in the face we have much more to do. If the baby-talker is cross-eyed, if the cerebral palsied girl has not learned to button her coat we have certain fundamental differences with which to contend. So far as possible, we should attempt to eliminate or minimize all conspicuous differences which provoke social penalty if we are to remove the emotional fraction of the total handicap.

There are various ways of eliminating these differences after they have been discovered. If the difference is of a physical nature (cross-eyedness, protruding teeth, obesity, club feet, and so on), we may be able to find surgical, dental, or medical methods for eradicating it. If the difference is environmental or economic, we may be able to eradicate it by enlisting the various social agencies or by removing the child from his present environment. If the difference is behavioral, we may be able to re-educate his parents and associates or to alter his environment so as to remove the irritating stimuli that set off the inadequate behavior. We must always remember that a *difference* implies a relationship, a comparison between two or more individuals, and we may eradicate a difference by having its possessor join a group of individuals who possess similar traits. Thus we often find a swift release from emotional conflict when the speech defective enters a speech clinic and discovers many other individuals with similar peculiarities. His own difference is minimized by such association. When he is able to include himself as a part of normal society by perceiving that its members, too, possess penalizable differences to which they might react inadequately, much progress has been made. For this reason, one technique useful in speech correction is the conduction of a class dealing with personality and behavior problems or a class in public speaking, taught from the mental-hygiene point of view. The speech defectives in these classes soon learn that the so-called normal speakers have their own differences and insecurities. When carried out under the direction of an able clinician, exhibition and discussion of these differences seem to have much value. Confession and verbalization provide excellent means of reducing their influence, and good-humored admissions or exaggerations tend to diminish the emotion with which they are invested. At any rate, the first task in the management of a personality problem is an attempt to eradicate or minimize those differences about which the individual has built his inadequate behavior. One case study may be cited:

E. G. was a cross-eyed girl of nineteen with a very severe stutter. Although of superior intelligence, she left school in the ninth grade and, from that time on, she very seldom left the confines of her home. She dominated her wealthy parents in every way and shirked every type of responsibility. When guests came for dinner, she had the servants serve her in her room. She spoke very little to anyone but read a great deal. Simulated heart attacks were used to control her parents. She refused to see any physician. Financial reverses and the death of her father forced her to do something about her speech defect after an attempt at suicide failed because of lack of courage. Enrolled in the speech clinic, she immersed herself in the literature on stuttering but failed to carry out any assignment which entailed any persistence, courage, or exhibition of her speech defect. Faced with dismissal, she pleaded that she wanted to co-operate but did not have the will power. She declared that she thought she would acquire some if she were permitted to remain. She was told that she could return if she would have an operation for her strabismus and carry out a certain set of assignments at home. The operation was very successful, and, when she returned a year later, her personality seemed to have changed entirely. She had performed not only all of the assignments given her but many more difficult ones as well. She had prepared herself for college entrance examinations, had taken dancing lessons, and had obtained and held a job in a restaurant for some time. For the first time she seemed to have some self-respect and courage to undergo temporary unpleasantness in order to achieve a future goal. Her stuttering was still present though its severity had decreased. She co-operated in every way and progressed rapidly in her speech work. Her explanation for the change was succinct: "Having my eyes fixed gave me my chance."

Eliminating and minimizing the penalties and unmerited approvals that produce maladjustment. Psychiatrists have often pointed out that the most inadequate behavior shown by maladjusted individuals occurs in situations in which there are features similar to those of traumatic or extremely unpleasant situations in the early history of the individual. This is especially true of penalties. Even the so-called normal person tends to react childishly at times, and those times are characterized by the presence of people or penalties bearing some important resemblance to childhood conflict situations. These present situations which are reminiscent of old maladjustment are the danger spots for which our speech defective must be prepared, and through our intensive study of the person, we teach our cases to recognize those persons and penalties which bear dangerous resemblance to old conflicts. This very recognition helps to prevent the almost involuntary response which is aroused by such reminiscent conditions. Many adults are not lying when they claim that they "just couldn't help" their inadequate behavior when confronted by old penalties. After the clinician helps them to be on their guard, they can develop the ability to inhibit the sudden overwhelming impulse to withdraw or attack.

Another useful technique in preventing the person or penalty from acting as a cue to set off the old response is to associate with it some other incompatible response, such as one that is humorous or absurd. The clinician may also deliberately create experimental situations, warning the speech defective beforehand, in which the old penalties or unmerited approvals are used. The speech defective is asked to react as adequately as possible and to substitute an adequate response for that which he commonly uses in such situations. He may also be asked to use similar penalties himself and to see how others react to them. Occasionally, the clinician should set up an experimental situation with the old penalties and give the student permission to react in the old way. With permission, the reaction becomes absurd. Paranoidal tendencies may be checked by assignments to exaggerate and burlesque them on a verbal level. A written diary of all suspected penalties as compared with those which are overt will also help.

Above all, it is necessary that all penalties and rejections be verbalized and confessed to someone—the speech correctionist or psychiatrist, as the case may be. Much of the emotion can be dissipated in this way, and the confession will serve as an excellent opportunity for dispassionate analysis and proposals of alternative reactions. Speech is one of the best forms of emotional catharsis we have in our clinical repertoire.

Of course, many of these suggested techniques cannot be used with young children. With them, it is necessary to educate the parents and associates to refrain from using those penalties and rejections that are producing the inadequate behavior. Occasionally this is not possible because of the personality problems or resistances to clinical recommendation which the parents or associates themselves possess. In this event, it is wise to try to take the child out of the old environment, at least for a time. Visits to more co-operative relatives are useful. Occasionally summer camps, private schools, or boarding homes provide such a change. It is also possible to change the environment to some extent by getting the speech defective to join new groups or to make new acquaintances who will react less savagely to the objectionable difference. Even when the parents seem willing to co-operate, it is wise to provide some clinical supervision, since parents find it difficult to change their ideas and penalties. Family conferences at the end of the day and weekly reports to the clinician in which the parents confess to each other, or to the clinician, their failures in following the new regime will help to ensure its success.

Eliminating the withdrawal and attack reactions which characterize the maladjustment. We must remember that eliminating the objectionable differences themselves will not always remove the inadequate behavior shown by the maladjusted speech defective. Withdrawal and attack reactions may become habitual responses to almost any type of insecurity. They may have originally been born and nursed by some former difference which no longer exists. Arising as specific responses to a specific situation, they tend to become generalized and stereotyped. Since they themselves become behavioral differences that are penalized by the group, they attain a permanence that is independent of their original causes. It is necessary, therefore, to focus some therapy directly upon the reactions themselves.

In general, the procedure to be followed is similar to that described in the last section. The withdrawal and attack reactions must be brought up to consciousness, confessed, guarded against, voluntarily practiced in unemotional or clinical situations, exaggerated, associated with humorous and other incongruous attitudes, freed from their satisfactions, penalized, and inhibited. Above all, their motives must be analyzed. They must be understood in terms of the past history of the individual and in terms of their contribution to the personal unpleasantness and social handicap.

It is not sufficient or possible merely to teach the speech defective to give up or inhibit his old withdrawal or attack reactions. He must be taught some substitute response to rejection, penalty, and all the other forms of insecurity. The substitute response usually taught is that which we have described in an earlier part of the chapter as the "objective attitude," or the intelligent unemotional acceptance of the objectionable difference as a problem capable of some solution. With some cases, it is impossible to teach this objective acceptance immediately, and a clinician will occasionally teach withdrawal reactions to an individual who habitually attacks, or aggressive reactions to the person who characteristically retreats. Even with these cases, the final aim is always the acquisition of an attitude that will face the facts realistically.

The nature of the objective attitude has already been discussed. Intelligent and well-informed parents teach it to their handicapped children when they are very young, and these children find it just as natural as other children find withdrawing or attacking. Among children as well as adults, the objective attitude is most easily taught through example. Attitudes are notoriously contagious, and if some of a child's associates, parents, or teachers adopt such an objective attitude, he will usually acquire it almost unconsciously. Occasionally, it will be necessary for him to be taught some verbalization of it, so that its expression will not be too hesitant or floundering when challenged by his associates. When possible, the child should be taught to accompany his unemotional admission of the difference with a statement of belief in its eventual disappearance. Thus one untutored cross-eyed child was overheard saying to his teasing associates, "Sure I'm cross-eyed and I'm going to Chicago some time and get it fixed." All teasing stopped. A difference about which the possessor was not sensitive was not worth wasting teasing upon—so reasoned the group. A well-conducted speech-correction class in which groups of children are taught together is a very efficient agent in the teaching of this attitude. They learn it from one another as well as from the teacher.

When working with older children or adults whose maladjustment is very marked, one must utilize the same indirect methods for teaching the objective attitude; but, in addition, more direct methods can be employed. The philosophy behind the objective attitude should be taught with emphasis on its reasonableness. The speech defective, for example, should be shown, through analysis of actual situations, how his withdrawal or attack reactions contribute to the present unpleasantness and perpetuation of his handicap. He should be shown that the speech defect is but a small part of his total handicap, that an emotional handicap is usually added to every physical or behavioral one, and that often the former far overshadows the latter.

We tend to think of speech therapy and psychotherapy as being two distinct areas of healing, but this need not and should not be the case. Every speech activity can involve psychotherapy. All learning and unlearning involves the whole person. Every success or failure adds or subtracts to the ego. The important point is that the therapist must conceive of his role as not only a speech therapist but a psychotherapist. Let us cite some examples:

Bernard, whose mother had a cleft palate, was unable to emit his *s* or *z* sounds orally. They always emerged in a snort from his nose.

He had a nasal lisp. His basic pattern of behavior was self-deprecation. He was always "running himself down." He continually apologized for his awkwardness, his stupidity, his very existence. He seemed to spend so much of his energy in verbalizing his inadequacies that he had little left for self-improvement.

A student speech therapist in his therapy plan one day had this activity: "I have rigged up a double platform device so that Bernard's nose will rest on the upper shelf and his mouth on the lower. By putting feathers on both shelves, I will ask him to try to blow off the lower feather while making a prolonged *s* without having his nasal snort displace the upper feather. I'm certain he can do it if he really tries, but I bet he'll fail."

The supervisor made this suggestion: "Tell Bernard most people with nasal lisps can do it successfully four times out of ten trials. People with normal speech can do it nine times out of ten. Ask him to make a guess as to how many successful trials he might get."

When the activity was carried out, Bernard guessed that he would only do it right two times at most. His actual performance was six successes to four failures. Then he was asked to make another estimate for another ten trials. He said he expected to make only four successes, still an underestimate since he made seven good responses. Nevertheless, we have here a change in the direction of reality. This use of aspiration and performance levels was a bit of active psychotherapy.

A public school speech therapist had a group of third grade children all of whom had severe articulation problems. Feeling sure that most of them had been frequently misunderstood and frustrated in their efforts to communicate, she began the sessions with the following activity. She put on a Halloween mask and said, "I'm the big person who can't understand when you try to tell me something. Today, you can get even. Whenever this big person says 'What?' or 'What did you say?' or 'Say that again' you can stick out your tongues and yell at me. Each of you listen to what the other children say so you can help yell it so I can't help but understand." She reported later that she made more progress in that one session than she had for a period of several weeks.

Another had a mildly spastic child who never participated in any of the group work until one day she took him aside and said, "Billy, will you help me remember something? I always forget to take my bag with me when I leave here. I'd sure appreciate it if you'd hold it all of our speech period and remind me to take it at the end of the period." The little ritual took place each time and Billy began to take part in the group therapy.

Cynthia was a frozen-faced little girl of nine. Only her eyes were alert and they were always on guard. She did what she was told but never volunteered. One day the speech therapist put on a puppet drama in which Zo-Zo the clown had a good many unpleasant things happen to him. Zo-Zo always laughed. Then when one of the other children said viciously to him, "Zo-Zo, your mother's dead," the clown stopped laughing and said sadly, "Oh why can't I cry? I want to cry. I don't want to laugh now. Please help me cry. Please!" At this point Cynthia broke into gales of tears. The class was dismissed but Zo-Zo and the teacher had quite a long interview with the girl which, with the release, finally led to the solution of her problem and a new out-going personality.

These examples are but a few of the host that could be given. Speech therapy always has some psychotherapy in it. Let us learn to use it wisely.

References

1. Allen, F. H., *Psychotherapy with Children*, New York, Norton, 1942, Chapter 3.
   T-F: A certain amount of authoritarianism is necessary to maintain control of the therapy situation.
   T-F: Little interpretation should be used in child psychotherapy.
   Essay: Why should children be permitted to express their hostility?
2. Axline, V. M., *Play Therapy*, Boston: Houghton Mifflin, 1947.
   One of the best books in the field of child psychotherapy through play.
3. Beckey, R. E., "The Children's Speech Clinic," *Hygeia*, 1944, Volume 19, pages 663–664.
   A popular descrip ion of speech therapy through play.
4. Bryngelson, B., Chapman, M. E., and Hansen, O. K., *Know Thyself*, Minneapolis, Burgess Publishing Co., 1951.
   T-F: The adjustment quiz is to be used by children from 8 to 10 years.
   T-F: It is wise for stutterers to advertise their stuttering.
   Essay: How can this book serve as an aid in psychotherapy?
5. Despert, J. L., "A Therapeutic Approach to the Problem of Stuttering in Children," *The Nervous Child*, 1943, Volume 2, pages 134–147.
   The importance of maternal attitudes in affecting the treatment

of stuttering in young children is clearly presented. The attempt to solve the child's anxieties is described.

6. Gustavson, C. G., "A Talisman and a Convalescence," *Quarterly Journal of Speech*, 1944, Volume 30, pages 465–471.

An excellent account of the introspections of an adult "cured" stutterer which is especially useful in illustrating the withdrawal reactions as the person himself feels them and in portraying the individual's attempts to free himself from their frustration.

7. Hinckley, R. G., and Hermann, L. M., *Group Treatment in Psychotherapy*, Minneapolis, University of Minnesota Press, 1951.

A detailed account of the principles of group psychotherapy. Many of the features described are similar to those commonly found in the group therapy for adult stutterers.

8. Lemert, E. M., and Van Riper, C., "The Use of Psychodrama in the Treatment of Speech Defects," *Sociometry*, 1944, Volume 7, pages 190–195.

Many different types of psychodramatic activity are cited to show their application to speech correction. Puppets, phonographically recorded dramatizations of interview material, and other similar agencies are used in the diagnosis and treatment of personality problems.

9. Rogers, C. W., *Counselling and Psychotherapy*, Boston, Houghton Mifflin, 1942.

The final part of this book is a transcription of a phonographically recorded series of interviews with a neurotic stutterer which led to excellent insight into the nature of his problems and provided their solution. The student can here see psychotherapy in action.

10. Whiles, W. H., "Treatment of Emotional Problems of Children," *Journal of Mental Science*, 1941, Volume 87, pages 359–369.

A common-sense approach to children's emotional problems with emphasis on environmental alteration.

11. Whitten, I. E., "Therapies Used for Stuttering: A Report of the Author's Own Case," *Quarterly Journal of Speech*, 1938, Volume 24, pages 227–233.

In this case report of a successful treatment of stuttering a preliminary psychiatric therapy was followed by speech therapy. Both are described in sufficient detail to give proper perspective to both.

12. Will, N., "A Six-Month Report on the Personality Development of a Thirteen-Year-Old Stuttering Boy," *Quarterly Journal of Speech*, 1944, Volume 30, pages 88–95.

The picture of the child's personality at the beginning and end of therapy is given, together with a description of the methods used in altering his behavior patterns.

5. How Children Learn to Talk

⊔⊓⊓

It may seem odd at first to the student of speech therapy that an entire chapter on the development of speech should be included in a text dealing with the speech disorders. The reason for its inclusion is simply this: the large majority of speech disorders date from infancy. The child has somehow failed to gain the proper articulation, vocal or fluency skills which normal children master without too much difficulty. Our culture demands a high standard of speech very early in life but few parents know how to teach a child to talk. It is difficult to understand the abnormal except by comparison with the normal. Moreover, we can learn much about therapy by studying how the normal child acquires his speech skills.

The problem. Many new parents seem surprised when asked if they know how to teach their baby to talk. They usually answer that babies learn to talk just as they learn to breathe or swallow. Let us examine this common assumption. James IV of Scotland deliberately isolated two children at birth under the care of a mute nurse, and it is said that when they first spoke they "spak very guid Hebrew," a conclusion which conveniently confirmed the royal prediction that any child exposed to such an environment would learn to speak in that tongue. However, Kaspar Hauser, who had been forcibly imprisoned when a child and kept in an isolated cell for sixteen years, had no speech at all. Nor did Lucas, the Baboon Boy of Africa, Victor, the Wild Boy of Aveyron, or Kamala, the Wolf Girl of India. An eight-year-old boy, Tamasha, when found in the jungle of Salvador in Central America, had only one actual word among his animal grunts and growls. Only after a long and difficult course of training did he develop a meager vocabulary.

It is true that many children learn to speak without any conscious or deliberate teaching on the part of their parents. Indeed, some children develop speech despite incredibly poor teaching methods, emotional conflicts, and parental neglect. In a similar manner, even though some children have learned to read by spelling out Burma-Shave signs along the highway, we still employ elementary schoolteachers who spend years preparing for their task of teaching children how to read. The skills involved in speech are far more complex than those in reading, yet, how many parents have ever read a word on the subject of teaching a child to talk? It is even difficult to find material related to the teaching of talking. Anyone who has observed the average parent bombarding his baby with the wrong type of speech material at the wrong time and in the wrong way will not marvel that there are so many speech defectives. Nor will he be surprised to learn that most of the speech disorders begin during the first years of life. Libraries are crammed with books on how to teach everything from advertising to zoology, but you will search long and far for a book on the teaching of talking, the most useful of all our communicative skills. Because of this basic neglect, the speech defective is with us still, usually as still as possible.

A question almost impossible to answer is "When did your child learn to talk?" The skills involved in speech begin to be acquired as soon as the child is born and are seldom perfectly mastered, even during a lifetime. Much of the speech learning during the first six months is relatively independent of the stimulation given by the child's parents. Even in the crying and wailing of infants the short, sharp inhalation and prolonged exhalation so fundamental to true speech are being practiced. Lip, jaw, and tongue movements involved in the production of all the speech sounds in all human languages are repeatedly performed. The early awareness of these movements and their accompanying sounds provides the foundation for speech readiness. Throughout the first years of life there are many ways in which parents can help or hinder the development of speech. Their knowledge or ignorance determines whether the child shall learn to talk because of his parents' efforts or in spite of them. Their application of principles, so obvious that we wonder why they should ever be violated, will determine whether the child's speech will be an asset or a handicap. Time after time the speech correctionist tries to trace the cause of a stutter or an articulatory defect, only to lose it in the vague parental memories of childhood. It is vitally important for the student of speech correction to know how speech develops.

First Through Sixth Month

Crying, whimpering, reflexive sounds. The child is learning to talk when he draws his first breath and lets out the yell that announces his arrival. He is learning to talk as he sucks and swallows, belches and smiles, for co-ordinations used in these activities are used in speech.

However, many of these activities are reflexive in nature. The birth cry itself seems to be nothing more than the automatic intake of air across taut vocal cords. During the first two weeks, most of the infant's vocalization is of this sort. It seems to have no intent or meaning. Variations in intensity account for practically all the variety that can be heard in the squall. Most of the vocalization occurs during pain, hunger, cold, or some other discomfort, but the nature of the irritation cannot be distinguished by the type of squall.

Even during the first month, the vocalizations vary from child to child. One infant may coo and laugh when taken from the breast; another may whimper; and still another may kick and scream. Research indicates that even at this period there are more vowels and consonants used in noncrying vocalizations than in whimpering, and more sounds used in whimpering than in ordinary crying.

The noncrying sounds are composed of grunts, gurgles, and sighs, and include most of the front vowels, the consonants *k*, *l*, *g*, and the glottal catch. These particular consonants involve contacts and tongue movements similar to those used in swallowing. All of these sounds are accompanied by movements of the arms, legs, or trunk. They sometimes occur during the act of sucking or immediately after feeding. Compared to later vocalizations, the noncrying sounds produced by a healthy baby during the first month are relatively infrequent. More crying is done than whimpering, and more whimpering noises are produced than noncrying ones. Perhaps it was this fact which led one scientific father (4), faithfully and no doubt solemnly, to record his baby's wails, first phonographically and then in the phonetic alphabet. After a profound mathematical analysis of the records, he concluded that the wails increased in pitch. Most night-walking fathers would agree that the wails also increase in loudness and meanness.

Many parents seek to prevent all crying, although a certain amount of it does exercise the child's vocal and respiratory coordinations as well as its parents' patience. They jounce their baby up and down, juggle it back and forth, or rock it, pat it, and whirl it until it is dizzy enough to end its crying through unconsciousness. Other parents resolutely ignore their newborn's howls because of a mistaken fear that they might spoil the child. These babies may cry away so many of their waking hours that their speech-sound repertoire will be necessarily limited. As we have seen, fewer sounds are used in crying than in noncrying speech. Again, many parents interrupt their children's automatic vocalization by embracing them or conversing

TABLE 1

SUMMARY OF MOTOR AND SPEECH DEVELOPMENT
(First Through Third Month)

	Motor Development	Response to Adult Stimulation	Speech Development (type of vocalization and conditions under which it occurs)	
			Type	*Conditions*
FIRST MONTH	Occasionally can lift head. When one part of the body is stimulated, the whole body becomes active.	Will push away adult's finger if pressed against baby's chin. When laid prone on flat surface, makes crawling movements. Reflex smiling movements to tactual, organic, or kinesthetic stimulation.	**END OF FIRST MONTH** *Crying:* Vowels (usually nasalized): æ, ɛ, ɪ, e, ʌ. Consonants: l, h. *Whimpering:* Vowels (often nasalized): i, ɪ, e, ɛ, æ, ʌ. Consonants: k, g, h. *Noncrying* (sighs, grunts, explosives, etc. Not likely to be nasalized): Vowels: i, ɪ, e, ɛ, æ, ʌ, ʊ, u. Consonants: h, k, g, l.	Hunger, pain, discomfort, fatigue, lack of exercise, strong sensory stimuli. Has intense conditions of the types listed above. Relief from conditions of discomfort.
SECOND MONTH	Able to follow a horizontally moving light with eye movements. Can lift head and chest off the floor when prone. Can turn from side to side.	Soothing voice will occasionally stop crying. Social smiling and laughter if eye contact and smiling accompanies adult's voice.		
THIRD MONTH	Sits with support. Holds head steady.	If adult interrupts child's vocalization by voice, child will either increase own vocalization or stop altogether. Occasionally will imitate exact intonation and phonetic form, but usually automatically responds to adult speech by own formerly practiced sounds. Responds to angry vocal tone by crying; to pleasant one by cooing, sighing, and other noncrying vocalization.	**END OF THIRD MONTH** Same sounds as above, plus a very few more. Pitch of crying slightly higher. Relatively more noncrying vocalization. If the child's attention is attracted (eye movements fixated on adult, who smiles and speaks to child) he will often respond by vocalization. Crying begins to be differentiated according to type of discomfort: pain, hunger, etc. In some children, repetitive chains of sounds ("gagagaga") appear in states of comfort. Back consonant (k, g, ŋ) sounds relatively frequent.	

TABLE 2

SUMMARY OF MOTOR AND SPEECH DEVELOPMENT

(Fourth Through Sixth Month)

	Motor Development	*Response to Adult Stimulation*	*Speech Development* (type of vocalization and conditions under which it occurs)
Fourth Month	Will reach for, but miss, dangling objects. Will accept and hold an object. Sits up easily with support.	The typical (imitative) response of infant vocalization to the mere hearing of speech and voice seems to decrease in frequency at this time, not to reappear until the ninth month. Interruption of babbling by adult speech usually causes silence unless adult is not sensed as a meaningful stimulus.	More babbling and vocal play (repetitive chains of syllables) than ever before. They occur more frequently when the child is alone. They are accompanied by smiles, laughter, gurgles, and other sounds indicatory of comfort and well-being.
Fifth Month	Sits alone momentarily. Turns from back to side. Pulls hair and nose.	Responds to human voices in absence of visual contact by head and eye turning. Responds automatically to friendly tone by smiling and angry tone by crying. Vocalizes displeasure if loved toy is removed.	Occasional reinforcement of babbling if parents interrupt with the syllable being spoken by the child and speak it softly in the proper rhythm so it creates no interruption.
Sixth Month	Squeaks a rubber doll. Can reach for object and put it in mouth. Rolls from back to stomach. Can grasp dangling object. Sits alone thirty seconds or more. Can hold two cubes.	Child no longer reacts automatically to friendly or angry tones but rather to the accompanying features of the situation. Follows a vertically moving object with eyes.	The babbling not only consists of more or less regular patterns of phonetically similar syllables but there is also a marked rhythm. These chains of sound often begin in a whisper, rise to a crescendo of intensity (though not of pitch), and then subside. More noncrying sounds than at three months. Nasal sounds begin to appear in babbling as well as in crying.

97

with them. They should let the vocal play period complete itself. During this first period the muscular development of the tongue may be delayed and abnormally high palatal arches may be produced by bottle feeding with improper nipples. These organic conditions may delay speech development.

In the baby's second and third month he begins to respond to human speech by smiling and vocalization. This vocalization has little resemblance to adult language. The coos, gurgles, clicks, grunts, and sighs do include a few consonants and vowels that we may recognize, but the father should not become discouraged if he says "Daddy! Daddy!" and the child responds with "wah." At least the baby is producing vocalization, and as anyone who has ever worked with a deaf-mute knows, that achievement is no small one. Parents should encourage this almost instinctive tendency to vocal play by combining a few gentle vowels with smiles, and then waiting the four or five seconds the baby needs before he responds. Most parents never give their children this necessary time interval. They should! A good share of this vocal play is carried on when the child is alone and it disappears when someone attracts his attention.

One child played with her babbling each morning after awakening, usually beginning with a whispered "eenuh" (Lina) and repeating it with increasing effort until she spoke the syllable aloud, whereupon she would laugh and chortle as she said it over and over. The moment she heard a noise in the parents' bedroom this babbling would cease and crying would begin.

The parents who joyfully rush in and ruin this speech rehearsal are failing to appreciate its significance in the learning of speech. The child must simultaneously feel and hear the sound repeatedly if it is ever to emerge as an identity. Imitation is essentially a device to perpetuate a stimulus, and babbling is self-imitation of the purest variety. When the babbling period is interrupted or delayed through illness, the appearance of true speech is often similarly retarded. Deaf babies begin to babble at a normal time, but since they cannot hear the sounds they produce, they probably lose interest and hence have much less true vocal play than the hearing child. Mirrors suspended above the cribs of deaf babies have increased the babbling through visual self-stimulation.

Babies babble most freely after food and drink—even as you and I—and yet most parents use this postfeeding period to bombard the infant with such a hodge-podge of verbal, visual, and tactual sensations that they are bound to inhibit the self-stimulation that might occur. They tickle his feet, tell him he looks like his Uncle Oscar, lift him up to test his poundage, and flood his ears with endearing verbiage. It must be difficult to be a baby trying to learn to talk.

The next major advance in the use of speech material may be called the stage of socialized vocalization, and it begins, in the majority of children, about the fifth month. The child begins to use his vocalization (with more vowels than consonants) for getting attention, supporting rejection, and expressing demands. Frequently he will look at an object and cry at the same time. He voices his eagerness and protest. He is using his primitive speech both to express himself and to modify the behavior of others. This stage is also marked by the appearance of syllable repetition, or the doubling of sounds, in his vocal play. He singles out a certain double syllable, such as *da-da* and frequently practices it to the exclusion of all other combinations. Sometimes a single combination will be practiced for several weeks at a time, though it is more usual to find the child changing to something new every few days and reviewing some of his former vocal achievements at odd intervals. True disyllables (*ba-da*) come relatively late in the first year, and the infant rejects them when the parent attempts to use them as stimulation.

Seventh Through Ninth Month

Practice of inflections. The next stage appears during the seventh to ninth months and is marked by the appearance of tone variation and inflection in the vocal play. The child practices

TABLE 3

SUMMARY OF MOTOR AND SPEECH DEVELOPMENT

(Seventh Through Ninth Month)

Motor Development	Response to Adult Stimulation	Speech Development (type of vocalization and conditions under which it occurs)
Sits alone easily. Stretches out arms to mother. Cutting first teeth.	Usually rejects adult demands for imitation but occasionally will form sounds with silent mouth movements. Responds by pursuit or flight movements to coaxing or threatening gestures if accompanied by vocalization.	Much more variety, occasional disyllables heard in babbling—occasional periods when same sounds are repeated for several days.
Stands with help. Begins to crawl. Will offer toy. Cutting first teeth.	Begins to combine babbling with gestures of reaching, rejecting. Calls for attention. If adult interrupts by imitating child's rhythmic pounding, clapping, or the motor play, the child will show marked perseveration in the activity. Toward the end of the eighth month, the child will imitate adult's physical rhythmic movements (clapping, nodding, etc.).	Toward the end of the eighth month the child begins to inflect his babbling, changing the pitch suddenly, repeating the commanding, complaining, declaring, questioning intonations of adults. Begins to duplicate in his own private vocal play the "mama," "dada" and "bye-bye" words spoken so often by his parents but does this as a form of babbling rather than as a response to adult stimulation. More phonetic variety in crying as well as in babbling. More back vowels used in both.
Stands, holding furniture. Sits up alone. Stepping movements. Sways to music.	Responds to strangers by retreating or crying and to other children by exploration or crying. Beginning about the ninth month the child will hold out arms if adult prepares to pick child up by showing same activity.	Higher pitch level and more pitch variation. Crying (yelling) often used to get attention. Babbling proportionately more frequent form of phonation than at five months.

inflections of every sort, those of questioning, command, surprise, and many others never used by the parents. It is interesting to note that during these months the child frequently repeats over and over sounds and inflections which are too complicated for an adult to imitate.

We have previously spoken of various stages of development, but it should be made very clear that, although most children go through these stages in the order given, the activity in any one stage does not cease as soon as the characteristics of the next stage appear. Grunts and wails, babbling, socialized vocalization, and inflection practice all begin at about the times stated, but they continue throughout the entire period of speech development.

It is during this period that the baby begins to use more of the back vowels (u, ʊ, o, ɔ) in his babbling. According to Irwin and Curry (10), 92 per cent of all vowels uttered by babies are the front vowels as compared to the 49 per cent figure for adult speech. They say, "It is evident that a fundamental process of development in early speech consists of the mastery of the back vowels." It is interesting that when we work with adult articulation cases we prefer syllables such as *see* and *ray* and *lee* to those involving the back vowels like *soo* and *low*. Front vowels seem to be more easily mastered.

The baby, through his vocal gymnastics, gradually masters the co-ordinations necessary to meaningful speech. But it must be emphasized that when he is repeating *da-da* and *ma-ma* at this stage, he is not designating his parents. His arm movements have much more meaning than those of his mouth. It is during these months that the ratio of babbling to crying greatly increases. Comprehension of parental gestures shows marked growth. As the summary (Table 3) indicates, the second period of imitation begins. The child now responds to the parent's stimulation, not automatically, but with more discrimination. His imitation is more hesitant but it also seems more purposive. It begins to resemble the parent's utterance. If the father interrupts the child's chain of *papapapapapapapapa* by saying *papa*, the child is less likely than before to say *wah* or *gu* and more likely to whisper *puh* or to repeat the two syllables *puh-puh*. During this period, simple musical tones, songs, or lullabies are especially good stimulation. The parent should observe the child's inflections and rhythms and attempt to duplicate them. This is the material that should be used for stimulation at this period, not a long harangue on why mother loves her little token of heaven.

After the Ninth Month

Some time during the period between the tenth and eighteenth month the normal child learns to say his first true words. Comprehension shows a great spurt of development at this time. As Table 4 indicates, gesture and imitation grow in complexity. The baby suddenly becomes a very human being. He learns to walk and to talk and to feed himself, three of the most fundamental of all human functions. He's quite a fellow indeed. Let us see how he masters his first words.

Teaching the child to say his first words. It is usually thought that the child learns to talk by imitation, but if by imitation is meant the exact reproduction of that which is seen or heard, certainly no such imitation occurs. It is true that, during the last months of the first year, most children seem to make some attempts to reproduce movements which they witness, but rarely are these movements exact. Imitation, as used in the larger sense to denote attempted reproduction, seems to be motivated by the desire to perpetuate the stimuli which intrigue one's interest. It is the child's way of maintaining his interest. The child's memory span is very weak and short, and to compensate for this deficiency he seeks to perpetuate the stimulus by repeating it. This accounts for the doubling and repetition of syllables in the vocal play and for the persistence with which he pounds the rattle on the table.

When the process of speech imitation is studied, we discover that it begins when the parent starts to imitate the child. This

TABLE 4

SUMMARY OF SPEECH DEVELOPMENT
(Tenth Through Twelfth Month)

Response to Adult Stimulation

Begins to comprehend a few words when accompanied by gestures or presentation by adults ("no-no," names of family).

Will fix object with eyes when its name is pronounced.

Responds discriminatively to words spoken in friendly and angry tones.

Will patty-cake when parent pronounces the words or even the rhythm of the rhyme when other vowels are used.

Great interest and attention paid to isolated adult words if they are always associated with things or activities important to his needs.

Fights with playmates for desired objects.

Will imitate two tones sung by adult.

Should imitate "dada" by twelve months.

Child will occasionally imitate sounds produced by clocks, dogs, cows, and adult exclamations without demand.

Child often responds to parental demand for imitation by a partial duplication. He will say "p" for "pap." If parent gives a disyllabic word, child often responds by reduplication.

Speech Development

Pronounced efforts to imitate are marked at this stage, especially if adult interrupts vocal play by speaking the sound being produced.

Will imitate number of syllables as well as sounds involved.

Readily imitates sounds already practiced and occasionally sounds new to the child or ones not present in the contemporary vocal play.

Echolalia occurs if the adult's words are introduced unobtrusively into the child's vocal play. (Echolalia—in a dream—is much more accurate than voluntary imitations.)

Occasionally, the child will respond to adult verbal stimulation by a delayed speech attempt.

Will accompany gestures by vocalization.

Some children acquire first true words.

may sound paradoxical, but its truth will be apparent when the situation is defined. During vocal play the child happens to be repeating the syllable *ma*. The hearing of the sound interests him, and so he repeats it again. Suddenly the sight of his mother interrupts his response to his own stimulation, and he lapses into silence. But the mother, unaware of the perfection of her technique, says to him, "Mama? Did you want mama?" and immediately the interesting stimulus is there again. Wishing it to continue, he makes the same vocal coordinations he made when alone, and again the same interesting sounds are heard, *mamaamaama.* Whereupon the mother rushes to the phone to tell her husband that the child has spoken his first word.

This, of course, is not strictly true, for only when the child uses the word as a definite tool of communication with such a meaning as "Mother, come here," or "Mother, lift me up!" can we say with certainty that he has acquired his first word. Nevertheless, the process of word acquisition has been described. The first step in teaching a child to talk should be the imitation of the sounds being made by the child during his vocal play. This should be preceded, if possible, by the parental imitation of other movements, such as pounding the table. If the child can be stimulated to return to his own former pounding by watching the parent pound, half the battle is won, for the first requisite is gained: the perpetuation of a stimulus given by another person. In imitating the speech of the child, the parent should seek to interrupt the child's activity before it is completed. For example, if the child is saying *da-da-da* over and over, it is wise to interject the parental *da-da* as soon as the child's first *da* has been produced. This will produce the most favorable conditions for getting the child to return to his own former activity, and usually he will maintain it much longer and much more loudly than he usually does. At first only a few sounds should be used in this way, preferably those that later can be used to represent the people doing the training. Thus the child will acquire *mama* in a situation which always represents her presence, and it is wise for her to say the word whenever she picks the child up. Thus the child will come to associate the interesting sound with the person, and it will thereby come to have meaning.

The child should be given such training until he responds consistently with eager repetition whenever the parent has interrupted vocal play by imitating his vocalizations. After that it is wise for the parent to utilize the silence periods which occur during the babbling as intervals of strong stimulation with the sounds previously used by the child. For example, the child has been babbling and suddenly becomes silent. The parent then attracts his attention and repeats *mamama* (or any other syllable which the child has been practicing). If the child will respond to this stimulation by attempted repetition, a second step in word acquisition has been taken. After considerable training involving the practices of both steps, the parent having been careful to pick the appropriate times, the child will suddenly surprise everyone by using the word very meaningfully, perhaps accompanying it with the gesture of reaching. In similar fashion, other early words may be taught.

In one sense, it may be said that the first words are acquired through stabilization. Out of all the vocal tangle of sounds produced by the baby, certain monosyllables or repeated syllables appear as familiar entities. They already have meaning for the child since they have expressed his needs or bodily conditions. He has played with them on so many pleasant occasions that they are old friends. He knows them well. Now, these same syllables become associated with certain conventional gestures (*bye-bye*) or consistent objects (*mama*) which appear repeatedly in his daily life. The first words have been his for a long time. They merely get a stabilized adult meaning.

One parent, whom we studied with some interest, tried by every device of conditioning known to educated idiots to have his boy say the word "Ralph" (the father's name) as his first meaningful word. He worked with the boy for hours. When the first word did arrive (fourteen months late) it was "teetee" and referred to a cat.

Even as certain gestures such as reaching become stabilized from the wild undifferentiated arm-swinging of the infant, so, too, do the first words from their early matrix of vocal play.

Gesture is very important in stabilizing the first words. Sometimes it is almost too powerful.

We observed one child who had the following history. At nine months the mother stretched out her arms to the child whenever the latter asked through gestures to be taken up. At nine months, eight days, the child would imitate the mother by reaching out bimanually whenever the mother did so. The mother then began to say "mama" whenever she used the gesture. At 9:14, the child would say it with the mother as they stretched out their arms. At 9:16, the child said "mamama" as she responded to the mother's silent gesture of reaching. On the same day she also said "mama" as she reached for her cup. At 9:19 she said "mama" to the father when he reached out to take her. Long after she could say "Daddy" imitatively and spontaneously, the gesture of reaching was always accompanied by "mama."

Fortunately, the effect of the accompanying gesture is seldom so persevering. Phonetic and intonation patterns of adult vocalization usually accompany the gesture and are perceived by the child as a whole. He responds not merely to the warning shake of the parent's head but to his own imitative head wagging and to the peremptory tone of the phrase "No. No!" and, if these fail, to the swat on his bottom as well. Even the mother's turning of her head or body as she recognizes and says "Daddy" is a meaningful gesture. Comprehension of speech for the baby consists of his interpretation of gesture, intonation patterns, and the presence of syllables which he has previously practiced. Those gestures spontaneously used by the child are much better than any that parents could think up. If you interrupt his hand-waving by your own similar gesture, and say "bye-bye" and then take him outdoors, the word will be learned fairly easily. But if you try to teach him to kiss his father's picture and say "Daddy" at the same time, the work will be long and hard and perhaps useless.

These first words of the child may sound very much like those of adult speech, but they differ greatly in meaning. Some of them are no doubt "abracadabra" words. The child says "mama" and magically she appears. Other early words are mere signs of recognition or acquaintanceship. "Ba" may mean, "I know you. You're a ball. You're that round smooth thing I throw and bounce." He utters it with the same smug self-satisfaction that our friends manifest when, hearing a familiar musical phrase, they pat their egos and murmur, "Brahms, of course!"

Speech at eighteen months. At eighteen months, the child is toddling about the room pushing chairs and toys from one position to another. He climbs without discrimination. He spills with a spoon but manages to feed himself after a fashion. His handedness is pretty well established. Extremely active, he seldom plays with any one object or activity very long. As fond of music as before, he now prefers marches to lullabies except before bedtime. When angry, he screams, kicks, or holds his breath, but this mass activity is not focused or directed against any particular person. He initiates games such as "Peekaboo" and seems to take great pleasure in "making" adults co-operate. A large empty box is his dearest toy. He usually plays beside other children rather than with them, and he plays better alone. He relies on adults for assistance and attention but shies away from strangers. He should never be asked to speak to them at this age.

At eighteen months the child's speech activity consists of *a few meaningful words*, a little solitary *vocal play*, some *echolalia*, and a great deal of what we shall call *jargon*. Again, let us repeat that we are discussing the mythical average child. The average child has acquired from ten to twenty meaningful words with which to manipulate his elders and express his needs. He not only has names for members of his family but for many other things. Some typical examples are: (mo) for *snow;* (ɔgɔn) for *all gone;* (baɪbaɪ) for *bye-bye;* (aɪt) for *light;* (kækə) for *cracker;* (pap) for *pot.* Many of these are used as one-word sentences and they are very general in their reference. (kækə) can refer to *cracker* or *bread* or even to the fact that the dog is chewing a bone. Many parents lose a great deal of pleasure by not trying to solve these little crossword puzzles of infancy.

Parents of our acquaintance put the problem to us in these words: "Why does our eighteen-month-old daughter refer to both the cat and a champagne bottle by the same word *dih* (dɪ)?" At the time we could not answer, but during the child's third year the word *dih* changed to *ding* (dɪŋ), then to *dink* (dɪŋk), and finally to *drink*. The child had been fascinated by the sight of the cat drinking its milk.

Occasionally the use of one word will spread to include a great many unrelated objects. The child feels little of his parents' confusion when he uses the word *behbuh* (bɛbə) to mean first "baby" then "bib," then "bread and butter." In this instance, the referential spread was no doubt due to the phonetic similarity of all these words. Had the parents taught them at different times or with different intonation or stress, the spread would not have been so great. Soldiers and others who suffer damage to the brain show these same symptoms.

Many early words are generalizations because they are so few and must serve a child so often. When a child who learns the word *puppy* as the designation for his varying perceptions of dogdom is suddenly confronted by a pony, he must needs make *puppy* do for both until he gets a new term. One child used the sound *fffff* as a generalized word for flowers. We also use a similar generic term. But he used *fffff* for perfume, for cigarette smoke, and for the figures on the wall paper. As the child comes to discriminate between objects, he needs terms to fix the contrasts involved. As long as ponies and dogs are merely big creatures with four legs on the corners and a hairy coat, they require but one word, and *puppy* is adequate. But when he realizes that ponies neigh, and he can ride on them, and they are bigger and eat carrots and never sleep by the fireplace— then a new word is needed, and it is acquired.

How, then, do children acquire these new words? The answer seems to be that at the moment when the child is undergoing some new experience in perception, or has an urgent desire to manipulate some new object in order to know it better, the adult intervenes, supplying a new word. If the child perceives this vocalization as part of the total experience, and at the same time produces the word through imitation, he finds he has a more efficient tool than the old generalized word. As the process repeats itself, the child comes to realize the greater expressiveness of conventional language forms. The whole process is, of course, also influenced by other factors: by the child's growing discrimination, by the strength and constancy of adult intervention at the crucial moments, and even by the natural responsiveness of the child.

These first words are used by the child even in his play. He yells "bell-bell-bell" (or a reasonable facsimile thereof) to himself as he rings it. He repeatedly labels the eyes, nose, and ears, not only of the mother who taught him but of his dog or doll, and he pokes them in the labeling. The early words are still accompanied by gesture or pertinent activity. He needs the parents' gestures in order to comprehend their utterances, and so he gestures and speaks in his turn. Only about one fourth of his speech attempts on these words can be understood by strangers. Each family seems to elect one of its members as interpreter. Nevertheless these first ten or twenty words of the eighteen-months-old child are a wonderful achievement. His manner shows that he knows it even if you do not. One child beat his chest and war-whooped whenever he used a new word successfully.

Jargon. The largest share of the average eighteen-months-old child's speech is *jargon*. This unintelligible jabber is probably more important for speech development than people realize. It is the lineal descendant of vocal play, but it differs from the earlier babbling in its rich variety and its seeming purposiveness. The child seems to be talking to other people or to his toys, rather than playing with the sounds themselves. He seldom repeats the same syllable.

One boy, aged 19 months, was observed banging a teddy bear with a hammer and between wallops addressing his victim as follows: "Gubba! Dadda bo-bo!" (Another hammering.) "Show gubba mahda." (Hammers again.) "Ashlee? Baá!" (Throws teddy bear over his shoulder.) In phonetics, the discourse was transcribed: gʌbə dædə bobo . . . ʃo gʌbə madɑ . . . æʃli . . . bɑ . . .

Often this conversational jargon includes words he has mastered. Reaching out his dish for more ice cream he said, "ɛːɛ adə mamə iːɪ nænə aɪ kim ʃlæ?" The words which we have underlined are certainly understandable, and perhaps (nænə) refers to "banana," a favorite food, but the other syllables are difficult to interpret. And most of the child's jargon is even less intelligible.

As Gesell (6) phrases it, "At eighteen months her jargon was beguiling. She would talk confidentially for minutes at a single stretch, uttering not a single enunciated word but conveying much emotional content." As this quotation hints, jargon is probably the child's practice of fluency. Most young children swim in a river of fast-flowing meaningless adult jargon. Why should they not imitate their elders in fluency even as they copy their speech sounds and inflections? Certainly the gap between the few halting words of the child and the ceaseless ebb and flow of adult speech is very wide. Jargon is the bridge. It reaches its peak at eighteen months, dropping out rapidly, and it is usually gone by two years. A few children never use any jargon. When words fail they gesture or cry or remain silent. Most babies are like adults. They must talk whether what they say makes sense or not.

Vocal play and echolalia. The babbling play of infancy still appears, usually when the child is in bed or alone. He plays with repeated syllables or prolonged sibilant sounds. His new teeth enable him to produce new whistling sounds and so he must practice them. Often you can hear him whispering to himself and working up to the crescendo of vocalization. Prolonging sounds with his finger in mouth, or fumbling rhythmically with lips, he discovers again (and not for the last time) how fascinating he is. Jargon is his vocal response to a vocal world. Vocal play is his private rehearsal.

Echolalia appears very markedly in some children during this period, and it probably occurs in all children occasionally.

By this term we mean the parrotlike echoing of words he hears. Occasionally whole phrases and sentences will be repeated so faithfully that the parent fairly jumps. In one instance a year-and-a-half-old girl almost wrecked a church service by saying, "and ever and ever amen!" fourteen times in the middle of the preacher's sermon. She had only spoken a few words prior to this event and she never uttered the phrase again for years. Parents frequently use echolalia to teach their children nursery rhymes, most of which are first learned backwards. The parent says, "The cow jumped over the moon." "Moo," says the child automatically. Soon the parent begins to hesitate before the last word, and the child fills in.

Echolalia occurs almost instantly and unconsciously as if in a dream. The child's attention is elsewhere. Feeble-minded adults show a great deal of echolalia, as do aphasics and some psychotics. Any fairly normal person who has ever held a conversation with one of these echolalics will never forget the experience:

Are you ten years old?
Ten years old?
Yes.
Yes.
I mean . . .
I mean . . .
When is your birthday?
Birthday?
Yes.—Oh let it go!
Let it go.

There madness lies. But in little children echolalia is a normal stage of development and, sensibly, they pass through it in a hurry. It is seldom observed in the normal child after two and a half years.

Speech at two years. By the time the child reaches his second birthday he should be talking. Speech has become a tool as well as a safety valve or warning siren. He is saying things like: "Where Kitty?" "Ball all gone." "Want cookie." "Kiss baby."

"Go bye-bye car." "Shut door." "Big horsie cry." "Put 'bacco in pipe."

Simple and compound sentences are often heard. The jargon is almost gone. His articulation is faulty; his speech rhythms are broken; his voice control ranges from loud to louder, but he has learned to talk. He may still turn out to have any of the speech defects, but he isn't mute. Not by a good many decibels, he isn't.

In summary, we may say again that children *learn* to talk. Their parents do the teaching, and it is usually very poor. Because of the widespread ignorance concerning speech development and the teaching of talking, many children: (1) fail to practice their speech sounds in vocal play; (2) do not learn how to imitate sounds; (3) do not learn that sounds can be meaningful and useful tools; (4) do not practice or profit from their jargon; (5) resort to gesture and other substitute behavior rather than develop a growing vocabulary, and therefore they (6) lay the foundation for defective speech.

The prevention of speech defects. Much has been written about the correction of speech defects but little about their prevention. The reason for this state of affairs is the general ignorance concerning the development of speech, especially during the preschool years. And yet it is precisely during these years when the majority of speech defects first appear. Stuttering begins during this period; the lispers fail to master the pronunciation of the sounds which other children are achieving; the whining voice of the little girl is reflecting that of her complaining mother. If parents knew how to teach their children to talk, and how to aid them in mastering the speech skills required in adult speech, there would be fewer cases for the speech clinic or the speech correctionist.

The young child has much to learn in the months that surround his third birthday. Prohibitions become important in his life and he becomes negative in turn. Bursting with energy, he meets frustrations at every turn. He must learn to become a social being, whether he wants to or not. The world of words becomes vastly important to the three-year-old. Through speech he finds expression for his emotion. By means of talking, he manipulates his associates and satisfies his needs. He has great need for fluency and precision of utterance.

The few infantile words that he learned during his first two years cannot possibly serve his growing needs. He now needs to express relationships and qualifications. He needs plurals and gender. He becomes conscious of the past and the future, and these demand new verb forms. The whole problem of English syntax presents itself as a challenge to the three-year-old. At the same time, his needs for a larger vocabulary are increasing. "What's that? What's that?" is a game which every parent learns to play, on the answering end. The three-year-old is into everything strange. He tests and tries everything, including the patience of his associates. These explorations yield him many moments of confusion when something never before seen has no name to identify its impact. Thus one three-year-old, who had shown precocious speech development with few if any breaks in fluency, suddenly observed a parachute descent and cried out "ε-ε-ʌ-ʌ-ε -bʌ (gesture of pointing and excited breathing), -bʌd-bʌd- goʊ-bum." At the time, her normal speech was being recorded, and therefore the transcript was accurate. Her usual speech was rhythmic and fluent. It is interesting also that she showed a return to earlier phraseology: "go boom" for the "fall down" which she had been using for over a year. Under the pressure of haste, the unfamiliarity of the experience, the confusion of *airplane* (εꝪ) and *bird* (bʌd), both of which were probably felt to be inadequate, the child's fluency broke down and she showed hesitant speech similar to that of primary stuttering.

Besides learning the conventional forms of syntax and acquiring a new vocabulary, the young child must also perfect his pronunciation and articulation. He has many errors to eliminate: the reduplications "goggy" for "doggy"; the use of the labial *w* for the tonguetip *l* and *r* sounds; the use of the *t* and *d* for the *k* and *g* plosives; the omissions of many of his final sounds. He also has many new co-ordinations and sound combinations to master: the precise grooving of the tongue for the sibilants; the transitional timing of the vocalization and movement on the affricatives (tʃ) and (dʒ) and the glide (j); the preparatory positioning of the tongue for the second sound in such blends as *sl, fr,* and *pl.* If these seem like a lot for a three-year-old to master, it must be said that we have only mentioned a few of them. All these and many other articulation skills must be mastered and perfected until they can be used at fast speeds and under conditions of excitement.

Finally, the child is attempting to conform to the patterns of the parent's speech with respect to fluency and phonation. Just as he imitates his father's pipe-smoking or his mother's sweeping with extreme fidelity, so, too, will he imitate their inflections and voice quality *and* attempt to imitate their fluency. It is in this last item that much of our trouble with stuttering begins. Children of this age do not have the vocabulary or the other skills well enough in hand (or mouth) to be able to keep their fluency up to adult standards. The adults about them speak to one another and to the children themselves in compound-complex sentences, in paragraphs that flow one after the other in endless series. If they pause, it is for so short an instant that the child cannot get his speech under way. Grown-ups often penalize interrupting children, but they will interrupt the child's speech with impunity. They finish the child's sentences before he has been able to get them half said. They interrupt to correct a plural or a pronoun or a past participle, and often seize the opportunity to rush on with their own flow of verbalization. When a child tries to adopt an adult fluency pattern of which he is not capable, or if he is bombarded by many of these parental interruptions, he will have hesitant speech. Anyone who has tried to speak a half-learned foreign language with a fluent native will understand what little children undergo. The average parent does not realize what has happened until the child's speech fails to develop normally.

If this childish urge to speak as fluently as his parents when he has neither the vocabulary nor the other necessary skills can precipitate stuttering, we should try to decrease its intensity. Whenever frustration is produced by having an aspiration level far above the person's performance level, we should try to reduce the former. In the case of the child learning to talk, the problem can be solved fairly simply. If the parents will speak to the child, using short phrases and sentences, using simple words whose meaning he can comprehend, using the simplest of syntax, the child will never need to feel speech frustration. He can achieve these fluency patterns without too much difficulty. We have been able, clinically, to free many children from primary stuttering by merely getting their parents to speak more simply. As an example let us quote from a parent's report:

Each evening, as you suggested, we have been holding a family conference and confessing to each other our errors in handling Ruth. Among other things, we found ourselves constantly talking over her head. Today, for instance, I said to her, "Ruth, do you suppose you could go to the bath room and bring down some of the dirty towels and washcloths? Mama's going to wash." She looked at me intently, then went upstairs and came down with some soap, and said, "Woothy wa-wa-wa-wash bath bath. . . ." and she stuttered pretty badly. So I thanked her for the soap and said, "Ruthy go upstairs. Bring Mama washcloth, please." Her face lit up, and she ran upstairs and down again in a hurry, bringing me the washcloth and a towel too. Then she said, "Woothy bwing wash coth. Nice girl." I begin to see what you mean by speaking more simply.

One need not talk baby talk in order to speak more simply. We must merely give our children fluency models within their performance ability.

If we are to prevent speech defects, we must prevail upon parents to change their present policy of sporadic correction and *laissez faire*. They must learn how to help the child master the difficult skills with which he is confronted in adult speech. They must learn how to keep from making speech learning difficult. They must not do all the wrong things so blithely.

Helping a child gain vocabulary. Most parents are eager

enough to help the child to get his first twenty or thirty new words. Some parents are even too ambitious at first; they try to teach such words as "Dorothy" or "Samantha." But their teaching urge soon subsides. The child seems to be picking up a few words as he needs them. Why not let him continue to grow at his own pace? Our answer does not deny the function of maturation in vocabulary growth. We merely say that parents should give a little common-sense help at moments when a child needs a new word, a label for a new experience. When parents notice a child hesitating or correcting himself when faced with a new experience, they should become verbal dictionaries, providing *not only the needed new word, but a definition in terms of the child's own vocabulary*. For example:

John was pointing to something on the shelf he wanted. "Johnny want . . . um . . . Johnny want pretty pretty ball . . . Johnny wanta pretty . . . um . . . " The object was a round glass vase with a square opening on top. I immediately took it down and said, "No ball, Johnny. Vase! Vase!" I put my finger into the opening and let him imitate me. Then we got a flower and he put it in the opening after I had filled it partially with water. I said, "Vase is a flower-cup. Flower-cup, vase! See pretty vase! (I prolonged the *v* sound slightly.) Flower drink water in vase, in pretty vase. Johnny, say 'Vase!'" (He obeyed without hesitation or error.) Each day that week, I asked him to put a new flower in the vase, and by the end of that time he was using the word with assurance. I've found one thing though; you must speak rather slowly when teaching a new word. Use plenty of pauses and patience.

Besides this type of spontaneous vocabulary teaching, it is possible to play little games at home in which the child imitates an older child or parent as they "touch and say" different objects. Children invent these games for themselves.

"March and Say" was a favorite game of twins whom we observed. One would pick up a toy telephone, run to the door of the playroom and ask his mother, "What dat?" "Telephone," she would answer, and then both twins would hold the object and march around the room chanting "Tɛpoʊn, tɛpoʊn" until it ended in a fight for possession. Then the dominant twin would pick up another object, ask its name, and march and chant its name over and over.

In all of these naming games, the child should always point to, feel, or sense the object referred to as vividly as possible.. The mere sight or sound of the object is not enough for early vocabulary acquisition. It is also wise to avoid cognate terms.. One of our children for years called the cap on a bottle a "hat" because of early confusion.

Scrapbooks are better than the ordinary run of children's books for vocabulary teaching because pictures of objects closer to the child's experience may be pasted in. The ordinary "Alphabet Book" is a monstrosity so far as the teaching of talking is concerned. Nursery rhymes are almost as bad. Let the child listen to "Goosey Goosey Gander, whither dost thou wander" if he enjoys the rhymes, but do not encourage him to say the rhymes. The teaching of talking should be confined to meaningful speech, not gibberish. The three-year-old child has load enough without trying to make sense of nonsense. When using the pictures in the scrapbooks, it is wise to do more than ask the child to name them. When pointing to a ball, the parents should say, "What's that?" "Ball." "Johnny throw ball. Bounce, bounce, bounce" (gestures). Build up associations in terms of the functions of the objects. Teach phrases as well as single words. "Cookie" can always be taught as "eat cookie." This policy may also help the child to remember to keep it out of his hair.

How to prevent hesitant speech. Hesitant speech (pauses, accessory vocalization, filibusters, abortive speech attempts) occurs as the resultant of two opposing forces. First, there must be a strong need to communicate, and second, this urge must be blocked by some counterpressure. Some of the common counterpressures which oppose the desire for utterance are:

1. *Inability to find or remember the appropriate words.* "I'm thinking of- of- of- of- uh- that fellow who- uh— oh yes, Aaronson. That's his name." This is the adult form. In a child it might occur as: "Mummy, there's a birdy out there in the . . . in the . . . uh . . . he's . . . uh . . . he . . . he . . . he wash his bottom in the dirt." Similar sources of hesitant speech are found in bilingual conflicts, where

vocabulary is deficient; in aphasia; and under emotional speech exhibition, as when children forget their "pieces."

2. *Inability to pronounce or doubt of ability to articulate.* Adult form: "I can never say 'sus-stus-susiss-stuh—stuhstiss— oh, you know what I mean, figures, statistics." The child's form could be illustrated by "Mummy, we saw two poss-poss- uh- possumusses at the zoo. Huh? Yeah, two puh-possums." Tongue twisters, unfamiliar sounds or words, too fast a rate of utterance, and articulation disorders can produce these sources of speech hesitancy.

3. *Fear of the unpleasant consequences of the communication.* "Y-yes, I-I-I- uh I t-took the money." "W-wi-will y- you marry m-me?" "Duh- don't s-s-spank me, Mum-mummy." Some of the conflict may be due to uncertainty as to whether the content of the communication is acceptable or not. Contradicting, confessing, asking favors, refusing requests, shocking, tentative vulgarity, fear of exposing social inadequacy, fear of social penalty in school recitations or recitals.

4. *The communication itself is unpleasant, in that it re-creates an unpleasant experience.* "I cu-cu-cut my f-f-f-finger . . . awful bi-big hole in it." "And then he said to me, 'You're fi-f-fired.' " The narration of injuries, injustices, penalties often produces speech hesitancy. Compulsory speech can also interrupt fluency.

5. *Presence, threat, or fear of interruption.* This is one of the most common of all the sources of speech hesitancy. Incomplete utterances are always frustrating and the average speaker always tries to forestall or reject an approaching interruption. This he does by speeding up the rate, filling in the necessary pauses with repeated syllables or grunts or braying. This could be called "filibustering," since it is essentially a device to hold the floor. When speech becomes a battleground for competing egos, this desire for dominance may become tremendous. More hesitations are always shown in attempting to interrupt another's speech as well as in refusing interruption.

6. *Loss of the listener's attention.* Communication involves both speaker and listener, and when the latter's attention wanders or is shifted to other concerns, a fundamental conflict occurs. ("Should I continue talking . . . even though she isn't listening? If I do, she'll miss what I just said. . . . If I don't, I won't get it said. Probably never. . . . Shall I? . . . Shan't I?") The speaker often resolves this conflict by repeating or hesitating until the speech is very productive of speech hesitancy. "Mummy, I-I-I want a . . . Mummy, I . . . M . . . Mumm . . . Mummy, I . . . I want a cookie." Disturbing noises, the loss of the listener's eye contact, and many other similar disturbances can produce this type of fluency interrupter.

If we are to help prevent the disorder of stuttering from getting started, especially when there seems to be some familial or natural tendency toward fluency breaks, it would be wise to arrange the child's environment so as to eliminate these disturbing influences as much as possible. The situations which produce them can easily be avoided. When they have occurred and have produced hesitant speech, the parents can introduce other speech-play experiences which will facilitate fluency. Most parents have no knowledge of the influence of these conditions on speech, and forewarned is forearmed. We have been able effectively to change many a young stutterer's speech environment so that his symptoms entirely disappear by giving his parents this summary of influences productive of hesitant speech, and asking them to record and report each instance of their occurrence. Let us help our children learn how to talk and decrease the malinfluences that upset or retard speech development.

How to help the child master his articulation skills. There are three main ways in which parents can help their children eliminate baby talk and attain normal pronunciation skills: (1) Children should be taught the characteristics of the various speech sounds. (2) They should be given help in vocal phonics. (3) They should be taught to correct themselves. In a short five- or ten-minute period daily, simple speech games should be played to help the child identify the characteristics of each of the consonants. At first these games should consist of simple prolongations of some continuant consonant, the sound being used to identify the movement.

We used a little porcelain kitty of which he was very fond to help him get acquainted with the *s* sound. We played a sort of peekaboo game. Whenever we thought Bob was occupied we would poke the porcelain kitty around the corner and say *ssss*. Soon he was calling the toy *ssss*. He would say, "Gi' Bobby *sssss* kitty." Three weeks after we started this game he used his first good *s* in a real word, the word *ice*. Previous to this time he had either left off the *s* or used a *t* instead.

Many modern nursery schools are incorporating speech play as part of their daily activity. Here are the games used in one nursery school of four-year-olds. Modifications of them for individual home work are easily made.

1. *The "m" sound.* Have the children press a forefinger against one nostril then against the other as they hum *m m m m mee mee.* Have them pretend to be a band and play simple tunes using their noses as horns.

2. *The "p" sound.* Give each child a very thin strip of paper and, holding it vertically over the mouth by a finger pressed under the nose, make it move out as they say *puh, puh, puh.* Tell them they are motor boats and have them move across the room as they say *puh, puh, puh,* blowing the paper with little puffs of air.

3. *The "k" sound.* Tell them they are crows whose tongues got stuck under bottom teeth and can only whisper *kuh, kuh, kuh.* Show them how their tongues got stuck by anchoring your tonguetip below your front teeth and saying the sound. See if they can fly all the way around the room saying the crow whisper without having their tongues get unstuck. Look in their mouths as they come back and listen to their sounds.

4. *The "g" sound.* Tell them that in a kind of Indian talk "ugh ugh" means "yes" and "oog oog" means "no." Ask them simple questions and have them answer you in Indian talk. Tell them that these Indians always hold their hand under the base of the chin when they answer questions. (This will help them feel the *g* sound.) Give them a feather for their heads and play an Indian game.

5. *The "f" sound.* Tell them to wet the side of their forefinger and hold it crosswise on the chin. Tell them to blow *f-f-f* until it feels cold. Call this the "freeze-your-finger" game. Feel the fingers to see which is coolest.

6. *The "v" sound.* Have them hold their fingers along the upper edge of the lower lip and make it buzz by prolonging the *v-v-v* sound (Do not say *vee,* just *v*). Tell them or show them that it gives a sound just like singing through the tissue paper over a comb. Have them sing some tunes with the finger-buzzing sound. See who can hold it the longest.

7. *The "sh" sound.* Choose one child to be the teacher and give each of the others a certain sound to say over and over until a hodge-podge or mumbo-jumbo of sound is produced. The moment the child-teacher puts her finger vertically to her lips and says *sh* . . . all the others must do the same thing. The one who stops last is the teacher.

8. *The "ch" sound.* Have the children form a line holding onto each other's hips and play train, starting up from the station when the conductor says "all aboard" and "choo-chooing" in unison as they move around the room. Have one person blow a whistle to stop the train. Repeat.

9. *The "j" sound.* Have the children sit on their haunches pretending to be frogs saying *jeo-joom* repeatedly. Choose a child to be a heron bird, and as he comes nearer the frog pond the children make their *jeo-jooms* softer and softer until finally they whisper and become silent. The bird says, "I guess there aren't any frogs here," and goes away.

10. *The "s" sound.* Have the child blow up his cheeks like automobile tires. As the teacher goes around the room she punctures them and they go *s-s-s-s* until all the air is gone. The one whose tire leaks the slowest gets to puncture the cheek tires the next time.

11. *The "z" sound.* Tell half of the children they are flowers and the other half they are bees gathering pollen to make honey. The bees hold a thin strip of paper in their teeth and must touch the flowers with it, saying *zzzzzzzzzz* as they do so. After they have touched all the flowers they must return to the hive and drop the papers on the teacher's desk without using their hands. The bees then become flowers.

12. *The "r" sound.* Have the children go to the blackboard (or use arm movements in the air) and roll a chalk hoop ꝋꝋꝋꝋꝋꝋ all the way across the entire blackboard space saying *r-r-r-r.* Show them how to make the sound louder and softer as they draw continuous circles.

13. *The "l" sound.* Have the children open their mouths and do exercises with both their tongues and arms together. As their arms are swinging in a side arc over their heads, they lift their tongues up to the upper gums and say *lll* (not *ell*). As they drop their arms they also drop their tongues saying *ah,* thus producing *la.* Repeat, using other syllables *la-lo-lie-loo.*

14. *The unvoiced "th" sound.* Have the children cool off their tongues. Tell them to pretend to eat some hot soup and then put their tongues just outside the door of their teeth and blow on it until it is cooled off. The sound which should be demonstrated is, of course, the unvoiced *th* as in *think.* Prolong it.

15. *The voiced "th" sound.* Make their tongues buzz against their fingers by holding their fingers vertically against the lips as they make the voiced *th* sound, as in *then.*

The above exercises can and should be varied in many ways as they are repeated. Different durations of the sound may be required, the sounds may be repeated any given number of times, or the intensity of the sound may be increased or decreased. Different vowels can be used to make up different nonsense syllables. They may be whispered or sung.

The important thing to remember in inventing new games or variations is to keep the identification of the sound as constant as possible. Thus the *f* sound should always be the "finger-cooling sound," the *s* sound the "punctured-tire sound," and so on. Thus the child can be asked to cool all of his fingers in turn with this *f-f-f* sound, or to cool another child's fingers, or to repeat the finger-cooling sound as he marches or until he finds a hidden object. Variation is excellent, provided the identity of the sound remains constant. The children are confused so far as the consonants are concerned. These games and exercises will help to eliminate this confusion.

Vocal phonics. Children during their third and fourth years are fascinated by rhymes and word play of every kind. They chant such sequences as these even when alone:

High chair, high tair, high bear, kigh kare, care care, bear tear, tear bear all up.
Sally, mally, silly sally, sabby, babby, sally babby.
I got a letter in the mail, in the pail, in the tail.
I like soup, sook, soos; do you like soot?

When their playmates seem puzzled by this punning, they laugh uproariously. If word play is the lowest form of wit, it may also be the earliest. But its major significance in the development of speech lies in its phonic training. Many children persist in their articulation errors because they never learn that words are composed of a series of consecutive sounds. They hear words as wholes—as chunks of sound. The word *fish* to these children is not a series of three sounds, *f*, ɪ, and ʃ, but a single sound. Thus the pronunciation of *fish* and *pish* if spoken quickly enough are much more alike than they are different, and the child fails to perceive any error. Very often, he may echo the word after his parent without error, and yet in the very next sentence he may use the *pish* again. Many parents consider their children obstinate because they do not use these words consistently with correct sounds. Yet, parrotlike repetition has little to do with mastery of true speech. The Mongolian idiot can often echo very long words and yet be speechless in the true sense of the word. The child must be able to perceive his own errors and to create his own standards of pronunciation before he can be expected to speak correctly.

The child must learn that words have beginnings and end-ings—heads, middles, and tails. He must learn that the word "fish" must start with the "lip-biting, breathy, finger-cooling sound" (or some similar identification) and with no other. He must learn that "cup" must end with a lip-popping puff of air. (kʌ) is not enough. There must be one more sound.

Most children learn these elementary facts of vocal phonics unconsciously through vocal play and listening. Many articulation cases never learn that words are made up of parts, and that if one part is wrong, the whole word is incorrect. These observations may seem absurdly simple to the student of this text, but he will appreciate their truth once he starts to teach some lisper an *s* sound.

> Say *sssssssssssss.*
> *Sssssssssssssss.*
> Fine! Now say *soup.*
> *Thoup.*
> Oh, oh. You said *thoup.*
> No, I didn't. I thaid it right: *sssthoup.*

The best way of teaching vocal phonics to young children is through guessing games, rhyming, indexing, and rhythmic vocal play. Here are three typical vocal phonics games which we have used successfully with children of three to five years.

1. Make circles on the floor with chalk and give each circle a "sound name" (*ssss* or *mmmm*). The child must make that sound whenever he is in the circle. Thus, as he jumps from circle to circle, he could produce the word (s) (æ) (m) or *Sam.*

2. *Guessing game.* "Show me your *n-o-se* (noʊz)." Separate the sounds at first, but gradually shorten the intervals until the child realizes that (n-oʊz) is a slow way of saying *nose*. Then use other words such as (ʃ u), (f-eɪ s), (maʊə), and so on.

3. *Collection game.* Give the child some gaily covered boxes and have him collect toys or objects whose names begin with an *s* sound and put them into the *m* box, and other objects whose names begin with an *s* sound and put them into the other box. Demonstrate first, and be sure to sound out the words so that he hears the *m* or *s* sound of the objects collected. Also demonstrate rejection thus: "Let's see. Here's a phone. Does this belong in the boxes? Let's see: *f-f-f-o ne*. No, that begins with a *fff* sound, not a *mmmm* or *ssss*. We don't say *mone* or *sone* do we? Let's just get things that begin with the *mmmm* or *sssss*. You bring them to me and I'll sound them out."

It is astounding to observe how a very few sessions of this vocal play will improve the young child's speech. Until the child knows one sound from another, and until he can analyze or synthesize words, he can hardly be expected to correct himself. If parents would spend half of the time they now waste in trying to correct the child's errors in a systematic effort to get him to recognize sound sequence and the characteristic features of the individual consonants, few articulation problems would result.

Teaching the child to correct himself. Once the child has become able to recognize the individual speech sounds, and has some concept of vocal phonics, the parents can begin to teach him to correct himself. It is odd that so few parents ever get this concept. They feel that they must do the correcting, that the little child is incapable of the task. No greater fallacy has ever produced so much speech difficulty. The methods used by the average parent to correct her child's errors are truly bad. The child is interrupted within the sentence; he is subjected to penalty; he is corrected sporadically rather than consistently; he is corrected on the whole word rather than on the sound that is mispronounced; no attempt is made to analyze the errors or to identify the correct sound. The parent merely yells: "Don't say wabbit; say *rabbit!* Why in the world can't you learn to talk like other children?"

Yet the child of three and four can easily learn to correct himself if the parents adopt a consistent policy of helping him to do so. First, they should confine their correction to those sounds that he should be expected to master at his age. We have known parents to try to get a child to say strawberry before he could even say the *s* or *r* sounds. The blends should never be subjected to correction in the early preschool years. In general, we may say that the first sounds to be mastered are those that involve a few large and coarse movements rather than many small and delicate adjustments; those that are easily seen rather than those whose movements are made in the back of the mouth; those whose frequencies are closer to the frequency of the vowels rather than those of the very high frequency ranges; and those involving a few of the speech organs rather than those that demand the use of all.

Thus, the first sounds mastered are the vowels, then the labials, then the dentals and gutturals (front- and back-tongue sounds, "t, d, n, k, g, ŋ"), then the complicated lip and tongue sounds (f, v, l, r, s, z, ʃ, ʒ, dʒ, tʃ), and finally the blends ("st, gr, bl," and so on). The ages at which these sounds are mastered completely are given for the average child: labials at three years, dentals and gutturals at about three and a half to four years, the *f* and *v* at about five years, the complicated tongue sounds during the sixth year, and the sibilants and blends during the early part of the seventh year. These sounds, however, are mastered much earlier by children who have been given definite training.

Most parents who become concerned about their children's delayed speech development want to know how well normal children of the same chronological age can talk. Fortunately, in Metraux's study (15) we have an answer. She provides a clear picture of the pronunciation, voice, fluency, and language facility for children of 18, 24, 30, 42, 48 and 54 months of age. Since most parents start to worry about the time children are about two years old we provide Metraux's norms for that age.

Second, it is important that only one sound be subjected to

parental attention at one time. Thus, for several weeks only the *k* sound should be the vehicle for teaching the child to correct his speech. Then the *f* sound, if that is incorrectly produced, may be worked upon. This concentration of effort on one sound at a time will do wonders to unravel the confusion which the average parental correction creates in the mind of the child.

Third, it is important that the parents help the child to locate his errors in terms of the sound sequences (the words) in which they occur, and that they help him identify both the correct and incorrect sounds. And finally it is important that all the correction be done without emotion and at appropriate times.

Suppose, then, that the parents have carried out the identification and vocal-phonics games and exercises and that the child continues to make some errors. How then can the parents help? We believe that the general procedure could be illustrated thus: As soon as the child has finished his sentence, say to him something like this: "You know, Johnny, you didn't say one of the words the way big people do. You said *dipper* instead of *zipper*. You forgot that *zipper* starts with the bumblebee sound: *zzzzzzz*. Hear it? *Zzzzzipper, zzz-ip-er*. Now let's pretend we've got some zippers on our shirts. Watch me *zzzip* mine up! Now you pretend you are that bumblebee, and make your sound *zzzzz* as you zip up your shirt. Now say *zzzzz-ipper*. Fine, I knew you could." Yes, this type of teaching takes a bit longer than "Oh, don't say *dipper* say *zipper!*" but it will save time in the long run.

In summary, then, let us say that parents should help their children to recognize the individual speech sounds, should train them in vocal phonics, and should teach them to correct themselves. This sort of a policy in the home will solve much of the speech-correction problem in the school. Speech defects can be prevented if parents will try intelligently to teach their children to talk.

References

1. Allport, F. H., *Social Psychology*, Boston, Houghton Mifflin, 1924, pages 181–183.

The classic description of how children learn to say their first words: 1. The child stimulates himself to repeat a syllable by hearing it. 2. Adults who pronounce the same syllable evoke the same response. 3. Perception of object at same time that others pronounce the syllable and evoke the child's response associates the syllable with the sound. 4. Perception of object evokes the child's production of the syllable.

2. Anderson, J. E., "The Development of Spoken Language," *Yearbook, National Society Studies in Education*, 1939, Volume 38, Part 1, pages 211–224.

A general summary of language growth from birth, with especial emphasis on its development during the preschool years.

3. Blatz, W. E., Fletcher, M. L., and Mason, M., "Early Development in Spoken Language of the Dionne Quintuplets," *University of Toronto Studies; Child Development Series*, 1937, No. 16.

The children were more retarded than twins in language development, due, perhaps, to their mutual imitation. Annette was imitated more than the other children. Graphs and charts of language development are provided.

4. Fairbanks, G., "An Acoustical Study of the Pitch of Infant Hunger Wails," *Child Development*, 1942, Volume 13, pages 227–232.

The author applies scientific analysis to the auditory characteristics of his infant's crying. The pitch varies, and so does the intensity!

5. Froeschels, E., *Psychological Elements in Speech*, Section II on "Infant Speech," Boston, Expression Co., 1932.

A discussion of the development of infant speech, pointing out analogies in the development of infant speech and in disorders of speech. The disorders of speech mentioned in this connection are aphasia, articulatory disorders, initial stuttering, and development stuttering.

6. Gesell, A., *The Psychology of Early Growth Including Norms of Infant Behavior and a Method of Genetic Analysis*, New York, Macmillan, 1938.

A scientific discussion of the transformation of motor capacities into motor abilities in the child, and his achievements in health and uninterrupted progress. It considers five fields of behavior for human psychomotor development—postural, prehensile, perceptual, adaptive, and language.

7. Hawk, S. S., "Can a Child Be Taught to Talk," *Journal of Speech Disorders*, 1939, Volume 4, pages 173–179.

The concept of speech readiness is explained, and with it the motokinesthetic method for teaching the sounds and words suitable to a young child's speech.

8. Hurlock, E. B., *Child Development*, New York, McGraw-Hill, 1942, pages 124–156; 157–186.

The first section of this book listed in the above reference gives an excellent account of the child's motor development. The second summarizes language development from birth onward. The material is presented interestingly and thoroughly.

9. Irwin, O. C., "Research on Speech Sounds for the First Six Months of Life," *Psychological Bulletin*, 1941, Volume 38, pages 277–288.

A summary of the studies on infant vocalization.

10. Irwin, O. C. and Curry, T., "Vowel Elements in the Crying of Infants Under Ten Days of Age," *Child Development*, 1941, Volume 12, pages 99–109.

Data interpreted comparatively to show a trend during speech development to increased use of back vowels.

11. Leopold, W. F., "Speech Development of a Bilingual Child: A Linguist's Record. Volume I. Vocabulary Growth in the First Two Years," *Northwestern University Studies in the Humanities*, 1939, Volume 6.

All the words, both English and German, were transcribed phonetically, with the date and circumstances under which they were produced.

12. Lewis, M. M., *Infant Speech*, London, Paul, Trench, Trubner, 1936.

A book outlining the development of a child's speech from the birth cries to the beginning of conceptual use of speech. This is based upon some statistical observations, and to a large extent upon the observation of a particular child. It discusses early utterance, babbling, imitation, comprehension of conventional speech, meaningful utterance, the mastery of conventional forms, the expansion of meaning, and further progress in conventional use. The appendices contain charts of the various data collected.

13. Low, A. A., *Studies in Infant Speech and Thought. Part I: The Development of Sentence Structure in Infancy from the Viewpoint of*

Grammar; A Quantitative Analysis of the Continuous Speech Record of Two Infants, Urbana, University of Illinois Press, 1936.

The report of a study to evolve a method that would show the language development of a child. It gives the observations of two mothers, and records and analyzes the utterances of their two children. The study includes many charts and tables summarizing the analyses of the language responses.

14. Merry, F. K. and Merry, R. V., *From Infancy to Adolescence*, New York, Harper and Brothers, 1940, Chapters 3 and 4.

This book not only summarizes the motor, physical, and social development, but also the language growth, of very young children. There are many excellent transcriptions of the speech of children at the different age levels.

15. Metraux, R., "Speech Profiles of the Pre-school Child 18 to 54 Months," *Journal of Speech and Hearing Disorders*, 1950, Volume 15, pages 37–53.

16. Miller, N. E. and Dollard, J., *Social Learning and Imitation*, New Haven, Yale University Press, 1941.

This book is especially noted for its exposition of imitation as a form of learning. It clearly illustrates the proposition that one cannot imitate any activity one has not previously practiced. Examples of imitation in children are given.

17. Poole, I., "Genetic Development of Articulation of Consonant Sounds in Speech," *Elementary English Review*, 1934, Volume 11, pages 159–161.

A study of the ability of 140 preschool children to articulate consonant sounds in words. The results showed that a child who is developing normally both physically and mentally may be expected to have reached maturity of articulation at least by the age of eight, with the median girl reaching that stage shortly after the age of six, and the median boy at age seven. The author concludes, then, that, unless definite pathological conditions were present to alter prognosis, no special help in articulation need be given to children younger than these ages.

18. Van Riper, C., *Teaching Your Child to Talk*, New York, Harper and Brothers, 1950.

A description of better ways of teaching a child to talk than those in current use. Written primarily for new parents.

6. Delayed Speech

In our classification of the various disorders of speech we found some difficulty in placing delayed speech in any one symptomatic category. There is usually a deficiency in vocabulary, a retardation in the development of conventional sentence structure, and often a marked inadequacy in the formulation of ideas. In this sense, delayed speech is a disorder of language rather than speech. The child just does not have the means of communication available. Thus delayed speech would seem to find its best fit in the disorders of symbolization. Let us watch such a child in action.

Don was five years old, physically normal, and his parents were completely convinced of his intelligence. His hearing was good and so were his coordinations. He seemed to comprehend speech very well and could follow directions with ease. Possibly because of an early isolation on a farm with few playmates, he had few friends and preferred to play alone. He was well behaved and his lack of speech and of interest in socialization seemed to be his only real difference. His parents had become quite anxious about his delay in learning to talk but seemed to love him. He was an only child. With this brief introduction, let us give you the observer's report. The observer watched the child and his parents through a one-way mirror and heard him over a hidden intercommunication system.

Father told Don to take off his hat and coat and to hang them on the rack. Boy did this without hesitation, then returned to play table and looked at toys. Father told him to help himself. He worked the little pump and when the little ball came out of the spout he smiled, looked at the father and said, "uhn, uhn, uhn" and pointed to the ball. Father told Don to put ball back into upper hole of pump. Don did, then pumped handle but ball was stuck. Looked at father who was not paying attention. Took pump to father and said, "oo." Father shook pump and ball came out. Don put ball back and shook pump. Ball did not come out so he put it down and put his thumb in his mouth. Father withdrew it without comment. Don said, "no," and put thumb back in mouth. Father said, "Cut it out, you hear me?" Don obeyed but held thumb in other hand. Father opened picture book and said, "See cow? Say cow." Don looked but did not respond. Father said, "Say cow. Try it anyway." Don said, "uhn." This was typical of the entire half hour of observation. The only recognizable word was "No." Boy used monosyllables to call attention and then conveyed his meaning with gestures. If he could not make himself understood, he just gave up, waited quietly or turned to something else.

This case is not typical. In fact, one of the major characteristics of delayed speech problems is its variability. But the child's reliance upon gesture, grunting and attention-getting phonation is commonly found. Some of these children have so little interest in speech that they not only will not make any effort to talk but also they show no interest in listening. Some of them have in consequence been sent to feeble-minded institutions or to schools for the deaf or treated as aphasics. Children who cannot send messages by mouth have little incentive to receive them by ear. In examining them we must be careful to explore thoroughly for instances in which they did respond or attempt to communicate. The general picture may lead to a false diagnosis.

Another fairly common pattern of delayed speech is the child who vocalizes constantly but speaks a gibberish which cannot be understood:

One of the children we examined vocalized every minute of her stay with us. She was a restless, wandering child whose attention constantly shifted. As she picked up one toy, threw it down, ran to the window, tapped at the pane, shook her skirt, sucked her thumb, laughed at her reflection in the mirror, and performed a hundred other

consecutive activities, she accompanied each with a constant flow of
unintelligible jabber. By using a hidden microphone, we were able to
record some samples of her speech. The speech sample together with
the object of her attention ran like this:

"Yugga boo booda . . . iganna min . . ." (jʌgə bu budə igæ nə
min.) Picked up the toy automobile and threw it down. "Annakuh
innuhpohee . . . tseeguh . . . tseekuh . . ." (ænakə inəpohi tsigʌ
tsikə.) Looked out window and tapped at pane.

In this case we were unable to recognize any mutilations of
familiar words, though in most cases of delayed speech careful
analysis will isolate a few words, consistently used, which bear
some resemblance to their conventional cognates. Both of these
general types of delayed speech can result from fixation at an
infantile level of speech development. They can also occur re-
gressively as the result of a sudden accident, illness, or emotional shock, even when the previous speech development has
been excellent. Both mutism and unintelligibility are relative
terms, since noises are made by all mutes, and even in the worst
jargon faint resemblances to meaningful words are occasionally
found. The problem of delayed speech, however, is more than
that of a severe articulation defect. These children are also
handicapped linguistically and semantically. They often do not
comprehend the language of others, nor are they particularly
interested in vocal symbols even when they can understand
them. The longer they go without receiving help in attaining
a normal method of communication, the more they tend to
ignore the speech of others. There certainly does seem to be a
time when each child is ripe for speech learning. According to
Stinchfield, the *speech readiness period* lies primarily between
the ninth and twenty-fourth months of a child's life. He
may be taught to talk much later, but it is during this period
that he will learn his speech skill most quickly and thoroughly. However, our own clinical practice has independently
convinced us that any child who does not begin to speak intelligible two-word phrases by thirty months should be referred
to the physician and the speech correctionist. The longer speech
is delayed, the more difficult it is to teach.

Examining the delayed speech child. In order to understand the problem with which we are confronted we must first find out the extent of the disability. To do this we must place the child in a situation where the need to communicate is very strong, and yet one in which the child's security is not so threatened. If the therapist can see the child in his normal home situation, the examination is more likely to be adequate. But we can observe the child and his parents, or the child with his playmates in school, or the child in the schoolroom and begin to understand the problem. At times it is possible to establish a pretty good rapport with the child immediately and personally and to create the communicative conditions necessary for the diagnosis. However, we must always remember the difference between leading a horse to water and making him drink Most of these children refuse speech when it is demanded of them. They have heard too often: "Say this" and "Say that!" But when the conditions are appropriate and they do not feel under threat, most of them will interact enough to help us understand the problem.

The first task, once the child is responding, is to estimate the amount of communicative ability possessed by the child. The following summary of the examination of another delayed speech case will make this clear, and also demonstrate the exploration into the causes of the disorder which is always required.

EXAMINATION FOR DELAYED SPEECH

Case: James B.   *Age:* 5:2   *Observer:* Kay B.   *Interviewer:* Ruth F.
Informant: Mother

A. Symptom Summary:

Observed situation: (Describe in detail.)

Father and child were playing with the airplane that comes apart. Child was helping to take it apart and put it together. They appeared at ease and unaware of the fact that I was watching and listening through the one-way mirror.

1. *List recognizable words and phrases actually heard:*

Da . . . (Dad?); uh-uh (no?); no, puh da (put down? Gesture of lowering); meemee (uttered questioningly while looking at door, perhaps referring to mother. Father said, "Mama will be back pretty soon."; bye; ow (ouch.)

2. *List words reported by parents to have been spoken meaningfully* (not repetitively, but spontaneously). Give informant:

Mother; bye-bye, milk, no, go car, all wet, down, cookie, no, mama, daddy, baby, night-night, potty (and others she could not remember).

3. *Frequency of above word usage: and conditions under which words occur:*

Direct observation: Never spoke these words except when father failed to understand pantomime and gesture. Most of the time played silently.

Mother's testimony: Seldom tries to talk. "Usually speaks his few words when frustrated or distracted." Silent most of the time.

4. *Jargon and babbling:* (Give frequency and conditions for occurrence.)

Jim only grunted twice, and this was when he was making a strong effort to take the tail off the airplane. Said, "uhng-uhng" once when spinning the propeller.

Father says the boy occasionally talks to himself when in the workshop alone, but that "He doesn't make sense and stops as soon as he knows some one is listening." Cries loudly enough and laughs normally. Scolded puppy once "for quite a while" but father couldn't understand him.

Mother claims child babbled very little during first year of life. "He was sick too much of the time." "Has babbled little since." "What he says, he says clear, but he doesn't say enough."

5. *Comprehension:* Boy understands everything, according to both parents. Was unable to follow directions given by examiner verbally. It was occasionally hard to hold his attention, but when examiner had it, the boy could cooperate. Seemed normal for his age.

6. *Response to verbal stimulation:* Refused to attempt any sound or word given by examiner or parents. No anger, just refusal. Would not automatically finish unfinished sentences. No mouth formations of words presented by examiner.

7. *Gesture and pantomine:* Unusually good, parents could always understand. So could examiner.

8. *Reaction to listener's* failure to comprehend utterance or gesture. Child was quite passive. Just gave up trying to communicate

9. *Interest in speech:*

Always listened when we were talking about him. Ignored other conversation.

10. *Interest in sounds:*

Quite normal. Reached for bell rung behind his back. Played with whistle and varied tone duplicatively. Listened to record and laughed when recording laughed. Refused to respond to recorded appeal.

11. *Imitative ability:* Very good, but only motor activities—not speech.

B. Possible Causes: (Cite appropriate case history, interview or test data.)

1. Low intelligence: Parents feel child is bright. Gesell Developmental Schedule shows boy up to age norms except in speech. Terman-McCall-Lorge Non-Language Multi-Mental Test indicated child was superior. Can follow directions intelligently. This cause very doubtful.

2. Hearing loss: Unable to give audiometric examination. Parents are sure child hears normally. Heard watch tick when watch was unseen. Child seems normal in this area.

3. Poor co-ordination: No evidence. Generally well co-ordinated. Ties shoes, cuts with scissors, draws well. No athetosis or evident spasticity. Walked crack well. Moved tongue independently of jaw and rapidly in lifting to hard palate when imitating.

4. Illness: Parents claim "Child was ill during most of first and second years." Cried a lot. General intestinal upsets, colic, pneumonia, frequent colds and chickenpox. No high fevers or coma.

5. Lack of motivation for speech: A probable cause. Parents anticipate desires and understand gestures. Child has been out of contact with other children most of his life. Parents baby him "because he was so sickly."

6. Poor teaching methods: A probable cause. Parents have not been consistent. Much speech demand at inappropriate times and for difficult material. Labeling, and demand for imitation, only techniques used. Much fast adult talk.

7. Bilingual conflicts: None.

8. Shift of handedness: None. Seems thoroughly right handed.

9. Emotional conflicts, trauma, etc.: Parental anxiety over child's

speech retardation. No shocks or accidents. Some trouble over family finances. Parent relationships seem pretty good.

10. Aphasia: No evidence except lack of speech.

' Another child with delayed speech might present a totally different picture, but the need for sizing up the problem in the terms of the above items will be equally necessary. Before we can cope with a disability we must know what that disability is. But this information is far from complete. We must also know something of the causes for the child's speech retardation.

Causes of delayed speech

In the treatment of delayed speech it is important that a careful and thorough study of the child's development and environment be made. Every child will learn to talk unless some important factor prevents speech acquisition. In no other speech disorder is it so necessary to find and eliminate the cause, and the teacher should leave untapped no source of information which might lead to a knowledge of the origin of the child's lack of intelligible speech.

The common causes of delayed speech, all of which should be considered in exploring the child's history, are: low mentality, deafness, poor co-ordinations due to disease or paralysis, prolonged illness (especially in the first two years of life), lack of necessity or motivation for speech, improper teaching methods used by parents, shift of handedness or confused hand preference, necessity for learning two or more languages simultaneously, shock during the act of speaking, emotional conflicts, and aphasia. Each of these will be discussed in turn.

Low intelligence. The teacher must be careful in deciding that the cause of the child's delayed speech is low intelligence. Indeed, the reverse relationship often seems to be the case, since several authorities claim that children gain from ten to thirty points in IQ as the result of having been taught to talk. The Binet examinations are especially dependent upon the acquisition of speech, and even many of the performance tests presume a familiar acquaintance with activities that these speechless children would find difficult. Recent studies in the field of intelligence testing have indicated that IQ's can be raised by providing young children with a stimulating environment, and it is easily seen that a child who has no speech responses would not be likely to meet as much stimulation as would the speaking child. Nevertheless, children of low intelligence are generally helped with special techniques known to the teacher of subnormal children. These children need speech training even more, perhaps, than the usual course of study given them would seem to indicate. Training in the manual and domestic arts should be supplemented by much speech training.

Hearing defects. It is well known that children who are born deaf do not speak unless they are painstakingly taught to do so. It is not so well known that children who have lost their hearing as a result of illness or accident frequently lose intelligible speech to such a degree that many of the speech sounds are never regained. Nor is it well known that there are types of deafness which permit the child to hear certain pitches but not others. So-called regional deafness, of which high-frequency deafness may serve as an example, can produce distortions of speech so peculiar that the child's parents are convinced of a lack of intelligence. Some of these children have often been placed in schools for the totally deaf, although properly designed hearing aids could permit them to attain adequate speech. These children should be referred to an otologist for a thorough examination. An audiometric examination is vitally necessary, and the physician should use some of the newer techniques suited to the responses of young children.

Poor co-ordination. Although certain children present the picture of precocious speech together with defective or immature co-ordination, the majority of children who are definitely retarded in the motor sphere are similarly retarded in speech. The child with St. Vitus's Dance (chorea), or the one who has suffered from infantile or spastic paralysis, seldom acquires intelligible speech before four or five years of age. It is usually unwise to do much speech work with these children before they have acquired some degree of control over the larger movements. Physiotherapy, especially for the paralytics, will improve speech much more than concentrated speech correction in the early years of the child's life.

Illness. Prolonged illness during the first year usually interferes with the babbling and vocal play so necessary to the beginning of speech. The first speech attempts seem to emerge, not from the squalling of hunger, irritation, or pain, but from the noises of relief or contentment. An ill child seldom gets enough of this early speech practice, and since all speech sounds used later in life are practiced during the babbling period, he usually presents delayed speech. Uninformed parents often fail to realize the importance of this babbling and, feeling that the child should then be talking, insist upon his learning meaningful words immediately. They should stimulate him to babble as much as possible. His environment should be one of much vocalization, especially of the repetitive vocal play that many parents coo to their infants. Repetition of syllables immediately after feeding or when the child is content or free from pain will soon provoke a similar response from him. Meaningful purposive speech can be taught later and the child should be encouraged to talk to his pets and toys, to accompany rhythmic movements with vocalization which is either sung or spoken, and to indulge in all the vocal play he wishes. Even six-year-old children with a history of early illness and delayed speech should be taught to babble.

Lack of motivation. One of the first causes of delayed speech which speech correctionists look for in the child of less than six years of age is that of a lack of motivation. Children will not learn to talk unless they realize the utility of speech. The law of least effort is a rather fundamental determinant of human effort, and when children can get their wishes fulfilled without employed speech, they never acquire this all-important tool. We adults, who speak so easily, often fail to realize that our vocal skills were not mastered without some difficulty. Children will avoid this difficulty if they can, and some parents seem to help them in this avoidance. Some mothers become so skillful at anticipating their child's every wish that the performance astounds the bystander. This appalling situation arises especially when the child is an only child or has been ill a great deal or is handicapped in some way. Excessive overprotection and solicitude can not only delay speech acquisition but often prevent it altogether. The child develops an excellent understanding of the speech of others and frequently develops a gesture language which would do credit to a Charlie Chaplin, but he steadfastly refused to make any speech attempt of his own.

Often the parent declares that she has tried to get the child to speak but he refuses, and that she does not know what to do. This is usually true, but when the manner of teaching has been examined, it will be found to be sporadic and perfunctory. Only a consistent, patient, and extended program of speech teaching will be effective. This program must follow some such sequence as this:

1. Insist that the child accompany all gestures by some vocalization. This vocalization may be some meaningless vowel. The parent should sound the vowel whenever the child gestures so as to provide the stimulation necessary to produce the child's response. The parent should explain to the child that no wish will be satisfied until he does vocalize, and the parent must maintain this standard for at least a week before giving up. We have never had a failure when this has been done. Usually two or three days are necessary before all gestures are accompanied by vocalization.

2. Once vocalization has been accomplished, select some favorite plaything or favorite food, and demand a modification of the vocalization whenever the child desires the object. For example, if the child wants a ball, he should be told that he must press his lips together firmly before vocalizing, thus producing a sound similar to the *b* sound, in the syllable *ba*. Even if this sound is not exactly the true word for the object, it

should be given him with much praise. Only one such "word" should be worked for at a time. If the child refuses the object and turns to others, he should be placed in an empty room where this object is the only toy. No normal child can resist such a program. The word should be reviewed frequently, and much social approval should be given. Pictures of the object can be hidden about the room, and games may be invented to show the child the usefulness of naming. Once a word has been mastered, other words can be acquired in a similar manner. Monosyllabic words should be used and, as we have said, they need only approximate the real word. Babbling, echoing, and other speech games will help. Usually, when the child has acquired one or two words, the problem solves itself.

Poor speech standards. Another cause of delayed speech is the prevalence of poor speech standards in the home. This condition is closely related to a lack of motivation, although the latter usually refers more to the substitution of a gesture language than to the presence of a primitive vocal language which results from the parental acceptance of distorted speech. Many a child of four and five is brought to the speech correctionist with speech so unintelligible that no one save the mother can understand what the child is trying to say. Twins and children of similar ages often develop a serviceable speech of this sort. One pair of twins used much vocalization when communicating with each other but used only gestures when speaking to adults. In their primitive vocabulary, the following words seemed to be used consistently: "we-we" (meaning either "I" or "you"); "eee" (any adult); "bam" (ball); "bam-aa" (apple). There were other similar distortions and substitutions. In general, this type of speech consists of the more primitive lip, nasal, and tonguetip sounds used with the neutral or front vowels. Most of the words are approximations of those used by adults, with the distortions produced by substituting easier sounds for more difficult ones. Since the parents or associates of these children accept this counterfeit speech, the child has no incentive to improve it.

These poor speech standards are occasionally due to parental baby talk, but more often they are the result of illness or handicap which has made the parent reluctant to put any extra pressure on the child. After the illness, the parents resolve to insist upon good speech, and so they nag and correct and scold the child for a period of days. This procedure seldom produces any great change, because a strong penalty or pressure placed upon any activity as unconscious as speech tends to stamp in the error and to make it more permanent. Moreover, the mere command, "Don't say 'eee', say 'mama'!" does not show the child how he can make the new co-ordinations. And again, constant nagging about the child's poor speech will surely arouse an emotional conflict, for not even an adult can watch his speech continually. Therefore, the parents usually give up the attempt and hope the child will outgrow his poor speech habits.

Better methods than those suggested in the last paragraph will be discussed in some detail later in this chapter. But it can be emphasized that good speech standards must be built gradually and that the child must be shown how to make the desired words. The parents should concentrate their efforts on not more than five words, and these words should be composed of the easier speech sounds. The child must be taught to make the sounds which comprise these words and should be able to make them at will. This teaching of sounds should be confined to a few situations or speech periods which are part of the child's daily routine. Only good-natured and humorously vivid penalties should be used, and rewards should be stressed. When the child is first able to make the desired word, corrections should still be confined to these nucleus speech periods. But as these words and nucleus situations become completely mastered, the requirements may be extended until all words and all situations must conform to the adequate speech standards.

Improper methods used in teaching the child to talk. An authority on child care once said that children learn to speak not because of parental teaching, but in spite of it. The average child certainly does seem to exhibit a remarkable ability to acquire speech when the teaching is so poor that it hardly merits the name. All that most young parents know of the teaching of talking is that they should hold out an object and repeat its name over and over. Meanwhile, they hope that the miracle will happen, and it usually does. But some children need more skillful teaching and do not acquire speech until such teaching is forthcoming. Some of the common errors made by parents in the teaching of talking are: stimulation at the wrong time, too much or too little stimulation, the wrong kind of stimulation, disregard of the need for motivation, and improper use of association to provide meanings.

Some parents begin to try to get the child to imitate them as early as the third and fourth months, whereas no attempts should be made until about the seventh month, and imitation of motor behavior should always precede imitation of speech. Stimulation at a time when the child has not reached the proper level of maturation is not only useless but also actually harmful, since it merely reduces the child's interest in the stimulation. Other parents will wake the child out of a deep slumber or will interrupt such prepotent activities as feeding to ask him to say "bye-bye." The first teaching of talking should be confined to the child's vocal play periods.

Even intelligent parents frequently overstimulate or understimulate the child and use improper types of stimulation. Children who are neglected, even in the interests of modern child education, will be delayed in their speech. Then, too, children who are bombarded from every side by crowing parents, by masses of endearing or admiring verbiage, can hardly be expected to respond selectively. Parents who have heard of the evils of using baby talk (which certainly is an evil at a later stage of speech development) confine their stimulation to such words as *bicycle*, *mother*, and *nurse*, and they occasionally rebuke their unlucky offspring for such achievements as *ba* for *ball*. As we have seen, the first stimulation should be the imitation of the child's own vocal play; and the next should be monosyllables or double syllables which the child has practiced previously. Later, after the child has learned to enjoy and to use speech and shows eagerness for new names, the true disyllables (such as water) can be used.

Many parents, made unintelligent by the presence of a new object for their self-love, seek to anticipate their child's every wish. They rush to give the ball to the child if he so much as looks at it. Were they wise, they would move it a little closer and provoke some speech attempt, thus using the situation for the teaching of talking. Probably the most frequent functional cause of delayed speech is this parental overeagerness. Children won't talk unless they profit from the attempt. Speech is a tool, and if it is not needed, it will not be used. Parents should be very careful to prevent the formation of such a condition, for only by careful and systematic retraining can it be broken down.

Finally, parents make the mistake of tearing down associations as fast as they are built. Instead of concentrating their teaching on a few simple words and their associated objects, they overwhelm the child with synonyms and adjectives and terms of endearment, a hodgepodge of stimulation which would make a nonspeaking adult with an IQ of 150 give up in despair. The use of a little applied intelligence, and some consideration of the child's outlook, will solve this problem.

Shift of handedness. A relatively infrequent cause of delayed speech is the shift of handedness insisted upon by many parents of left-handed children. Occasionally a child is found with no definite hand preference and speech which is very much delayed. Most of these children show a spontaneous acquisition of speech as soon as they show a preference for one hand. Studies in aphasia demonstrate that the part of the brain which controls speech is also that which is responsible for the control of the preferred hand. Therefore, it is wise to determine which hand the child naturally prefers and to prevent any prejudice on the part of the parents from affecting his natural choice. The child should be observed in those activities which have

been least affected by environmental training, and these activities are those which demand little speed, strength, or accuracy. Writing, sewing, or cutting with scissors are not good
criteria of natural handedness. The teacher or parent should
make careful observations of the child's one-handed activity
and then take the child to some psychological or speech clinic
where the proper apparatus is available for diagnosing the true
hand preference.

Once this has been done, a program of manual activity should
be initiated. New skills should be acquired with the correct
hand, and the old skills should be transferred to the proper
side. It is often wise to ask the child to vocalize as he uses his
hand in such activities as ball tossing, writing, and hammering.
The child should be trained in larger activities first, and then
in those which involve the use of specialized movement. Almost
miraculous results follow a program of this sort. With no speech
training, but with intensive concentration on motor skills, the
child suddenly begins to speak.

Bilingual conflicts. Some parents deliberately attempt to
teach their children two languages at the same time, a procedure which is usually disastrous. Studies indicate that ineffi-
ciency and confusion result from such training even in adulthood. Most children in foreign-language homes learn the foreign
speech first, and then make the shift when they enter school.
This can usually be done without much danger, but when older
children in the family insist upon speaking English, the situation becomes dangerous. The teacher must educate the parents
to insist upon one language until the child has acquired a mastery of it. If this procedure is followed, no delayed speech will
result.

Emotional shocks and accidents. As we have mentioned,
speechless children are often found whose histories show that
they talked at one time. These individuals often lose their
speech because of some accident, severe illness, or shock to the
central nervous system. Occasionally a severe fright or other
powerful emotion will produce a speechlessness which persists.

One child injured his tongue and mouth cavity with a pair of scissors and refused to talk long after the wounds had healed. Another child of five was talking to his mother when knocked down by a large dog. At eight years he was still using pantomime for all communication.

The majority of these cases will respond to the intensive treatment to be described later. However, when the loss of speech followed a strong psychological or emotional shock, it is often wise and necessary to take measures to minimize the effects of the shock. The procedure usually consists of the following steps. (1) Someone, such as a teacher, psychologist, psychiatrist, who has had no former connection with the child's unfortunate experience, wins his confidence and respect. (2) The original shock situation is re-experienced in such a way as to provide a successful solution. The child must somehow recreate the original situation and master it. (3) Attitudes of humor should be associated with the experience. (4) When speech does return or is relearned, the child should verbalize both the situation which caused the shock and the one which canceled it.

As an illustration, the treatment of the child who lost the power of speech after being knocked down by a dog may be described:

The speech correctionist to whom the child was referred spent a week of fifteen-minute daily periods in gaining the child's confidence. In these periods games were played in which the child's dominance over toys, teddy bears, and so on, was stressed. The clinician never spoke to the child but used sign language entirely. Gradually, games were introduced in which activity was accompanied by vocalization. There was a spiral maze in which a little train traveled the grooves when pushed by the humming clinician. If the child pushed the train without humming, the clinician shook his head and took the toy away from him. Pictures of dogs were hidden about the room and the child learned to say "dah-dah-dah" until he found them. A stuffed toy dog was provided and the child was encouraged to roll a large ball in the attempt to knock it over. The clinician then held the toy dog and made it prance and dodge the ball. All activity by this time was accompanied by some kind of vocalization, and the clinician occasionally used one or two words such as *dog, train,* and *here.* A puppy which had previously been trained to play the ball game was brought in, and when the child appeared for his conference the clinician was playing ball with it. The child was given the ball, and, rolling it at the puppy, knocked it over. "Look, look, I did it," he said spontaneously, and from that time on, speech returned swiftly. The child seemed very cruel to the puppy for a while, but gradually this attitude changed. Later, the clinician taught the game of "Knock-down," in which alternately the child and the clinician and the puppy pretended to attack and to be knocked over. The child was very amused by this game and kept a running conversation going all the time in imitation of the clinician.

Emotional conflict. Another frequent cause of speech loss is emotional conflict. One child stopped talking when the courts, after his parents were divorced, assigned him to the custody of the father. Another, the youngest child and only boy in a family of six children, all of whom were extremely rapid speakers, finally gave up the battle for speech until he entered school, where the competition was not so great. Another child, urged to confess his guilt in a rather serious misdemeanor, refused and was punished severely. He did not speak again until after a course of psychological treatment. Other emotional speech conflicts which have produced speech loss are: forcing the child to recite or perform when he feels himself incapable of doing so successfully; too high speech standards in the home; constant repression at home or in school; deprivation of attention or so much overattention that an abnormal hunger for attention is created, both resulting in speech loss as a symptom which will satisfy this thwarted desire; and subjection to unreasonable (from the child's point of view) compulsion to such an extent that the only way in which he can resist is to refuse to talk. In each of these instances, the treatment requires elimination of the cause by treating the environment rather than the child.

Speech teachers who do not realize the importance of emotional etiology frequently find themselves working vainly. The child will appear to make progress and then will unaccountably relapse into as much or more error than he had at the beginning. The speech correctionist is frequently required to map out an entire program of home adjustment before her work can begin. She must teach the parents how to react to the child's negativism and demand for attention. The former may be taken care of by commanding and requesting the child to do things he really wants to do, and then, when he refuses, accepting his refusal. An example of this may be given:

The teacher said to the child in a rather peremptory tone, "Johnny, you go down to the drugstore this very minute and get youself an ice-cream cone!" The child answered "No" and the teacher asked another child, who accepted and returned to eat the ice-cream cone under Johnny's regretful nose. Such a program soon brought a discriminatory answer to requests and commands, and when reward for positive response was added, together with humorous attitudes toward the negativism, the child's whole attitude changed, and his speech soon became normal.

At times, the child's refusals may be chalked up on the board and matched by the teacher's or parent's refusals. The demand for attention, if reasonable, should be satisfied in other ways. If unreasonable, it can be eliminated by teaching the child that he will get a lot of attention at certain times during the day but not at other times. Penalize all unreasonable demands by humorous disregard.

In addition to the emotional etiology, emotional conflicts will frequently produce a rapid, careless speech, or a repressed speech with minimal articulatory movements, which lead to sound substitutions, omissions, and distortions.

Poor auditory memory span. Another cause of delayed speech seems to be an inability on the part of the child to retain sequences of sounds. He frequently can repeat a sound or a word immediately after it has been pronounced but seems to be unable to retain it for more than a few seconds. Simple sounds appear to be retained more easily than words of one syllable, and polysyllabic words present an insuperable difficulty. Many parents who fail to recognize this condition attribute the child's speech failure either to stubbornness or to a lack of intellect, and penalize the child severely. This causes a negativism which complicates the situation.

Most of the children who possess short auditory memory spans can be trained to retain auditory impressions long enough to acquire good speech. The training must include teaching the concept of sequence and the delayed response. Many exercises for teaching these factors will be found in the chapter on the treatment of articulatory disorders. Young children must be taught the concept of sequence by identifying sounds with objects. Thus, in one case, the concept of sound sequences was attained in the following manner:

Three different dolls were named "wa," "ba," and "ma." After the child learned their names, the teacher pretended that the dolls were going to school, and as they entered the door the child was to say their names. Sometimes, two entered the door in a hurry, and so the child had to say "ma" and "ba" in swift sequence. By varying this situation in many ways, the child soon learned to point out the dolls in their proper sequence and to give their names in proper order. By insisting that the child cross the room to whisper the names to her mother, the delayed response which necessitated the retention of sound sequences was taught, and from this simple beginning a sound plan of treatment was constructed which resulted in good speech.

Aphasia. One of the more uncommon causes of delayed speech is aphasia, which is usually the result of a severe birth injury or an injury to the head. It is always necessary to rule out the other causes, especially those of high-frequency deafness and feeble-mindedness, before aphasia is considered.

The child may appear to be congenitally deaf, but if there is a history of occasional response to air-borne sound (rather than to sounds which might be carried through the floor or other vibrating bodies), the child should be carefully examined by a specialist in this field. Highly emotional situations often produce such responses when they are not apparent in ordinary activity. Other signs of aphasia manifest themselves in what seems to be a "forgetting" of the purposes of well-known objects such as a pencil or spoon. The treatment of these cases is difficult and must be carried out through the development of a serviceable gesture language, to which vocalization may later be added. The kinesthetic method of teaching speech sounds is effective with many of these children. In any event, the parent and teacher should seek to find other avenues of speech teaching than those normally used, and they should study carefully the more recent works on this subject. The references at the end of this chapter will serve as a primary bibliography. The disorder is so rare that few teachers ever see an aphasic child.

General principles of treatment. The therapy plans for each delayed-speech case will naturally vary with the particular needs discovered. We must design our therapy play in such fashion as to eliminate the causes or minimize their influence. If the child's intelligence is low, we may have to delay treatment for a few years, or set up goals, within his capacity, which will help him express his basic needs. With these children, we should teach the single words, simple phrases, and sentences from the beginning, always rewarding any utterance but patiently presenting the necessary phrase in its proper context. The word "eat" should be heard over and over again during his time at the table, this and little else until it is mastered.

The child whose delayed speech is the result of a hearing defect will require auditory training, lip reading, and the other techniques described in the chapter concerned with these individuals. The specialized therapy for children with brain injuries will also be found in the chapters devoted to those disorders.

Where illness has been a contributory cause, it is wise to encourage a great deal of babbling, of playing with noises, tones and inflections. Often the speech therapist slights this very important phase of the work, although it probably does more to help such a child get speech than any other single technique. The etiological (causal) treatments for the other important types of delayed speech have already been outlined. Much of this type of therapy can be combined with the speech therapy which we now present.

The most common aims of therapy for retarded speech are these: (1) Create a need for verbal communication; (2) Train the child in the alphabet of sound; (3) Train the child to combine sequences of sounds; (4) Build a useful basic vocabulary; (5) Make the new speech a communicative tool.

1. Creating a need to communicate verbally. Some of our delayed-speech children already have accomplished this aim. They cannot refrain from jabbering. But there are many others who have not realized how important and how satisfying a tool speech can be for manipulating their elders and satisfying their desires. They simply don't think that learning to talk is worth the trouble. They find it possible to get along without verbal communication. Pantomime and gesture are sufficient for a child in a home where everyone else tries to learn his language instead of the reverse. Parrots and mynah birds have little incentive to talk either until their trainers pay some attention to motivation.

Silent gestures must therefore remain unrewarded. The best policy to follow is to withdraw the parents' granting of the pantomimic requests in a gradual fashion. The first day, collect two instances in which they pretend not to understand the gesture requests, guessing incorrectly until the child is pretty frustrated by their stupidity. The next day they do it four times, scattering the misunderstandings at random. Gradually most of the child's gesturing is being unrewarded. The guessing part of this technique should always be in single words:

Today I was carrying out your suggestions. Bobby wanted me to hand him down the ball from the shelf. He kept pointing and reaching and saying "a . . . a . . . a." I looked at him in a puzzled sort of fashion, saying, "Dish? Dish? Bobby want dish." They I tried "cap" and "cup" and "box," reaching up and taking down each, and pretending to be trying hard to understand. It certainly seemed cruel, but I did it. He finally got mad and began to suck his thumb. Is this what you want me to do?

It was, but it should not be used alone. All spontaneous utterance should be rewarded by providing attention, sharing through imitation, and a little extra loving. With a severe case, even grunts and babbling should receive rewards. If the child makes any attempt at all to say the right word, or indeed for some children who do not talk at all, if any utterance accompanies the gesture it should be reinforced by pleasantness.

Another technique which creates a need to talk is to have the parent or therapist do a lot of self-talk, commenting on what they see or do. A sample of this running commentary is as follows:

Mummy do dishes now. Wash cup . . . put cup here . . . Where glass? Oh, here glass . . . Glass dirty . . . Now glass soapy . . . Wash . . . Jerry wipe . . . Towel . . . Rub, rub . . . Glass clean . . . Glass on shelf . . .

If some of this simplified self-talk is done several times each day, the child who watches will begin to participate, first silently with inner speech and later aloud.

It is important in the speech therapy sessions that the therapist talk in this abbreviated way. Often in the first meetings it is wise to do as little talking as possible. Try to get down on the child's own level of non-verbal, gestural communication, then accompany gestures with single words, and then go to these brief phrases and sentences. The constant flow of adult speech is so fluent and complicated that most delayed-speech children feel it is too difficult to achieve. Once it is simplified it seems easier and within his reach. For the same purpose we should cut down on the amount of reading to the child that parents do. Its fluency provides an almost unobtainable goal. We have had several cases in which the elimination of oral reading by itself produced the climate productive of spontaneous speech attempts.

2. Acquainting the child with the alphabet of sound. Most delayed-speech cases tend to use only a few of the consonant sounds. Those with a lack of language tend to begin to talk in much the same way as the normal baby, with the simplest sounds, and will continue unless stimulated with the entire repertoire. Those whose speech is largely jargon tend to use one or two favorite consonants for all others, though a large variety of vowels may be used. If a child is to learn to speak his mother tongue he must become acquainted with all the sounds within it. He must learn his alphabet, not of letters, but of sounds. It would be difficult to write comprehensibly if you only had six or eight letters. It is difficult to talk sense until you have all the speech sounds at your command. Most of this work with the younger child must be done in play but it must not be omitted. The more identifying of isolated sounds the child can do, the sooner he begins to talk understandably. We need a solid foundation for intelligible speech and the alphabet of sound provides it. Here is a picture of some of this therapy:

1. Blindfold the child. Make the sound from several different places in the room. Ask the child to point to where the sound came from or to find you.

2. Pretend that each of you is a certain animal or machine that makes the sound. Have him run around the room with you as you produce the sound.

3. Procure a calendar mailing tube or similar device. Hold one end to the child's ear as he winds a string upon a spool. The moment the teacher stops making the sound, he must stop winding.

4. Certain objects are set aside as demanding the hearing of the correct sound before they can be touched. Such rituals appeal to children and compel attention.

5. Prolong or repeat the sound rhythmically. Ask him to clap his hands or put his fingers in the ear whenever you make it very loudly.

6. Tell the child a story or rhyme and prolong the selected sound whenever it occurs in a word. The important thing is to accent the particular sound you are working on.

7. Tie a rope on the child and tell him to walk back and forth as you pronounce the sound. Whenever you cease making the sound, jerk the rope.

Indirect methods for combining sounds and movements. (Do these first in unison, making the sound a part of the activity.)

1. Snap off the light—say *ow*.
2. Shoot a toy gun—"bang," *ba, boom,* or *pow*.
3. Turn an egg beater—any vowel on which you rhythmically change pitch.
4. Saw a board—*ee-ee* or *ay-ay*, or *zzz-zzz*.
5. Hit piano or xylophone and sing any vowel.
6. Wind a toy—*mmmm-mmmmm*.
7. Pull the cork out of a bottle—*puh* or *buh*.
8. Pull or push any toy animal and say its sound: Cow—*moo*, dog—*bow-wow*, and so on.
9. Move a zipper: *zzz* or *sss*.
10. Rock in a chair or bounce—any vowel or consonant.

Direct methods for combining sounds and movements.

1. *For "m."* Have child flip or stroke your lips as you make the *m* sound. Then you stroke his lips as he makes it.
2. *For "puh."* Have child hold his whole hand flat over your closed mouth with cheeks full of air. Ask him suddenly to pull it away as you explode the *puh* sound. Reverse the process.
3. *For "buh."* Hold or have child hold a feather or strip of tissue over your mouth. Then explode the *buh* sound so that the feather or strip moves or falls. Reverse positions.
4. *For "tik."* Cup hands around your mouth and ask the child to look inside and hear the clock. Say *tik-tik-tik*. Then have him be the clock.
5. *For "dee."* By folding a cardboard provide yourself with a series of ten holes each large enough to insert a finger in. Have child hold it in front of himself and as you insert your finger in each hole say *dee*. Then you hold it, refusing to let him hit the hole until he says *dee*.
6. *For "nnnnnn."* Have child place finger on side of your nose as you open your mouth and say *nnnnnn*. Ask him if he feels the little noise. Then ask him to open his mouth so you can feel his little noise (and nose).
7. *For "oo(w)."* Have child watch your rounded lips as you blow into a tube of paper or into a bag or horn. Then have him do it. Then blow the *oo* sound "out loud." Always call this the "blowing sound."
8. *For the "guh."* Call this the "squeezing sound" or the "choking or collar sound." Ask the child to choke you with both hands as you laugh and say *guh-guh-guh*. Reverse, but be gentle.
9. *For the "kuh."* Call it the "coughing sound" and play some sort

of a coughing game. For example, put a feather into the mouth and cough it out with *kuh-kuh-kuh-kuh-kuh.*

10. *For the "f."* Call this the "blow on the finger" sound. Hold your finger laterally across the child's lower lip, pushing it inward. Then ask him to blow on your finger to cool it off. Then set his own finger in position and repeat.

11. *For the "v."* Ask him to watch you in the mirror as you "bite your mouth (or lip) and blow out loud." Then ask him to do it.

3. Teaching the child to combine sound sequences. Another basic part of the foundation of normal speech is the ability to form sequences of sounds and to vary them so that they will fit a given pronunciation model. Few delayed-speech children have done much of this and they need to learn the skill. Again, it too must be taught through play. If "I-E" equals "ice-cream" in the child's mind and speech, it will remain there no matter how many people try to correct him unless he realizes it is possible to add, subtract or change sounds. To put it differently, and more accurately, the pronunciation of any certain word represents a pretty stable configuration, and it remains intact. We must introduce the idea of change; we must perceive it from a different point of view, if we can hope to vary it.

One reason why so many children develop a jargon or gibberish is that they fail to realize that a word is made up of a series of sounds blended together. They hear the word as a whole and pronounce some sound which bears a certain likeness to it. Some children can be taught some real words immediately by these sound-sequence games. The majority, however, need much practice in "vocal phonics," in combining and blending sounds without regard to meaning, before true words are taught. Most successful teachers of delayed-speech cases first teach blending sounds as an interesting game and skill; then they teach sound combinations which they call nonsense names; then, finally, real and familiar words.

1. Let the teacher perform two of the previously practiced movement-sound combinations then ask the child to imitate her. If this is too difficult, alternate before combining.

2. Let the child perform the activities while the teacher makes the sound, then reverse.

3. Trace a circle to form syllables. Have top arc of circle represent one sound, bottom part another. Trace slowly first, faster gradually for advancement, and divide circle into more parts and sides and sounds.

4. Have squares on floor for certain sounds. Say these sounds while stepping in squares. Form words or syllables.

5. Use different notes on the piano for different sounds.

6. Mount two or more cardboard bells on a piece of tag board so that they can be moved when strings are pulled. Color differently and let each represent a sound. Have child pull the strings as you make the sounds. Then exchange places.

7. Cut shapes of paper for various sounds. Arrange two or three in a row on the table for child to sound out after he learns the sounds for them.

8. Roll a ball across the room, having child say the sounds as the ball moves in the various spaces.

Exercises for sound sequences.

1. Select short one-syllable words, which begin with the continuant sounds: *m, n, w, y,* or *v,* or any vowel. (*Examples: nose, yell, neck, man, way, egg.*) Prolong the first sound, pause, then say the rest of the word, asking child to point to object, or indicate by pantomime, what was spoken. Then prolong the pause for several seconds and try the same procedure except for this variation. Next, separate the vowel from the final sound also and repeat exercise. Then increase number of sounds in the words used, allowing child to guess the word. If difficulty is experienced, repeat sounds more swiftly and with shorter pauses between sounds.

2. Show the child some pictures which include a number of objects. Sound out one of them.

3. Select some simple word, sound it out, ask child to help, and then sound it in unison. Ask for identification of word sounded out.

4. With chalk, divide the floor into sections, a sound for each. As child walks across the room saying each sound, ask what word is formed.

5. Sound out words and have child listen to see if he can count the sounds.

6. Tell child to say some nonsense syllables such as *an* just after teacher has pronounced another sound. (*Example.* Teacher says

mmmmm, child says *an*. Teacher asks child what word they have spoken together. Child should guess *man*.) Then use other combinations, *puh-an*, *pan*, *can*, and so on.

7. Sound out, in the fashion indicated, direction which the child must carry out. (*Example:* "Sh-uh-t th-uh doh-r.")

8. Give each finger the name of a sound. Child says each sound as he lifts (or teacher lifts) the appropriate finger.

4. Building a basic vocabulary. For the delayed-speech case it is as necessary to teach a basic vocabulary of tool-words as it is for the normal infant. Some of our delayed-speech cases already have a good many words when they come to us but they are hidden and buried in the jargon. It is necessary to separate them out, get the child to use them meaningfully, and then reward them. Many of these children show great spurts of progress as soon as they come to realize that they can speak many words correctly. They also show surprise, since over-correction, rejection or other penalties may have convinced them that they cannot talk correctly and they have accepted this judgment and made no further attempt to improve.

With the child who has little or no speech, it is necessary to teach the first words. The first project should not contain more than five or ten words, and they should begin with the easier sounds, *m*, *b*, *p*, or *w*. If possible, they should be monosyllabic or should consist of repeated syllables, such as "mama." They should be names of things or activities which the child enjoys. If the child has some distorted speech sounds which he habitually employs for naming favorite objects, it is wise to select new toys or new activities which he has not previously named. When this principle is followed, no unlearning is necessary. Nonsense names can be used if the true names are too difficult or begin with the wrong sounds, since the object of this first training is to teach the child to use speech as a tool and to set up proper speech standards. Later on, the child can be given the more difficult task of unlearning old incorrect names and substituting correct ones for them. The parents and teacher alike must use the nonsense name, however, when referring to the object in the presence of the child. We usually include about two true names among each set of five words used in building the primary vocabulary. Thus, one child was taught the following names in the order given:

1. "Moop" (the name given to an oddly shaped mass of modeling clay which was used in a hiding game). 2. "Wap" (the sound made by the child and teacher in unison as a signal for a Jack-in-the-box to pop out). 3. "Boom" (the name of a toy cannon). 4. "Papa" (the name he used for himself when he pretended to be his father, a physician, engaged in treating the teacher, who pretended to be sick. The boy was given an old medical satchel and tongue depressor and left the room to knock at the door. Whereupon, the teacher asked "Who's there?" and refused to open the door until she knew who was knocking). 5. "Ba" (the name for "ball," or the sound used as the boy bounced it).

After the child has been taught to make the sounds that are included in the five or ten words previously selected, the teacher's next task is to teach him to combine those sounds to form words. There are two major ways of accomplishing this: by teaching whole words and by teaching sound sequences. Both methods should be used for almost all cases of delayed speech, and, for both, ear training should precede actual performance. Generally speaking, the whole-word method should be used for simple monosyllabic words, whereas the sound-sequence method should be used for those of more than one syllable.

In one case, the word *mop* was among the first five words to be taught. After the child had been given ear training in saying the *m* and *p* sounds by themselves, the teacher began the ear training necessary to the production of the whole word. She left the room in a very mysterious manner, returning with a bottle of colored water and a mop. As soon as she entered the room, she went solemnly to each corner and said *mop, mop, mop*. Then she made another circuit of the room with the child, and in each corner she said the word *mop* into the ear of the child. On her third circuit, she spilled a little water in each corner, uttering the same word three times, prolonging the *m* slightly and emphasizing the *p*. On her fourth circuit, she took the mop itself and wiped up the water with it, saying the word rhythmically as she worked. She motioned to the child to help her, and as he took hold of the handle he began to say the word in unison with her, somewhat to her surprise. In this case, the vivid stimulation and identification with an activity were sufficient to produce the spontaneous response.

When the sound-sequence method is used, the word should not be broken into all of its component sounds, for the vowel should always be spoken in connection with the consonants that precede or follow it in the syllable. Thus the word *wipe* should be sounded as *wi-p*, and the word *cookie* as *kooh-kee*, never as *w-i-p* or *k-oo-k-ee*. The reason for this is that consonants vary in their formation according to the sounds that follow or precede them, and the child must not be asked to break up words into any finer elements than necessity demands.

Useful words for a basic vocabulary. The following words employ the easiest sounds and are most frequently used in children's speech. However, if a child prefers others or seems interested in learning others, always follow his desire.

The words that are the easiest to say are: *baby, bacon, bee* or *be, bib, big, bite, boat, book, bow, boy, buggy, cake, can, coat, comb, come, cookies, cow, cup, dig, eat, egg, eye, go, got, gum, gun, hat, home, hot, ink, keep, keys, kitty, man, me, meat, neck, pig, pin, no, talk, tie, top, two, wagon, walk, window,* and *wood.*

Those not quite so easy to say are: *bag, bone, can, cap, come, daddy, deep, do, door, egg, fat, game, gate, hand, he, make, mama, milk, money, moon, night, open, point, pound, put, talk, top, wait, walk, want, we,* and *you.*

Those that are the least easy to say are: *bad, ball, banana, big, book, car, cold, corn, dinner, dog, farm, fight, goat, good, hide, monkey, nose, O.K., paint, paper, pen, potato, take, tongue, water, wind, wing,* and *yes.*

Other suggestions:

1. Keep a list or notebook dictionary of all words correctly spoken without help. Make the child feel that each new word is a wonderful accomplishment.

2. Reward the child for each new word acquired.

3. Tell a story but omit the new word whenever it occurs. The child must say it. Also use the word to end a rhyme.

4. Hide objects or pictures representing the new words then cover your eyes. The child must hunt and tell what he finds.

5. Make a phone call and ask the child to say a word for you. (Use this method in ordering groceries.)

6. Send the child home, or to a friend's house, with the picture and word to "show off" how well he can talk.

7. Whenever the child masters a new word, his mother must write in one of the squares of a large calendar. He should "read" these every day.

8. Pin a picture to the door of a room or to a favorite chair. Child must say its name whenever he sees it.

5. *Making the new speech a communicative tool.* **Parents** of these children must be cautioned not to use the good new speech for exhibition purposes. These new words and phrases are tools, not ornaments. One of the most effective ways of rewarding the acquisition of new words is to have the child use them to manipulate the big people around him.

One whole session was spent by a speech therapist in turning the light off and on, in climbing upon a table and crawling under it, in banging the table. The four-year-old with whom she had been working had just acquired these new words and was busy using them: "ight" (light), "ight a' gone," "up," "down," and "bang." He shouted with joy whenever his command was followed by her obedient behavior. He had suddenly learned to rule by words. Speech had suddenly become good and useful and very important. From this session onward the therapy proceeded very swiftly and easily although preceding sessions had been very stormy and frustrating.

As soon as the child has mastered a few words, have him use them in as many meaningful ways as you can invent. Review frequently. Draw pictures of them. Send them home or to the regular teacher to practice. Have the child play games with them, perhaps combining them with activities. Make the child realize that the words are useful in these games and give him great praise for their acquisition.

As soon as the child has had some experience in making

words, you should begin the building of a group of words which can serve as a foundation for good acceptable speech. Scrapbooks of pictures clipped from magazines and catalogues, and certain comic strips or cartoons, carefully selected so as to produce certain words, are useful devices to review and "set" this basic vocabulary. Try to get the child to speak these words as spontaneously as possible. Work them into his contacts with other children and adults, into his errands as well as his play. Drill is much less important than use in real life situations. Provide them.

Cautions: There are two major pitfalls in the terminal therapy for delayed-speech cases. First, we must be sure that his incentive for speaking does not far outdistance his actual skills. Once a child begins to realize the miracle of speech as a means of social control, he may hunger to talk so much and so fast that a great deal of hesitation and frustration may ensue. Stuttering has developed from such backgrounds, especially when parents have pushed the child in their desire to have him catch up to his playmates. By keeping the child in a speech environment of slow, quiet, easy talk, this misfortune can be prevented.

The other pitfall also comes from over-eagerness, this time usually from the parents who tend to correct his articulation errors too frequently. They must be helped to realize that no child emerges from delayed speech without going through a transitional period in which many articulation errors and inaccurate word-choices occur. The best way that parents can help is to make errors in their own speech occasionally, stop and think, and then correct them. By this means they will set a model for the child which he can follow without anxiety. It is helpful for such parents to have the concept of "speech age" as well as chronological and mental ages. If a child has begun to talk at the age of four, he should not be expected at six years to have the same mastery of language as another child who began to talk at two. If he has made a good beginning he will catch up to his fellows, usually within three years, in our experience.

References

1. Beckey, R. E., "A Study of Certain Factors Related to Retardation of Speech," *Journal of Speech Disorders*, 1942, Volume 7, pages 223–249.

T-F: Low mentality causes the majority of delayed speech cases.

Essay: List five causes of delayed speech and illustrate.

2. Carrel, J. A., and Bangs, J. L., "Disorders of Speech Comprehension Associated with Idiopathic Language Retardation," *Nervous Child*, 1951, Volume 9, pages 64–76.

T-F: There are many behavioral similarities in delayed speech and brain-injured children.

Essay: List and illustrate the three main goals of treatment.

3. Chapin, A., and Corcoran, M. A., "A Program for the Speech Inhibited Child," *Journal of Speech Disorders*, 1947, Volume 12, pages 373–376.

This outlines a therapy program for delayed speech children who are not mentally deficient.

4. Davis, E. A., "The Development of Linguistic Skill in Twins, Singletons with Siblings, and Only Children from Age Five to Ten Years," *University of Minnesota Child Welfare Monographs*, Series No. 14, 1937.

Twins are much retarded in speech development. Reasons are discussed.

5. Day, E. J., "The Development of Language in Twins. I. A Comparison of Twins and Single Children," *Child Development*, 1932, Volume 3, pages 46–52.

An experimental study of language development in twins showing marked retardation, presumably due to the use of the other twin as a language model or as a social substitute for language need.

6. Dupont, H., Landiman, T., and Valentine, M., "The Treatment of Delayed Speech by Client-Centered Therapy," *Journal of Consulting Psychology*, 1953, Volume 17, pages 122–125.

This is the report of an eight-year-old boy with delayed speech whose problem was based on feelings of rejection. The authors show the value of treating certain cases with child-centered psychotherapy rather than speech-centered therapy.

7. Froeschels, E., *Psychological Elements in Speech*, pages 72–86, Boston, Expression Co., 1932.

An excellent description of the treatment of a speechless child who seemed to be aphasic. The author also mentions the prevalence of behavior problems as a consequence of the inability to express oneself.

8. Gens, G. W., and Bibey, M. L., "Congenital Aphasia: A Case Report," *Journal of Speech and Hearing Disorders*, 1952, Volume 17, pages 32–38.

T-F: On non-verbal tests Bobby was only slightly retarded.

T-F: The child, according to the author, could be called a congenital aphasic.

Essay: Describe the treatment used.

9. Gesell, A., Amatruda, C. S., Castner, B. M., and Thompson, H., *Biographies of Child Development*, New York, Hoeber, 1939, pages 129–146.

Two case histories of delayed speech are analyzed in terms of their developmental causes and treatment.

10. Hawk, S. S., "Moto-kinesthetic Training for Children with Speech Handicaps," *Journal of Speech Disorders*, 1942, Volume 7, pages 357–360.

A description of moto-kinesthetic methods for teaching correct speech.

11. Hurlock, E. B., *Child Development*, New York, McGraw-Hill, 1942, pages 183–186.

The causes of delayed speech are listed and discussed.

12. Konigsberg, E., "Speech for the Slow Learner," *Bulletin of the National Association of Secondary School Principals*, 1948, Volume 32, pages 148–151.

Suggestions to teachers of slow learners who have delayed speech. A full year's program with achievable goals is outlined.

13. Mason, M. K., "Learning to Speak after Six and One Half Years of Silence," *Journal of Speech Disorders*, 1942, Volume 7, pages 295–304.

A detailed description of methods used in treating a delayed-speech case together with notations as to progress.

14. Metraux, R. W., "Speech Profiles for the Child 18 to 24 Months," *Journal of Speech and Hearing Disorders*, 1950, Volume 15, pages 37–53.

This reference is useful here in providing a yardstick of normal speech development against which the delayed speech case may be measured.

15. Peacher, W. G., "Neurological Factors in the Etiology of Delayed Speech," *Journal of Speech and Hearing Disorders*, 1949, Volume 14, pages 147–161.

T-F: The "speech readiness period" is over at four years of age.

T-F: After reviewing the literature, the author comes to the conclusion that there is no such disorder as congenital aphasia.

Essay: What are the arguments for and against the concept of congenital aphasia?

16. ———, "The Neurological Evaluation of Delayed Speech," *Journal of Speech and Hearing Disorders*, 1949, Volume 14, pages 344–352.

The different forms of the neurological examination are presented.

17. Rigby, M., "A Case of Lack of Speech Due to Negativism," *Psychological Clinic*, 1929, Volume 18, pages 156–162.

A general discussion of some of the causes for delayed speech is followed by a very detailed case study of the case mentioned in the title.

18. Rigg, M., "A Superior Child Who Would Not Talk," *Child Development*, 1938, Volume 9, pages 361–362.

Emotional conflict as a cause of delayed speech.

19. Russell, C. M., "Three Hours a Week with a Word Deaf Child," *American Journal of Mental Deficiency*, 1943, Volume 47, pages 456–461.

An account of the treatment of a delayed-speech case, due probably to aphasia.

20. Stinchfield, S. M. and Young, E. H., *Children with Delayed or Defective Speech*, Stanford University Press, 1938.

Topics discussed in this monograph are: characteristics of normal and delayed-speech development; results of speech, mental, hearing, and physical examinations given to a large number of delayed-speech cases; a detailed description of the kinesthetic method for teaching new speech sounds.

21. Van Riper, C., "Children Who Are Slow in Learning Speech," Chapter 5 in Johnson, W. (editor) *Speech Problems of Children*, New York, Grune and Stratton, 1950.

A general survey of the causes and treatment of delayed speech.

22. Weiss, D. A., "Speech Retarded Children," *Nervous Child*, 1951, Volume 9, pages 21–30.

Essay: List the differing behavioral characteristics of children who are (1) aphasic, (2) psychotic, and (3) feeble-minded.

23. Werner, L. S., "Treatment of a Child with Delayed Speech," *Journal of Speech Disorders*, 1945, Volume 10, pages 329–334.

An interesting account of the treatment of a delayed-speech case by indirect means, games, play, and so on.

7. Articulation Disorders

What sounds are defective? Lisping, lalling, baby-talk, oral in-accuracy, dyslalia, all these are labels for the disorders of artic-ulation. There are many others. *Sigmatism* for defective sibi-lants such as *s* and *z*, *rhotacism* for a distorted *r*, *gammacism* for a defective *g* are only a few of the names used to designate specific difficulties with pronunciation. These Greek terms add something to our pomposity but relatively little to our working knowledge. Besides we have known more than one mother who would have fled in terror or hated us for our seeming profanity if we had diagnosed her child's trouble as a sigmatic, kappacic, lambdacic dyslalia instead of telling her that his *s*, *z*, *k* and *l* sounds were defective.

Yet these terms point out something. They indicate that one of the first things we have to do in diagnosing an articulation disorder is to find out what sounds are being mispronounced. We must analyze the speech *phonetically*. If we say that a per-son lisps, we are making such a phonetic analysis, since the word "lisp" refers to a cluster of defective sounds, the sibilant fricatives such as *s* and *z*. "Baby-talk" is an ill-defined term, used more by parents and teachers than by speech therapists, but so far as it does have meaning, it refers to a series of char-acteristic errors: the *w* for the *r*, *t* for *k*, *y* for *l* and so on. This too is a crude diagnostic term which implies a phonetic analysis.

Speech therapists tend to make their phonetic diagnoses more

164

accurately than a mere listing of defective sounds would permit. They also want to know the type of phonetic error. If the
k is defective, is it distorted or omitted? Is some other sound
used in its place? Is the utterance defective because other unnecessary sounds have been added or inserted?

These are some of the questions the speech therapist must
ask of himself in sizing up an articulation problem. He must
analyze the phonetic errors in terms of substitutions, omissions, insertions and distortions. The child who says, "Tally
taw me tee-tawing" is substituting the *t* for the *s* (We record
this: t/s). The child who says, "Oh ook at the itto doggy" is
omitting the initial *l* sound but substituting an *o* for the final *l*
(We would record this as: −l[I] and o/*l*[F]). The letters in the
parentheses indicate the location of the error. We use *I* (for
"initial") if the error is found at the beginning of words, *M*,
if in the middle, and *F*, if in the final position. The minus sign
(−) indicates that the sound has been *omitted;* the plus sign
(+) represents an *insertion* such as the pronunciation of "blue"
as "brrlue" (+r); the diagonal represents a *substitution:* th/s
equals a frontal lisp; *distortions* are substitutions of sounds
foreign to our language, and we use adjectives or symbols to
describe them.

A lingual-frontal lisp is a substitution: (th/s). Let us analyze
a lateral lisp which has distortions. We have no unvoiced *l* in
our language. Welshmen do, and much of their speech seems
lisped to us. One common variety of our lateral lisping is the use
of a whispered *l* for the *s*. If you will attempt to say "*LLLLL*ee
the *LLLL*un" and whisper the *L* sounds, you will be saying
"See the sun" with a lateral lisp. These are distortions, and so
we write them "S (I, lateral-emission)" or more simply:
−s−(I,). If the *s* were laterally emitted in every position of
the word, it would be recorded: −s−(I,M,F). If the student
has mastered the International Phonetic Alphabet with its
modifying marks, he can record many of the distortions accurately, and as substitutions. For example, it is difficult to
record on paper the *l* which is produced by holding the tongue-

tip down and using the middle of the tongue for making the contact against the palate. It seems to be a distortion. The best we could do is to call it "a dark *l*" or a "retracted *l*." However, there is a way of recording it in the phonetic alphabet directly and without vague adjectives. To those who know phonetics, the upside down symbol (λ) will represent the distortion better than adjectives ever could. The child who says (bɔλ) for "ball" probably comes from Mexico.

To summarize, we cannot understand or diagnose an articulation case without making a *phonetic* analysis of his speech in terms of (1) the sounds which are defective; (2) the type of error in terms of substitution, omission, insertion or distortions; and (3) the location of the error within the word (initial, medial or final). This sort of analysis is not academic. It has vital importance for therapy. It helps us answer such questions as: "With what sound or sounds should we first begin? Does the case ever make the sound correctly? How much ear training will be required?"

One of our student speech therapists gave an articulation test to a boy of seven and came out with the astounding summary that although he had thirty-two defective sounds, his speech was perfectly intelligible. When we checked her findings we found that the child actually was doing only one thing incorrectly: He was *forming* the final sounds of every word but he was not pronouncing them audibly. The student therapist had been right in finding that thirty-two sounds were defective, but this actually had no significance, or importance. Our therapeutic task was clearly to teach the child to strengthen his terminal sounds.

To show you what a brief report of a typical phonetic analysis would be like, we submit this one of an eighteen-year-old college student whose tongue had been badly cut during the first grade of his schooling:

Name of case: K. J.   *Examiner:* Leith   *Date:* 1/4/53   *Rapport:* O.K.
Summary of errors: y/l(I,M); o/l(F)
                 w/r(I,M); -r(F)
                 t/ch(I,M,F)
                 —s—(Lateral, I,M,F)
                 —z—(Lateral, I,M,F)

Why are these sounds defective? Besides a phonetic analysis such as we have described we also need a *kinetic* analysis. It is important to know which sounds are being mis-uttered, but we need also to know how they are being produced. The label "lisp" is a *phonetic* term; the modifying adjectives "lateral," "occluded," "inter-dental," or "nasal" are *kinetic* terms. They describe how the error is being made. They refer to the *manner of production*. The term "lalling" is such a kinetic or kinesiologic term. It refers to the type of speech produced when the individual characteristically makes most of his speech sounds without raising the tip of the tongue from the floor of the mouth. It tells us only that this tongue position is at fault. If you were told that a child was a *laller*, all you could guess about his actual speech would be that certain of the consonants which normally are made with an elevated tonguetip would be defective. You could be sure that the *r* would be defective; the *L* probably would be poor, and perhaps the *ch* and *j* or even the *t, d*, and the sibilants. Those would be the probabilities but you could not be certain. Only by analyzing the manner of error-production could you know what the person is doing incorrectly.

Each of the speech sounds can be incorrectly produced in several ways. The most frequent error of such *stop-plosives* as *k* and *g* seems to be due to (1) the wrong location of the tongue contact. Other errors include (2) the wrong speed in forming the contacts; (3) the wrong structures used in contacts; (4) the wrong force or tension of the contacts; (5) too short a duration of the contacts; (6) too slow a release from contacts; (7) the wrong mode or direction of release; (8) the wrong direction of the air stream; and finally (9) sonancy errors in which voiced and unvoiced consonants are interchanged. Examples of these errors are now given for illustration:

1. The child who says "tandy" for "candy" is using a tongue-palatal contact, but it is too far forward.
2. A breathy *k* sound (*xki*) for (*ki*), results when the contact is formed so slowly that fricative noises are produced prior to the air puff.

3. A glottal catch or throat click (ʔæt) for (kæt) is often found in cleft-palate cases. They make a contact, but with the wrong structures.

4. Insufficient tension of the lips can result in the substitution of a sound similar to the Spanish *v* (φ) for the standard English *b* sound.

5. When the duration of the contact is too short, it often seems to be omitted entirely. Thus the final *k* in the word *sick* (sɪk) may be formed so briefly that acoustically it seems omitted (sɪ).

6. Too slow a release from the contact may give an aspirate quality to the utterance. "Kuheep the cuhandy" (kʰip ðə kʰændɪ) is an example of this.

7. The lowering of the tonguetip prior to recall of the tongue-as-a-whole can produce such an error as "tsen" for "ten" (tsɛn) for (tɛn). In this error the case is not inserting an *s* so much as releasing the tongue from its contact in a peculiar fashion.

8. Occasionally the direction of the air stream is reversed and the plosion occurs on inhalation. Try saying "sick" with the *k* sound produced during inhalation, and you will understand this error.

9. The person who says "back" for "bag" illustrates a sonancy error.

Most of the errrors in making the *continuant* sounds are caused by: (1) use of the wrong channel for the air stream (using an unvoiced *l* for the *s*); (2) use of the wrong construction or constriction ("foop" for "soup"); (3) use of the wrong aperture (a lateral lisp); (4) use of the wrong direction of the air stream (nasal lisp; inhaled *s*); (5) too weak an air pressure (acoustically omitted *s*); (6) the presence of nonessential movements or contacts (*t* for *s*, occluded lisp); and (7) cognate errors (*z* for *s*, or vice versa).

Most of the errors in making the *glide* sounds are produced by combining the types of errors sketched above. They may be generally classed as movement errors. They include: (1) use of the wrong beginning position or contact ("yake" for "lake"); (2) use of the wrong ending position (fɪu) for (fɪɚ); (3) use of the wrong transitional movement in terms of speed, strength, or direction (rweɪd) for (reɪd); (4) the presence of nonessential contacts or positions (tjɛlou) for (jɛlou); (5) cognate errors (wɛn) for (hwɛn).

It is necessary to analyze any given articulation error according to the above scheme so as to understand its nature. It is not sufficient merely to start teaching the correct sound. We must also break the old habit. Many of our most difficult articulatory cases will make rapid progress as soon as they understand clearly what they are doing wrongly. Insight into error is fundamental to efficient speech correction.

To show you how we would record the results of a *kinetic* analysis, let us present the summary report of both the phonetic and kinetic procedures:

Name of case: P. T.   *Examiner:* Wensley   *Date:* 2/5/53
Rapport: Good

	Phonetic	Kinetic
Summary of errors:	k/g (I,M,F)	Confusion of voiced and
	t/d (I,M,F)	unvoiced sounds; cognate
	f/v (I,M,F)	or sonancy errors.
	s/z (I,M,F)	Ditto: Vocal cords silent.
	ө ʒ (I,M,F)	" " " "
	w/r (I,M)	" " " "
	-r (F)	Uses lip glide instead of tongue glide. The *r* position was made but it was unvoiced.

This case mastered all of his errors at once except the w/r. He was taught the concept of cognates: that there are pairs of sounds, articulated in much the same way but one is voiced or sonant while the other is unvoiced or surd. He learned that the *v* was made by having his vocal cords vibrate as he made the lip-teeth position for an *f*. He found out that the *s* was a whispered *z*. By feeling both his own and his clinician's throat as the pairs of sounds were produced, he learned to discriminate between them. By holding his fingers in his ears as he shifted from a prolonged *ssss* to a prolonged *zzzz* he learned to recognize one sound from its twin.

Under what conditions do the articulation errors occur? In studying any articulation case it is also necessary to discover the circumstances in which the errors occur. Some of our lispers have difficulty with their sibilants only when emotional. We worked with an exasperating case who never made an error when speaking at a normal rate of speed but who became unintelligible when hurried. Some children can utter words perfectly when repeating from a model and yet substitute, omit and distort their speech sounds in spontaneous speech. Some children who can produce every consonant correctly in isolation or in nonsense syllable will seem to be unable to use them in meaningful words. All of these observations point to the necessity for studying the articulation errors in terms of the type of communication being used. The importance of these factors in therapy is obvious. It would be silly to spend a lot of time drilling a child to produce the *r* sound in nonsense syllables if he has always been able to do so. For these reasons, we examine each error in terms of the following: (1) Type of communicative situation; (2) Speed of utterance; (3) Kind of communicative material; (4) Discrimination ability. Here is a typical summary report:

Our analysis of the conditions under which articulation errors occurred is as follows: Jackson substituted Θ/s (I,M,F) and ð/z (I,M,F) consistently in swift, emotional speech, swift non-emotional speech, when carefully trying to speak correctly in oral reading, and when repeating single words after the examiner. One exception occurred: he said "six" correctly when repeating it carefully. He made the same errors on nonsense syllables when they were spoken at fast speeds but had good final *s* sounds occasionally when the nonsense syllables were spoken slowly. He produced good isolated *z* sounds when prolonged with teeth closed. The *s* was only occasionally good in isolation, even with strong stimulation by examiner. He is always able to hear the error in another's speech but does not seem to be able to hear his own except on isolated words.

The only reason for such diagnostic procedures is that they may help us in therapy. In the above case, the therapy plan called for the teaching of the *z* sound prior to the teaching of the *s*. A great deal of discrimination ear training was used. Recordings and auditory training units which enabled Jackson to hear his own *z* and *s* at high amplification were used. The *s* sound was first taught by isolating it from the key word "six" and no attempt was made to have oral reading or conversation employed in therapy until the new sounds were thoroughly habituated. The *s* sound was used in the final position of nonsense syllables (ees-oss-oos) and in the final position of familiar words (house, glass, ice) before it was taught in the initial position (see, sandwich, sick). By analyzing the conditions under which errors occur, we are able to treat our cases much more efficiently.

Now let us present a complete articulation test report which will combine the *phonetic* analysis, the *kinetic* analysis and the conditions under which errors occur.

A Typical Articulation Test Report

Name of case: *Examiner:*   *Date:*

Summary of errors: t/k (*I,M,F*)   Except in slow nonsense syllables repeated after examiner. Wrong location of contact.

               d/g (*I,M,F*)   Same as above, but said "go" correctly. The case can hear these errors when imitated by examiner at both slow and fast speeds, but cannot hear his own errors except in slowly spoken nonsense syllables.

               t/s (*I,M*)   Except in slow production of isolated sound after strong stimulation by examiner. Can always hear own error except in fast conversation. Doesn't realize no contact is needed.

               -s (*F*)   Makes no attempt to produce it. Evidently does not hear it as a part of the word when it comes in the final position.

Organic factors.   High narrow palatal arch, but teeth are normally placed and tongue assumes good lateral contact with the teeth in making the *z* sounds. Makes the contacts for defective *k* and *g* sounds too far forward and with blade of tongue. When he tries to produce a gen -

ine *t* or *d* he uses the tonguetip against the upper teeth.

Motor co-ordinations: Excellent in every respect.

Emotional factors: Not particularly sensitive. Will try persistently to follow instructions even when failing. Mother says he will try to say a word correctly for his father but not for her. "I'm too impatient, I guess." Boy seems to be mature for his age.

Developmental factors: Had been seriously ill the majority of his first year and a half. Onset of speech at 32 months.

Perceptual deficiencies: Very poor phonetic discrimination except for isolated sounds. Auditory memory span O.K. Poor ability to analyze component sounds of words. Could not recognize "mouth," "shirt," or "nose" when they were sounded out phonically.

Prognosis: Good.

Finding the articulation errors. The conductor of a large symphony orchestra is said to be able to hear any mistake made, whether by piccolo or bass viol. Some speech therapists of long experience and training also have this gift. They can listen to the conversation of an articulation case and come up with a detailed presentation of each error, how it was made and under what conditions. Most of us are not so adept. We must arrive at the same result by a systematic testing program.

Articulation Tests

Articulatory disorders, as we have defined them, are characterized by errors of sound substitution, addition, omission, and distortion. Each speech correctionist devises his own procedure for giving the articulatory examination. Even when students have been trained according to one standard technique, they find it necessary to make modifications to fit the individuality of each case they examine. For this reason, we have described various procedures under each of the types of articulation tests and have provided word lists, sentences, and reading passages which the student may use as he sees fit. His task is to determine the nature, number, and characteristics of the articulatory errors as they occur in the case's speech.

Spontaneous production of a speech sound may be tested in

Fig. 2. Typical sets of articulation test pictures. Note the arrangement according to initial, medial, and final positions of given sounds. In the lower part of the illustration is a metal shield with an exposure window.

several ways, two of which are most commonly used. These are the naming of pictures and the answering of question riddles. For both, a common set of objects or activities is used, the names of which include all the speech sounds in all three word positions. Such a list, with the sounds classified according to manner of articulation, is given at the end of this section. The words are chosen from the lists given in *A Reading Vocabulary for the Primary Grades*, by A. I. Gates, and therefore are suited to small children as well as to adults. The technique of administering this test is simple. After gaining rapport, the teacher points to the picture and asks the child to name it. Or, for example, when using the question riddle to get the sound of voiceless *th* in the final position, she says, "Watch me bite my finger. What did I bite my finger with?" Pictures representing the words in the test list may be cut from old magazines, and every teacher should have such a scrapbook.

The same word list may be used in administering the part of the articulatory analysis which requires the subject to repeat after a model provided by the teacher. The teacher merely asks the child to listen carefully, to wait a moment until the teacher lifts her finger as a signal, and then to repeat what the teacher has said. In addition to the word lists, it is often wise to use nonsense material such as "tho, otho, oth" to determine if a child can follow a model when the effects of training are minimized. Nonsense pictures may be drawn and named with nonsense words containing the sound to be tested. The speech correctionist may also ask the child to repeat "monkey-talk" words.

Both the spontaneous production of the various speech sounds and the student's ability to repeat them after stimulation can be tested by having the student read material that has been organized to include all the speech sounds in all three positions within the word. In addition to the word lists given, the reader will also find individual sentences, one for each of the speech sounds. A continuous passage, "My Grandfather" (see page 178) may be used for this purpose when only a little time is available.

An especially excellent collection of articulation test pictures is provided by Bryngelson and Glaspey (33). Other articulation testing material is provided in the references at the end of this chapter. Two other methods for evoking the spontaneous production of the various speech sounds for children who cannot read the sentences we have listed in this chapter are often

TEST FOR ARTICULATION

FRANK ROBINSON

WESTERN MICHIGAN COLLEGE OF EDUCATION

With Drawings by H. J. McCook

Kalamazoo, Michigan

I would like to have you help me read a picture letter just like one that you may get some day. It has some words and some pictures in it. I'll read the words and I want you to read the pictures. It goes like this

There was a big white – – – – →

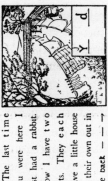

in front of the ↑

That's all there is to it. Now you turn the page and we'll read.

Dear.....

I want to tell you about last Saturday when my mother and I went downtown. We really had a wonderful time. I got up early and went out to feed my – – →

d__g

and my bunny – – – →

r_b_t

The last time you were here I just had a rabbit. Now I have two pets. They each have a little house of their own out in the back – – – →

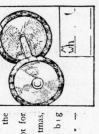

Y__d

Remember when the rabbit was just a little bunny and I would let him suck on my →

θ
th_mb

Now he is big and I can't let him do that, but I do take him and my dog for rides in my →

w_g_n

That's the one I got for Christmas, with the big red —

θ
wh__l

Fig. 3.

employed. In the first, the pictures are drawn or pasted on a continuous strip of paper which passes through guides behind a window in a cardboard shield. Children love these "movies" and will readily name them as they appear. In the second method, a picture letter is used, the teacher reading the words and the child naming the pictures which fit into the context.

We now provide some word lists and sentence lists which the student may use to prepare his own picture test or which he may use for oral reading, repetition after the examiner, or question riddles to evoke spontaneous speech.

ARTICULATORY TEST MATERIAL

Lip sounds: P—pie, apple, cup; B—boy, rabbit, bib; M—mouse, hammer, drum; WH—wheel, whistle; W—window, sidewalk, sandwich; F—fork, telephone, knife; V—valentine, river, stove.

Tonguetip sounds: TH (*unvoiced*)—thumb, bathtub, teeth; TH (*voiced*)—the, feather, smooth; T—top, potato, cat; D—dog, Indian, bird; N—nose, banana, man.

Back of tongue: K—cup, basket, clock; G—girl, wagon, flag; NG—monkey, swing; H—house, schoolhouse.

Complicated tonguetip sounds: L—leaves, balloon, ball; R—rug, orange, chair; S—Santa Claus, bicycle, glass; Z—zebra, scissors, eyes; SH—shoe, dishes, fish; ZH—pleasure, treasure; CH—chicken, pitcher, peach; J—jelly, soldier, bridge; Y—yellow, onion.

Blends: TW—twenty, between; DW—dwarf; BL—black, bubble; CL—clown, declare; FL—flag, snowflake; GL—glass; PL—please, airplane; SL—slim, asleep; SPL—split, splashed; -DL—cradle; -TL —turtle; -ZL—puzzle; BR—bring, umbrella; CR—cry, across; DR— drop, children; FR—friend, afraid; GR—grandma, angry; PR—prize, surprise; SCR—screw, describe; SHR—shrub; SPR—spring; STR— string, destroy; TR—trip, country; THR—thread, three; SK— school, asking, desk; SM—smell, smoke; SN—snow, sneak; SP —spool, whisper, clasp; ST—stop, upstairs, nest; SW—swing, swim; FS—laughs; -LS—else; NS—once, bounce; -PS—cups, pups; -TS— cats, puts; -STS—vests, tests; -THS—months; -BZ—tubs, bibs; -DZ—birds, reads; -LZ—girls, balls; -MZ—drums, homes; -NZ— pans, runs, rains; -NGZ—songs, rings; -THZ—clothes, breathes; -VZ—lives, moves; -LK—milk, milking, silk; KW—queen, require; SKW—squirrel; -KS—packs, except; -GZ—eggs, rugs; -NG—sing, hang, wrong.

Vowels: i—eat, meat, tree; ɪ—it, pig; ɛ—egg, bread; ɛɚ—bear, pear; æ—at, cat; ʌ—up, cup; ɚ—turkey, mother; ə—away, banana; u—moon, shoe; ʊ—book, cooky; ɔ—all; a—arm, star; eɪ—age, cake, day; aɪ—ice, kite, pie; oʊ—old, boat, snow; aʊ—owl, house, cow; ɔɪ—oil, noise, boy.

Reading Sentences

Lip sounds: 1. *P*—The pig ate his supper with the sheep. 2. *B*—The baby robin is in the tub. 3. *M*—The man hammered his thumb. 4. *WH*—Why is the wheel off? 5. *W*—We found a wagon. 6. *F*—The farmer drank coffee with his wife. 7. *V*—His vest is over by the stove.

Tonguetip sounds: 1. *TH (voiceless)*—I think the baby needs a birthday bath. 2. *TH (voiced)*—The baby's mother will bathe him. 3. *T*—Take the pretty coat to her. 4. *D*—Get the doll ready for bed. 5. *N*—At night through the window we see the moon.

Back-tongue sounds: 1. *K*—Come and get your broken kite. 2. *G*—Let's go again and find a frog. 3. *NG*—She sang as she was dancing. 4. *H*—He likes horses.

Complicated tonguetip sounds: 1. *L*—Let me bring a tulip and an apple. 2. *R*—The rabbit likes four carrots. 3. *S*—We saw a see-saw on the grass. 4. *Z*—The zoo is the home for bears. 5. *SH*—She washes every dish. 6. *ZH*—It is a pleasure to have a treasure hunt. 7. *CH*—The child went to the kitchen for a peach. 8. *J*—Jack saw a pigeon under the bridge. 9. *Y*—Your dog ran into the barnyard.

Blends: 1. *TW*—The twin stood between the others. 2. *DW*—The dwarf is a little man. 3. *BL*—He blew a bubble from a black pipe. 4. *CL*—The clown climbed a tree to declare he was king. 5. *FL*—The flag flew in the snowflakes. 6. *GL*—He broke the big glass. 7. *PL*—Please let me have an airplane ride. 8. *SL*—The slim little boy fell asleep. 9. *SPL*—I will splash some water on you. 10. *-DL*—Put the baby in the cradle. 11. *-TL*—See the little turtle. 12. *-ZL*—I like a puzzle. 13. *BR*—Bring me a brown umbrella. 14. *CR*—You could hear him cry across the room. 15. *DR*—The children dropped their balls. 16. *FR*—My friend is afraid of the dark. 17. *GR*—Grandma was angry with me. 18. *PR*—Won't the prize surprise her? 19. *SCR*—The screw is described in the book. 20. *SHR*—There is a shrub by our barn. 21. *SPR*—Spring is coming. 22. *STR*—The string has been destroyed. 23. *TR*—A trip to the country will be nice. 24. *THR*—She has three spools of thread.

25. *SK*—I am asking for a new desk at school. 26. *SM*—Do you smell smoke? 27. *SN*—Let's sneak out and play in the snow. 28. *SP*—They whisper about the lost spool. 29. *ST*—Stop upstairs and see the robin's nest. 30. *SW*—We will swim over to the dock. 31. *-FS*—She laughs at all the jokes. 32. *-LS*—Give me something else. 33. *NS*—You can bounce my ball once. 34. *-PS*—The little pups can drink out of cups. 35. *-TS*—She puts the cats to bed in the barn. 36. *-STS*—He slipped the tests in one of his father's vests. 37. *-THS*—It took him two months to read the book. 38. *-BZ*—Mother washed the bibs in the tubs. 39. *-DZ*—He reads about birds every day. 40. *-LZ*—The girls took our balls away. 41. *-MZ*—They have drums in all the children's homes. 42. *-NZ*—The water runs over the pans when it rains. 43. *-NGZ*—Teacher rings the bell for us to sing more songs. 44. *-THZ*—I have some new clothes. 45. *-VZ*—The fish lives and moves in water. 46. *-LK*—Don't wear a silk dress when you are milking a cow. 47. *KW*—The queen requires that we obey her. 48. *SKW*—That squirrel has a bushy tail. 49. *-KS*—Bring all the packs except one. 50. *-GZ*—Mary dropped the eggs on the rugs. 51. *-NG*—We all sang the wrong song.

Vowels: 1. i—The dog can eat his meat under the tree. 2. ɪ—Give the rest of it to the pig. 3. ɛ—Let's eat an egg with the bread. 4. ɛɚ—That bear went up our pear tree. 5. æ—Don't throw a tin can at the cat. 6. ʌ—Take the cup up from the table. 7. ɝ—Mother put the turkey on the platter. 8. ə—Throw away that banana skin. 9. u—Can you look in the moon and see a shoe? 10. ʊ—I like to eat a cooky when I read a book. 11. ɔ—All of us like corn. 12. a—Point your arm up at the biggest star. 13. eɪ—At the age of ten I will have a cake on my birthday. 14. aɪ—If the ice doesn't freeze over night, I will make you a pie. 15. oʊ—The old boat was lost in the snow. 16. aʊ—The owl hooted from the house and the cow was afraid. 17. ɔɪ—The oil lamp made so much noise that the boy couldn't sleep.

The following passage may be used for a quick survey of the student's ability to produce correct speech sounds. It includes all of the speech sounds, and may either be read by the student or be repeated phrase by phrase after the examiner.

My Grandfather

You wished to know all about my grandfather. Well, he is nearly ninety-three years old; he dresses himself in an ancient black frock coat, usually minus several buttons; yet he still thinks as swiftly as ever. A long, flowing beard clings to his chin, giving those who observe him a pronounced feeling of the utmost respect. When he speaks, his voice is just a bit cracked and quivers a trifle. Twice each day he plays skillfully and with zest upon our small organ. Except in the winter when the ooze or snow or ice prevents, he slowly takes a short walk in the open air each day. We have often urged him to walk more and smoke less, but he always answers, "Banana oil!" Grandfather likes to be modern in his language.

Templin's Word Test[1]

1. reaching	11. grass	21. throw	31. cracker
2. skate	12. cloth	22. present	32. zipper
3. brother	13. there	23. shrink	33. pleasure
4. shoe	14. flower	24. swing	34. larger
5. splashing	15. spring	25. drum	35. onion
6. snow	16. thumb	26. stove	36. bird
7. yellow	17. truck	27. glass	37. straw
8. cherry	18. valentine	28. scratch	38. music
9. sled	19. spoon	29. fresh	39. twins
10. anything	20. jump	30. smooth	40. queens

Templin's Sentence Test[1]

1. In spring we play outside.
2. We throw balls and catch them, too.
3. The twins gave crackers to the birds.
4. Mother scrubbed the floor.
5. Martha shouted, "Slide! It's fun."
6. Smoke came from the train.
7. Here's a long piece of red string.
8. Charles jumped in the pretty snow.
9. Come quick! I dropped my skates.
10. Where is my clean sweater?
11. I brush my teeth every day.
12. I use a green and yellow brush.
13. The soldiers are marching.
14. I like shredded wheat.
15. The thin girl splashed in the water.
16. The stove is very smooth.
17. William measured the zipper on his coat.
18. Grace is washing the spoons.
19. I'm glad you like carrots.

In using this material we must always remember that it is a person who is being tested instead of an articulation test being

[1] M. C. Templin, "A Non-Diagnostic Articulation Test," *Journal of Speech Disorders*, 12:393, 1947.

administered. To go through every word and every sentence
first using oral reading, then repeating, then evoking spontaneously, would be more than any person, child or adult, could
take. Usually, we make a quick screening test consisting of the
single words with small children, or using the reading sentences
with adults. We usually start with the material representing
the most frequently defective sounds in adults. This will give
us the major articulation errors. Then we explore these further
by testing them in isolation, in nonsense syllables, in spontaneous speech. While this is going on, we listen for other errors
and, if they appear, we check them with the appropriate words
and sentences. For a very quick screening test, the author shows
the case a picture of a little girl watching a television set and
asks the child to say this sentence: *"This girl thinks the cowboys
in the television set are real."* It tests all of the most frequently
defective sounds, though not in all positions. The clues received
then lead to the more formal testing with the regular articulation material.

As we listen and analyze and record the errors, we do something else. We listen intently for words in which the sound
usually mispronounced is made correctly. These words we call
key words. They are very useful in therapy, since the correct
sound can be isolated from them. Spriestersbach and Curtis
(28) summarize some research findings which corroborate what
all speech therapists know: that many of the articulation errors
are inconsistent. In some words, and under certain conditions,
the usually defective sound is made perfectly. The examiner
must listen not only for errors, but for the correct sounds as
well.

The public school speech therapist often has to examine
many children for articulatory defects and she must do so
swiftly. Her screening methods must of necessity be brief. Here
is a test passage used by one of them. It is repeated after her,
sentence by sentence.

My mother thinks I like to hear Roy Rogers on the radio. . . . I
don't. I choose Gene Autry. . . . I'd even rather listen to him than

to the Lone Ranger. . . . The Lone Ranger's horse is called Silver. . . . All the Lone Ranger has to do to get Silver to hurry to him is to call or whistle. . . . He sure can run fast. . . . When I'm big I'm going to be a cowboy too. . . .

This passage has all of the most frequently defective sounds in most of the positions and as it unfolds sentence by sentence it interests the children and distracts them so that they do not remain on guard. If certain errors are found, they are checked by subsequent passages of the same sort. Suppose, for example, the child substituted a *d* and a *t* for the *th* sounds in the above material. The speech therapist checks these errors by having the child repeat these sentences after her:

This is my thumb. . . . I put my thumb in my mouth . . . but I don't bite it with my teeth. . . . That would hurt. . . .

Many similar checking paragraphs can be invented for other errors.

Some of the children we have to examine are so severely handicapped that to give a regular articulation test would be not only a chore but meaningless as well. As with delayed-speech children, if there are so many errors that the speech is almost incomprehensible, it would be wiser to record a list of the sounds and words that the child speaks correctly. When such a child repeats sentences after the examiner, it is wise for the latter to record the speech in the phonetic alphabet. In these cases it is wise to put on the articulation test report some estimate of intelligibility. Can the child be understood easily despite his errors? Can he be understood only if his listener knows what is being talked about? Are any words recognizable? What effect does speed of utterance have upon his intelligibility? Would other children be able to understand him? Are his own parents often unable to comprehend his requests?

There are various ways of recording the errors systematically. The following chart will insure that the examiner has heard all of the speech sounds in all positions, and has checked the errors:

PHONETIC ANALYSIS

Consonants				Comments	Vowels				Comments
Sounds	I	M	F		Sounds	I	M	F	
p					ɑ				
b					e [eɪ]				
m					i				
n					ɔ				
t					o [ou]				
d					u				
k					æ				
g					ɛ				
ŋ					ɪ				
f					a [ɒ]				
v					ʌ				
θ					ʊ				
ð					ɑɪ				
s					ju				
z					ɔɪ				
ʃ					ɑʊ				
tʃ					j				
dʒ									
l					List all defective blends:				
r									
h									
w									
ʍ					List "key words" in which defective sound is used correctly:				

Why does this person have an articulation disorder? Some of the causes of defective articulation may have been lost in the mists of speech development by the time the person comes to us. Some may no longer be effective, though at an earlier period they may have been highly potent. Certain factors may have created habits of defective articulation which persist long after they themselves have been removed.

A preacher who came to us for help with his lateral lisp had no organic abnormality, hearing deficiency, poor co-ordination or any other of the usual causes of such a disorder. No one else in his family had such a defect. Finally, however, he recalled that during his second and third years of life he had a nurse-maid who was his constant companion and who had no upper teeth at all. When listening to the recording of another lateral-lisper, a woman, he said, "That sounds just like Nana's voice. She was my nurse."

Frequently several factors may be found, each of which could help to create or perpetuate the defective sounds. At times the defective consonant is merely the product of bad teaching, and its continued presence is due to habit alone. In view of this picture of a wide range of symptoms and causes, we have felt it advisable to devote an entire section to the genesis and analysis of articulation errors.

Some teachers who would investigate the background of a stutterer with great care seem prone to disregard the etiology of articulatory disorders. They merely notice, for example, that their victim mispronounces (among a good many sounds) the consonant *s*, and so they start "correcting" this consonant without further ado. Such a teacher may be occasionally successful, but she will fail with the cases who most need her help. The professional speech correctionist never slights his diagnostic methodology.

The causes of articulation disorders will be discussed under the following headings: (1) developmental influences; (2) emotional conflicts; (3) motor in-co-ordination; (4) organic abnormalities; (5) perceptual deficiencies.

(1) *Developmental influences.* Any examination of an articu-

lation case would be incomplete that did not explore his developmental background by means of interviews and testing procedures. In order that the student may realize some of the possibilities of this type of exploration, we shall now present a few significant facts which proved of importance in the treatment of some of our cases. These bits of information will be organized in terms of the major divisions of the general case history. (See Appendix.)

Parental and Family Influences

Names. If the names of the parents are foreign, the child's consonant errors might possibly be due to imitation of parental brogue, or to the learning of similar consonants belonging to another language. Thus, in one of our cases, the child who substituted *t* for *th* (ɵ), did so because he imitated his father's pronunciation of *th* words. The father's name (which gave us the first clue) was Molo Zymolaga.

Age. When the age of the parents seems somewhat unusual in terms of the child's age, certain emotional factors may be influencing the latter's speech development. Thus, Peter, age 7, had parents aged 22 and 24, and (as we found out by following the clue) was an unwanted child, neglected, unstimulated, and untrained. His articulatory errors were easily understood against this background. Or, consider Jane, who astonished her 49-year-old father and 45-year-old mother by being born. Their excessive attention and demand for adult speech standards too early drove the child into a negativism which made her reject their constant corrections and persist in her errors.

Speech defect. Imitation is often a causal factor in articulation, but we must be sure that the symptoms are similar. All five children of a family living on an isolated farm had nasal lisps. Organically, they were perfect specimens, but their mother had a cleft palate. It is often wise to explore to ascertain whether or not the parents had possessed a speech defect in their own childhood, since such an event would affect their attitudes toward the child's difficulty.

Physical defects. If the mother is deaf, we can easily understand how a child's articulatory errors would receive little attention from her. Here are two other items from our case history files which had significance in our understanding of the child's speech problem: a father whose tonguetip had been shot off in a hunting accident; a "nervous" hyperthyroid mother so unstable that she screamed whenever the children made noise or mispronounced a word.

Emotional conflicts. Conflicts between one parent and the other, or between parent and child, can arise in each of the other areas mentioned in the case history: handedness, religion, education, occupation, and so on. Other people living in the home or closely associated with the child may have significant malinfluences on the child's speech development.

Developmental History

Birth history. Severe birth injuries have malformed the mouth cavity and wrecked the alignment of the jaws or teeth. They sometimes produce, through their injury to the brain, not only feeble-mindedness but the unsure, trembling or spastic co-ordinations of cerebral palsy.

Physical development. When we learn that a child was delayed in sitting alone, in feeding himself, in walking, we usually probe to discover whether the speech development was similarly retarded. Almost any factor that retards physical development also retards speech. Many articulation cases with sluggish tongues and palates have histories of slow physical development.

Illnesses. These have importance according to their severity and sequellae. Certain illnesses such as scarlet fever may impair hearing. Others may so lower the child's vitality that he does not have the energy to learn the difficult skills of talking correctly. Prolonged illness may result in parental attitudes of overconcern or of overprotection. The parents may anticipate the child's needs so that he learns to talk relatively late. They find it difficult to "correct" the speech of a sick child. If illness occurred during the first year of life, the child may not have had the necessary babbling practice. Injuries to the tongue may make certain sounds defective. One child who had burned his tongue started immediately to lall and continued in this articulatory disorder long after the tongue had healed. Many children lose their speech after a prolonged illness with high fevers and find it difficult to master it again.

Mental and educational factors. It is often the unpleasant chore of the speech correctionist to help parents face the fact that their child is feeble-minded, and that his general retardation is not solely the consequence of his delayed speech. When we find such children, we usually postpone speech therapy until they have a mental age (on a nonverbal test) of from five to six years.

Failures in the school subjects, especially in reading, may be a direct consequence of defective articulation, and remedial reading can frequently be combined with remedial speech. Children who fail in school are likely to be resistant at first to speech correction. If they have been penalized for their school failure, they may become so emotional over their speech handicap that their tension prevents new muscular adjustments of the articulatory organs. One of our cases made no progress in his speech until he was transferred to another grade. The hatred he felt toward his teacher constantly reflected itself in our work with him.

Play. Children adopt the consonant errors of their playmates as well as their grammatical errors. In one instance, children from three different families in the neighborhood acquired a lisp by identification and imitation of a dominant older boy. It is said that *s* and *z* are pronounced as *th* (θ, ð) in Castilian Spanish because a certain king of Spain lisped and his courtiers adopted his pronunciation of the sibilant sounds. Little tyrants in every child kingdom similarly impose their speech peculiarities upon their subjects.

Home conditions and emotional problems. A knowledge of the home conditions, the tempo of life lived therein, the attitudes of its inmates, is often vital to the understanding of the articulatory problem. Parents may bedevil a child for his social blemishes merely because they are sensitive about their own. An unhappy home can make our speech correction difficult. The list of emotional problems given in the case history can give us some indication of the child's reaction to his speech defect. The child who is always fighting, hurting pets, setting fires, or performing similar aggressive acts must be handled much differently from one who withdraws from the challenges of existence. Articulatory disorders, like stuttering, can be primary or secondary, according to the manner in which the child regards his difficulty. We have known lispers to substitute easier words for those which included sibilant sounds. One boy's speech was so halting that he was referred to us as a stutterer. Extremely maladjusted and antagonistic, he avoided speech whenever he could. Asked to recite in school, he would growl, "I don't know and I don't care." Investigation showed that he had been penalized severely by his classmates for his lisp. His breaks in fluency and his behavior problem disappeared simultaneously with his lisp.

Language development. The chapters of this book on learning to talk and on delayed speech have provided many instances of the factors which can cause articulation errors to persist. By and large, poor teaching methods are no doubt responsible for more defective articulation than is any other factor. We always try to interview the parents of a young articulatory case to determine how they attempt to correct his errors. Observation of this parental correction at work will often

demonstrate penalties, confusions, and impatience as well as ignorance.

(2) *Emotional conflicts*. Some of our most difficult articulation cases are those in which the child failed to acquire adult
pronunciation because of emotional conflicts.

For over two years we worked with a co-operative girl who had
what seemed like a fairly simple frontal lisp. She seemed to do her
utmost; she obviously disliked the penalties which it evoked in her
college classes, but she consistently failed to master the correct *s* and
z sounds. We interviewed her at some length but were unable to discover any emotional blocking. Then her father visited us and said:
"Dorothy always gets what she wants from me. If I say no, she just
crawls up on my lap and puts her arms around me and talks baby
talk. I'm a sucker, but she hooks me every time. That lisp of hers
cost me $800 last year. Put it into a car she wanted."

The desire to remain a child or to return to childhood security has produced many symptoms of articulation disorders.
Speech therapy alone with these cases is useless. Consciously
they may desire to overcome their infantile errors, but they
will cling to them with a compulsiveness that must be experienced to be understood. West (59) cites numerous cases to
show that articulation errors can be due to a sensitivity of one
kind or other. He says, "Malocclusions have their greatest effect on speech disorders psychologically." We have had cases
whose mumbling, half-articulated syllables were clearly the result of unsightly teeth.

Social penalties upon unconscious habits can often make
them very difficult to eliminate. The parent who scolds or ridi-
cules a child for his articulatory errors may make it impossible
for the latter ever to attempt to correct himself. We have
known lispers to become so emotional over their errors that
they could not make an intelligent attempt to produce the *s*
sound in a different way. One girl smashed a radio with a mallet
upon hearing a "comedy" program in which an articulatory
defect was assumed for humorous purposes. Another fainted
when she heard a recording of her speech.

(3) *Motor deficiencies.* Articulation cases are occasionally seen who could truly be called the "slow of tongue." They can scarcely protrude the tongue even in the expression of impudence without having it lall around and droop over. Sometimes, these poorly co-ordinated movements seem to be localized about the mouth. The tongue, jaw, soft palate, all are sluggish. But in most of these clumsy-mouthed individuals the other co-ordinations are similarly affected.

Not all articulation cases are thus poorly co-ordinated, but those who are so handicapped must be given therapy devoted to their needs. In earlier speech correction, tongue exercises had the status of a religious ritual. All speech defectives were given rigorous training in this routine. In modern speech correction, the emphasis on tongue exercises has almost disappeared. Yet for certain of the "clumsy-tongued" individuals with whom we work, modern forms of these exercises are very valuable.

A good many diseases and neuromuscular malconditions reflect themselves not only in muscular in-co-ordination but also in distorted speech. The speech correctionist is often able to refer them to the physician they need. The student of speech correction should therefore be able to recognize the general symptoms of paralysis, both flaccid and spastic, and pronounced neuromuscular in-co-ordinations. Besides the tests mentioned in the references, other simple activities which may demonstrate poor co-ordination are: walking a straight line; extending arms above head and dropping them suddenly; beginning with hands resting on knees as one sits in a chair, alternately touching nose with forefinger of each hand; standing first on one leg and then on the other, with eyes closed; skipping; standing on tiptoe for five seconds.

It is possible to get an excellent estimate of the sluggishness of the articulation apparatus by measuring the rate of jaw movement. Maximum rates are achieved in about ten seconds, but several short practice sessions should be used to ensure understanding of the task. Demonstrate the opening and closing of the jaw with a clicking of the teeth on the closure. Instruct the case to imitate you as rapidly as possible, and count the number of clicks in five seconds. Be sure not to create fatigue. Jenkins (16) gives the following norms for this dia-dochokinesis of the jaw in number of jaw closings *per second:*

	NUMBER OF JAW MOVEMENTS PER SECOND	
AGE	*Males*	*Females*
7	3.5–3.8	3.7–4.0
8	3.6–3.9	3.8–4.0
9	4.0–4.4	4.0–4.3
10	4.1–4.3	4.2–4.3
14	4.9–5.1	5.0–5.2
15	5.1–5.3	5.2–5.4
Adults	5.2–5.4	5.4–5.6

The tongue seems to be of greater importance in articulation than the jaw. We therefore cite the research of Blomquist (6), who found that children of nine years averaged 4.6 jaw move-ments for the syllable "tuh" (tə); 4.6 for the syllable "puh"; and 4.0 for the syllable "kuh." When these syllables were com-bined in the nonsense word "puhtuhkuh" (pʌtəkə), children of nine could utter the word 4.5 times per second. At eleven years of age, the corresponding figures were p:5.3, t:5.2, and k:4.7. Lundeen (18) tested diadochokinetic rates for ten consonants, finding the following order (from fast to slower rates): t, d, p and b. These are the sounds which can be repeated most quickly; then follow f and v; and slowest of all were the sounds s, g, and z. We have found that training in diadochokinesis is extremely valuable with most articulation cases who are slow in it.

Lest the student come to the improper conclusion that all articulation cases need muscle training, we cite the research of Mase (21) who found no group differences between articula-torily handicapped and normal speaking school children either in five tests of diadochokinesis or in rail-walking, a general motor-skill activity. But when we deal with an individual case we want to know whether or not he needs help and training in his motor skills.

Here are some tests to measure the rapidity of the articulatory structures:

A. "As soon as I give the signal repeat what I say very slowly and carefully: 'Puh-puh-puh.' . . . . Now, I am going to say it five times but this time as fast as possible. Now, let's see how fast you can say it five times. Ready—go!" (Examiner times the five trials.)

B. and C. Repeat the above, but use first the syllable "tuh" and then the syllable "kuh."

D. Repeat the instructions above but use the nonsense word "puh-tuh-kuh." Children of from seven to nine years should, according to Rainey's research, be able to utter this word at least once per second.

From Mase's monograph (21) we select the following alternate tests, citing the means of his fifth and sixth grade boys:

E. With mouth open, subject is to move his tongue repeatedly from left corner to right corner. Examiner counts total number of cycles in two trials of ten seconds. Norm: 23 cycles.

F. Subject is required to say "Daddy" as many times as he can in each of two five-second trials. Examiner totals both trials. Norm: 25 times in ten seconds.

It would seem important to have tests for accuracy as well as speed of movement, but so far as accuracy of the tongue or jaws is concerned, little research has been published.

(4) *Organic abnormalities.* Most parents are anxious to discover an organic cause for a child's articulatory disorder: a tongue-tie, a sluggish velum, an abnormally high arched palate, spaced or missing teeth. Yet many persons with perfectly normal speech can be shown to possess these abnormalities, and many articulation cases have perfectly normal articulatory organs. We must be careful that we do not miss significant functional factors in our search for something organic. Froeschels[2] declares that missing front teeth are not the cause of frontal lisps:

---

[2] Froeschels, E. and Jellinek, A., *Practice of Voice and Speech Therapy*, Boston, Expression Co., 1941, pages 162–163.

Of some 800 cases who passed under our observation we found only three who used the opening formed by the abnormal teeth for protruding the tongue. All other cases lowered the jaw to make room.

He also suggests the hypothesis that the dental abnormality may have been caused by the speech defect:

The pressure of the tongue against the teeth, namely against the incisors . . . or against the lateral teeth, is the cause of the abnormal position of the teeth.

There have been several cases reported in which a person whose tongue had been amputated was subsequently able to achieve intelligible speech.

Fairbanks (12) and his students in a series of careful experiments has shown that there is no consistent or statistically significant difference between groups of normal speaking and articulatorily defective adults so far as organic differences are concerned.

Nevertheless, the presence of a badly overshot jaw, or an excessively long tongue, or any other of the many organic abnormalities which we look for in examining the speech defective must certainly be a handicap in achieving normal pronunciation. Bright children from homes with high speech standards, who are badly tongue-tied, will no doubt be able to learn other compensatory ways of making their sounds, but less intelligent children whose parents show little interest in their speech improvement will continue to lall. We must not exaggerate the importance of organic factors, but we must not ignore them either. We have been able to teach a good many children with very marked dental, palatal, or lingual abnormalities perfect speech sounds, but we usually find that the organic anomaly makes our work more difficult. In some cases, the organic peculiarity is interpreted by the case as a sign of hopelessness so far as good speech is concerned. Backus (8) cites the case of a ten-year-old boy whose tonguetip had been cut off. She says, "There was no organic reason why he could not make the back-tongue sounds (k, g, ŋ), yet the fact remained that he did not make them, nor did he use the tongue much even for vegetative purposes." Later, he was taught to make these sounds as well as all others. We once worked with an adult who mistakenly believed that he had an extremely large tongue, and who did not progress in his speech correction efforts until convinced that his tongue was of normal proportions. It may be that many organic causes are of this order.

As we shall see when we come to our discussion of the treatment of articulation disorders, it is often necessary to teach compensatory or nonstandard ways of producing a given speech sound when dealing with a child who shows a marked organic abnormality. A soldier with a one-sided paralysis of the tongue can be taught to make an excellent *l* sound, but it will seldom be made with the tonguetip against the midline of the upper gum ridge.

The presence of organic defects is therefore important and must be taken into account both in diagnosis and therapy. However, the presence of some organic abnormality need not discourage the speech correctionist even when it cannot be eliminated or changed.

Examination for organic defects. It is wise to make a special examination of the mouth, nose, and throat of every speech case, but such an examination is needed especially for voice and articulatory disorders. While it is true that many normal speakers have organic defects in these speech structures and that such defects therefore cannot be termed essential causes of the speech defect, nevertheless the presence of an overshot jaw or of an excessively long tongue must certainly be a handicapping factor in speech development. Some of us can compensate for these defects because of either training or natural desire for speech perfection, but many others cannot. Hence the presence of these defects is important and must be taken into account in both the diagnosis and the treatment. However, the presence of some anatomical abnormality is of no importance in itself unless it stands in functional relation to defective speech sounds. For example, the presence of a harelip in a child whose sole speech error is an inability to produce the *k* sound is of no causal significance. It is also necessary to caution the inexperienced teacher not to make a hasty diagnosis. Other causal factors may be of far greater importance than the organic defect.

Although a head mirror or laryngoscope is more convenient, an adequate examination may be made by placing the subject slightly to one side of a flashlight or a window and reflecting this light, by means of a little mirror, into his mouth. Tongue depressors, probes, and tooth props are tools easily procured. The examiner should develop a systematic routine involving quick, sure movements and requests. He should examine each structure, not only in quiescence, but also in its relation to the appropriate speech sounds. He must record all evidence of handicapping abnormality, together with a notation as to any evidence of compensatory movements in the production of speech. A convenient sequence for the examination is as follows:

1. Examine lips for presence of scar tissue or harelip. Examine during performance of *p*, *b*, and *m*.

2. Examine jaws in relaxed occlusion to note overshot, undershot, or asymmetrical jaw formation. Examine during performance of *f*, *v*, and *th*, and note whether tongue movement is compensatory during performance of *s*, *l*, and *r* due to the relative displacement of tongue with respect to the upper teeth.

3. Examine teeth to note malocclusion. Record whether it is due to the upper, lower, or both sets of teeth. Record also whether it is on the right, left, or both sides. Note spaced or missing teeth according to a similar scheme. Note whether tongue habitually plugs gaps in silence or in making the following sounds: *s*, *z*, *sh*, *ch*, *j*, *zh*. Note relation of teeth to jaws and lips.

4. Note tongue to determine gross abnormality of width and length. Have subject lap tongue several times, finally leaving it out. Note any evidence of atrophy, in terms of area on both sides of midline, and of wrinkling. Have subject touch right and left corners of mouth alternately to determine possibility of unilateral sluggishness or paralysis. Note proximity of frenum to tonguetip. Can subject lick above upper margin of upper lip without showing bowing effect of frenum? Is there evidence of past tongue-tie? Can subject groove tongue at will? Can subject touch hard palate with tonguetip easily? Have subject touch tongue depressor held one inch out from the

teeth as you count rhythmically at a rate of three counts per second for five seconds. Note action of tongue in making *th, s, l, r, d, t, k, g.*

5. Examine roof of mouth to note gross abnormality in height and width of hard palate. Note tongue placement for *r* and *l, k* and *g,* to determine compensatory positions. Note slope of hard palate from alveolar ridge. Note whether any evidence of present or past cleft exists.

6. Examine velum for presence of cleft, shortness, uvular abnormality, atrophy, or asymmetry. Is uvula pulled to one side? Is it so long as to stick to back of tongue? Have subject phonate vowel *a* and note action of velum and pharynx. (A guttural mirror may help in this part of the examination.) Is velum too short for good closure? Note action of velum in producing *k* and *g* sounds. Determine whether gag reflex exists. Note size and condition of tonsils and part they play in velar action. Note injuries or scar tissue on pillars of the fauces. Note inflammation of the velum and surrounding tissues. Ask student to swallow a large mouthful of water. Note if any comes out of the nose. Ask student to blow up a balloon.

7. Examine pharynx as subject nasalizes vowel *a* and as he phonates a normal *a.* Note presence of adenoids, using guttural mirror. Note inflammation and amount of mucosa. Have subject alternate *m* and *ba* sounds as rapidly as possible for 5 seconds. He should be able to average at least 2 per second if a child, and 3 per second if an adult. Note presence and condition of adenoids. Is there a constant nasal drip from the nasopharynx?

In so far as possible it is always wise to examine the articulatory organs (the tongue, lips, teeth, jaws, and soft palate) as the incorrect sounds are being attempted. Occasionally we must insert a tongue depressor between the teeth to observe the action of the tongue or palate. This does not give a normal picture of the manner of sound production, but it does help to identify basically incorrect movements and contacts. Thus, one adult who could not produce a normal *ch* (tʃ) sound was observed beginning this sound from a contact of the tonguetip and the soft palate. A passable *ch* (tʃ) sound can be made in this way but not at conversational speeds. Helping him to locate the normal starting position on the upper teeth or gum ridge soon cleaned up his difficulty. Many cases of lateral lisping will be observed lifting the tonguetip to the contact for an unvoiced *l* as a substitute for the *s*. It is often impossible for these cases to adopt a new correct method of sound production until they can identify the old one. We cannot break an unconscious habit except by bringing it up to consciousness. By studying the action of the articulatory organs as they produce the incorrect sounds, we can plan a much better treatment.

(5) *Perceptual deficiencies.* In our opinion, it is in this area that most of the causes of articulation defects occur, but we have to admit that most of the research does not support that opinion. Studies of auditory memory span and of phonetic discrimination have generally failed to show marked differences between groups of normal speakers and articulation cases.

Despite the general negative tone of these research findings most clinicians feel that their articulation cases need a great amount of training in auditory perception, in sensing the location of focal articulation points, in feeling where the tongue is and what it is doing. Case after case shows a marked inability in synthesizing a series of isolated sounds to make a familiar word (recognizing that n . . . o . . . z can be combined to make "nose"). Case after case finds great difficulty in recognizing his own errors, even though he may show excellent discrimination of the errors of others. Many such persons may know that a word is incorrectly pronounced without being able to isolate the particular part of the word which is defective. The research has not tested these basic difficulties, and in its absence, we must do what we can to discover whether or not they exist in the case we are examining.

Like diadochokinesis, *vocal phonic ability* increases with age, varies with sex and many other factors, including intelligence. Our own very tentative norms for a group of twenty first-grade, twenty third-grade and twenty fifth-grade normal speaking children on the following test are given in terms of number of items missed. The sounds are given at a rate of one per second.

Vocal Phonics Test

"I am going to say the name for this thing (pointing to nose) in a funny way: 'nnn . . . . o . . . . zzzz.' Do you know what I'm saying? 'nnn . . o . . zzz,' . . . 'nn . o . zz,' . . . 'nnnozz,' nose. Yes,

I said 'nose,' didn't I? Now see if you can guess what these words are?"

NUMBER OF CHILDREN UNABLE TO RECOGNIZE WORD

	First grade	Third grade	Fifth grade
aɪ...z (eyes)	1	0	0
ʃ....u (shoe)	1	0	0
f....e.....s (face)	3	1	0
n....aɪ.....f (knife)	4	1	0
m...aʊ....ɵ (mouth)	3	2	0
æ...p.....l (apple)	4	2	1
m...ʌ.....ð.....ɝ (mother)	5	3	0
l....æ.....m.....p (lamp)	7	4	1
k....ʊ.....k......i (cookie)	4	1	0
s....ɛ.....v......n (seven)	7	2	0

We insert this crude test and inadequate norms in the hope that someone will investigate this very important area of perception. Meanwhile, you may judge the vocal phonic ability of your articulation cases against these figures.

An individual who cannot synthesize a series of sounds into a word usually seems to have more difficulty in the opposite function, the ability to analyze a given word into its component sounds. We test this ability by giving the above test in reverse, giving the case the word, and asking him to say the sounds that compose it. This is usually more difficult, and we have no norms available, but this skill is vitally important for the correction of articulation errors. If a case is to correct himself, he must analyze the word he has just spoken, recognize the defective sound, and replace it with the correct one. We have found clinically that systematic training in both the analytic and synthesizing forms of vocal phonics speeds the therapy greatly with most of our cases.

Auditory memory span. In testing the articulation cases' auditory memory span, several methods may be used. We may follow the procedure used in intelligence testing and determine how many digits a child can recall. We may use a series of isolated nonsense syllables with two-second intervals (23), or we may use a series of nonsense words in which the syllables are combined as in "goulabi." Research has not shown any conclusive difference between groups of articulatory cases and groups of normal-speaking individuals on auditory memory-span tests, but certain individuals are found whose auditory memory spans are so short that this factor must be taken into account during treatment. The purpose of these tests is to discover these individuals.

Some norms for auditory memory-span tests are now given:

I. For repeating digits at one-second intervals (Robbins):

Age	Number of Digits
3	3
4	4
7	5
10	6
14	7
18	8

II. For repeating nonsense syllables (kʌ, pʌ, and so on) (Metraux) at two-second intervals:

Age	Number of Syllables
5	2.0
6	2.3
7	2.6
8	2.6
9	2.8
10	3.0
11	2.9
12	3.1

III. For repeating nonsense words (Beebe[3]):

Age	Number of Syllables per Nonsense Word
4	4
5	3.8
6	4.3
7	4.3
8	4.6

---

[3] Beebe, H. H., "Auditory Memory Span for Meaningless Syllables," *Journal of Speech Disorders*, 1944, Volume 9, pages 273–276.

Phonetic discrimination ability. Ordinarily we combine our examination of the case's ability to hear differences among the various speech sounds with the general articulation tests. We do this by determining whether he can tell his errors from the correct sounds when both are produced in random fashion by the examiner. But occasionally we find a case who seems to be especially lacking in phonetic discrimination. In order to be certain that this is indeed an important factor, we administer a more formal type of test. The one which we have found most useful is the modification of the Travis-Rasmus test used by Templin (30). It is simply administered by requiring the case to write down on a sheet of paper his judgment of whether or not the two sounds given by the examiner are the *same* or *different.* A short practice session is given to clarify the task. The series of paired syllables used by Templin in the short form of her test are as follows:

SHORT TEST OF SOUND DISCRIMINATION

Examples:	*Key:* All D Except:
te-de	A. 1, 8
ere-ere	B. 1, 6, 8, 10
os-og	C. 3, 6, 8, 9
	D. 4, 9, 10
	E. 3, 9
	F. 3, 7
	G. 3, 6

A	B	C	D
1. te-te	1. ne-ne	1. fo-θo	1. pe-ke
2. hwe-we	2. dʒe-tʃe	2. vo-ðo	2. tʃo-ʃo
3. ne-me	3. ʃe-tʃe	3. zo-zo	3. ki-ti
4. ðe-de	4. im-iŋ	4. ʃe-ʒe	4. eb-eb
5. fi-vi	5. hwi-wi	5. fi-θi	5. ehwe-ewe
6. he-pe	6. ge-ge	6. ze-ze	6. en-em
7. se-ze	7. dʒi-tʃi	7. mai-nai	7. eð-ed
8. θe-θe	8. fai-fai	8. θe-θe	8. ehe-epe
9. ʒe-dʒe	9. ðe-ve	9. he-he	9. ov-ov
10. vo-bo	10. pe-pe	10. dʒi-ʒi	10. eθ-eθ

E	F	G
1. eʒ-edʒ	1. eð-ev	1. if-iθ
2. ov-ob	2. et-ep	2. aim-ain
3. ed-ed	3. ep-ep	3. eθ-eθ
4. en-en	4. of-oθ	4. ini-iŋi
5. edʒ-etʃ	5. ov-oð	5. ef-ep
6. eʃ-etʃ	6. ed-eg	6. eð-eð
7. imi-iŋi	7. em-em	7. idʒ-iʒ
8. ihwi-iwi	8. eð-ez	8. ep-ek
9. eg-eg	9. airai-aiwai	9. otʃ-oʃ
10. is-iz	10. eʃ-eʒ	10. ez-eð

Our own norms, based on 30 normal-speaking children from each of the grades 2 through 6 are as follows:

Grade	Average Number of Errors
2	14.2
3	11.8
4	10.1
5	10.2
6	10.1

Great care must be taken to ensure attention and to prevent fatigue. From a consideration of the test data, we would not feel justified in considering a person markedly deficient in phonetic discrimination unless he made ten or more errors above the averages given.

Summarizing the diagnosis. At the end of the examination it is always necessary to put all our information together in a systematic and meaningful way. Only when this is done is it possible to get a clear picture of the case with which we will be working. If a therapy plan is to be constructed which has a real chance for success, the information gained from the examination must be organized. The following form can be used for this purpose·

DIAGNOSTIC CASE SUMMARY

Case:　　*Age:*　　*Grade:*　　*Address:*　　*Phone:*
Type of disorder:
Results of Articulation test:

Phonetic errors: *Manner of error production:*   *Conditions:*
Phonetic transcription of conversational speech:
Intelligibility:
Key words (Underline sound usually defective):
Case history data:
Intelligence:
Hearing:
Emotional conflicts:
Motor in-co-ordinations:
Organic abnormalities:
Perceptual deficiencies:
Attitude toward prospective therapy:

Treatment

The first task of the speech therapist, once the examination has been completed, is the construction of a therapy plan. This is often slighted due to the assumption that articulation defects are less serious than the other abnormalities of speech. But to the man who owns one there is no such thing as a minor speech disorder. Some of our cases who possessed a single sound distortion, e.g., a lateral lisp, have proved to be as difficult to treat as any stutterer or cleft-palate case. Equally prevalent is the belief that all that is required is the administration of drills consisting of the repetition of words or sentences loaded with the difficult sound. Modern speech therapists have given up tongue-twister therapy. The "ragged rascal" is no longer compelled to "run around the rock" a thousand times by our lalling cases. If "Susie cannot sell sea shells at the seashore" it is all right with us. The important necessity before us is that we outline a comprehensive program of remedial help which will eliminate the causal factors still existing and facilitate the unlearning of an articulatory error and the learning of the correct sound which must replace it.

Therapy plans are constructed primarily in terms of subgoals leading toward the acquisition of normal speech and secondarily in terms of the activities necessary to the achievement of these sub-goals. A typical therapy plan will illustrate these features.

But let us first present our case.

DIAGNOSTIC CASE SUMMARY

Case: Robert Johnson   *Age:* Ten   *Grade:* Fifth   *Referral:* by teacher
Informant: Mother   *Examiner:* Jackson   *Date:* March 2, 1953
Previous Therapy: None.   *Type of Disorder:* Articulation
Articulation test results:

> t/k (I. M. F) -k (F)
> d/g (M. F)   -g (F)
> w/l (I. M)   -l (F)
> o/l (F)

> All l blends (sl, pl, etc.) have the l omitted. All k and g blends defective. Occasionally defective r (I) distorted by lip protrusion.

Manner of error production: This case tends to anchor the tonguetip on the lower gum ridge and produces the acoustically correct *t, d,* and *n* as well as the defective sounds by raising the blade of the tongue instead of the tip.

Conditions under which errors occur: Case can produce the *k* in isolation (kə) but only with strong stimulation and at slow speeds. The *g* can be produced in isolation and in nonsense syllables in all positions by repeating after the examiner and without need for strong stimulation. Case also uses *g* occasionally in his conversation. Fails consistently if excited or hurried. Omissions of both these sounds in the final position are most prominent in swift conversation. Discrimination of correct versus incorrect sounds as made by examiner is good. Self discrimination is poor. Child cannot produce or discriminate a good *l* sound even with strong stimulation. Error on this sound always occurs.

Intelligibility: Generally good. Occasionally when speaking swiftly or excitedly some difficulty in understanding a word or two was experienced by examiner. Other children and his parents and teacher understood him readily.

Key words: The following words were produced correctly: "O.K." "*g*o" "*g*um" and "*l*i—" (like).

Case history data: No foreign language background; parental speech and attitudes toward child, good. No evidence of imitation as a factor.

Birth history normal. Developmental history: child experienced great difficulty in sucking; bottle fed with large opening in nipple required; digestive troubles during first two years of life; much crying, "little babbling." Normal physical development. Usual childhood diseases were mild. Cut tonguetip with paring knife at 22 months; no permanent injury or scar tissue; intelligence normal: Binet I.Q. at 8 years was 108; good student and excellent reader (silently); well adjusted child with no pronounced emotional conflicts or behavior problems; interests normal for his age; first words spoken at 13 months and was speaking in "long sentences" by his second birthday; parents tried to correct child by demanding he repeat his difficult words after them but this method failed and no further attempts have been made except by the kindergarten teacher who also had no success. Child is aware of the fact that he does not talk correctly but is not too concerned. Some teasing to which he reacted by laughing and making his speech even worse.

Hearing: Audiometric examination reveals no hearing loss.

Organic examination: No abnormalities. Palatal arch fairly high but within normal variation. No frenum interference.

Motor coordinations: Large muscular coordinations adequate for his age norm. However, child seems unable to move tongue independently of jaw except at very slow speeds. Tongue thrust and strength seem normal. Tongue curling and lifting are accomplished with great difficulty. Cannot sustain half-lifted tonguetip in a fixed position. It always returns to lower gum ridge, or teeth.

Perceptual deficiencies: Auditory memory span normal; cannot discriminate *w* from *l* and made one error on *t* and *k;* cannot locate or recognize own errors in conversation or in single words; vocal phonics very poor: could only integrate two stimulus sounds (sh-oe); failed consistently in trying to integrate three sounds. Has little conception of words as sound sequences. Poor rhyming ability. Hears words as "chunks of sound."

Attitude toward prospective therapy: Fifteen minutes of trial therapy were administered in which discrimination of *t* from *k* was attempted. Child seemed interested. Cooperative. Rapport easily established. Should be a good case if motivation can be achieved.

How then should we treat Robert Johnson? Our final goal of course is to have him pronouncing correctly all of his defective sounds as unconsciously and automatically as other children do. But what are the sub-goals which lead to this final result? The therapy plan for this case should answer these questions. It is phrased in the form of the report to the therapist who was planning to help the boy.

. . . In addition to the preceding case summary, we are providing a tentative therapy plan which may assist you in organizing your treatment. We cannot, at this time, be certain that it will be adequate to the child's needs. Actual therapy alone will indicate the modifications necessary, but it should provide a framework for those changes.

Therapy Plan for Robert Johnson

Each therapy session, we feel, should be partly devoted to building a stronger foundation of essential skills and abilities and partly to the unlearning of an articulation error and the mastery of the correct sound which it replaces. Accordingly, we suggest that each session include some activity aimed at achieving each of these goals:

1. Convincing the child that it is essential that he achieve better speech.

2. Improving his ability to move the tongue independently of the jaw; increasing his precision and control of tongue postures. Also try to free tongue lifting from lip-rounding.

3. Teaching him to recognize the location of the upper gum ridge as an important landmark in speech production not only for the *l* but also for the *t*, *d* and *n* which are so often dentalized. Get him to explore the geography of the mouth so that he can distinguish the posterior focal articulation points needed for *k* and *g*.

4. Improving his vocal phonics. Much training is needed here if he is ever to learn to recognize his errors or to master the correct sound in words.

5. Ear training to help him (a) locate his errors within his utterance; (b) to discriminate between the correct sound and his error; (c) to recognize and identify the essential characteristics of the new sound to be learned; and (d) to receive enough strong stimulation with the isolated new sound to permit mastery.

6. As soon as the child shows real success in the ear training activities and you feel that Robert has shown improvement in tongue coordination and vocal phonic ability, we suggest that you devote a good share of each therapy session to teaching the new sound in isolation. However, this new sub-goal should not replace the five previously mentioned. They must receive a due portion of the therapy time.

7. When the boy can produce the new sound easily upon request, you should proceed to strengthen it, first in isolation, then in non-sense syllables or nonsense words. This strengthening should form the dominant part of the session at this stage, but again each of the pre-ceding sub-goals must be reviewed in any therapy session.

8. Once Robert can make the new sound swiftly and easily in nonsense material you should begin to help him learn to incorporate it within meaningful words. The transition must be carried out with care using such techniques as signal practice and reconfiguration. Concentrate first on a few key words and continue on these until thoroughly mastered. Then proceed to the correct pronunciation of many words, using them in meaningful situations.

9. Finally, help him to use the new sound habitually, employing such techniques as negative practice, alternation of correct and in-correct sounds at swift speeds with rewards or token penalties by the use of checking devices in actual communicative situations. The child must be able to recognize his mistakes and to cancel them with cor-rectly spoken words before you start working with one of his other defective sounds. This must be done without prompting on your part or reminder by others.

We suggest that you begin first with the g then the k, then the l and finally the r and the blends. You will probably find that careful training on the g will produce swift or even spontaneous mastery of the others. If it is possible, therapy should be individual, though group therapy can be employed, especially in the latter stages of the treatment. Since the boy's motivation to speak correctly is not very great, you will no doubt be forced to cast many of the therapeutic activities in the form of games or experiences suited to his age and intelligence. With good rapport, you may be able to work directly on the problem once he recognizes it. We feel his prognosis is very good. We doubt that any fewer than two therapy sessions per week for at least a semester will produce the desired progress.

In the following sections of this chapter, the techniques for achieving these and other sub-goals of treatment will be given in detail. Robert Johnson is a fairly typical case although many children have much more severe and complicated problems. The personality problems of articulatory cases may vary widely from that of Robert Johnson. The degree of severity may range all the way from a simple failure in discrimination of a voiced g from its unvoiced twin, the k. But the large majority of our cases show a pattern of symptoms and underlying difficulties similar to the example provided here.

General principles of treatment. With the exception of neurotic lisping and neurotic baby talk, the treatment for all of the articulatory disorders follows the same general plan. Many variations must be made for individual problems, but these will be provided for within our discussion. Lalling, lisping, baby talk, oral inaccuracy, foreign speech, sound substitutions, omissions, and distortions of all kinds may be eradicated in much the same way. The neurotic disorders seldom respond to such treatment and require emotional retraining and adjustment prior to actual speech correction.

The course of treatment for the majority of articulation cases may now be outlined. (1) The speech defective must be convinced that he has errors which he must eradicate. (2) The causes of the disorder, if still existent, must be eliminated. If those causes are no longer present, their influence must be counteracted. (3) Through intensive ear training, the old word configurations are broken down so that the correct sound and the error may be *isolated, recognized, identified,* and *discriminated.* (4) Through various methods, the speech defective must be taught to produce the correct sound in isolation and at will. (5) The new and correct sound must be strengthened. (6) The new sound must be incorporated within familiar words, and the transition to normal speech must be accomplished. (7) The use of the correct sound must be made habitual, and the error must be eliminated.

In cases where the person makes more than one error, it is well to work with the sounds according to their usual developmental order: first the lip sounds, then the dentals, then the gutturals, then the complicated tongue sounds, and, finally, the blends. It is usually wise to work with the sound first in the initial position, then in the final position, and, finally, in the medial position. One should continue working with one sound until the person can make it alone at will, can use it in all three word positions when he watches himself, and uses it habitually on about ten common words. Then we may rely on parental and teacher co-operation to do the rest.

Convincing the Student that He Makes Speech Errors

The child must be convinced that he has a problem which he must solve. This is not so easily done. Owing to sheltered environments and the tolerance of associates who have become accustomed to the speech difference, many speech defectives grow to adulthood without ever having been made aware of their speech disorder, although it may be so noticeable that it shrieks its presence whenever its possessor opens his mouth. If friends and acquaintances will not mention it, certainly the average stranger will not. We seldom hear ourselves speak. Instead, we listen to our vocalized thinking. And so the speech defective himself has little chance of becoming fully aware of the nature or frequency of his errors.

Although many articulatory cases are thoroughly aware of their speech disorder, they do not seem to recognize all of their errors; and there are other cases who seem totally unaware of any speech difficulty. Small children, especially, need to be convinced that they have sound substitutions, additions, omissions, or distortions before they will cooperate or respond to treatment. The older ones must learn to recognize error whenever it occurs. A vague, generalized feeling that something is wrong with the speech will not provide sufficient motivation for the type of retraining that is necessary.

Teachers frequently ask whether or not it is advisable to work upon the child's speech in view of the self-consciousness and embarrassment which might be produced. The answer to this question is that the quickest way of getting rid of these errors is to make the child aware of them. The habits should be broken before they become fixed. Moreover, it is perfectly possible to work on a speech defect without shame, and if the teacher makes the child understand that a certain skill is to be learned and a problem is to be solved, no insecurity will be created. If she adopts a calm, unemotional attitude herself, empathic response will ensure a similar attitude in the child.

There are various ways of teaching an articulatory speech defective to recognize his errors, and some of them are given in the next paragraphs. One mother patiently corrected her child on every mispronounced word for three successive days, and he responded by refusing to talk at all for a week. With small children, no such nagging is necessary or advisable. The teacher should select five or six common words in which the child uses the error and should try to create in the child the feeling that in these words he is doing something incorrectly. She may tell him that there are other troublesome words, but she should set up as the first definite project the correction of these five or six. By narrowing the disorder to such a slender nucleus, the task is made easier and specific. The child must learn to recognize these words as "wrong words" and must come to realize that in these words he is likely to use "wrong sounds."

Sample exercises for teaching the child to recognize his errors:

1. The teacher reads a story to the child in which the five or six error words are used many times. The first time she reads it, she imitates the child's errors, cupping her ear every time she does so. The child is asked to do the same thing. The second time, the teacher reads it correctly except for one word. The child is asked to cup his ear when he hears the one error.

2. The teacher reads a list of words among which are included the error words. The child repeats all but the error words after the teacher, who pronounces the error words twice, first correctly, then incorrectly.

3. The child tells a story or recounts some experience and the teacher rings a bell whenever she hears the child mispronounce one of the error words.

4. One of the error words that is the name of a certain object is selected. The teacher draws two pictures of the object and asks the child to scribble over one of them. The teacher then names the two pictures, pronouncing the scribbled one with the child's error, and pronouncing the other one correctly. She then tells the child a story, sometimes using the word correctly and sometimes incorrectly. The child is asked to hold up the appropriate picture. The child then tells

a story while the teacher holds up one picture, usually the scribbled one.

Sample exercises for teaching the older child or adult to recognize errors:

1. The student silently reads prepared material which illustrates the error: Thus: He thaw/saw the bird fly to the netht/nest. The teacher then reads it aloud.

2. Have the student write from dictation, putting down in phonetic spelling the errors which the teacher purposely makes.

3. Teacher speaks a word five times, once with error. Student signals when error occurs. The same assignment can be made but with the teacher saying the word correctly only once out of five trials.

4. Same as above but with student immediately imitating teacher's error. (*Note.* Speech penalties are more effective than any other penalty.)

5. Using material with *s* words (or other error-sound words) underlined, have student (1) make judgment as to error occurrence as he reads; (2) pause after attempt on *s* word while teacher imitates and asks for judgment of right or wrong; (3) pronounce the *s* in three different ways, raising finger for the incorrect pronunciations; (4) repeat each *s* word three times, making judgment as to which attempt was the best; (5) repeat *s* sound five times before proceeding, while teacher makes judgments for each; (6) prolong *s* sound and make judgment.

6. Use the same assignments as above but (1) reading lists of words, one at a time; (2) saying prewritten speech; (3) using conversation.

7. Student uses telephone and teacher interrupts conversation by hanging up immediately upon occurrence of error.

8. Teacher requires student to do something absurd (such as going to mirror, shaking head, and saying "Oh, oh") after each error.

9. Student confesses and points out own errors each time they occur.

10. Student imitates own error whenever it occurs, exaggerating it.

Elimination of the causes of articulation defects. In the preceding chapter we have discussed the various causes of articulatory errors. In this chapter we are primarily interested in the methods available to us for eliminating these causes or canceling their effects. While it is true that often the articulatory errors are habits that can persist long after their original cause has disappeared, there are many cases in which the causes are still potent factors in maintaining the disorder.

Organic abnormalities can certainly act as contributory or maintaining causes. There are two methods for minimizing their influence: (1) reconstruction of defective organic structure through surgery and orthodontia, and (2) the teaching of compensatory movements in speech-sound production.

In recent years, orthodontia has made great strides, and almost unbelievable changes in dental, palatal, and jaw structures have been accomplished. The speech-correction teacher should refer all children with marked mouth deformities to these specialists and should begin her work after the reconstruction has been carried out. Unfortunately, such reconstruction is expensive, and many cases cannot be taken care of in this way. Nevertheless, the speech-correction teacher should acquaint herself with the resources in the orthodontic field so that she will not waste months of effort in teaching compensatory movements to a child whose speech problem can be taken care of through surgery or the displacement of structures. Similarly, she should realize that palatal abnormalities are frequently associated with those of the jaws, and that orthodontic projection or retraction of the jaw can facilitate tongue contact with the roof of the mouth. Modern surgery also offers a wide variety of repair and reconstruction techniques. Scar tissue can be excised, and grafts can be made which will provide the necessary mobility. High palatal arches can be lowered, and the velum can be modified to almost any desired degree. Much of this work should be done early in childhood, and the speech-correction teacher is often responsible for seeing that it is done. Frequently, parents postpone such remedial work until too late, but they may often be convinced of its necessity by the teacher who points out the social maladjustment which such defects may produce.

Paralyzed structures occasionally can be helped by exercises, and a professional physiotherapist should be consulted in planning a remedial program if the physician's report indicates a possibility of success. Such remedial work usually consists of recourse to the more biological functions and the tying up of the specialized movement with gross muscular action. Spaced practice, well motivated by graphs of successes, is advisable.

Hearing disabilities frequently necessitate the use of hearing aids, visualization, phonetic diagrams, and schemes of muscular contractions. In deaf and blind children, manipulation

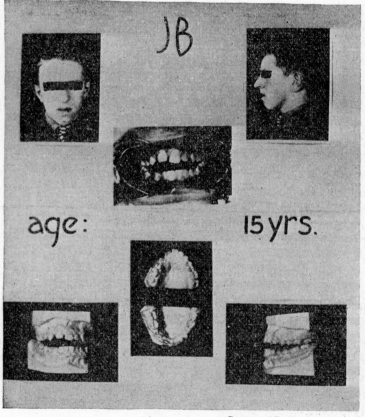

Courtesy of Dr. Kurt von Frowine

FIG. 4. A child in urgent need of orthodontia. This child omitted *f* and *v* sounds and had a lateral lisp.

by the teacher to set the jaws, mouth, and teeth is sometimes required. In cases of mental deficiency, many articulatory disorders occur, and the speech correctionist is called upon for aid. Although it is recommended that speech correction be carried out by the regular special-room teacher, the speech specialist should plan the program, fitting the technique to the typical traits of the feeble-minded.

Teaching compensatory movements. As we have said, many cases showing severe organic defects cannot be helped by the orthodontist or plastic surgeon because of age or financial reasons. The picture is by no means hopeless, however, since all of the speech sounds may be made in various ways. The art of the ventriloquist demonstrates compensatory activity of the tongue for that of the lips and jaws. Many normal speakers have profound anatomical abnormalities, occasionally so marked as to excite wonder in the speech correctionist familiar with the ordinary production of the speech sounds. Perfect *t* and *d* sounds, for example, have been made by individuals so tongue-tied that they were unable to lift the tonguetip to contact the upper teeth. Inmates of prisons frequently learn to talk out of the side of the mouth—the one farthest away from the guard—with but minor jaw movements.

In order to teach compensatory or nonstandard ways of making any speech sound, it is first necessary to make a phonetic analysis in terms of the type of sound to be produced. For example, the production of an *s* sound requires the propulsion of a narrow stream of air past a cutting edge. The cutting edge should be placed at about right angles to the air stream in order to produce a clear *s*. The average person produces this narrow stream of air by placing the sides of the tongue along the side teeth, thereby cutting off all lateral escape of air, and by grooving the center of the tongue so that the air stream is projected directly past the cutting edge of the front incisors. Lacking these front teeth, or having them widely spaced, the person can get an equally good *s* by directing the air stream past the cuspids or bicuspids on the side of the mouth having the better teeth. This new mechanics, however, is not quite so simple as the preceding sentence might imply. The tongue must adjust itself so that on one side it makes a larger occlusion and the groove is diagonal. The lips must plug the former opening and part at the appropriate side. Frequently the mandible must be moved sidewise so that the best upper and lower teeth will be brought together. Thus the teacher must plan the type of compensatory mechanics necessitated by the particular mouth deformities involved. In this plan, the teacher should take into account or seek to minimize as far as possible the following factors: complexity of performance (the fewer adjustments, the better), ease of transition from other sounds, amount of facial contortion, distinctness of kinesthetic and tactual sensations, and the motivation and co-operation of the subject.

In teaching compensatory mechanics, then, the teacher should follow this general outline. (1) Note how the student articulates the defective sound. (2) Make a phonetic analysis to determine what the essential mechanics of the sound must be. (3) Discover what structures the student might possibly use to satisfy these requirements. (4) Give the student a thorough course in ear training, stimulation, and discrimination along the lines of the program sketched in a future section. (5) Through manipulation, phonetic diagrams, mirror work, imitation, and random activity, try to get the student to produce a sound similar to that made by the instructor. (6) Once achieved, do not let the student move a muscle of face or body until he prolongs, repeats, and uses it in nonsense syllables many times. (7) Build up its strength through techniques suggested in the next section. (8) Do not worry about exaggerated movements used by the student in making the sound. At first, most students will use facilitating movements of other structures as a baby uses gross movements prior to specialization. We frequently encourage head and jaw movements or modifications of smiling, chewing, biting, and swallowing as accessory tools. These extraneous movements drop out as the new performance pattern becomes habitual. (9) Increase the speed with which the new performance pattern can be initiated. No compensatory movements will become habitual if they cannot be used quickly and easily. (10) Be careful to change the transition movements as well, working for new and quick patterns of change from one speech sound to another.

Functional causes. Besides the organic factors previously described, we have a large number of functional causes. The emotional causes of articulation disorders are best remedied by following the procedures outlined in Chapter 4. The case must be given insight into his problems. His social assets must be increased; his liabilities diminished. His habitual reactions of attack or retreat must be altered so that he can be freed from social penalty. He must learn to adopt an objective attitude toward his differences and to carry out a campaign of self-improvement. As he begins to fulfill his potentialities and meets social acceptance, the emotional causes will no longer hamper his efforts to eliminate his speech difference.

The developmental factors which cause articulatory speech defects can be overcome by following the general methods described in the chapter on delayed speech and the one on the development of speech. The child must become familiar with the major characteristics of the various speech sounds and he must learn the elementary facts of vocal phonics. Activities aimed at these goals can easily be added to the general speech correction procedures to be described later in this chapter. Even as tongue exercises are often a part of the daily sessions used to teach a new sound and eliminate an error, exercises in identifying the isolated speech sounds can also be made an integral part of the program. When the child has developed habitual antagonistic or frustrating attitudes toward any type of correction because of scolding or impatient methods of the parents, we must be careful to follow the child's own interests in devising our assignments or activities. One of our adults felt sure he could never acquire a normal *r* sound and passively resisted every attempt on our part to help him do so until we gave him the task of helping a girl correct her lisp. He became so interested in the project that his whole attitude toward his own errors changed and he quickly succeeded in eliminating them.

It may be said that anything which puts a great deal of pressure on speech will tend to produce speech defects of all kinds, and, if this pressure is exerted during the development of speech, articulatory disorders frequently occur. Some of these factors are: fear of interruption, habitual urge to interrupt others, oral confession of guilt, too high speech standards in home or school, public recitation or speaking of pieces, too much excitement, ridicule, fear of punishment or sarcasm, speech when fatigued, bluffing, too great parental or teacher pressure for school progress, speaking while confused, general unhappiness or emotional strain, and constant need for speech to strangers. There are many others, and the average teacher can readily devise ways for eliminating or minimizing these conditions after she discovers what they are.

Imitation and poor environmental speech standards are difficult factors to eliminate, but the best approach seems to be through frank recognition of the problem, the adoption of other models, and the provision for contacts with other environments which have high speech standards. The teacher should not berate the parents or companions whose speech is not acceptable or ask the child to adopt a speech which is foreign to his environment. A better policy is to tell the child that he may continue to use the jargon and poor speech of his home and neighborhood while he is there, but that he should learn a different type of speech for other situations. He should be shown other environments and future opportunities, and the necessity for adequate speech therein. Without such a horizon, no permanent progress will be made. Very seldom can the home or neighborhood speech standards be changed, and the speech correctionist may as well face that fact.

Weak auditory memory span. The factors of poor auditory discrimination and short auditory memory span are usually taken care of in the intensive ear training that is the keynote of modern articulatory therapy. Many exercises to take care of these factors may be found in later pages of this text, and it is well to give the child a preliminary course in discrimination, recognition, remembrance of sound sequences, and self-hearing. We have found that most inadequate auditory discrimination or memory span is due to a lack of directed attention and that it will respond to appropriate treatment. Some special techniques for improving one's auditory discrimination or memory span follow.

1. Auditory memory-span drill. Teacher pronounces a series of digits or words. Student repeats them after intervals varying from 1 to 60 seconds. This assignment should be followed by the student's giving himself his own series, waiting the prescribed interval, and then repeating. Errors should be checked, and this procedure should be strongly motivated. The above drills can be carried out through phonograph records, the student being asked to write down the series.

2. Jabber-repetition. This consists, like the above, of stimulation and repetition. The teacher says certain nonsense words (polysyllabic) such as "wahwo-kadda-makeree-samma." The student repeats these after a certain interval, which should be gradually increased. As in the last assignment, the student should then give himself the jabber stimulation and attempt to repeat as closely as possible. The syllables may also be recorded phonographically for stimulation.

3. Student distorts certain speech sounds and then attempts to repeat these distortions exactly. The teacher should illustrate using the "dark *l*" sound or the lateral lisp.

4. It is often wise to begin these assignments with the direction of the speech defective's attention to the duration of his sounds, since this feature is more easily recognized and judged. Thus the student is instructed to repeat after the teacher the nonsense word *laaaaaaalo*, seeking to keep the relative and total durations of the repetition as close as possible to those of the stimulation. Other similar nonsense words, including those which prolong the continuant consonants, are given. Phonograph records in which the duration can be identified are used in providing a checkup. The student should then give himself similar stimulation, and repeat it after an appropriate interval, while the teacher checks.

5. Assignments similar to the above but using inflections as the stimulus material are helpful in training the individual to listen to his speech.

6. The student is told to pronounce certain continuant consonants or vowels (both in words and by themselves) five times, prolonging the consonant or vowel slightly each time. The same type of assignment may be used for inflected vowels and consonants. The teacher checks. Written material may be used for this, such as *sso, ssso, sssso, ssssso*.

7. The student, using a stage whisper, prolongs, inflects, or distorts certain vowels or continuants. He then repeats vocally, as closely as possible.

8. The student should be given frequent self-listening periods, in which he makes a sound and listens closely to it. Not more than two or three words should constitute a period, and the student must be extremely alert. Later in the treatment it is wise to have the student use these periods for judgments of correct sound production.

When poor muscular co-ordination is an important factor in producing the articulatory errors, we devote part of our therapy to improving the speed and precision of the articulatory musculature.

Tongue exercises. Many speech defectives, especially younger ones, or those with some abnormality of the tongue, who have had mouth injuries or paralysis, need these exercises. Their tongues do not move with the speed and precision demanded by good speech. They can assume only the simplest tongue positions. Therefore, they raise the front or middle of the tongue instead of the back, and protrude it rather than lift it. It is difficult for them to curl the tip or groove the tongue. Tongue exercises are useful and necessary for these cases.

The exercises that follow are given in a form suitable for adults where we may be direct in our therapy. For children, it will be necessary to cast the same activities in the form of games. The principles governing the use of tongue exercises are as follows:

1. Learn to recognize the movement as part of some familiar biological movement such as chewing, swallowing, coughing, or others to be mentioned later. Practice these basic activities.

2. The finer movements should be taught first in conjunction with larger movements, then alone.

3. The movement should be used with increasing speed, strength, and accuracy.

4. The movement should be combined with other movements (breathing, phonation, and so on) used in speech.

5. The emphasis in this training should be on the activities (lifting, thrusting, drawing, tip-curling, and grooving) and the contacts (upper gum ridge, lower teeth, interdental, palatal) and the positions actually used in speech, rather than random and generalized tongue movements.

6. Not only the tonguetip, but the blade, middle, and back of tongue should be exercised.

7. In any drill period, use a few from each of the lists of exercises under each major activity heading rather than complete one section at a time. Practice the activity exercises *A, B, C, D,* until these are fairly well mastered before using contact exercise *E.* Use position exercises *F* last.

8. Avoid fatigue and hurry. Identify movement by imitation or mirror observation rather than by oral description. Identify contacts by stroking or pressure. Identify new positions in terms of their variation from other well-known positions.

9. After movement is well learned, combine it with production of other speech sounds.

10. Compare, contrast, and combine the various movements.

A. *Lifting*

1. Chew in an exaggerated fashion with mouth openings and hand movements for thirty seconds.

2. In a manner similar to the chewing exercise, alternately do the following two sets of opposite movements:

a. Beginning with open mouth, lower your head and as you do so shut your jaws and lift your tonguetip in unison. (Be sure that tongue lifts itself and is not merely lifted by jaw.)

b. As you raise your head, open your jaws and let your tongue flop back to the bottom of your mouth. Do this to a simple rhythm tapped out by teacher, very slowly at first, then increasing speed. Finally combine with pretended chewing.

3. Repeat exercise (2) but omit large head movements. Hold head still and merely move lower jaw in unison with the lifting or lowering tongue. Use rhythms and increase speed.

4. Repeat exercise (2) but hold head still and mouth open (do not move lower jaw) and merely lift tongue. Use rhythms and increase speed.

5. Repeat exercises (2), (3), and (4) one after another. Then repeat again and again, using rhythms and increasing speed.

6. Repeat exercise (5) but breathe out first silently then in an audible stream as in a stage sigh. Then repeat vocalizing the vowels *ah, ee, a, o,* and *oo.*

7. Protrude lips and at a sudden signal lift tongue. Then alternate protrusion of lips and lifting of tongue, using rhythms and speed.

8. Practice sudden shifts from prolonged consonants *m, n, v, th,* to the upward movements of the tongue. Follow procedure of exercise (7).

9. Get a small piece of sponge rubber and sterilize it by boiling. Put into the front of the mouth and repeat exercise (5), forcing rubber to roof of mouth and compressing it with the tonguetip. Use this device to strengthen tongue.

10. With spoon or tongue depressor hold tip of tongue down. Mouth is held open. Use rhythms and increasing speed in lifting tongue against the pressure.

11. *Repeat those of the above exercises which can be modified to employ the back of the tongue. Do the same for the blade or middle of tongue.*

B. *Thrusting and withdrawing*

1. Using imitation and mirror observation, practice licking lips and cleaning teeth and cheeks with the tongue. Use tonguetip as a suction cup, pressing it firmly against back of teeth then quickly pulling it away. This results in a sound often spelled as "tsk" and used as a mild reproach.

2. Practice using imitation and mirror observation (1) tongue-sucking, (2) several varieties of tongue-clucking or -clicking (with mouth open), (3) Bronx-cheering (tongue between lips and forced into rapid vibration by expelled air blast, (4) tongue-wobbling (rounded lips and phonation of vowel *o* as tongue rapidly and alternately protrudes and withdraws), (5) cheek-pumping (alternately puffing out and pulling in cheeks, which results in small back-and-forth tongue movements).

3. Round lips and hold sterilized blunt pencil or heavy probe in hole so that the tonguetip, pressing and yielding against it, can make it move in and out like a plunger. Begin with half-inch oscillations then increase to in-and-out movements of at least an inch each way. Use slow rhythms and gradually increase speed. Give frequent rests. Repeat, exerting enough pressure on plunger so that tongue will become stronger.

4. Use rhythms and increasing speed in performing the activities of exercise (2).

5. Protrude tongue as far forward (*not* up or down) as possible. Use rhythms and increasing speed. Allow head and jaw movements at first but end with head and jaw fixed. Then get set and protrude tongue to its farthest extent the moment a sudden signal is given. Work for an almost automatic reaction.

6. (*a*) Blow out a stream of air and then protrude tongue to its farthest limit without stopping the blowing. (*b*) Repeat but phonate the vowel *ah* as you protrude tongue. Repeat this exercise until it becomes very smooth.

7. Shut teeth and suck air through them as you inhale. Then as you blow through the teeth thrust your tongue lightly against them. Make sure that some part of the tonguetip is in contact with the teeth as the air is exhaled.

C. *Curling*

1. Practice licking stick candy or spoon or other object held at right angles to and in contact with the upper teeth. Lick a thin scattered sprinkling of sugar from a plate.

2. Facing a mirror, hold a sterilized probe or match horizontally about half an inch from the mouth. Reach out with tongue and, by curling the end of it, pull it back to the teeth. The strength of this action may be increased by holding match more firmly.

3. With mouth wide open (and allowing jaws to close with the tongue action), thrust tongue out and then curl the tip to touch exact center of the upper edge of the upper lip. Use rhythms and increasing speed.

4. Repeat exercise (3), but with jaws barely open enough to let tongue through; and do not permit any jaw or head movement.

5. Open mouth and curl tonguetip as in preceding exercises but do not protrude tongue. Keep it entirely within mouth.

6. Repeat exercises (3) and (5) but curl tongue during forced exhalation.

7. Repeat exercise (5) but use a sudden signal to set off an instantaneous tongue-curling. Work for quick reaction to the signal.

D. *Grooving*

While many people with perfectly normal speech do not have the ability to form a narrow tubelike groove in the tongue which they can maintain even when the tongue is protruded, some form of shallow grooving is essential to the production of the *s, zh, sh* and *z, j,* and *ch* sounds.

1. Round the lips as in producing the vowel o͞o, and as you do so protrude tongue barely between teeth, then cough easily several

times. Observe self in mirror and you will see that the tongue is grooved as you cough. Practice this until, you can hold the groove even after the cough is completed. "Listen" to the muscular sensations coming from the tongue when it is in this position. Shutting your eyes will help you to focus your attention. Finally, produce the groove by merely getting set to cough.

2. Repeat exercise (1) but insert sterilized probe or pencil in mouth so as to help the rounding or grooving of the tongue. Withdraw probe but maintain groove.

3. With mouth open wide and tongue relaxed, place bowl of spoon on front third of tongue. Ask child first to squeeze the sides of the spoon without lifting, then to squeeze and lift. After this is successful, pretend that you are using an imaginary spoon and repeat. Repeat this but with teeth together.

4. Practice whistling between the teeth.

5. Practice forcing tonguetip against upper teeth (when teeth and lips are closed). Then suck air through narrow lip opening. Then exhale through same opening. Alternate exhalation and inhalation, increasing speed.

6. Once grooving has been clearly identified (without mirror) and can be produced at will, use rhythms and increasing speed in producing the movement.

7. Practice grooving tongue (do not insist on tubular groove; a shallow groove is adequate) while lowering jaw, while rounding and unrounding lips, while smiling.

8. Using different varieties of grooving produce many different sibilant sounds, ranging from a high-pitched whistled *s* to a sloppy *sh* sound.

Delayed speech development. We have mentioned the fact that interruptions in speech development seem to produce typical errors. Severe illnesses often occur during the first years of a child's life, and these may interrupt the practice of inflections, or the babbling period, or the naming period. Occasionally, very clear case histories point to these interruptions as causal factors, and it is interesting to note that these cases progress much more rapidly if they are allowed to begin with the type of activity they have missed. In many cases, it is impossible to get definite histories of the type of speech being used by the child at the time the illness or accident occurred. Nevertheless, we have found that if illness occurred during the babbling period it is well to have the student practice some of this vocal play. From this activity, many adults seem to get a peculiar pleasure, which is out of all proportion to its novelty, and without suggestion from the clinician they proceed to go through many of the same phases which the child experiences, using doubling first, then true disyllables, then inflections. Certain combinations are practiced much more than others, and frequently the sounds which they have never been able to say are used over and over, although they are so lost in the matrix of the babbling that a keen ear is needed to distinguish them. We often recommend that they combine swallowing, chewing, biting, and smiling movements with this vocal play. The student should do it alone, and with a clear understanding of its purpose, to avoid self-consciousness. He should keep out analysis and purposeful combinations, and should relax and let the babble go where it may. After the student has practiced babbling in this way for about ten five-minute periods, scattered throughout several days, the speech correctionist should try to get him to repeat certain combinations of the nonsense material as they occur in the babbling.

Ear Training

The vast importance of ear training. Many texts in speech correction agree that the first step in remedial treatment of articulatory cases should be ear training, and most speech correctionists employ it. The exact nature of this ear training is too often vague, unsystematic, and perfunctory, although it is probably the most important tool in the clinician's kit. If the preliminary ear training is done well, little difficulty is experienced, even with the most severe cases. The speech-correction teacher is prone to slight it because immediate results are not forthcoming, because it demands strong motivation, because it necessitates lesson preparation and clever techniques, and because she does not realize its nature or importance. Many parents and teachers feel that all they need to do to get rid of such a speech defect is to tell the child that he has said the word wrong and must try it again. Often they attempt to show him by increasing the loudness of the correct word as though he were hard of hearing, a proceeding which is obviously poor pedagogy. *It may be said with the utmost emphasis that no teacher should attempt to get a child to try to make a new speech sound without first giving him systematic ear training.*

The teacher of the articulatory case must appreciate the point of view of the speech defective with respect to the errors involved. To the uncorrected lisper, for example, the substitution of *th* for *s* in the word *soup* is entirely natural. He is often unaware that any substitution has occurred. The liquid's name just happens to be *thoup*. The auditory sensations for *s* and *th* are fairly similar even when produced by some other person. Unless one has learned to isolate them from the words in which they normally occur, or has associated them with some specific object such as a goose's hiss, or has produced them with different tongue movements, there will be very little discrimination in hearing them. Discrimination of sounds involves, as we shall see, recognition, identification, association with symbols, and differential bodily reactions. The lisper without correction or training has no power of discrimination because he has none of these attributes of discrimination. Frequently the lisper can be taught to tell the difference between the *s* and the *th* when produced by another person without being able to recognize his own substitution of those sounds. This is due to the fact that a speech sound is a complicated combination of hearing and feeling. Both are blended and integrated into a perceptual whole, into a configuration. Thus, to the lisper, the *s* and *th* sounds are not different enough to overrule the similarity of the habitual tongue movements which he has always made in identical fashion for each. If he attends to the auditory sensations alone, he can tell the difference, but, if he must also attend to the feel of the tongue, which is similarly placed for both sounds, the sounds will be perceived as being more alike than different.

If this is the case when the sounds are isolated, it is clear that, when the sounds are incorporated within the unitary sound sequences called words, there will be even less chance for discrimination between correct and incorrect sounds. As students of phonetics know, there are no such things as syllables in speech, although there may be in orthography. In most spoken speech, even the words are but parts of the sentence as a whole, and may not be considered as units. Therefore, within the word, any individual sound can have little perceptual importance. Most children learn words as wholes, and not as sound sequences. Each word is a complex configuration, having within it patterns of muscular movements, patterns of sequences of auditory sensations, and a unitary meaning. It is a unit and an organized whole.

Recognizing this unitary nature of the word and the subordinate nature of the sounds which compose it, we can easily understand why the articulatory case does not recognize his errors and why he frequently refuses to believe that the correct sound, when used in an old familiar word, is indeed correct. Indeed, the correct sound frequently appears to these cases not only as strange and unfamiliar but as definitely incorrect. Moreover, the fact that the lisper has so thoroughly incorporated the *th* sound in the configuration whose meaning is *soup* gives us the explanation for the curious relapse that occurs when a new sound is used in familiar words without previously being strengthened. Many lispers, for example, can learn to make a good *s* when it is isolated, but, if the teacher insists upon their using it in familiar words, they go right back to their old error, and frequently lose the ability to make it even in isolation. It therefore becomes necessary to build up the new sound in isolation and in simple configurations, to tear down the old configurations and isolate the error, to synthesize the new sound with various sound sequences and meanings, and thereby to produce the new and standard configurations—the correct words.

If the student has not been convinced by this time of the

urgent need for ear training as a prerequisite to speech-sound production, he will probably have to learn the same truth through sad experience with persistent error, frequent relapse, and slow progress. When articulatory cases are seen daily, it is customary to spend at least a week or two in intensive ear training before the student ever attempts to produce the correct sound. Most teachers and speech defectives hurry this part of the work. They are impatient to see actual results, to get to the correction of the speech errors; and because of this attitude, they interfere with future progress. Adequate ear training is the best insurance for successful speech correction where articulatory and voice cases are concerned.

Types of ear training. Ear training should consist of definite exercises and activities fitted to the age, interests, and understanding of the speech defective. There are four main types of this ear training, and every one of the early speech periods should include exercises of each type. The four types, with their distinguishing characteristics, are as follows:

Isolation—training in listening to sound sequences, nonsense words, or connected speech in order to detect the presence of certain sounds; training in isolating any sound, correct or incorrect, from its context; training in breaking up unitary speech-sound configurations into sequences of fairly independent sounds.

Stimulation—training which bombards the speech defective with a barrage of the correct sound.

Identification—training in identifying the characteristics of the correct sound and in identifying the characteristics of the error. No comparison is involved. The student learns the distinguishing traits of each.

Discrimination—training in comparing the correct sound with the error, in hearing the differences between the two sounds, and in recognizing the contrasts involved.

In the following paragraphs, we outline some of the techniques through which the four goals mentioned above may be obtained. Those cited are, of course, but a few of the techniques that may be used. Any worth-while teacher can and will invent others. Moreover, it is seldom necessary to use all of them with any one case. The medicine must be fitted to the symptoms.

However, each case should be given an intensive course of ear
training to convince the child that he has a speech defect and
enable him to isolate, recognize, identify, and discriminate between the correct sound and the error.

Isolation techniques. We have pointed out that, as long as a
sound is lost within a word, it cannot be heard or felt with any
clarity. The word configurations must be broken up so that
the correct sound can be heard by itself. One adult declared
that he had sincerely tried to hear the sound that his teachers
said he used incorrectly, but, when they pronounced the words,
the part in which he was interested was gone before he could
perceive it. This adult could make the sound at will when he
said it separately, but was unable to use it in familiar words.
To the child speech defective, spoken words are lumps of sound.
Indeed, he hears them as single sounds rather than as sound
sequences. The older methods of teaching reading, in which
children learned to sound out their new words, probably helped
the articulatory cases much more then the new methods, which
stress the acquisition of whole words. It is possible for an articulatory case to learn new word-wholes in which the correct
sound is used, but it is much more economical, in terms of time
spent in remedial work, to teach him to disrupt the incorrect
word-wholes, to recognize the error, and then to integrate the
correct sound into a sequence that is acceptable. He will then
be much more likely to recognize his errors, and he will be able
to master new words by himself.

A few illustrative exercises in isolating sounds from their
contexts may be given. The individuals concerned were lingual
lispers—hence the use of *s* as the sound illustrated. Any other
sound may be used in the same exercises, and many other similar exercises may be easily invented.

Sample isolation techniques for children.

1. The teacher hides, in different places about the room, nine or ten
pictures of various objects, one of which begins with the *s* sound. The
moment the child finds this picture, he can run back to the teacher
and ring a bell.
2. The teacher gives the child an old catalogue and a pair of scissors.

A box is shown the child, and he is told that when he gets five pictures whose names begin with the *s* sound and one picture whose name ends with that sound, he can open the box and have what is in it. He does so and gets the jelly bean.

3. The child is covered with a bath towel and told to play Jack-in-the-box. The teacher tells him that she has three funny word keys, only one of which will open the box. The word key that fits has the *s* sound in it. The child is to jump and throw off the towel and say *boo* when the teacher uses the proper key. The three keys are nonsense words or sound sequences such as "mo-bo-to-pay," "ka-pa-la-tha," and "ro-ssso-fa-ta." The length of the nonsense word key and the location of the *s* sound within the word may be varied to fit the needs of the child. Word keys may be simple monosyllables at first.

4. The teacher arranges five boxes on a table and tells the child that she is going to put a word in each box. He is to watch and point to the box in which there is a word with an *s* sound in it. The teacher may use word lists first and then progress to interesting sentences.

5. The teacher sounds out words and asks the child to locate the appropriate picture, putting all *s*-word pictures in a special envelope.

Sample isolation techniques for adults or older children.

1. Student reads silently, underlining all *s* sounds (not only *s* letters). He reads the passage and notes how many he missed in silent reading.

2. The teacher and student read from the same material (or recite sentences previously agreed upon), the teacher omitting all *s* sounds and the student speaking them, or, in the earlier stages, the student reading and omitting all *s* sounds and the teacher speaking them. Thus:

    Student: Thi . . can . . ertainly run fa . . t.
    Teacher: *ss*   *ss*   *ss*

3. The student should make a list of words in which the *s* symbol refers to some other sound (as in "measure" or "his"), and also a list of words in which other symbols are sounded as *s* ("ice," "extra").

4. The student should talk while having pencil and paper before him, writing the symbol *s* each time it occurs in the teacher's speech. This can also be done for each time it occurs in his own speech.

5. Pause for a count of five after each occurrence of the correct or incorrect *s* sound in his speech. Repeat, pausing prior to the sound.

6. Teacher stimulates student by omitting, prolonging, or repeating *s* each time it occurs. Use reading material in which the *s* sounds have previously been underlined.

Stimulation techniques. It is not sufficient to isolate and identify the correct sound during the preliminary period of ear training. The student must be stimulated with the sound so thoroughly that it may almost be said to ring in his ears. Every available agency should be used to provide this stimulation. Parents, friends, and classmates can help. Through various devices, the speech defective's attention to the sound must be focused and heightened. He must become aware of it not only in isolation but also as it occurs within spoken words. If there is any law governing speech acquisition, it is the law of adequate stimulation.

Obviously, many of the techniques used in isolating the correct sound may be modified to provide adequate stimulation. The adult should be required to listen carefully and discriminatingly to variations in intensity and rhythmic presentation of the stimulus. He can be required to write the symbol simultaneously with the teacher's utterance. He may signal his perception of the presence of the sound within a jumble of nonsense material. Phonograph recording may be used, and so also may such tongue twisters as "Sally sold silk and satin at the store on Saturday." The student, of course, does not pronounce these sentences. This is the period for ear training. He merely listens, or writes from dictation.

A correct attitude on the part of the speech defective is of the utmost importance to the success of this auditory stimulation. Koepp-Baker[4] gives this advice to his adult articulatory cases:

When your clinician produces the sound, over and over again, for you, it is highly important that you pay the strictest attention. This listening must not be a passive act, but a highly active one. You must be listening—not just sitting. It would be much the same kind of listening you would do if you were studying a piece of music being played by an orchestra or single performer, to determine the nuances, variations, and subtleties of execution. Should you grow tired, inattentive, or disinterested, tell the clinician at once, for auditory stimu-

---

[4] By permission of the author, from *A Handbook of Clinical Speech*, Ann Arbor, Edwards Brothers, 1936, Volume 2, pages 346–347.

lation is of value only when you are fully participating in the process of listening.

As you listen, try to determine exactly in what way the sound which you are hearing differs from all other sounds of speech and in what way it is like them. Remember that your ability to detect the slight differences in sounds which give them their identity will develop slowly. At first you will hear nothing of any significance. *As you learn to listen discriminately*, you will discover much you have missed before.

Do not be misled by the fact that your clinician *seems* to be doing all the work during the auditory stimulation period. His part is relatively simple and makes no great demands of him. On the other hand, your task of actively listening far transcends his in importance. All that really happens occurs in you. What you do during these stimulation periods determines the extent of any improvement to occur in your speech habits. Psychologically, the most important thing which will ever happen during your speech training is happening as you listen. Don't be fooled. Listening is hard work—and of greatest importance.

The co-operation of adults may usually be enlisted by such direct reasonable appeals, but younger children must be motivated to listen by the interest inherent in the activity itself. It is always wise to call for some type of performance to indicate the efficiency of the student's reception of the stimulation.

Sample stimulation techniques for children.

1. Procure a calendar mailing tube or similar device. Hold one end to child's ear as he winds a string upon a spool. The moment the teacher stops making the sound, he must stop winding.

2. The teacher, parents, or classmates act as animals, machines, or objects which produce the sound. The child may be asked to tell a story in which these objects are mentioned, and, whenever he mentions them, the teacher makes the sound. Little dramas may be invented in which the child, for example, pretends to be an automobile with a flat tire in need of air, and the teacher is the station attendant who fills the tire with hissing air.

3. Certain objects are set aside as demanding the hearing of the correct sound before they can be touched. Such rituals appeal to children and compel attention.

4. A secret signal is arranged between the child and the parent or teacher. Whenever the child makes it, the parent or teacher must respond by a prolonged *s* sound.

5. A certain room in the home is set aside as a room which the child cannot enter until he knocks three times and hears the *s* sound.

6. Alliterative sentences using the correct sound in the initial position of most of the words are used as commands or requests. The child performs the activity.

7. Nursery rhymes, jingles, and even tongue twisters may be read to the child.

8. One minute of each hour is set aside as the *s* minute. Some associate of the child must pronounce the sound for a full minute. The child or teacher records the time in a little book.

Sample stimulation techniques for adults or older children.

1. The teacher prolongs or repeats the correct sound, using variations in rhythm or intensity. The student follows the type of stimulation by drawing a continuous line or separate lines on a sheet of paper, using dips to indicate decreases in intensity and crests to show increases. Rhythms may be indicated by spacing.

2. Phonograph records which carry variable durations of the correct sound can be played. The student is requested to time each of the durations until he makes a perfect score.

3. The teacher dictates to the student, prolonging all the *s* sounds.

4. The teacher holds a conversation with the student, interjecting the correct sound between all words.

5. Two students, one of whom is the lisper, sit side by side, with their eyes closed. The teacher produces a prolonged *s* sound as she slowly walks away from them. They indicate by raising their hands when they can no longer hear the sound.

Identification techniques. As we have said, it is necessary to make the correct and incorrect sounds very vivid if the child is to learn to discriminate them in his own speech. The techniques for isolating and recognizing the sounds do a great deal toward this end, but they need to be supplemented by other methods which give the sounds their identities or personalities. This identification is largely a process of observation of the sound's characteristics, in terms of both audition and mechanics. It is also a process of association.

Each correct sound and the error must come to have an individuality and an identity. Many people fail to realize that before we can have discrimination we must have identification.

All good teachers of speech correction give personalities to the sounds with which they work. They give them names, traits, and even faces. From such identification comes recognition; from recognition comes discrimination; from discrimination comes success.

Sample identification techniques for children.

1. It is always well to begin the identification by giving names to the correct and incorrect sounds. These names are frequently those of objects which make noises similar to that of the sound in question. Thus *th* is called the windmill sound; *s*, the snake or goose sound; *ch*, the train sound; *r*, the growling-dog sound; *k*, the coughing sound; *f*, the spitting-cat sound. Many others are easily invented, for literalness is not nearly so important as repetition of the name.

2. Many teachers of speech correction find it advisable to give faces to certain sounds. These may be drawn on cards and used for stimuli. The faces can illustrate some of the more simple mechanics of making the sound. Thus *f* has a face with the upper teeth biting the lower lip; *s* is smiling; *th* is barely protruding a very red tongue; *l* seems to be looking for peanut butter, with his tongue exploring the roof of his mouth. Mirror work also helps.

3. It is wise to associate the sound with a symbol, either in script or printing. Children readily understand that the snake sound looks like a snake, and that it is entirely natural for the sound with the lip-biting face to wear a sweater bearing the monogram *F*. Hiding cards with such symbols around the room and requesting the child to find them, during which time the teacher keeps repeating the sound, will prove useful. So also will be the technique which calls for the child to pick out the symbol, whose sound the teacher speaks, from a pile of cards.

4. Little stories, frequently repeated, about the sounds will often produce associations which will help identify them. No one can tell just what will best identify the sound for any one child, but once the child shows a clear and strong reaction of emotion or curiosity, that association should be remembered.

5. It is not well to get too many traits associated with any one sound. Not the number of traits, but their pertinence, interrelationship, and contrast to the traits of the error give them their value. It is important that the teacher work for close co-ordination of the asso·· tions with any one sound. The sound of *s* should bring to mind immediately the snake, the symbol, the smile, and the story of how

the snake hissed when the filling-station man turned the air hose on him. It should also bring to mind that the little red tongue is never between the teeth as it is with the *th* sound.

Sample identification techniques for older children and adults.

1. Identification for the adult can also be enhanced by giving names to the correct and incorrect sounds. Thus, for one adult lateral lisper, the correct sound was always referred to as the "whistled hiss," while the incorrect one was called the "old sloppy shush." Derogatory adjectives which need not be truly descriptive are often used. The auditory characteristics of the sound also may give rise to the names used. Consequently, we speak of the "high-pitched" and "low-pitched" *s* sounds, the "whispered *f*," and the "sounded *v*." They may also be identified by names descriptive of the shape of the lips, the position of the tongue, or the use of the nasal opening. The teacher should always bestow some name on both correct and incorrect sounds. Other traits and characteristics of the sound are thereby given a nucleus about which to cluster.

2. Phonetic diagrams, palatograms, and models of the articulatory positions characteristic of the correct sound and the error may be used as identifying agents. The student should be examined in his production of the incorrect sound, and his performance should be described in detail. He should examine the teacher's mouth as the teacher produces the correct sound and the error. Observation in the mirror is also useful. A tongue depressor may be inserted within the mouth to probe and investigate tongue positions. A slender-handled throat mirror may be employed for those sounds in which access to the speech organs is difficult. From all these data, the student should finally attain an integrated picture of what the teacher does when she makes the correct and incorrect sounds. It is often wise to insist that the student write out a complete description of this picture. Even though phonetically accurate descriptions are not obtained, the procedure has identification value.

3. Since adults and older children have associated incorrect sounds with the printed or written symbols, it is often necessary to use nonsense symbols to represent the new sound. All of the characteristics of the correct sound should be associated with this rather than with the old symbol. The student must be taught that his task is to learn a new sound rather than to change an old one, that the new sound has characteristics that he must discover, and that, for the time being, he should use a new symbol to represent this new sound. Typical

nonsense symbols for several of the speech sounds will be found in the section of this chapter concerning methods for strengthening new sounds.

Discrimination techniques. The final step in ear training is that of discrimination, and, if the preceding types of ear training have been carried out, it should not be difficult. Discrimination consists of comparing and contrasting the correct and incorrect sounds, both in isolation and in incorporation within regular speech. Selecting, matching, and signaling techniques are used. They are employed even when the student discriminates successfully, for the practice is valuable in itself.

These discrimination techniques frequently call for an ability which many untrained teachers do not possess—the ability to mimic or produce a reasonably accurate imitation of the student's error. While such substitutions as *f* for *v* or *t* for *k* make no great demands upon the teacher's histrionics, the imitation of a lateral lisp, dark *l* or guttural *r* often present great difficulties. Nevertheless, the teacher may be assured that a little practice will soon bring about an approximation so close to the student's error that it will serve well enough for the usual discrimination exercises. In a sense, all preceding steps are pointed at facilitating this auditory discrimination, for it is the essence of the necessary ear training of which we hear so much. Without the ability to differentiate correct sound from error, the student becomes discouraged, the treatment becomes blind drill, and the teacher wishes she had taken up library work.

Sample discrimination devices for children.

1. *Selection.* Show the child an object such as a cake of soap. After a short review of the identifying characteristics of the correct sound and error, the teacher pronounces a series of isolated sounds or nonsense syllables, such as *k, p, th, s, f, r, n, s, f, th,* and requests the child to hand her the object when he hears the sound that starts the word when it is made correctly, but to hide it when he hears the sound that starts it when it is made incorrectly.

2. *Selection.* The teacher and student begin the game with ten toothpicks each. The teacher holds up a series of pictures, one at a time, pronouncing the name of each. In naming one of the pictures

she uses the child's error. If the child recognizes it, he can demand the picture and one toothpick. If he fails to recognize it, he loses a picture and toothpick.

3. *Matching.* The teacher produces two sounds, declaring that they begin words which name objects in the room. The student is required to find three objects for each sound.

4. *Matching.* The child is blindfolded and sits with his hands outstretched on the table in front of him. He is allowed to pull only one hand away at a time. The teacher names one hand as possessing the correct and the other hand as possessing the incorrect sound. She then pronounces the sound name of one of the hands, rapping it lightly with a pencil as she does so. This helps to speed discrimination and the children enjoy it.

5. *Signaling.* The teacher asks the child to ring a bell and to rap the teacher's hand whenever the teacher uses the wrong sound. The teacher then tells a story, occasionally using the error. After every signal the teacher repeats the word correctly.

6. *Signaling.* The teacher reads a list of *s* words with her back turned to the child. The moment the child signals, she must pronounce the next word using the incorrect sound. If she fails, the child gets some small reward.

Sample discrimination devices for older children and adults.

1. *Selection.* The teacher tells the student that she will pronounce a series of thirty isolated sounds, some of which are correct and some incorrect. The student is given a sheet of paper on which the thirty numbers are printed and is asked to encircle those numbers in the series on which the teacher used the correct sound. The teacher then pronounces the sounds and checks up on his discrimination.

2. *Selection.* The teacher pronounces three nonsense words such as "pa-sa-no-see." She tells the student that each word will contain two correct sounds, two incorrect sounds, or one correct and one incorrect sound. She teaches the student to recognize the three types, then dictates ten or twenty of them, which he is to write phonetically or in any way he wishes, classifying them according to type.

3. *Matching.* Using the symbols taught the student in the identification exercises, the teacher dictates a list of words, occasionally using the error. The student is asked to write down the symbol corresponding to the sound used.

4. *Matching.* The teacher slowly reads a newspaper article, occasionally using the student's error. The student is asked to name each correct and incorrect sound, using the names taught in the

identification exercises. He must interrupt the teacher to do this naming.

5. *Signaling.* The student is asked to raise his right hand the moment he hears the correct sound and to raise his left when he hears the error. The teacher pronounces a series of nonsense syllables, slowly at first, but with a gradual increase of speed.

6. *Signaling.* The teacher reads tongue twisters, occasionally using the error. The student is asked to rap on the table the moment he hears the error. If his response does not occur until after the teacher has said the next two words, he has failed. The procedure is continued until he collects five successes.

Besides these selecting, matching, and signaling devices, it is advisable to use a little direct comparison of the right and wrong pronunciations of common words, whether one is working with children or adults. Some such sequence as this is used: The teacher imitates the child as he says the word. Then the child says it. The teacher points out the similarity. Then the teacher says it correctly and very clearly, pointing out the contrast. The contrasts and similarities are put in the identifying terms previously used.

Methods for Teaching a New Sound

After the speech defective has been given a well-planned and thorough course of ear training, during which he has made no attempt to produce the correct sound, he is ready for the next step. The goal of this next step is the ability to make the correct sound by itself and apart from its usual context in familiar words. Remedial work must be continued until he can make the sound whenever he wishes. He must be able to produce it consistently and at will. There are a great many methods whereby a new sound can be taught: the stimulation method, the phonetic placement method, the modification of other standard sounds or biological functions, the babbling method with identification of chance production of the sound, and the method which uses a few words or imitative sounds in which the usually defective sound is made correctly. Each of these will now be described in detail.

Stimulation method. This method, which is the simplest and easiest, depends upon the preliminary ear training for its value. It should be tried first, for a sound taught by this method is much more stable and permanent than a sound acquired by one of the other methods. In a sense, it may be said that this is the natural method of sound acquisition. The baby hears and discriminates sounds. He is stimulated intensively by them. He listens. Then he makes the attempt, and lo!—he has produced the correct sound. In a similar fashion, when the teacher feels that the student has been given adequate ear training, she goes through a brief review of some of the isolation, identification, stimulation, and discrimination techniques and concludes with a request similar to this:

TEACHER: Now, Johnny, I'm going to let you have your first chance to make the snake sound, *sss*. Remember not to make the windmill sound, *th-th*. This is the sound you are to make: *sss, sss, ssssss*. Now you try it.

If the ear training has been adequate, this simple routine, in which the wrong sound is pronounced, identified, and rejected, then followed by the correct sound given several times, will bring a perfect production of the correct sound on the first attempt. Occasionally it will be necessary to repeat this routine several times before it works, and the student should be encouraged to take his time and to listen carefully both to the stimulation and to his response. He should be told that he has made an error or that he has almost made it correctly. He should then be encouraged to attempt it in a slightly different way the next time. No pressure should be brought to bear upon him, and a review of discrimination, stimulation, and identification techniques should preface the new attempt. He should be asked to make it quietly and without force. The procedure may be slightly varied by asking the child to produce it in a whisper. After the sound has been produced, the teacher should signal the child to repeat or prolong it and to sense the "feel" of it. The attempt should be confined to the isolated sound itself or to a nonsense syllable beginning with it. This stimulation method will produce excellent results in all but a very few cases, and it should always be tried thoroughly before the other methods are used.

Phonetic placement method. The phonetic placement method of enabling a speech defective to produce a new sound is the old traditional method. For centuries, speech correctionists have used diagrams, applicators, and instruments to ensure appropriate tongue, jaw, and lip placement. Children have been asked to watch the teacher's tongue movements and to duplicate them. Observation of the teacher's mouth in a mirror has also been used. Many very ingenious devices have been invented to adapt these techniques for children, and often they produce almost miraculous results. Unfortunately, however, the mechanics of such phonetic placement demand so much attention that they cannot be performed quickly or unconsciously enough for the needs of casual speech. At best, they are vague and difficult to sense or recall. The positions tend to vary with the sounds that precede or follow them, and to teach all of these positions is an almost impossible task. Frequently dental abnormalities will make an exact reproduction of the standard position inadvisable. Many speech correctionists produce the sounds in nonstandard ways, if, indeed, there is a standard way of producing any given speech sound. Despite all of these disadvantages, the phonetic placement methods are indispensable tools in the speech correctionist's kit, and, when the stimulation method fails, they must be used. They are especially useful in working with individuals with hearing defects, and they certainly help to identify the sound.

Excellent diagrams and descriptions of the various speech sounds may be found in the texts to which references are given at the end of this chapter. The speech correctionist should have these texts available and should know the mechanics of articulation thoroughly enough to interpret the diagrams and assume the positions illustrated and described. The teacher should be able to recognize any sound from its description and diagram.

In using methods of phonetic placement, it is necessary that the speech defective be given a clear idea of the desired position prior to speech attempt. If an adult, he should study diagrams, the teacher's articulatory organs in position, when observed both directly and in a mirror, palatograms, models, and the written descriptions of the mechanics whereby the sound is produced. Every available device should be used to make the student understand clearly what positions of tongue, jaw, and lips are to be assumed. It is frequently advisable to have the

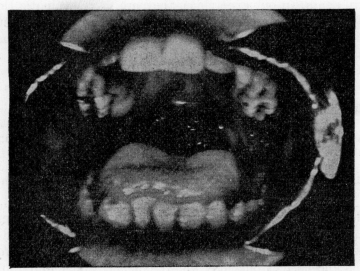

Courtesy of Dr. Kurt von Frowine

FIG. 5. Photograph of the mouth of a child who had suffered a severe lye burn. The tongue is being lifted as high as possible. Despite the handicap, the child had learned compensatory movements sufficient to give him perfect speech.

student practice other sounds that he can make easily, using diagrams and printed descriptions to guide his placement. This will familiarize him with the technique of translating diagrams and descriptions into performance.

Various instruments and applicators are used to help the student attain the proper position. Tongue depressors are used to hold the tip and front of the tongue down, as in the attempt to produce a *k* or *g*, or they may be used to touch certain portions of the tongue and palate to indicate positions of mutual contact. Tooth props of various sizes will help the student to assume a proper dental opening. Thin applicators and wedges are used to groove the tongue. Curious wire contrivances are occasionally used to insure lateral contact of tongue and teeth. Small tubes are used to direct the flow of air. The old texts by Borden and Busse and by Scripture provide examples of these instruments. In our experience, they are more dramatic than useful. Enforcing a certain tongue position through some such device produces such a mass of kinesthetic and tactual sensations that the appropriate ones can seldom be attended to. Usually, the moment the instrument is removed the old, incorrect tongue position is assumed, because, as Travis puts it:

If a child used *p* for *f* from pressing the lips too tightly together, a thick stick or finger was stuck between the lips so that they could not close tightly. As far as the child is concerned, he is still making *p* regardless of whether a stick or finger was stuck between the lips or not. A sound cannot be broken up into its component parts, as into lip movements or tongue movements. It is a unit, a whole, and can be learned only as such.[5]

If these devices and instruments have any real value, it seems to be that of vivifying the movements of the tongue, and of providing a large number of varying tongue positions, from which the correct one may finally emerge. Many individuals have difficulty in realizing how great a repertoire of tongue movements they possess, and instruments frequently enable them to attempt new ones.

Tongue exercises. The same result may be attained through various articulation exercises. Although the value of tongue, lip, and jaw exercises has been questioned and denied by many workers in the field of speech correction, they can be said to be useful in teaching the student to manipulate his articulatory apparatus in many new and unaccustomed ways. Too many articulation cases have only one or two stereotyped tongue

---

[5] Travis, L. E., *Speech Pathology*, New York, D. Appleton-Century Co., 1931, page 193.

movements in their speech repertoire, although they may have many more in their functions of swallowing, laughing, chewing, or sneezing. They need to learn how adaptable the tongue really is. Whenever possible, the articulatory exercises given should proceed out of the movements used in the biological functions or in babbling. The old, formal tongue exercises are of much less value.

When the correct sound has been produced (and frequently a lot of trial and error must be resorted to before it appears), the speech defective should hold it, increasing its intensity, repeating it, whispering it, exaggerating it, and varying it in as many ways as possible without losing its identity. He should focus his attention on the "feel" of the position in terms of tongue, palate, jaws, lips, and throat. He should listen to the sound produced. Then he should be asked to leave the position intact but to cease speech attempt, resuming it after a long interval. Finally he should let the tongue assume a neutral position on the floor of the mouth and then attempt to regain the desired position. Sounds produced by phonetic placement are very unstable and must be treated very carefully or they will be lost. Strengthen them as soon as possible and keep out distractions. After a successful attempt, one should insist that the student remain silent for a time before taking part in conversation. This will permit maturation to become effective.

Modification of other sounds. Another special method of teaching a speech defective a new sound is that which involves the modification of other sounds, either those of speech, those that imitate noises, or those that imitate other functions, such as swallowing. These methods are somewhat akin to those of phonetic placement, but they have the advantage of using a known sound or movement as a point of departure for the trial-and-error variation which produces the correct sound. The modification method may take many forms, but in all of them the sequence is about the same. The student is asked to make a certain sound and to hold it for a short period. He is then requested to move his tongue or his lips or jaws in a definite manner while continuing to produce his first sound. This variation in articulators will produce a change in the sound, a change which often rather closely approximates the sound that is desired. An illustration of this method may be given. A lateral lisper is told to make the *th* sound and to prolong it. Then, while continuing to make the sound, he is required to draw in the tonguetip slowly and to raise the whole tongue, slowly scrape its tip upward along the back of the upper teeth, and finally bring it to rest against the alveolar ridge. The *th* sound will change as the tongue rises, and a rather good approximation to the desired *s* will be produced. If this is combined with ear training and stimulation, it will be found to be very effective.

There are many of these modification methods, and each speech-correction teacher invents others. The student should go through the references given at the end of this chapter and collect examples appropriate to each of the commonly defective sounds for his notebook. The text by Nemoy and Davis is especially useful in this regard. Most of these techniques have been used by all speech correctionists for decades, and they are part of the standard equipment of any worker in the field.

We shall now provide some supplementary methods for getting the articulation case to produce the correct sound. The student should be warned not to use them indiscriminately. They have value only in their ability to get the child to make the sound in a new way, in varying his attack on the desired sound. The essential task remains the same: to give the articulatory case a clear auditory, kinesthetic, and tactual picture of the sound.

S *and* Z *Sounds*

1. Have the child protrude the tongue between the teeth so as to produce the sound *th* for the beginning of such words as *saw, glass,* and *rose.* Have him think of *th.* Then when he is thinking of producing the *th* for the *s,* force the tip of his tongue inward with a thin instrument such as a thick blunt toothpick. The result will be an *s.* The

principle involved is that the child's thinking the *th* drives the air over the tip of the tongue. The value of directing the child's attention to the tip of his tongue when he is producing sibilant sounds is that he will eventually feel the current of air being emitted over it.

2. Have the child protrude the tongue as in the preceding exercise, and form the sound of *th*; but as this is formed, have him slowly and gradually withdraw the tongue and, while still attempting to make the *th*, scrape the tonguetip along the back of the front teeth and upward. The result will again be an *s*, which he should be asked to match with the *s* produced by the instructor until an adjustment is made which gives an excellent lispless *s*.

3. Have the child begin by forming a *t* in a word like *tea*. Have him pronounce it with a strong aspiration (*tuh-hee*), with a strong puff of breath after the explosion of the *t*, before the vowel begins. Then, instead of this sudden explosion or puff, take away the tip of the tongue from the teeth-ridge slowly. This will give the sound *ts*. Hold onto this sound and you will have the *s-s-s-s*. The child must not think he is saying *ts* as in the word *oats* or he will use his usual pronunciation. Keep him rehearsing the steps of this procedure till they are fixed in his mind, before showing him that he is making a good *s*.

4. Have the child hiss, seeking to raise the pitch of the hiss until it approximates that held by the instructor. Often it is wise to tell the student to experiment with the tonguetip positions during the production of his hiss, not before. Sometimes, the instructor should change his hiss from the faulty one used by the student through several degrees until the correct *s* is made.

5. Have the child go through some brisk tongue exercises with special stress paid to the grooving of the tongue. The tongue should be grooved and protruded and the air should be blown through this groove. From this protruding position the tongue should be drawn back slowly while the blowing is continued, concentrating the attention meanwhile on the tip of the tongue. Sometimes use a thin stick or instrument to help the groove.

6. If the child can make a good *z* sound, take such a word as *zero* and ask him to listen carefully and to feel where his tongue is when he whispers it, prolonging the first sound. This is the sound which must become the child's model.

7. Put upper and lower teeth together. Ask child to stroke (with tongue) the back of his upper teeth as he blows a stream of air.

8. Put upper and lower teeth together and press lips tightly together. Keep teeth together but part lips to let a small hiss escape.

K *or* G *Sound*

1. Ask child to repeat the sequence *puh-tuh-kuh* in unison with the teacher. Teacher should give several samples first.

2. Ask child to imitate the teacher as she coughs up an imaginary wishbone in this fashion, *kuh-kuh*.

3. Ask child to anchor tongue against lower teeth and hold hand in front of his mouth so he can feel the puff of air as he imitates his teacher.

4. If the child can make the *ng* sound, ask him to do so and then give a little puff of air against his hand or a feather held in front of his mouth.

5. Ask the child to say *uhkuh* in a strong whisper.

6. Explore the child's vocabulary to see if he can say any word in which the word ends with a good *k* sound. Then ask him to repeat many times and repeat last sound, imitating teacher, thus: *sick-kuh-kuh*.

7. If child can say "guh" ask him to whisper it because the "(kʌ) is a whispered (gʌ)."

8. Press underneath child's chin and ask him to say *kuh* in a whisper as you release the pressure suddenly.

9. Tell the child of two Australian birds, one a big one who has a long tongue that moves up and down and who always says *tee-tee-tee* and the other who doesn't have any tongue at all that you can see move and who always says *ook-ook-ook*. Ask the child to imitate both birds.

L *Sound*

1. Give strong stimulation through humming or singing the non-sense syllables *lay, lee, lie*, then ask child to hum or sing.

2. Give tongue-lifting and -lowering exercises, first in silence, then while blowing, then while whispering *ah*, then while saying *ah*. Gradually lift tongue higher and higher until it finally makes the contact at the right place.

3. Form mouth for *ah*. Keep whispering it softly as you place tongue in firm contact with upper gum ridge. Then suddenly say the "ah" loudly as the tongue is released and a long *l* is subsequently made.

4. Practice this sequence very swiftly: *tah-dah-nah-lah*.

5. With a match or tongue depressor stroke the back of the upper

gum ridge until child touches it with tongue. Ask him to stroke the spot with his tongue. Ask him to stroke it as he says *ee*.

6. Practice making the sound using a mirror and a wide-open mouth.

SH *Sound*

1. Tell the child to round his lips and flatten his cheeks and "slush" the air out between his teeth.

2. Ask the child to make an *s* sound and pull back the base of tongue with a pencil stuck between the teeth.

3. Ask child to make a *th*, then to pull back the tongue, shutting the teeth and continuing to blow.

4. Ask child to whisper an *er* sound, holding it for some time during which he gradually brings his teeth together.

5. Ask child to round lips and raise tongue and shut teeth as he whispers a prolonged *ee*.

6. Put spoon in mouth, rim up. Ask child to shut teeth over handle and to produce the *sh* sound.

7. If child can say "measure" have him whisper it and prolong the sound.

8. If child can make the *ch* sound, have him "let it leak out," prolonging it rather than releasing it suddenly.

9. During the production of an *s* sound, pull tongue one-half inch toward the back of the mouth.

F *and* V

Tell the child that today he is to have his first chance to make the new sound. Then say, "Now watch me. See how I bite my lower lip. Can you bite your lip in the same way? Now let's look at ourselves in this mirror. Don't bite hard, just lay the teeth on the lower lip. See how I do it? Now let's hold our mouths like that and suck in some air. All right. Now, don't move your mouth but blow some air out, like this, *f-f-f-* [give strong stimulation]. Now do it again and make this sound in a whisper *fuh, fffuh, fffuh.*" Give child a little rest then some new trials. Then have him say *fuh* whenever you raise a finger. Spend some time talking about the new and old sounds, showing him how they differ. Tell him that the new sound may feel wrong but that it "sounds" right, and that he must *listen* rather than feel.

1. Ask child to hold lower lip against upper teeth, with a finger laid crosswise, then to blow.

2. Ask child to smile broadly as he tries the sound.

3. Have child bite far down beyond the upper lip (toward the chin) as he blows.

4. By holding a feather against the mouth, show child that *p* is a puff of air while *f* or *v* is a gradual stream of air.

R *Sound*

1. Ask child to say *l*. Then with the depressor gently push the tip of the tongue back until you can insert the depressor between the tip and teeth-ridge or until *r* sound results.

2. If this fails and the child can say *z*, ask him to make the sound and continue it while the jaw is dropped until the teeth are separated about one inch or until *r* results.

3. Have the child imitate you as you trill the tonguetip. Then use this trill to precede the vowel $\overline{ee}$.

4. Spread the sides of the child's mouth with your fingers; ask him to produce a prolonged *n* sound, then to curl the end of his tongue backward as he continues making the sound.

CH (tʃ) *Sound*

1. If child is able to make the *t* sound and the *sh* sound separately, these sounds can be combined to make a good *ch*. The *ch* sound is a combination of these two sounds. Have the child form his teeth and tongue as for the *t* sound, and then say the *sh* sound instead. You might also have him say *she* by first forming the *t*.

2. Tell the child to pretend to sneeze. Often a child who cannot follow instructions about tongue and lip formation will make a perfect *ch* sound this way. Playing train, and saying *ch-ch-ch* like an engine may work, too.

3. Have the child prolong *sh* as though to tell someone to be quiet. When you signal by clapping or raising a finger from the table, have him quickly touch the gum of the roof of his mouth, and then go right on with *sh*. This will produce a prolonged *sh* with a *ch* in the middle.

The babbling method. This method for producing the desired speech sound is probably as close as any method to the one used by the child in learning to talk. Its greatest disadvantage is its lack of economy, for much time is needed to teach the student to throw off his inhibitions and to babble thoroughly at random. Most students resent this procedure and must be convinced of its utility before they will consent to give up their dignity and attempt it. It is usually wise to outline in advance the purpose and type of babbling desired. Both the teacher and the student should babble in unison. They should relax, get the babbling started, and then let it continue almost automatically, ranging where it will. For the first several periods, no attempt should be made to notice the sounds produced or to look for the sound desired. Random vocalization should be the goal for the time being.

After the student seems to be babbling adequately, the teacher should cease intermittently, and, finally, allow the student to babble alone. Then, when the teacher gives a prearranged signal, the student should repeat the sound being used at the time the signal occurred. He should repeat it over and over. In this type of babbling, the speech defective makes all the speech sounds, even those which he cannot make voluntarily or in words. The teacher's task is to get the student to select, out of the complex hodgepodge of vocalization, the sound which he has difficulty in making, to focus his attention upon it, and to make it voluntarily. The sounds attained by this method are very unstable and must be strengthened immediately.

Using words in which the usually defective sound is made correctly. As we have seen, one of the items in both the voice and articulation tests requires the examiner to record all words in which the usually defective sound is made correctly. Many teachers of speech correction fail to realize the value of these words in remedial work. They may be used to enable the student to make the correct sound at will and in isolation. They are also extremely valuable in getting the student to make clean-cut transitions between the isolated sound and the rest of the word. Finally, they serve as standards of correctness of sound performance. Speech defectives need some standard with which to compare their speech attempts at correct production of the usually defective sound. Although occasional cases are found who never make the sound correctly, the majority of speech defectives have a few words in which they do not make the error. The teacher should be alert enough to catch these when they do occur. Often these words are those which have the usually defective sound in an inconspicuous place—that is to say, the sound occurs in the medial or final position, or is incorporated within a blend; seldom is it found in an accented syllable. The teacher must train her ear to listen for it in the student's speech or it will escape her. At times it occurs in words in which an unusual spelling provides a different symbol for the sound. To illustrate: A child who was unable to make a good *f* in any of his words using that printed symbol, said the word *rough* with a perfect *f* sound. This was probably due to the strong stimulation given by the child's spelling teacher.

These words are worth the trouble needed to discover them, for they simplify the teacher's work tremendously, since it is possible to use that sound as a standard and guide and to work from it to other words in which error normally occurs. The experienced teacher greets these nuclei words as veritable nuggets. Similarly, even when the student is highly consistent in his errors, there comes a stage in his treatment when he is saying a few words correctly. These words may be used to serve the same ends as those mentioned in the preceding paragraph.

The procedure used in this method is roughly as follows: The teacher writes the word on one of several cards (or uses a picture representing it). Then she asks the student to go through the series one at a time, saying the word on each card ten times. Finally, the special word to be used is repeated a hundred times, accenting, and prolonging if possible, the sound which in other words is made incorrectly. Thus the lingual lisper who could say *lips* correctly repeated the word one hundred times, prolonging the *s*. He was then asked to hold it for a count of twenty, then thirty, then forty. Finally, he was required to hold it intermittently, thus; *lipssss.ssss..sss*. The purpose of such a gradual approach is that the sound must be emphasized in both its auditory and its motor characteristics to prevent its loss when the student becomes aware of it as his hard sound. For example, one baby talker made the initial *r* in *rabbit* perfectly until told that he did. Immediately the child changed to the *w* substitution and was unable to make the initial *r* again.

After the child has emphasized the sound a large number of times, has listened to it and felt it thoroughly, and can make it intermittently and in a repetitive form, he may be asked to think the word and to speak the sound. It is often wise to underline the sound to be spoken, asking the student to whisper all but the letter underlined. Other sounds and other words may be similarly underlined if a careful approach is necessary. Through these means, the child finally can make the sound in isolation and at will.

Strengthening the New Sound

One of the greatest causes for discouragement in treating an articulatory case may be traced to the parent's or teacher's ignorance of a very important fact. A new sound is weak and unstable. Its mechanics are easily forgotten or lost. Its dual phases of auditory and motor sensation patterns are easily confused. Many people believe that a complicated skill (such as that involved in a speech sound) once achieved is never lost, although any musician or tennis player will tell us that a new stroke or fingering sequence must be practiced and strengthened a great deal before it can be used in competition or concert. Many speech-correction teachers become discouraged and blame the speech defective for his frequent relapse into error or his sudden loss of the sound he had been taught to make. Many children, who can at will make the correct sound, never learn to incorporate it within familiar words. All of these unfortunate occurrences are due to the fact that a new sound must be strengthened before it can win the competition which the error provides in the speaking of common words. A lisper who has said "yeth" for "yes" several thousand times cannot be expected to say the latter as soon as he has learned to make the *sss* sound in isolation. Perhaps that sound has been performed only three or four times. Yet parents and teachers constantly ruin all of their preliminary work by saying some such sentence as this: "Fine, Johnny. That was fine! You said *sss* just as plainly as anyone. Now say 'sssoup.' " And Johnny, ninety-nine times out of one hundred, will say triumphantly, "thoup." Most speech correctionists have to train themselves to resist this urge to hurry. When the child has been taught to make the new sound, the utmost patience and restraint are needed.

There are two main types of techniques used for strengthening a new sound: those using the sound by itself, in isolation, and those using the sound in nonsense material. Included under the first classification are prolongation, repetition, exaggeration, attending to kinesthesia, shortening initiation time, inclusion in babbling, and simultaneous talking-and-writing. Included in the second classification are the methods which use nonsense syllables, symbols, and names, and those which employ signal practice and other transitional techniques. Although no one case will ever require all of the techniques, we shall describe some of them under each heading. All cases should be given some strengthening technique of each type.

Techniques for strengthening the new sound in isolation. In general, it is advisable to use these techniques before those employing nonsense material. As we have said, after the new sound has been obtained, it should be repeated and prolonged immediately. During this repetition and prolongation, the student should be told to keep a poker face and to move as little as possible. A sudden shift of body position occasionally produces a change in the movements of articulation as well. As soon as the new sound tends to lose its clear characteristics, the teacher should insist upon some rest and should then review the procedure used to produce the sound. Rest should be silent in order to let maturation take place. Little intensity should be used, and when working with a pair of sounds, such as *s* and *z*, the unvoiced sound is preferable. Often sounds such as *l* and *r* should be whispered or sung.

After the speech defective is able to produce the sound readily and can repeat and prolong it consistently, the teacher can ask him to increase its intensity and exaggerate it. He should be asked to focus his attention on the "feel" of the tongue, lips, and palate. Shutting his eyes will help him to get a better awareness of the tactual and kinesthetic sensations thereby produced. Ask him to assume the position without speech attempt and, after a short period of "feeling," to try the sound. Many other supplementary devices will occur to the teacher.

After the student reaches the stage where he has little difficulty in producing the new sound, he should be encouraged to shorten the time needed to produce it. A sound which the student takes too long to produce will never become habitual. This speeding up of the time needed to initiate it may be accomplished by demanding fast repetitions, by alternating it with other isolated speech sounds, and by using signals. In this last activity, the student should keep his articulatory apparatus in a state of rest or in certain other positions, such as an open mouth, and then, at a certain sharp-sound signal, he should react by producing the new sound immediately.

One of the most effective methods for strengthening a new sound is to include it in babbling. The babbling should be initiated in the manner described in the preceding section, and the student should attempt to incorporate the new sound within the vocal flow as effortlessly as possible. It should not stand out and there should be no pausing before it. Doublings of the sound should be frequent. These babbling periods should be continued daily throughout the course of treatment.

The most important of all strengthening devices is the use of simultaneous talking-and-writing. In this procedure, the student writes the script symbol as he pronounces the sound. The sound should be timed so that it will neither precede nor follow the writing of the symbol, but will coincide exactly with the dominant stroke of the letter. Since this dominant stroke varies somewhat with different persons, some experimentation will be needed. At first, the teacher should supervise this talking-and-writing very carefully to ensure clear vocalization of the new sound and proper timing. Later, the student can be assigned to hand in several pages of this talking-and-writing every day. The continuant sounds should be pronounced by themselves (*sss, vvv, lll, mmm*), and the stops should use a lightly vocalized neutral vowel (*kuh, puh, duh*). Simultaneous talking-and-writing techniques not only provide an excellent vehicle for

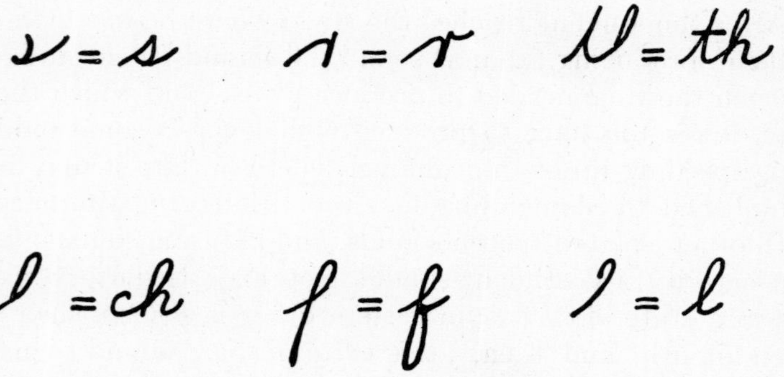

Fig. 6. Typical nonsense symbols used in talking-and-writing exercises for articulatory cases.

practice of the new sound, but also give a means of reinforcing it by enriching the motor aspect of the performance. They also improve the identification, and, as we shall see, make possible an effective transition to familiar words. For children who cannot write, the sound may be tied up with a movement such as a finger twitch or foot tap. In this case, as in writing, the timing is very important.

Strengthening the new sound through use of nonsense material. The second group of strengthening techniques includes those which use nonsense syllables, symbols, and names. It is obvious that such material provides a very effective means of practicing the new sound in all of its various combinations with other sounds. The student meets none of the competition which the error produces in speaking familiar words. He need not add to the speech attempt the burden of rejecting the error. Fewer confusions arise. New sound sequences are strengthened, and new articulatory co-ordinations are learned.

The first type of nonsense material to be considered is the nonsense syllable. These syllables can be readily constructed

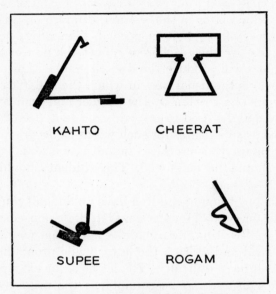

Fig. 7. Nonsense pictures used to provide names which children with articulatory defects can learn to pronounce more easily than familiar words.

by combining the new sound with the fourteen most common vowels and diphthongs. The first nonsense syllables to be practiced are those in which the transitional movements from consonant to vowel involve the fewest and simplest co-ordinations. For example, *ko* involves less radical transitional movements than does *kee*. The next nonsense syllables should be those which use the new sound in the final position (*ok*), and, finally, those in which the new sound is located in the medial position (*oko*) should be practiced. Double nonsense syllables may also be used, but simple doublings are preferred (*kaka*).

These nonsense syllables should be practiced thoroughly before familiar words are attempted. The talking-and-writing technique can be used to facilitate their production if any difficulty is experienced. The student should speak the new sound as he writes the symbol until he gets to the end of the line, then should add the vowel, thus: *s s s s s s saaa*. Signal practice, such as that described later in this section, can also be used to form the nonsense syllable if it is needed. Generally, however, a simple request by the teacher to repeat the nonsense syllable he pronounces will produce the desired results. This repetition from a model is the usual way in which the syllables are used. They may also be written by the teacher and read by the student. They may be used to precede each sentence of conversation or used as substitutes for such words as *the* or *and*. Lists of them may be used for practice, and all the various vowel combinations should be employed. The student should practice them finally at high speeds.

Although most young children have no difficulty in using the standard letter symbol for the sound in these nonsense syllables or talking-and-writing, many adults and some young children who have read and written the letter while pronouncing it incorrectly will have difficulty. The letter *s*, for example, means *th* to such a lisper, and he cannot use the usual syllables in talking-and-writing. For these cases, it is wise to use a nonsense symbol in place of the standard letter. In general, the symbols should be parts of the standard symbols, though the student should not realize this fact until later. These symbols should be used for identification techniques and for all strengthening techniques. After the student has finally begun to use them in regular words, he may be shown that the nonsense symbol is really a part of the true symbol for the sound.

It is also advisable to use nonsense names and meanings to provide new words in which the new sound can be incorporated. The fingers and toes may be given nonsense names. The doorknob may be christened. The teacher can make nonsense objects out of modeling clay, giving them names which include the new sound. Nonsense pictures may be drawn and named. Card games using these nonsense pictures seem to be peculiarly fascinating to almost all cases. Through talking-and-writing techniques, repetition from a model, reading, conversation, questioning, and speech games, these nonsense names can be used repeatedly. The various sound combinations are thereby practiced, and remarkable progress will soon occur. Examples of some of the nonsense pictures are given in Figure 7.

Making the Transition to Familiar Words

After the new sound has been strengthened sufficiently, the speech defective may attempt to use it in familiar words. If the preliminary work has been done carefully, there will be little difficulty, even though this is probably the most difficult and critical stage of the whole treatment. The teacher must always keep in mind that the speech defective has said these words in the wrong way thousands of times and that these words are units which include the error as a part of them. In retraining, we do not merely substitute one sound for another. We build new words, new configurations. The student must unlearn the old and learn the new. This process involves many techniques, among which the following may be cited: training in reconfiguring, signal practice, transitional techniques, and talking-and-writing.

Reconfiguration techniques. Frequently the reconfiguration techniques must be carried out rather gradually. Their purpose is to teach the individual that words are made up of sound sequences and that these sound sequences can be modified without losing the unity of the word. If, for convenience, we use a lingual lisper as our example, the reconfiguration techniques would follow somewhat the same sequence: (1) The student reads, narrates, and converses with the teacher, substituting the sound of *b* for that of *f* whenever the latter occurs in the initial position. He reads, for example, that "Sammy caught a bish with his hook and line." The purpose of using these non-error sounds is to make a gradual approach. (2) The student substitutes his new sound for other sounds, but not for the error. Thus: "Sammy sssaught a fish with his hoos and line." (3) The student substitutes another sound for the *s* in the same material. Thus: "Bammy caught a fish with his hook and line." (4) The student omits the *s* in all words beginning with it. Thus: "—ammy caught a fish with his hook and line." (5) The student "substitutes" his new sound for the *s*. Thus: "Ssssammy caught a fish with his hook and line." Many similar techniques are easily invented. It may seem to the young speech correctionist that such techniques are far too laborious and detailed. But, after he has met with persistent error in his articulatory cases, he will appreciate the fact that careful and thorough training will produce a thoroughgoing and permanent freedom from error. Sketchy and slipshod training will enable a speech defective to make the correct sound and perhaps to use it in a few words when he watches himself carefully, but this is far from the goal that should be set. Too many speech-correction teachers have blamed the student for failure when they should have blamed themselves.

Signal practice. There are several other methods of getting the student to use the new sound in familiar words, but one of the most effective may be called signal practice. In this, the student prolongs or repeats the new sound and then, at a given signal, instantly says the prearranged vowel or the rest of the word. The student should be given a preparatory set to pronounce the rest of the word by preliminary signal practice. During this practice he waits with his eyes closed until he hears the sound signal which sets off the response. Thus, during the student's prolongation of *sssssss*, the instructor suddenly raps on the table, and the syllable *oup* is automatically produced. With a preparatory set, the response is largely automatic and involuntary, and thus the new sound is integrated within the word as a whole. Often it is wise to require the student to say the word twice. Thus: *sssssss*(rap)*oupsoup*. Signal practice can also be used with repetition. Thus: *kuh-kuh-*(rap)*atkat*. After some training with this type of signal practice, the student may use other signals, such as those provided by the timing of a rhythm. Thus: *s-s*, *s-s-soup* or *s-s-soup*, *s-s-soup*. The student may also be required to repeat over and over some nonsense syllable which he can make well, suddenly saying the new word when the signal is given. Thus: *ssi-ssi-ssi-ssi*(tap)*ssip*. The nonsense syllable and the new word may also be used alternately. The isolated sound may be used in the above exercises in place of the nonsense syllable. Various other combinations may easily be invented.

Simultaneous talking-and-writing. The simultaneous talking-and-writing techniques previously described will be invaluable if used properly. The student should talk-and-write the symbol alone for one line, and then, on the next line, talk-and-write the first letter, the first syllable, and, finally, the whole word. Thus: *s s s s s s s s s s; s si sick s si sick*, and so on. Later he can alternate the symbol and the word, and finally he can write only the symbol as he says the word. Assignments can be given for home practice. Frequently such a gradual approach is not necessary, and the student need write only the symbol and say any *s* word.

At times, difficulty will be experienced in making the transitions into the words. The student will say *rwabbit* and be confident that he has pronounced the word correctly. The error must be brought to his attention by the teacher's imitation and by the student's voluntary production of the error. Signal practice will help a great deal to eliminate this error.

Another invaluable technique is provided by a signal used in a slightly different way. The student is asked to form his mouth for the vowel which begins the rest of the word; *i.e.*, for the vowel *a* in *rabbit*. He may whisper a prolongation of this vowel. Then, at a given signal, he is to say *rabbit* as swiftly as possible. This preformation of the vowel will often solve the problem. Similarly, the practice of pairs of words, the first ending in the vowel of the second, will be effective. Using pairs of words in which the first word ends with the new sound and the second begins with the same sound is occasionally useful, although the student should be cautioned to keep out all breaks of continuity.

Still another method of eliminating this error is to use some nonsense symbol to represent the part of the word which follows the new sound. Thus, one individual was asked to say *oup* every time he wrote a question mark (?), and, after ten minutes of this, he was told to read the following symbols, *t?*, *kr?*, and *s?*. The last symbol was pronounced *soup* rather than *sthoup*, and no further difficulty was experienced.

How to Get the Child to Use the New Sound Consistently

One of the most important steps in the treatment of both articulatory and voice disorders is getting the child to use the new sound consistently in his daily conversation. It is not enough merely to teach the child how to make the correct sound; he must follow a systematic program of effecting the transition into casual speech.

Such a program should include, first of all, definite speech periods at school and at home, during which the child uses speech primarily for correction purposes. These periods should be short, varied, and well motivated. Such a program should also include the use of speech assignments in outside situations; the use of checking devices and penalties; the use of negative practice; and the use of persons, words, and situations as nuclei of good speech. Each of these activities is outlined in the paragraphs which follow.

Some suggested activities for school and home speech periods are:

(1) Making and using scrapbooks or flash cards wherein the pictures represent words containing the sound on which the child is working. (2) Hiding word or picture cards about the room, and requiring the child to say the word correctly until he finds the proper

card.   (3) Reading passages in which words containing defective sound are underlined.   (4) Teacher or parent uses error in his speech, asking child to correct him.   (5) Child writes new word containing defective sound on calendar each day.   (6) Use of jingles and sentences in which particular sound is emphasized.

Other speech games and activities can be readily devised by anyone truly interested in the child.

Speech assignments. Some typical speech assignments to illustrate methods for getting the child to work on his errors in outside situations are:

(1) Go downstairs and ask the janitor for a dust rag. Be sure to say *rag* with a good long *rrr.*   (2) Say the word *rabbit* to three other children without letting them know that you are working on your speech.   (3) Ask your father if you said any word wrongly after you tell him what you did in school today.

The teacher should always make these assignments very definite and appropriate to the child's ability and environment. He should always ask for a report the next day. Such assignments frequently are the solution to any lack of motivation the child may have.

Checking devices and penalties. Checking devices and penalties are of great value when properly used. Typical checking devices are:

(1) Having child carry card and crayon during geography recitation, making a mark or writing the word whenever he makes an error. (2) Having some other child check errors in a similar fashion. (3) Having child transfer marbles from one pocket to another, one for each error. Many other devices may be invented, and they will bring the error to consciousness very rapidly.

Similarly, penalties are of great service, when used properly. It should be realized, however, that painful and highly emotional penalties should not be used, for they merely make the bad habit more pronounced and cause the child to hate his speech work. Penalties used in speech correction should be vivid and good natured. Typical penalties used with a 10-year-old lisper were: put pencil behind ear; step in wastebasket; pound pan; look between legs; close one eye; say *whoopee*. Let the child set his own penalties before he makes the speech attempt.

Nucleus situations. Many parents and teachers make the mistake of correcting the child whenever he makes speech errors. It is unwise to set the speech standards too high. No one can watch himself all the time, and we all hate to be nagged. As a matter of fact, too much vigilance by the speech defective can produce such speech inhibitions that the speech work becomes thoroughly distasteful. Fluency disappears and the speech becomes very halting and unpleasant. Then, too, the very anxiety lest error occur, when carried to the extreme, seems to be able to increase the number of slips and mistakes themselves. Other errors sometimes appear.

Therefore, we recommend that the parents and teachers of the speech defective concentrate their reminding and correcting upon a few common words and upon certain nuclei speech situations. Use a certain chair as a good-speech chair. Whenever the child sits in it, he must watch himself. Have a certain person picked out who is to serve as the speech situation in which the child must use very careful speech. Use a certain speech situation, such as the dinner table, to serve as a nucleus of good speech, and, when errors occur in these nuclei situations, penalize them good naturedly but vividly. You will find that the speech vigilance and freedom from errors will spread rapidly to all other situations.

Finally, we recommend that, after a child has mastered a new sound and several words in which it occurs, he be required to say it occasionally in the wrong way. This is called negative practice, and it has no harmful effect. Indeed, it merely emphasizes the distinction between the correct and incorrect sounds.

Negative practice. By negative practice we mean the deliberate and voluntary use of the incorrect sound or speech error. It may seem somewhat odd to advise speech defectives to practice their errors, for we have always assumed that practice makes perfection, and certainly we do not want the student to become more perfect in the use of his errors. Nevertheless, modern experimental psychology has demonstrated that when one seeks to break a habit that is rather unconscious (such as fingernail-biting or the substitution of *sh* for *s*), much more rapid progress is made if the possessor of the habit will occasionally (and at appropriate times) use the error deliberately. The reasons for this method are: (1) The greatest strength of such a habit lies in the fact that the possessor is not aware of it every time it occurs. All habit reactions tend to become more or less unconscious, and certainly those involved in speech are of this type; consciousness of the reaction must come before it can be eliminated. (2) Voluntary practice of the reaction makes it very vivid, thus increasing vigilance and contributing to the awareness of the cues that signal the approach of the reaction. (3) The voluntary practice of the error acts as a penalty.

The use of negative practice is so varied that it would be impossible to describe all the applications which can be made of it. Variations must be made to fit each type of disorder and each individual case. There are, however, certain general principles which may be said to govern all disorders and cases. Make the individual aware of the reasons for his use of the incorrect sound, for unintelligent use of the error is worthless. Never ask the student to use the error until he can produce the correct sound whenever asked to do so. Negative practice is a technique for getting the correct sound into the student's speech; it is used to make the correct sound habitual.

Set up the exact reproduction of the incorrect sound as a goal. The use of mirror observation, teacher imitation, and phonograph recording is invaluable. This is a learning process and does not come all at once. The teacher should confine all negative practice to the speech lesson until the student is able to duplicate the error consistently and fairly accurately. One should begin the use of this technique by asking the student to duplicate the error immediately after it has occurred. That is to say, the student should stop immediately after lisping on the word *soup* and attempt voluntarily to duplicate his performance.

Work constantly to make the negative practice serve the purpose of comparing the right and wrong sounds. It is often well to provide lists of words for the students to work with, speaking each of them in this sequence: correctly, incorrectly, correctly, correctly. Work first on individual sounds, then on words, then on certain words in sentences containing two words which begin with the difficult sound, one of which is to be said correctly and the other incorrectly. Have the student read material in which certain words are underlined for negative practice.

Make speech 'assignments for the student's use in outside situations. Examples are:

(1) Collect (write down on cards) ten words on which you have used negative practice. (2) Write down on a card two words on which you have used negative practice during each hour of the morning. (3) Write the first sentences of five phone calls, underlining the words on which you are going to use negative practice. (4) Collect, during the day, twenty words which you have said wrongly and in which you have become aware of your error, have made a retrial and said them correctly, and then have made a second retrial using negative practice.

The preceding list of examples is merely indicatory of the type of assignments that may be used. It is vitally important that no assignment be made that does not call for an objective record of some kind. The teacher must ask for the card and discuss the fulfillment or nonfulfillment of the assignment. Assignment plus checkup will work wonders in the treatment of any speech defective. Vary the assignments to fit the case, and always make them purposeful, never a matter of routine or drill.

In concluding this section on articulatory disorders we wish to point out that in very few instances will it be necessary to spend more than five or ten minutes of individual work each day on any speech defective. Most of the work can be carried on in connection with the regular school activities, and so it should be, if the new habits are to be made permanent. Any teacher can see the possibilities for combining speech work with the language activities. In the names of the numbers themselves, arithmetic presents almost all of the speech sounds. Geography and science activities may be arranged so as to give the lisper recitations in which he is responsible for all new *s* words. Questions may be phrased so as to demand responses which involve the sound upon which error occurs. The teacher and student may have a secret signal for correction. The student should check all errors in a notebook. At times it is wise to post on the board a list of five words with which the student has trouble unless he watches himself. Occasionally, some other student may be asked to check on the speech defective's errors. Class recitations should be used not for teaching a new sound but for building up the strength of the new sound after the student can make it correctly.

Drill. Most texts on speech correction are heavily laden with lists of words, phrases, and sentences which contain the various speech sounds. Most of them imply or state that the speech defective must be drilled intensively on such material before he can hope to speak without error. Many of them advocate the use of tongue twisters and similar difficult sentences. Modern educational practice and theory are rapidly getting away from the older concept of drill as a valuable tool. If it provided any value at all, it was that of opportunity for stimulation and performance, both of which factors depend upon many other influences for their efficacy. Motivation, maturation, discrimination, and application to life situations are indispensable adjuncts of any therapy, and the old-fashioned drill lesson tended to kill their usefulness. In speech correction, very little of such dull routine is necessary. The teacher should constantly assume the role of a helper or an assistant, placing the entire responsibility upon the student. Even for little children it is wise to outline the major steps of treatment as soon as possible. The student must know what he is trying to do throughout the whole therapy. He should be cautioned against mechanical, unpointed repetition of sounds. He should always be dynamically learning or unlearning. Speech correction is an active, not a passive, process.

Nevertheless, since the errors occur in words, they must be eradicated in words, and for this purpose the word lists are very valuable. The speech-correction teacher should be familiar with the lists of Horn, and the words most commonly used should be practiced first and most frequently. The text by Schoolfield listed in the references at the end of this chapter is a most welcome addition to modern speech correction because the words most commonly used by children are classified according to sounds. These words should always be incorporated into games, errands, stories, or conversations. Practice of words in word lists will produce little transfer to real speech situations unless those words are taken out of their series and made part of the actual communicative function. Speech assignments such as those described in the preceding section need such word lists, and the good speech teacher can find many other uses for them; but they should never be used for meaningless, dull, repetitive drill. The meaningless sentences and tongue twisters can occasionally serve as challenges or speech games, but they should never take the place of intelligent speech correction.

ANECDOTAL ACCOUNT OF SPEECH THERAPY WITH LISPER

First Day

Today I had my first session with Sally. I told her how glad I was to be the one chosen to help her. We had an old magazine with us, and I asked her to find in it, and cut out with the scissors, pictures of (1) a can of *soup*, and (2) a bowl of *cereal*. Then I cut out pictures of (3) some *icicles*, (4) a *house*, and (5) a pretty little girl whom I told her we would call *Sally*. I told her these five words were the first ones we would learn to say in the right way, because she didn't say them like other children did. First, I pronounced each one of the five words and asked her to repeat it after me. She substituted the *th* for all the *s* sounds of these words. Then the second time I asked her to repeat the words after me. I repeated the word as *she* said it, prolonging the incorrect sound so she could hear which one it was. I explained to her that it was those sounds which made her speech sound a little different from the other children's (they had imitated her some at school). I asked her if she would help me so we could get the right sound into those words. She seemed eager to work so she wouldn't (as she said) always "talk like a baby." She asked if she could come again tomorrow.

Second Day

Sally was anxious to come in today. She told me she cut out 5 pictures at home just like the ones we found yesterday. I had a list of the 5 words we worked on yesterday printed in big colored letters. I said them slowly, asking her to repeat slowly, and then had her show me on the list which sound she made that was different from mine. We encircled those with a red crayon. Then I asked her to tell me what their house looked like. During her conversation I wrote down three more words she ended with the error sound, and I added those to her list. They were *fireplace, mess* (referring to her daddy's bookshelf), and *fence*. She repeated them slowly, and we encircled the incorrect sounds with the crayon. Then I told her I would hide the list, and she could try to find it. If she got close to it I would make the correct sound, and if she went away from it I would make the sound the way she makes it. She enjoyed the game immensely, and we hid the list three times. She showed no confusion when I said the correct and incorrect sounds to designate where the list was hidden. She suggested that she was good at that game because the "close" sound was a "Sally sound" because it always started her name. I praised her for the suggestion, and told her we would call it the *New Sally* sound, and would learn it in her name, as well as in lots of other words. I suggested she pin the pictures which she had cut out at home in her own room.

Third Day

I took the list of 8 words which we had collected the first two days, and asked Sally to shut her eyes. I told her I would say each word in both the right and wrong ways, and she was to shake her head (as for "no") when I used the incorrect sound in the word. She identified these very easily. Then I took a schoolbook, and read a page backward. I asked her to hold up both hands every time she heard a word with the sound we were working on. She missed only one of them. Then I had her make two columns on a paper—the right-hand one for the correct sound, and the left column for the incorrect. She was to make an X in the appropriate column as I read the words. I read the same page backward again, purposely using the error sound in 4 words. She checked all of those, but missed 2 words in which the sound was used correctly. These were in final positions. I made the "New Sally sound" 5 times before reading her a sentence from the story book, and asked her to hold up her hand whenever she heard the sound in a word. I read 4 sentences in this manner, and she designated all the "New Sally sounds" correctly. Next, I had her draw lines on the board as I produced a prolonged s sound. The longer I held the sound, the longer she was to draw the lines. Then I gave her a paragraph from a story in a child's magazine. I told her to take it home and ask her parents to read it to her slowly. She is to hold up her hand when she hears a word with the "New Sally sound," and they will encircle each word in which she makes an error. She will bring this clipping back tomorrow.

Fourth Day

I took the list of 8 error words, pronouncing them correctly and incorrectly at random, and asked Sally to pull her ear each time I said it in the wrong way. She did this easily. She brought back the clipping which her mother had read to her—there was only one error, on a medial s word. So I gave her a magazine and told her to cut out pictures in which our sound came in the middle of the word. She found pictures of *ice cream*, *candlestick*, and *bicycle*. Then I gave her a paper with the numbers 1–15 on it, and a red pencil. I combined the sound with different vowels (such as *sa*, *see*, etc.) and asked her to follow the numbers and put a red circle around the number of the syllable I said incorrectly. I purposely made errors on numbers 5, 10, and 15, and she checked them correctly. We decided that from now on we would use an "¿" (upside-down question mark) to show the "New Sally sound" when it was made in the wrong way. I showed her that if I said *song* incorrectly, she would write it *¿ong*. She was a little confused at first, but was enthusiastic over it when she understood, as she said "The wrong sound is no good, anyway." Then I read her a list of 15 simple words, and she printed them after I said them, using the ¿ symbol instead of the letter s when I said it incorrectly. She got the entire list correct, and asked hopefully if we could play that again tomorrow. Her discrimination is good, and she can judge between correct and incorrect sounds much more rapidly now.

Fifth Day

Using the first list of 5 error words, I read them several times, sometimes correctly, sometimes incorrectly. Sally printed the words as I read them, using the symbol when I used the sound incorrectly. She got these all right. Then I asked her to watch my lips and mouth as I made the "New Sally sound" in isolation. I did it slowly, prolonging the sound as I made it. Then I gave her a mirror and asked her to watch herself while she made the sound. She noticed that her mouth didn't look like mine and commented "I don't sound like you, either." I showed her that we could see her tongue when she made the sound, but when I made the Sally sound, you could only see my teeth. She began to imitate me so I hurried on to our next activity. I told her a short story and asked her to make an *X* whenever I used the *sssss* sound in a word where it didn't belong. She detected all 8 errors in the story. Then I told her I was going to say the sound by itself several times, and she was to write *¿* when it was right, and *s* when it was wrong. I used the sound between 40 and 50 times, and introduced the error sound only 5 times. I felt that in this way the error sound would be more distinct, and she would get maximum stimulation with the correct sound. Her co-operation was excellent, and she asked "When can I learn to make the New Sally sound right?" She wanted to hug me when she said good-bye.

Sixth Day

Today I used the first 5 error words and added 5 other *s* words, including *ice cream*, *candlestick*, *bicycle*, *mister*, and *saucer*. I used each word several times, in different order, asking Sally to clap her hands together whenever I made the *sss* sound in the wrong way. She designated those without an error. Then I told her that today she would have her first chance to make the Sally sound. I took the picture of the soup and said "Now you call this a can of *th*oup (sound it out slowly). Say it your old way. Now listen to the way I say it—soup—*ssss-ssss-ssss-* soup. That's the New Sally sound. You cannot see my tongue when I say it. Now look in the mirror and see if you can say it that way, without showing your tongue. *Ssss-ssss-ssss-* say it with me. Now you try it." Her first attempt was a good *s*, so I asked her to try it again. The third time she made the *th* again, so I repeated the above, showing her the difference between *th*oup and soup. Then I asked her to try it again. It was not clear, but resembled an *s* more than a *th*. We finished by repeating the syllable *suh* together 20 times. She tried to say her name as she was leaving, but I asked her not to try to make the sound alone yet, as we didn't want to put it in her name until it was a strong New Sally sound. She seemed very happy.

Seventh Day

We tried the exercise we did yesterday with *soup* and then I experimented with a few other ways of making an *s*, so there will be another alternative if the auditory-stimulation method fails. I asked her to say *soup* in the old way (*thoup*) and then told her to say it again, holding on to the first sound—*th-th-th*. As she did this I took a tongue depressor and pushed the tonguetip behind her teeth. I cautioned her to keep on making the *th*, and we repeated this several times. After I pushed the tonguetip back, I said the *s-s-s* sound with her. She got quite a clear *s* in this procedure. Then I showed her how to groove her tongue and blow the air through it. She did this easily, though sometimes it is necessary to use a long match or a small instrument to help her get the feeling of the groove. We practiced drawing the tongue back while it was grooved, blowing air through the groove all the time. After that I asked her to put her upper and lower teeth together and press her lips tightly together. Then she continued to hold her teeth together but parted her lips to let a small hiss escape. Finally, we slowly said the syllable *suh* together again about 20 times. Each time Sally approximated a good *s* sound she was very pleased. I told her to practice grooving her tongue and blowing air through the groove in front of a mirror at home. She enjoys having a home assignment to demonstrate to her mother.

Eighth Day

I read Sally the original list of 5 error words, using the correct *s* and prolonging it noticeably in each one. Then I asked her to groove her tongue and blow air through it as she drew it back behind her teeth. This seemed to be the most successful way to produce a good *s*. We did this several times. Then I told her I was going to count to 5, and after each number she was to make the Sally sound that many times. (After *one* she was to make it once, after *two*, twice, etc.) In this exercise, there were two *s* sounds made in the old *th* way. She had hurried too fast. I read a short story to her, and asked her to hold up her hand whenever she heard the *s* sound in a word and then to say the sound aloud for me. She missed only one of these words. She is so enthusiastic about her success at making some of these isolated sounds that I warned her again not to try to use the Sally sound in words yet, as it was not strong yet, and might get all mixed up with the wrong sound.

Ninth Day

I showed Sally again some of the ways we used to make the good Sally sound (grooved tongue, hiss, tongue depressor, etc.), and then asked her to make several after I made them. I did this because we must somehow get her out of her old tongue-thrusting habits. That tongue sometimes protrudes even when she hears me make an *s*. I told her I would count to 13, and after each number she was to make a good *ssss* sound. These came slowly but were very clear. I asked her several questions, such as "What are you going to do after school?" and she had to make three long *ssss* sounds before she gave me the answer to each question. I gave her a pencil and paper and asked her to make an *s* symbol each time she said a New Sally sound. If she said it incorrectly, she was to put down the (¿) symbol instead. I showed her how to do it, and she did half a page with only one error before our lesson was completed.

Tenth Day

After some tongue-grooving exercises I told Sally we were going to make the New Sally sound together, strongly. As we repeated the *s*, I gradually lowered my volume to hear how she was making the sound. Then I told her we would start together again. but I would quit in the middle of the exercise, and she was to keep on making *s* sounds until I clapped my hands. We did this 5 or 6 times, and her *s* was very clear. After that I told her to repeat the sound alone until I clapped my hands once, and then to start making it again when I clapped my hands twice. I varied the intervals, and she made only two poor sounds. She did several lines of talking and writing, then we tried the new sound with vowels. First I had her prolong an *ssss* until I added an *ah* or *uh*. Then I asked her to prolong the *ssss* until I tapped on the table with the pencil and then add an *uh* sound to it. We did this with *uh*, *ah*, and *oh*, and I shortened the time of the *s* prolongations. The exercise was quite effective and Sally said, "I'll bet I can make real words pretty soon." Her enthusiasm is a great help.

Eleventh Day

We practiced the Sally sound together about 10 times, then I let her continue saying it about 10 more times, as I gave her a signal to start by tapping my pencil on the table. After that we reviewed yesterday's exercises in which we added vowels to the *s* sound. She did this easily and accurately. Then I told her I would read a short story to her very slowly, and whenever I made the Sally sound incorrectly, she was to stop me by holding up her hand and saying the syllable *sah*. I read a three-page story and purposely made about 15 errors, all of which she detected and responded to with a good *sah*. I told her I wanted to ask her several questions, but before she could answer each one she was to first say *sah-say-soo*. I asked questions about her doll collection, which always brings enthusiastic responses, so there was some pressure on her, as she was so anxious to talk. In spite of that, only one *say* syllable had a bad *s* sound. Just before she left we tried her name—first separating the *s* from the *ally* with quite a long pause, then holding the *s* until I tapped for her to add *ally*. I gradually shortened the length of her *s*, until she finally said *Sally* twice with no noticeable break. She was a mighty happy child when she left, and I feel that giving her a successful experience with her name will add a lot of motivation for the next step.

Twelfth Day

Today I wrote Sally's original 5 error words in large letters on a piece of cardboard. We practiced sounding them out, sound by sound, and she imitated me after each one. Then we practiced the following sequence on each one. For example, on her name, we first said the sound alone three times—*s-s-s*. Then we added the *a* (æ) to it and said *sa-sa-sa* three times. Finally we said that whole word 3 times. First she did it with me, then alone. We used this on *Sally, soup, cereal, icicle,* and *house.* She had a failure when she first used the whole word *icicle,* but she insisted on retrial until it was correct. After this we tried some signal practice. I pointed to the word on the card which I wanted her to say, and she held the *s* sound until I tapped with a pencil and then finished the word. On *house* she prolonged the final sound until my signal. Then we used each word in several short phrases, which she repeated slowly after me, such as—"hot soup," "bowl of cereal," "big cold icicle," "new white house," "pretty girl Sally." She experienced no failures with these, and was almost jubilant because they sounded so well. She went out the door saying "pretty girl Sally," and I remarked how much prettier her name sounded now.

Thirteenth Day

We went through the same type of exercises that we used yesterday, first reviewing the original 5 words, and then adding 10 more common *s* words to the list. She had no failures with the sound or the words. Then I said a word at random from the list, and told her she was to repeat it after me and use another word with it. For example, when I said *bicycle,* she responded with "Johnny's red *bicycle,*" and when I said *house,* she said "pretty *house.*" Then we reversed the order, Sally saying the original word and I using it in a combination. This was so successful that she begged to try it again. We concluded this period by using short sentences containing one or two *s* words. I read them first, and asked her to repeat after me. Typical sentences were— "I want a nice white house" and "Let me ride your bicycle." Her parting comment was "Now I'm talking the New Sally sound!"

Subsequent Therapy

In each of the days that followed we did some of the following exercises:

1. Signal practice—(where Sally held the *s* sound till I signaled her to release it and finish the word).

2. Negative practice—(in which Sally purposely used her old error *th* sound in some of the common *s* words which I listed).

3. Ear training—(some of the old exercises to continue her discrimination between the old incorrect sound and the "New Sally sound").

4. New words containing the *s* sound—(we usually used this about five times daily, although the new sound carried over into many of these without actual drill).

5. Telling or reading a short story—(I clapped my hands if she used an *s* sound incorrectly, and then we repeated the word, first by sounding it out, then as a whole).

6. Use of nucleus situations in which she paid close attention to the "New Sally sound." (It is too much to ask a child that he watch every *s* sound. So we used telephone situations, experiences in which she took messages to other teachers, short recitations in certain classes, one meal at home each day, and conversations with one certain playmate. In these situations, when possible, another person also checked for any possible errors in *s* words. The schoolteacher often listed any words that were incorrect. Sally also brought reports from her mother noting any incorrect *s* sounds she used during conversation at lunch time.)

Finally she got to the point where she would voluntarily correct herself on any words which she had missed. After that she made all *s* sounds without conscious effort, and we discontinued the daily lessons, substituting a monthly conference which was devoted to spontaneous conversation.

References

1. Anderson, V. A., *Improving the Child's Speech*, New York, Oxford University Press, 1953, Chapter 6, "Articulatory Disorders."

T-F: Organic defects of the speech organs are the exception rather than the rule so far as causing articulatory speech defects is concerned.

T-F: Dental irregularities do not indicate a poor prognosis.

Essay: What is the relationship between personality factors and articulation errors according to the author?

2. Backus, O. L., "Speech Rehabilitation Following Excision of the Tip of the Tongue," *American Journal of Diseases of Children*, 1940, Volume 60, pages 368–370.

Not only the sounds made with the tonguetip were defective but other sounds as well, and remedial speech work was successful despite the injury.

3. Bangs, J. L., "A Clinical Analysis of the Articulatory Defects of the Feebleminded," *Journal of Speech Disorders*, 1942, Volume 7, pages 343–356.

T-F: Dental irregularities have little effect upon speech.

T-F: Chronological rather than mental age is a better determinant of articulation adequacy.

Essay: In what ways are the normal and feeble-minded children different so far as articulation errors are concerned?

4. Beckey, R. E., "A Study of Certain Factors Related to Retardation of Speech," *Journal of Speech Disorders*, 1942, Volume 7, pages 223–249.

This reference is important in stressing the relation between articulatory defects and the conditions surrounding the learning of speech. Illnesses, economic status, birth injury, parental coddling, and parental anxiety are listed as among the causes.

5. Berry, M. and Eisenson, J., *The Defective in Speech*, Crofts, New York, 1942, pages 74–75.

A discussion of the causes of articulatory defects with frequent citations from the literature.

6. Blomquist, B. L., "Diadochokinetic Movement of Nine-, Ten- and Eleven-year-old Children, *Journal of Speech and Hearing Disorders*, 1950. Volume 15, pages 159–164.

The speed of repeating single and joined consonants increases with age. Norms are given for *p, t, k* and *ptk* combined with schwa vowels.

7. Bryngelson, B., and Glaspey, E., *Speech Improvement Cards*, Chicago, Scott Foresman, 1941.

A set of cards with pictures used for testing and remedial work, together with a manual describing procedures.

8. Chess, S., "Developmental Language Disability as a Factor in Personality Distortion in Childhood," *American Journal of Orthopsychiatry*, 1944, Volume 14, pages 483–490.

The effect of defective speech on personality development is sketched. Behavior problems must be solved before therapy will be successful.

9. Curry, R., Kennedy, L., Wagner, L., and Wilke, W., "A Phonographic Scale for the Measurement of Defective Articulation," *Journal of Speech Disorders*, 1940, Volume 8, pages 123–126.

A series of phonographically recorded samples of defective articulation.

10. Everhardt, R., "The Growth and Development of Negro and White Elementary Children with Articulatory Defects," University of Michigan Ph.D. Thesis, 1953.

Investigates onset of speech, developmental factors and reading problems.

11. Fairbanks, G., *Voice and Articulation Drill Book*, New York, Harper, 1940.

The common errors for each of the consonant sounds are given, and a general discussion of the nature of articulatory defects is provided.

12. Fairbanks, G., and Bebout, B., "A Study of Minor Organic Deviations in 'Functional' Disorders of Articulation," *Journal of Speech and Hearing Disorders*, 1950, Volume 15, pages 348–352.

Very little differences between articulatory and normal speaking *adult* subjects in length of tongue or tonguetip, maximum tongue force, and ability to duplicate a given tongue position. One of a series of studies of organic differences.

13. Fletcher, H., *Speech and Hearing*, New York, D. Van Nostrand, 1929.

Frequency characteristics of the different speech sounds are given.

14. Hansen, F. M., "Application of Sound Discrimination Tests to Functional Articulatory Speech Defects," *Journal of Speech Disorders*, 1944, Volume 9, pages 347–355.

Three tests of sound discrimination were given to adult articulatory and normal speaking subjects. A vowel discrimination test is described.

15. Henry, J. and Henry, Z., "Speech Disturbances among Pilagra Indian Children," *American Journal of Orthopsychiatry*, 1940, Volume 4, pages 99–102.

They talk baby talk until they are seven years old, and substitute easier sounds for the more difficult ones in terms of co-ordination.

16. Jenkins, R. L., "The Rate of Diadochokinetic Movement of the Jaw at the Ages of Seven to Maturity," *Journal of Speech Disorders*, 1940, Volume 6, pages 13–22.

Summarizes other studies of the speed of jaw activity and presents original data to show that it increases with age up to 17 years. Females can move their jaws faster than males, a not surprising conclusion, if we may say so.

17. Keaster, J., "Studies in the Anatomy and Physiology of the Tongue," *Laryngoscope*, 1940, Volume 50, pages 222–257.

Cites cases to show that speech in tongueless patients is much less interfered with than chewing and swallowing.

18. Lundeen, D. J., "The Relationship of Diadochokinesis to Various Speech Sounds," *Journal of Speech and Hearing Disorders*, 1950, Volume 15, pages 54–59.

The consonants *t*, *d*, *p* and *b* can be repeated at significantly faster rates than can *s*, *z*, *k* and *g*. No differences between voiced and unvoiced sounds.

19. Palmer, M. F. and Osborn, C., "A Study of the Tongue Pressures of Speech Defective and Normal Speaking Individuals," *Journal of Speech Disorders*, 1940, Volume 5, pages 133–141.

Articulatory speech defectives are especially poor in tongue strength.

20. Patton, F. M., "A Comparison of the Kinesthetic Sensibility of Speech Defective and Normal Speaking Children," *Journal of Speech Disorders*, 1942, Volume 7, pages 305–310.

Articulatory cases are inferior to normal speakers in the kinesthetic perception ability as measured by Starling's tests.

21. Mase, D. J., *Etiology of Articulatory Speech Defects*, New York, Columbia University Teachers College Contributions to Education, Number 921, 1946.

Compared 53 pairs of boys with and without articulatory defects. Found no significant differences in phonetic discrimination, auditory memory span, coordination of large muscles and sense of rhythm. Tests are described.

22. McEnerny, E. T., and Gaines, F. P., "Tongue Tie in Infants and Children," *Journal of Pediatrics*, 1941, Volume 18, pages 252–255.

True tongue tie very rare. Only four per thousand speech defectives.

23. Metraux, R., "Auditory Memory Span for Speech Sounds of Speech Defective Children Compared with Normal Children," *Journal of Speech Disorders*, 1942, Volume 7, pages 33–36.

No important differences were found. Auditory acuity and auditory memory span are different functions.

24. Milisen, R., "Principles and Methods of Articulation Testing," *Speech and Hearing Therapist*, 1945, Indiana University Speech and Hearing Clinic, Bloomington, Indiana, February, pages 6–10.

One of the best articles on articulation testing ever written.

25. Ogilvie, M., *Terminology and Definitions of Speech Defects*. New York, Teachers College, *Columbia University Contributions to Education*, Number 859, 1942.

This monograph helps to clear up some of the confusion between the various terms used to designate the same articulatory disorder. It also provides a valuable bibliography for articles written prior to 1938.

26. Reid, G., "The Efficacy of Speech Reeducation of Functional

Articulatory Defectives in the Elementary School," *Journal of Speech Disorders*, 1947, Volume 12, pages 301–313.

T-F: The untreated group showed considerable improvement.

T-F: The trouble with speech correction is that it doesn't correct.

27. Sayler, H. K., "The Effect of Maturation Upon Defective Articulation in Grades Seven Through Twelve," *Journal of Speech and Hearing Disorders*, 1949, Volume 14, pages 202–207.

There is very little maturation to be counted upon to clear up articulation defects after the primary grades have been passed.

28. Spriestersbach, D. C., and Curtis, J. F., "Misarticulation and Discrimination of Speech Sounds," *Quarterly Journal of Speech*, 1951, Volume 37, pages 483–491.

T-F: Most articulation cases are consistent in their errors.

T-F: The blends are often easier than the single sounds.

Essay: What applications do the authors make to therapy?

29. Sullivan, E. M., "Auditory Acuity and Its Relation to Defective Speech," *Journal of Speech Disorders*, 1944, Volume 9, pages 127–130.

Articulation cases had more hearing loss than did the normal population.

30. Templin, M. C., "A Non-diagnostic Articulation Test," *Journal of Speech Disorders*, 1947, Volume 12, pages 392–396.

When repeating after an examiner, single words are just as good for testing articulation as are sentences.

31. Templin, M. C., "A Study of the Sound Discrimination Ability of Elementary School Pupils," *Journal of Speech Disorders*, 1943, Volume 8, pages 127–132.

A short test of speech-sound discrimination is described and compared with the Travis-Rasmus Test.

32. Templin, M. C., "Spontaneous Versus Imitated Verbalizations in Testing Articulation in Pre-school Children," *Journal of Speech Disorders*, 1947, Volume 12, pages 293–300.

T-F: The specific word used in articulation testing is unimportant so long as it contains the sound being tested.

T-F: Repetition is just as adequate as evoking spontaneous speech.

Essay: Why are the author's findings important?

33. Van Riper, C., *A Case Book in Speech Therapy*, New York, Prentice-Hall, Inc., 1953.

A paper and pencil case work book designed to give the student vicarious experience in diagnosis and therapy planning.

34. Wolf, I. J., "The Relation of Mal-occlusion to Sigmatism," *American Journal of Diseases of Children*, 1944, Volume 68, pages 250–252.

Types of mal-occlusion and their effect on speech are presented.

35. Wood, K. S., "Measurement of Progress in the Correction of Articulatory Defects," *Journal of Speech and Hearing Disorders*, 1949, Volume 14, pages 171–174.

A person with a defective sound used frequently in English has a more severe problem than one used infrequently. Suggests the use of a numerical index to indicate severity.

36. Wood, K. S., "Parental Maladjustment and Functional Articulatory Defects in Children," *Journal of Speech Disorders*, 1946, Volume 11, pages 255–275.

Parents of these children seemed to be less well adjusted. Counseling the parents may have assisted the child's acquisition of better speech.

37. Anderson, V. A., *Improving the Child's Speech*, New York. Oxford University Press, 1953.

T-F: Defective *sh* sounds require rounding of the lips.

T-F: Final consonants are usually weaker than initial ones.

Essay: How does Anderson use word and syllable pairs?

38. Ainsworth, S., *Speech Correction Methods*, New York, Prentice-Hall, Inc., 1948, Chapter 5.

T-F: A child with many errors need not work with only one sound at a time.

T-F: The characteristics of the error must be studied by the case.

Essay: Draw up a therapy plan for a child with a frontal lisp.

39. Backus, O., and Beasley, J., *Speech Therapy with Children*, Boston, Houghton Mifflin, 1951.

T-F: Group speech therapy can include all varieties of speech defects.

T-F: Conversational speech is the basic method.

Essay: Contrast the treatment expressed in this reference with that described in this text.

40. Baker, P., *Primer of Sounds*, Boston, Expression Co., 1943.

Contains a short discussion of baby talk and lisping. The material for teaching the blends, and some of the games, will be of value to public-school speech correctionists.

41. Berry, M., and Eisenson, J., *The Defective in Speech*, New York, F. S. Crofts, 1942.

Essay: What are the ten commandments for articulation therapy?

42. Cable, W. A., "Dynamic Factors in the Moto-Kinesthetic Method of Speech Correction," *Quarterly Journal of Speech*, 1945, Volume 31, pages 350–357.

T-F: The case is always treated while reclining.

T-F: Crying can be changed into speech by this method.

Essay: Describe this method.

43. Enquist, L. E., and Wagner, C. F., "Flannel Chart Technique for the Rehabilitation of Speech and Hearing Disorders," *Journal of Speech and Hearing Disorders*, 1950, Volume 15, pages 338–340.

Some devices for motivating groups of articulation cases in the public schools are presented.

44. Fairbanks, G., *Voice and Articulation Drill Book*, New York, Harper, 1940.

Especially useful for its lists of paired words for each sound, the one containing the correct sound and the other its most frequent substitution.

45. Heltman, H., *Handbook for Remedial Speech*, Magnolia, Mass., Expression Co., 1948.

Some excellent suggestions for teaching the individual sounds.

46. Hull, M. E., "Anticipatory Speech Response in Children with Articulatory Defects," *Journal of Speech and Hearing Disorders*, 1948, Volume 13, pages 268–272.

Be sure to prevent the child from making immediate erroneous subvocal articulations during stimulation.

47. Manser, R., *Speech Correction on the Contract Plan* (revised edition), New York, Prentice-Hall, 1942.

Progressive assignments in the form of contracts enable the student to work in the direction of complete mastery of his defective sounds.

48. McCullough, G. A., *Work and Practice Book for Speech Improvement*, Boston, Expression Co., 1940.

Sentences and other material arranged according to phonetic units.

49. Nemoy, E., and Davis, S., *The Correction of Defective Consonant Sounds*, Boston, Expression Co., 1937, pages 26–27.

Exercises are given for enabling the student to hear good tone production and normal sounds.

50. Obermann, C. E., "Improving Pupil's Speech; A Practical Program of Correction," *Nation's Schools*, 1941, Volume 28, pages 51–53.

Recommends the auditory-stimulation method as the best procedure. Criticizes phonetic placement methods.

51. Partridge, L. M., "Dyslalias of Southern Ohio," *Journal of Speech Disorders*, 1945, Volume 10, pages 249–254.

Dialectal variations and mild sound substitutions in Ohio college students are classified as dyslalias.

52. Porter, F., "Speech Correction in an Orphanage," *Journal of Speech Disorders*, 1945, Volume 10, pages 241–249.

A series of brief case reports of articulatory treatment is presented.

53. Roe, V., "Follow-Up in the Correction of Functional Articula-

tion Disorders," *Journal of Speech and Hearing Disorders*, 1948, Volume 13, pages 332–336.

Suggests ways of getting parents and teachers to carry-over a child's newly acquired correct speech sounds into daily life.

54. Scott, L. B., and Thompson, J. J., *Talking Time: For Speech Correction and Improvement*, St. Louis, Webster Publishing Co., 1951.

Provides interesting materials for articulation cases in early grades.

55. Smith, M. E., "A Clinician's Story," *Quarterly Journal of Speech*, 1948, Volume 13, pages 268–272.

A play by play account of a speech therapist's day, including a report of methods used in a five week program with a six-year-old boy with an articulation problem.

56. Stinchfield, S. M., and Young, E. H., *Children with Delayed or Defective Speech*, Stanford University Press, 1938.

The moto-kinesthetic methods are described in detail and there are many case reports which will be of interest to students in giving them concrete examples of the types of articulatory problems met in speech correction and the methods used by the authors.

57. Walsh, G., *Sing Your Way to Better Speech*, New York, E. P. Dutton, 1940.

The author advocates teaching sounds through singing and provides tunes and words arranged phonetically for articulation cases.

58. Welsch, J. D., and Nixon, G., *My Own Speech Reader*, Champaign, Ill., Johnson-Randolph Co., 1942.

Speech drills for articulation cases; designed to be read aloud.

59. West, R., Kennedy, L., and Carr, A., *The Rehabilitation of Speech*, New York, Harper, 1947 (revised edition).

Essay: What is meant by residual diathesis?

60. Wood, K. S., "Sound Substitutions and Omissions," *Bulletin of the Secondary School Principals*, 1950, Volume 34, pages 36–41.

A comprehensive therapy including speech hygiene is described.

61. Yoakam, D. G., "Speech Games for Children," *Quarterly Journal of Speech*, 1944, Volume 30, pages 85–87.

A very valuable group of suggestions about using games in speech correction. Cautions are given to subordinate the game to the acquisition of speech skill. Some modifications of well-known parlor games are described.

8.   Voice Disorders

⎍⎍⎍⎍⎍⎍⎍⎍⎍⎍⎍⎍⎍⎍⎍⎍⎍⎍⎍⎍⎍⎍⎍⎍

Chaliapin, the famous basso, once said that going to a party was like going to a symphony played by instruments all of which were out of tune. "All around me are voices blowing discords, squeaks, rasps, whines, grunts and growls. I can hardly bear it." Fortunately for most of us, our ears are not so sensitive. His observation, however, is more accurate than our calloused ears would be likely to admit. All about us are voices which could be improved, made more pleasant and efficient. And there are some so markedly unpleasant or peculiar that they are referred to the speech therapist. The singing teacher gets some of these, the speech teacher gets another group, the physician sees the pathological ones, and the speech therapist is usually called upon last.

Since the development of public school speech correction, some of these cases are caught early and helped before the bad voice becomes an integral part of the individual's personality. We asked some of our friends who do public school speech correction to describe some of their voice cases. Here are a few:

I have an eight-year-old boy with a very deep, low-pitched voice which is also harsh. The voice quality has a buzz in it and this, I think, accounts for the impression of harshness. The boy is not at all tense, either generally or in the laryngeal area. He has quite a range, going way up into the treble, and his singing voice is quite normal

277

for his age so far as pitch is concerned. The singing voice is, however, somewhat breathy. The speaking voice is pitched almost at the very bottom of his range. When he is heard for the first time, the effect is quite startling, and he has received a lot of teasing about it, to which he reacts good naturedly. The other children have nicknamed him "Bullfrog."

.   .   .

My most frequent voice cases are those of excessive nasality. Phoebe is typical. She whines when she talks, although she is not at all a chronic complainer. Instead she is rather shy and noncommunicative. Most of the nasality is of the assimilation type. Every word containing an *m* or *n* sound is completely nasalized and so also is the vowel *ae* and *ai*. For example, she can say the sentence, "If we are to go we'd better hurry," without a trace of this excessive nasality. But if she says, "Many men make money," it's one long whine. The effect on the listener is odd. Even I find myself wondering why all of a sudden she seems to be complaining, wondering what's wrong with her now. The palate seems to be entirely functional and there's no emission of air from the nose on the isolated vowels mentioned above. Maybe the velum is too short or sluggish. It's hard to tell. I have had a hard time with these cases and they haven't shown much progress. Would appreciate a few suggestions.

.   .   .

My worst voice case is a senior in High School this year and he's the son of the Superintendent of Schools. He's big for his age. A good athlete. No ear for music nor interest in voice improvement. What's wrong is that his voice keeps breaking, just like a boy's voice sometimes does when he reaches puberty. It will shoot up an octave from his usual baritone. It (the break) occurs most often when he gets excited or emotional. Very noticeable to others but boy comes to speech class under protest. His father insists or I'd get rid of him. He's been shaving since he was 14. He's eighteen now. Help, help.

.   .   .

The ones that trouble me the most are the children with soft voices, who just can't talk loudly enough to recite in class without having the teacher demand over and over again that they make themselves heard. Most of them are terribly shy, afraid of their classmates and, I think, of themselves. They just can't let go in anything. I've had my only success with these, and not too much at that if I'm to be honest about it, by working with them individually, building up their faith in me, giving them a chance to talk about their troubles and having them help me. One little girl though, Alice, isn't a bit shy; actually, she's quite aggressive but her voice is as soft as a baby chick's peeping, even when she tries to yell on the playground. She just doesn't seem to have any breath support for her tone, though she's full of energy.

. . .

I have trouble with the foreign kids, especially those who come to this country when adolescent. Their articulation clears up pretty good, but the foreign melody pattern of inflections stays with them, and they sound just as foreign as ever. The Latvians seem to be the hardest of them all. I can't seem to get them to stop going up in pitch before every pause. They're worse than the Swedes.

These are but a few of the voice disorders who come to the speech therapist for help. We also have the aphonics who cannot speak aloud, the husky, breathy voices, the falsettos, the denasal individuals who talk as though they had a permanent post-nasal drip, the monotones, the hoarse voices, the laryngectomized and many others.

Voice disorders account for only approximately ten or fifteen per cent of the speech correctionist's cases, but they are frequently the most difficult of all problems. The reasons for this difficulty are, no doubt, the lack of research, the complexity of the problem, and the fact that such cases have usually been treated by elocution and singing teachers rather than by members of the medical or speech-correction professions. The literature is scanty and scattered. Except for certain occupations such as the ministry, teaching, and entertaining, the average voice defect is not a handicap, since communication is still possible, a factor which does not hold true in stuttering or articulatory difficulties.

As we have said, there are almost as many names for voice disorders as there are adjectives to describe the voice; but in general they may be classified as disorders of *pitch, intensity*, and *voice quality*. Frequently any one case will be defective in more than one of these aspects, but for clearness of presentation we shall consider them according to the above classification.

Pitch Disorders

There are four major types of pitch disorders: too high an habitual pitch, too low a pitch, the monotone, and stereotyped inflection. Again we are faced with the necessity for defining a speech defect in terms of variation from the norm. When is a given voice too high? Some case presentations may help us understand the problem.

Joan P., a high school senior, referred herself to the speech clinic after hearing a recording of her voice. "Why, I sound like a little first grader," she complained. "After hearing that voice I'll never dare talk to a boy again over the telephone. Please do something!" Analysis of the average pitch levels used by the girl showed that she phonated about the pitch of middle C, a level which is well within the normal range for females of that age. When the test recording was played back, she said, "That's funny. That's a little bit higher than I thought I talked but not so high as the other recording. We then made another recording in front of a class and this time, the average pitch level did reach F above middle C. We explained to Joan that most females hear their recorded voices as seemingly higher in pitch just as most males hear themselves as possessing a deeper voice than they expect. We also explained the effect of tension and fear on the pitch level and the need for learning to adapt to the pressures of confronting a group. A series of experiences in making recorded talks to a group while trying to use the middle C habitual pitch of her conversational voice proved successful and no further difficulty was experienced.

Most of us tend to raise the pitch of our voices when communicating under fear or stress, or when trying to speak loudly. In examining a voice case, we must always be alert lest the case's uneasiness give us a false picture.

A boy of 17 was referred to us as a monotone, and most of his speech was pitched at D above middle C. He tended to use loudness instead of pitch variations to give the meaningful inflections necessary in asking questions, making demands and so on. For example, he would say this sentence with each syllable pitched at the one note, but saying the last word quite loudly. "Are you planning to GO?" The effect was often one of hostility which he did not mean to convey at all. The voice quality was rather harsh. Most strangely, he was able to sing in a very high tenor voice and sing very well. A series of counseling interviews and examinations resulted in our refusal to accept him as a case for therapy at that time. A year later, he was reexamined and his voice was entirely normal, being pitched at B below middle C, with a range of an octave and a half, and normal inflections and quality. He had meanwhile started to shave.

As the foregoing case implies, pitch levels are dependent upon many factors. The case mentioned was slow in acquiring the secondary sex characteristics. His larynx, at the time of our first examination, was child-like and under-developed. Highly conscious of this, he had endeavored to compensate for the natural high pitch by speaking at the very bottom of his range. This practice often interferes with the easy use of inflections, since if you cannot go below your habitual pitch level, you also find it hard to go upward from it. Also, harshness as a voice quality is often caused by speaking with tension at the bottom of one's pitch range. It is always necessary in studying a pitch disorder to determine the location of the habitual pitch level in terms of the total range. If the habitual pitch is too near the top of the range or too near the bottom, we tend to have voice difficulties of loudness or quality, as well as pitch. Sometimes the speech therapist is faced with a voice problem which has no pleasant solution:

Vera P., a college senior, after preparing for a teaching career, was refused placement service because in her practice teaching, she was constantly penalized by her students who called her "Bo-Peep-Peep" and mocked her piping little high-pitched voice. At 22, her larynx was very small, the vocal cords were only about half the length of a normal mature woman's. She spoke at a level approximately four notes above the bottom of the pitch range, had good flexibility and inflection, but the average habitual pitch was A above middle C. We were able to lower the pitch to E without causing undue tension and strain, but this still was conspicuously high and also it reduced her loudness to a degree which made her handicap worse. Our failure was conspicuous, and she became a typist and filing clerk. We should not have accepted her as a case.

The concept of a habitual pitch level must be clearly understood. Except in the case of monotones, it does not refer to a
certain fixed pitch upon which all speech is phonated. It represents an average or median pitch about which the other pitches
used in speech tend to cluster. For example, in the utterance
of the sentence, "Alice was sitting on the back of the white
swan," the fundamental pitch of each vowel in any of the words
may differ somewhat from that of the others. Moreover, certain vowels are inflected—that is, they are phonated with a
continuous pitch change which may either rise, fall, or do both.
Of course, each inflection has an average pitch by which it may
be measured, if the extent of the variation is also considered.
If all the pitches and pitch variations are measured and their
durations are taken into account in the speaking of the preceding illustration, we shall find that they cluster about a certain
average pitch, which may be termed the "key" at which the
speaker phonated that sentence. This may be determined experimentally through the use of the trained ear, as indicated
in the chapter on speech tests and the reference by Gilkinson
listed at the end of this chapter. It should be understood, of
course, that different pitch levels will be used under different
communicative conditions. Nevertheless, each voice can be said
to have a habitual pitch and a habitual pitch range, in which
most of the communication is phonated.

The pitch of the normal human voice presents many mys-
teries and much research needs to be done before we can hope
to understand its abnormalities. We know that the voice of a
young child is high pitched when compared with that of the
adult, and that in old age it tends to creep back again to higher
levels. We know that the major pitch changes occur at puberty,
the bottom of the girl's pitch range descending from one to
three tones with an equivalent gain at the upper limit. Boys'
voices usually drop a full octave and there is a less marked but
noticeable loss at the upper end of the pitch range. Usually,
but depending upon the onset of sexual changes, the voice
changes occur in boys between the ages of 13–15 with the girls

showing the same basic changes a year earlier. Occasionally, the change of voice has been known to occur very suddenly (usually when puberty comes late) but most frequently it lasts from three to six months on the average.

Pitch breaks. Most of us tend to think of the change of voice as occurring abruptly when it does occur, and the "pitch breaks" have been the subject for a good deal of amusement in our culture. However, recent unpublished research has shown that most children, boys and girls alike, do have these sudden shifts of pitch as characteristic of the period of voice change, and also, some children as young as seven and eight can show similar sudden shifts of pitch. We also are prone to think of the pitch changes as always shifting toward the higher notes, but when this does occur consistently, it does so only toward the end of the pubertal period. Voice breaks can be downward as well as upward. Curry (10).

The majority of the pitch breaks that do occur are generally an octave in extent in most children. They occur involuntarily, very suddenly, and the child seems to have little control over them, reacting at first with great surprise. The upward pitch breaks of boys according to Curry (10) start when the word spoken is pitched below the habitual pitch of the moment. It often seems as though, in the attempt to return to the level they feel most natural, they overshoot their mark. In a few children the experience is so traumatic that they resort to a guarded monotone, and develop a very restricted range.

The cause of the pubertal pitch changes is not entirely understood though we do know that profound alterations in the organs of voice occur at this time. The male larynx grows much larger and the vocal cords longer and more suddenly; the female larynx increases more in height than in width, and the vocal cords seem to thicken. The male vocal cords lengthen about one centimeter, the females only a third as much. At the same time the child is growing swiftly in skeletal development. The neck becomes longer, and the larynx takes up a lower location relative to the opening into the mouth. The chest expands greatly, and perhaps some of the cause of voice-breaks is due to the greater air pressure which suddenly becomes available. The following case may be illustrative:

One of our cases was a boy who had been delayed markedly in physical growth until his sixteenth birthday at which time a great spurt of development occurred. He grew six inches in three months and his voice seemed uncontrollable so far as pitch was concerned, so much so that he developed a marked fear of speaking and a profound emotional disturbance. Speech therapy was ineffective until he was taught by the speech therapist to fixate the chest and to use abdominal breathing as exclusively as possible. Immediately the pitch breaks disappeared and the technique tided him over the next six months at which time he returned to his normal thoracic breathing pattern without difficulty.

The above case illustrated another of the characteristics of the truly abnormal voice. Not only did he have many more pitch breaks than does the average boy, but also he showed shifts of pitch which were not of the usual type. Sometimes the break in pitch was of fourteen semitones. The speech therapist can often distinguish a pathological case who will not "out-grow" his adolescent pitch breaks by listening to the type of pitch shift which occurs. Curry (10) cites the following similar case from the German literature:

Case four is that of a 23-year-old girl with a mutation disorder; since age eight her voice had been continuously hoarse and accompanied by many involuntary breaks. These breaks from a higher to a lower pitch took place so rapidly that the voice was originally diagnosed as diplophonic (two-toned). In this instance, however, the apparent diplophonia is due to a rapid succession of different fundamentals rather than to different rates of vibration of the two individual cords. This case is of especial note because the difference between the two frequencies is not necessarily an octave.

Public school speech therapists who have to make surveys of large populations of school children should recognize the fact that the control of pitch during pubertal development can vary widely from day to day. Very often there is less control early in the morning than later in the day. We have also found that anger, excitement, fear and other emotions may give a false picture of the severity of the problem. Laughter, especially if uncontrolled, will also produce an unusual number of breaks.

Too high a pitch in some individuals, either male or female, may fail to make the necessary transition to the adult voice. The social penalties upon the male with a voice pitched too high are severe in our culture. Indeed, an old name for this voice problem was the "eunuchoid voice." The penalties upon the female are less severe. An occasional male may even find a "baby-voice" as attractive as a "baby-face." Nevertheless, the high-pitched voice is rarely much of an asset. We have seen some marked tragedies resulting from the disorder. Personalities have been warped by social rejection; vocational progress has been blocked; self-doubts have destroyed the person's ability to cope with the demands of existence. There is nothing humorous about a high-pitched voice.

Why do some people fail to make the normal pitch change? There are several reasons besides delayed sexual development. Some cases have voices which are high-pitched primarily because of infantile personalities, because they cannot or prefer not to grow up. This case study may help to make the point:

Charles J. was first referred to the public school speech therapist for his articulation difficulty at the age of twelve. He substituted *w* for *r* and *l, t* for *k* and *d* for *g.* He had a marked inter-dental lisp. He sucked his thumb, cried easily. He preferred the company of very young children and still played with dolls at home. He was rejected and despised by boys of his own age and bore the nickname of "Sister." He was an only child, pampered and babied and over protected by an anxietous mother. Although intelligent he had failed the third grade twice. He was absent from school a good share of the time for chronic headaches and stomach upsets. The articulation defects were very resistant to therapy and the child was not co-operative. Consequently, he was dismissed from speech therapy classes and referred to the school psychologist who was unable to solve the home problem because of the mother's attitudes.

At seventeen he was again referred to speech therapy, this time at a college clinic. No articulation defects were present, but the voice was very high-pitched, rather nasally whiny, and weak in intensity.

The secondary sex characteristics were present and he was quite fat. The personality was still infantile.

In such cases psychotherapy is the indicated treatment, although vocal training may be used along with it, either to make the psychotherapy more palatable or to help the person to make changes in the habitual pitch as he comes to accept and solve his psychological problem.

Another common cause of the high-pitched voice is tension. The tighter the vocal cords are held, the higher is the pitch of the tone produced. Tension in any area of the body tends to flow toward and focus in the larynx. Many individuals who, in their occupations, are compelled to speak very loudly will raise their voices to make themselves heard, and this raising also lifts the habitual pitch. Speech therapy will be of little avail unless the underlying cause of the tension can be eliminated or reduced.

The falsetto. The falsetto voice, which is partly a disorder of pitch and partly one of voice quality, is still not thoroughly understood in terms of its manner of production. Negus[1] declares that only the very edges of the cords vibrate and that they move upward and downward rather than outward and inward. When the higher falsetto notes are being produced, only a portion of the cords vibrate. In the male voice, the lowest notes cannot be produced in a falsetto, and the highest notes are more easily phonated in this manner. The falsetto is easily produced when phonating on inhalation, and it is seldom present in such biological activities as sighing or coughing. Although little air pressure is needed to produce this type of voice, constriction of the laryngeal musculature usually occurs. In treating this voice disorder, lowering the habitual pitch level, relaxation, and the vocalized sigh are the techniques commonly employed. The student is required to diminish the intensity of his ordinary speech and to follow each "break" into the old

---

[1] Negus, V. E., "The Mechanism of Phonation," *Acta otolaryngology*, Stockholm, 1935, Volume 22, pages 393–419.

falsetto quality by sighing and by using some stereotyped phrase or sentence such as "That is to say" or "What I mean to say is. . . ." These sentences are practiced sufficiently so that they provide an easy vehicle for returning to the new voice quality and pitch level.

Treatment of Pitch Disorders

In any of the voice disorders there is need not only for a comprehensive investigation into its causes but also for a careful analysis of the vocal abnormality itself. For example, if two men both had very high-pitched voices, the one who had many notes available to him below this habitual pitch would tend to be easier to work with than would one who had a very narrow range. Before we can work out a therapy plan for a voice case we must study the defective voice in a systematic fashion. A series of tests is therefore provided for this purpose. In order to administer them, the student needs a normal sense of pitch placement and discrimination and the ability to distinguish the abnormal from the normal. Many of these tests are highly subjective and not too reliable, but they are widely used by speech therapists in getting some idea of the voice problem presented to them.

Pitch analysis tests.

1. *Ability to discriminate pitch.* This may be tested by whistling pairs of notes at low, middle, and high pitches, and requesting the subject to tell whether the first is higher or lower than the second. Use ten pairs of notes at each of the pitch levels, using a random order. The same test can be given by humming the notes. Do not let the subject watch you, and keep the tones exactly two semitones apart. Record the number of errors at each pitch level. Students should practice giving this test under supervision until they are able to give adequate stimuli.

2. *Ability to produce a given pitch* This may be tested by humming the nasal *m* at a low, middle, and high pitch. After each stimulus, the

subject is required to attempt to duplicate it with his humming. Use different notes at each pitch level and continue the hum for at least five seconds. Score : s an error any performance which does not come within a semitone of the stimulus or its octave, but note any tendency to produce a harmonic such as a musical fifth.

3. *Ability to carry a tune in unison or alone.* Tunes chosen should be simple and familiar. Use the unison test first. Use the same tune for both.

4. *Ability to follow inflections.* In this test the student is provided with a pencil and paper and is shown the following graphs of inflection as they are phonated and drawn by the examiner on the vowel *a*: _____↑ _____↓ _____→ _____↓. He is then asked to follow with his pencil a new series given by the examiner, who phonates the inflections according to the following sequence of graphs: _____↑ _____→ _____→ _____↓ _____→ _____↓ _____↑. The examiner's inflections should not range above a full tone. Record number and type of error.

5. *Normality of inflections in speech.* Use phrases or sentences which ask questions, make statements, give commands, indicate surprise, and express disgust, and have the subject repeat them after the examiner. Some examples are: *What's that noise? I liked that movie. You get out of here! What a* BIG *fish! Oh, I'm sick of this lousy place.* Record marked differences from your own inflections.

6. *Relation between pitch and stress.* Using the sentences in the preceding paragraph, notice whether stress changes are used instead of pitch changes. Underline certain words in sentences and ask subject to emphasize them. Note whether any pitch changes occur. Ask subject to phonate some vowel several times, alternating stressed and relaxed production. Note whether stressed notes are higher in pitch.

7. *Determination of pitch range.* Hum a middle-pitched note as a model for the case to imitate. Then gradually hum down the scale until the case cannot phonate at any lower pitch. Do this several times and note the place at which the individual begins to strain and falter. Locate this note on a piano or pitch pipe. Then, beginning with the same original note, hum up the scale until the voice breaks into the falsetto. Instruct the subject not to use the falsetto if possible. Locate the highest note accomplished without straining or falsetto. The difference between highest and lowest notes may be called the pitch range. If the falsetto keeps breaking in, determine the highest note of its range.

The importance of pitch-range tests is that they help us determine whether the speech defective is using a habitual pitch that is too near the bottom or top of his pitch range. If this is the case, intensity and quality defects may result. Moreover, the optimal or natural pitch at which the subject is most effective is usually located at a point a few semitones above the lowest third of the regular pitch range. If the falsetto is included, the natural pitch is usually located at about the twenty-fifth percentile of the total pitch range.

8. *Determination of habitual pitch.* This is much more difficult for the untrained or inexperienced examiner to determine, since it involves the disregard of inflections and a process of mental averaging of the pitch changes which exist in propositional speech. Nevertheless, the trained ear can spot the average pitch of another individual's voice with amazing accuracy. The subject is asked to repeat over and over, ten times or more, the sentence: "Now is the time for all good men to come to the aid of the party." Disregarding the first and last words, the examiner hums softly up and down the scale until he finds his voice synchronizing with the pitch of the subject's voice. Continuing to hum this pitch, he goes to the piano and finds its notation, which he records. Through similar technique it is also possible to determine the extent of habitual pitch range used by the subject. The reference by Root is recommended if supplementary information is desired.

9. *Determination of natural pitch.* Ask the subject to close his eyes, to begin with a low pitch, and to hum slowly and continuously up the scale, attempting to keep the intensity constant. The observer will note a certain pitch at which the intensity swells. Hum this pitch until it can be identified on the piano and recorded. Repeat the process while humming a descending scale. Give three ascending and three descending trials, and consider the place at which these pitches seem to cluster as the natural pitch. A range of three or four semitones about this note may be considered as optimal for performance. The natural pitch level may also be determined from the pitch range as described in test seven of this section.

10. *Effect of special influences.* By controlling the testing situation in the appropriate manner, study the effect upon the subject's habitual pitch of the following variables: change in quality (have subject speak gutturally, nasally, and so on); changes in intensity (very loud and very quiet speech); relaxation; distraction; imitation of another's speech.

We now present a case summary which will illustrate the kind of information procured by such an interviewing and testing program.

VOICE CASE SUMMARY REPORT

Case: William T.   *Age:* 19   *Status:* College Freshman

Date: April 1, 1953

Referred by: Self   *Examiner:* Shearer

Type of voice disorder: Habitual pitch too high

Case history and interview data: William T. is a tall (6'2"), thin, asthenic individual, poorly coordinated and awkward, ill at ease in social situations. Bad case of acne. Wears glasses for myopia. Excellent high school grades but is doing poorly in college. Away from home for first time. Few acquaintances and no close friends here. Spends most of his time studying or going to movies or watching television in dormitory. Thinking of quitting school and "going away somewhere." Highly conscious of voice and tends to blame the high pitch for his lack of social acceptance. Low energy level, except when he speaks, which is done in a high-pitched, very swift, hastily-articulated voice. Marked tension at this time. Has not dated. No athletic ability. Many social fears. Anxiety about possibility of employment when he finishes his general degree. No vocational preferences. Only child. Parents separated but not divorced. Father paying for education with proviso that once this is finished no more support will be provided.

Premature birth with history of frequent illness up to school age. Case reported that his presence held the parents together until he graduated from high school. Felt they had often resented this situation. Parents highly approved scholastic achievement since neither had experienced much education. Parents had often criticized him for lack of social skills. They had pushed him into many social situations in which he felt inadequate but tended to exclude him "whenever they had company." Only close relationship was with a neighbor boy who "ditched me as soon as he entered high school and started going out with girls and participating in sports." Had been highly dependent upon this friend and felt loss keenly. Daydreams a great deal with fantasies concerned with girls and oratory. Reads escape literature of all kinds.

Physical development was uneventful until age of 13, at which time he "shot up at about six or eight inches a year." Pubic and facial hair appeared "about a year later." Experienced a few voice breaks in pitch about this time but "voice never did change." Speech development up to this time had been normal.

Only previous therapy had been a series of six lessons from a singing teacher at age of fifteen. No success. Feels that if he can just talk like other people all his problems will be solved.

Test data: Habitual pitch is about at the level of G above middle C. When emotional, it rises to B above middle C. The apparent range is twelve semitones or a full octave with B below middle C the lowest note he is capable of producing. However, when case was asked to sigh, to clear throat while vocalizing, and to grunt, he produced pitches as low as E below middle C.

His pitch discrimination is excellent; he can produce and sustain any pitch within his usual range; he sings and hums melodies without error; he is able to follow inflection stimulus patterns with accuracy; normal inflections are heard in his voice except when he is excitedly speaking at the top of his range. He is able to yodel. The falsetto quality, however, does not invade his ordinary speech. If he increases the loudness of his phonation, the pitch rises. Clenching the hands produced an increase in pitch. Relaxation could not be achieved.

Attitude toward therapy: Unrealistically hopeful. He said: "I feel it won t be too hard to get my voice down. All I need is the right exercises."

Organic examination: Laryngeal cartilages are of normal size. Vocal cords are of adult length with no pathology. In phonation, however, the thyroid cartilage is tilted and raised so that no space between it and the hyoid can be felt. Extrinsic structures are highly tensed. Resonating cavities are normal. Polygraphic recording of breathing shows much air wastage prior to phonation. Case tends to exhale most of his breath before beginning to speak. Some opposition between abdomen and thorax at this time.

The treatment of these disorders concerns itself primarily with the teaching of new habitual pitch levels and the teaching of new inflection patterns. Since disorders of intensity and voice quality are often due in part to the use of unnatural pitch levels, the techniques discussed in this section are useful in the treatment of all voice disorders. Disorders of intensity frequently demand the teaching of a higher pitch level, especially when the speech defective is male; but the large share of remedial work consists of teaching lower habitual pitch levels.

Methods for changing the habitual pitch level. The procedure for changing the habitual pitch should consist of the following techniques: (1) convincing the student of the inadequacy of his present habitual pitch; (2) ear-training techniques in the recognition and discrimination of pitch levels and variations; (3) methods enabling the student to use the desired pitch level and normal variations and inflections at that level; (4) techniques for making the new pitch level and range habitual. These will now be discussed in detail.

1. *Convincing the student of the inadequacy of his habitual pitch.* The most effective method of doing this is to provide an opportunity for the student to hear his own voice. Few of us are able to hear our own voices, for we are too concerned with the communication involved. It is difficult to consider discriminatingly anything that is very familiar. We are so "used" to the sound of our own voices that we cannot listen to them. The increased availability of voice-recording devices is of great value to the speech correctionist. Every voice defective should have a phonograph record made of his speech. Other individuals with good voices should repeat the same speech material on the same record so as to allow comparison. If the recording is a faithful reproduction, the student will recognize the adequacy of the other voices and the inadequacy of his own in so vivid a manner as to provide a true psychological shock. Such a shock is frequently needed to provide the necessary motivation. The record can also serve as a basis for the measurement of progress. Besides the voice recording, the teacher can require each student to speak before a class, the members of which should be asked to rate the speakers as to pitch and general adequacy of voice. Other methods may be invented.

Improper pitch levels produce so many of the disorders of voice quality that they cannot be neglected. Many individuals have learned improper pitch levels owing to their personality problems, their imitation of poor models, their desire to identify themselves with other individuals, and many other reasons. It is usually necessary to recognize these influences and to cancel them before the student will really co-operate. A few cases may illustrate these points.

Bullowa described the etiology of certain voice disorders suddenly occurring in a high school as follows: "In order to acquire the low, lady-like voice which high school children believe suits their condition as opposed to the shrill shout of elementary school days, many students close their mouths, and inaudibility and nasality result." [2]

Ridpath, pleading for better co-operation between singing teachers and the laryngologist, says, "It is a fact that most vocal teachers try to make sopranos of all girls and tenors of all men, with resultant failures, whereas if they would consider the individual from the physiologic point of view they would not expect a student who is anatomically unsuited to produce high tonal effects to become a tenor, and vice versa." [3]

Felderman, in speaking of the folly of using an improper pitch level, declares that self-consciousness prompts the aping of elders by using coarse, throaty, guttural, or nasal voices, the use of which is continued even after the child passes through adolescence and does achieve a lower pitch. "Invariably the imitation fails." [4]

T.S., one of the author's cases, a schoolteacher, was dismissed after one month of teaching because the students could not hear her. It was found upon examination that her habitual pitch level was less than three semitones above the bottom of her range, whereas her optimal or natural pitch level was at least six semitones above her habitual level. She possessed adequate intensity at the optimal level but declared she could not bear to speak in such a high voice. Investigation showed that a series of experiences in which high voices had been penalized had caused her prejudice, which was truly unfounded since her optimal pitch was that of middle C. The last of these experiences had been the scolding given by a critic teacher to another student. Therapy consisted primarily of having her make phonograph recordings of the voices of twenty successful teachers and analyzing them with respect to habitual pitch. Mental hygiene and insight into the role played by her early experiences in producing her old pitch level helped to convince her. A course in practice teaching completed the re-education, and she experienced no further difficulty vocationally.

---

[2] Bullowa, A. M., "The Need for Speech Work in High Schools," *Proceedings of the National Education Association*, 1912, Vol. 54, pages 870–874.

[3] Ridpath, R. F., "A Plea for a Better Understanding Between the Laryngologist and the Vocal Teacher," *Journal American Medical Association*, 1937, Vol. 109, pages 545–546.

[4] Felderman, L., *The Human Voice*, New York, Henry Holt and Co., 1931.

Perhaps the most important and frequent of all voice disorders due to improper pitch levels is the hoarse voice. Williamson (48) has shown in a study of seventy-two cases of hoarse voice that:

The most common principal cause of hoarse voice was the throat tension resulting from the effort to speak at a level far below optimum pitch. When optimum pitch was established, the principal problem of correction was that of eliminating habits of tension. Such "placing" the voice in an efficient pitch and removing throat tensions generally remedied the hoarseness.

Williamson feels that the throat tensions occurred as a result of trying to gain loudness while using such a low pitch level, and that they then became habitual.

2. *Ear-training techniques in the recognition and discrimination of pitch levels and variations.* Before the teacher makes any attempt to get the student to lower or raise his voice, the student should be given a great deal of ear training. This training should be concentrated upon the identification and comparison of pitch levels and the recognition of the types of inflections. Many of these individuals have great difficulty in carrying tunes, in matching the pitch given by the teacher, in running a scale, and in recognizing or using inflections. When all of these abilities are defective, the prognosis is not favorable, though ear training will occasionally accomplish wonders. Even when the student has no difficulty with these activities, he should be given a good deal of discrimination practice before he attempts performance.

The ear training should begin with the methods used in the voice tests. Pairs of tones should be vocalized by the teacher as the student records or designates which of the two is lower in pitch. If difficulty is experienced, very wide intervals should be used. The Seashore musical tests for pitch may be played repeatedly, and the student should be urged to better his score of correct judgments. Inflections, glides, and slides of all types may be used for stimulation. Care should be taken to prevent the student from making his judgment in terms of quality or intensity.

Often the teacher needs to accompany her presentation of this stimulation with sample pairs of sounds phonated while she raises and lowers her hand to indicate the pitch level used. The student should be required to follow pitch variations with similar movements, and after his judgments are consistently correct, he should make slight head movements to indicate higher or lower pitch levels. It is often necessary to use much of this kinesthesia in order to reinforce and recall the stimulation. After the student has been given some of this training with pairs of tones and inflections, simple melodies should be used, both in song and in speech. These should be followed by the student's head or limb movements. Empathic response to tonal variation should be encouraged. The teacher should then speak whole sentences in a monotone, at various pitch levels, asking the student to judge the pitch levels used. Finally, normal speech can be used for this presentation, first using higher, then lower, average pitches, and requiring judgment by the student. This system may be supplemented by having the student and teacher judge the pitch characteristics of the various members of a class during recitation. Through such methods, the student will soon acquire the necessary foundation for his later speech attempts.

The next phase of the ear training should consist of attempts to hear and match the pitch level used by some other person. Some musical instrument such as the piano should be used. The student listens to the single prolonged note, the sentence said in monotone, and the conversational sentence in turn, and attempts to find the pitch on the musical instrument which corresponds with that used in stimulation. He should be given a great deal of this matching practice. Pairs of notes, monotone sentences, and conversational sentences should next be used, and the student attempts to match them on the musical instrument. If the student possesses a very poor ear, the teacher should be content with his performance if he can indicate only the direction of pitch change given.

The final stage of ear training should consist of responding to stimulation by designated pitch variations. For example, the teacher hums a note and the student finds one on the musical instrument which is lower (or higher, depending on the level desired for the voice) than that given by the teacher. The teacher may give one sentence for a standard, then repeat it at various pitch levels, asking the student to designate the type he wishes. Occasionally during this practice, the teacher should give the wrong response in order to check up on alertness and discrimination.

We have found that the use of a hearing aid is very effective in this self-hearing. A good phonographic recording of one's own voice always seems strange despite its acoustic fidelity because one does not listen to the pitch or quality. It is often difficult to convince the speaker that the recording is accurate, and thus much of the technique value is often lost. A hearing aid which amplifies one's own voice while in the act of speaking seems to prevent this objection. We have found it invaluable in both voice and articulation cases.

3. *Enabling the student to use the desired pitch level.* After the pitch level which the student should use as his habitual pitch has been determined through experimentation and voice tests, the speech correctionist should stimulate him with that pitch through every means at his disposal. The note may be sustained and a phonograph record made of it. The piano and other musical instruments should be used to make him conscious of it. The speech correctionist should speak in a monotone on the given pitch, or, if that is impossible, on its octave. The student should then attempt to speak certain prepared sentences in unison with the teacher. If necessary, he should hum several pitches until the right one has been found. It should then be reinforced by the playing of the record or the use of the piano and the teacher's voice. The student should repeat the same material over and over, maintaining the pitch. Often only a

vowel can be used in this practice, but the student should progress to propositional speech as soon as possible. Attention to kinesthesia should be stressed. Accessory associative movements, such as those of head and arm, should be used after the student has been able to hit the pitch consistently. The speech used should have practically no element of communication.

As soon as the student has attained this pitch while speaking in unison with reinforcing stimulation, the latter should be gradually diminished until he is attaining the pitch alone. All strain should be avoided or eliminated. It is usually wise to stick to one sentence or one type of material until this can be phonated in the required manner. Then a short period of silence should be interjected, during which the student tries to maintain the pitch. After this, he tries to phonate again at the same pitch level. The silence periods are then lengthened and some distraction is introduced. After further reinforcement and repetition of the sentence on the new pitch, returning immediately to the former, the student should interject another sentence spoken at his old pitch. Such comparative activity should be stressed. The student must realize how much higher (or lower) his new pitch level is, and therefore the old pitch level may serve as a standard of reference. Often the difference in terms of the tonic scale may be used to indicate the amount of change. The teacher cannot hope to establish anything in the nature of the special talent of absolute pitch, but she can hope to establish a sense of the amount of deviation from the old pitch level. The exercises in maintaining a pitch are of great importance in providing the self-stimulation these voice cases need and in preventing the natural tendency to shift gradually back to the old pitch level.

For a time, the voice retraining should be confined to the teaching periods, and all of these should begin with ear training and end with monotone speech on the desired pitch. Then the student may begin to use other material than that with which he learned to use his new pitch level, and when speaking these new sentences he should be encouraged to use all the inflections normal to him. At first, he should alternate the key vowel or sentence and the new material, and the teacher should require the student to do much of the speech in unison with her, perhaps with the reinforcement of the phonograph record or piano. Gradually this reinforcement should be withdrawn, until the student is phonating easily and flexibly at his new pitch level. Frequent review of the methods for finding his new pitch level in terms of his old habitual pitch is necessary.

Although the above method for teaching a new pitch level is most effective, there are several others. One frequently employed uses the vocalized sigh or yawn to produce the desired pitch. These sighs and yawns must be accompanied by decreasing intensity and relaxation in order to be most effective. Another method employs exclamations of disgust or contempt in order to provide a lower pitch. Still another makes use of the grunts and noises symbolic of relief or feeding. Clearing the throat may also be used to provide a lower pitch. These methods are often effective with true monotones when the former stimulation or matching method fails. Many of the techniques included in the stimulation method are combined with the biological activity methods in order to provide the necessary stability of performance.

4. *Making the new pitch level and range habitual.* As in the treatment of the articulatory disorders, the new type of speech must be made habitual or the treatment has failed. The speech correctionist must realize how unnatural the new pitch level seems to the student and to his associates, who have become accustomed to the old pitch level. The student himself must gradually become accustomed to the new level or it will create such a psychological shock that he will not be able to stand it. One youth declared that he did not know himself when he used his new deep voice instead of the high-pitched piping tones he had always phonated, because it seemed to change his entire personality. It is usually wise to prescribe a great deal of oral reading at the new pitch level. This reading should consist of

simple narration or the recital of the lines of some dramatic character with whom the student can identify himself. The student should read alone before a mirror. Later, other people may be asked to enter the mirror situation to listen. Finally, conversation can be used. It will be found that, as this therapy is carried out in a few restricted situations, the voice in other situations will gradually change to the new level.

After the student has become thoroughly accustomed to his new level, definite procedures can be used to make the student consistent in its use. These procedures are the same as those outlined in a similar connection for the articulatory cases. There should be definite speech periods at school and at home in which the student concentrates on the use of the new pitch. Speech assignments to get the student to use the new voice in outside situations should be formulated and carried out. Checking devices and penalties will serve to motivate the student and to make him conscious of his return to the old pitch levels. Negative practice in which the student uses the old pitch levels serves a similar purpose. A consistent program including these activities will soon make the new pitch level and range habitual.

Types of intensity disorders. These disorders include too loud voices, too weak voices, and aphonia (the lack of phonated speech). Since the causes of too loud a voice are hearing loss, occupational influence (farmer's voice), personality problem (exhibitionism or overaggressiveness), or imitation, little special therapy other than that sketched in the first section of this chapter is required.

Voices which are not loud enough for efficient communication are fairly common, but they seldom are referred to the speech correctionist. Imitation, overcompensation for hearing loss, and feelings of inadequacy leading to retreat reactions account for most of them. Many pathological reasons for such disorders are common, but they are frequently accompanied by breathiness, huskiness or hoarseness, or other symptoms sufficiently evident to necessitate the services of the physician, who should rightfully take care of them.

Intensity tests. Although a few intensity voice cases whose disorder is due to too loud a voice are referred to the speech correctionist, most of these are due to defective hearing. The majority of defective voice intensity cases are of pathological or neurotic origin, or are due to overstrain and overuse. A laryngoscopic examination is usually required, and when the disorder is complicated by excessive breathiness an oto-laryngologist should be consulted. In cases of aphonia, or total loss of voice, the services of this specialist, and occasionally those of a psychiatrist, are recommended. Examination of the exterior of the throat will indicate whether a grossly malformed or underdeveloped larynx may be responsible. Since these cases are usually consistent throughout their speech in their weak intensity, no speech-sound analysis is necessary, except an aural scrutiny of the patient's speech to determine whether the vowels are being normally prolonged or the consonants sufficiently stressed.

1. *Maximum duration.* The subject is required to take three deep breaths and then phonate a front, middle, and back vowel. Each is held as long as possible, and the time recorded. Normal individuals should be able to hold any of these vowels for at least 15 seconds without difficulty. The vowels *i*, *a*, and *u* may be used, and the series should be given twice if the subject fails the first time.

2. *Breath economy.* The subject should be given a passage to read. Note the first words of sentences to determine whether the subject exhales abnormally prior to speech attempt. Also note the number of inhalations per fifty words of jumbled material, or in reading backward. Over eight inhalations per fifty words is definitely abnormal. It is wise to make a breathing record if possible, noting attack-exhalation, phonation on residual air, shallow breathing, and dysintegrations between thorax and abdomen. These can also be detected by the trained observer without such apparatus. Note also whether clavicular breathing is used.

3. *Muscular tension.* Firm pressure by the experimenter's fingers on both sides of the thyroid cartilage will discover hyper- or hypotonicity of the laryngeal musculature.

4. *Effect of special influences.* By controlling the testing situation in the appropriate manner, the examiner can study the effect of the following conditions on the habitual intensity: strong clinical demand

for more intensity; pitch change; change in voice quality and presence of masking noise; distraction; relaxation; strong physical effort made simultaneously with speech attempt; expression of rage or disgust. It is also wise to determine if the subject can discard speech inhibitions by asking him, for example, to call a dog from across the street in the manner illustrated by the examiner. Determine also whether, in certain speech situations, the person's voice is adequate in intensity.

Improper breathing habits. There are, however, certain speech cases possessing voice defects of weak intensity which require other treatment than that sketched in the section concerned with removing the causes of voice disorders. These individuals, owing to the influence of several of the functional causes above mentioned, have built up inadequate breathing habits which markedly interfere with efficient speech. They lack what the speech teachers and singing teachers have termed "support for tone." When the latter is analyzed in more objective fashion, using actual breathing records, support for tone is found to consist, not of deep inhalation, but of controlled exhalation. Inhalation for good speech is seldom any deeper than for silence. The air supply is merely expended very efficiently. Poor speakers, and especially those of the weak voice intensities, often speak on residual air. They sometimes attempt to speak while inhaling. They interrupt their exhalation by quick gasps, even though sufficient air is retained for speech.

Although Wiksell (see references) found in recent experimentation that for normal subjects there was no relationship between type of breathing and voice intensity, it is obvious from Figure 9 that individuals possessing such abnormal breathing patterns should tend to be handicapped in phonation. Efficient phonation demands continuous and sufficient air pressure below the vocal folds. Clinicians have found that training in breath control is of great usefulness in such cases.

Breathing habits for speech are difficult to modify. Retraining necessitates a carefully planned program which must be based upon the breathing anomalies habitual in each case. The speech correctionist should first make a careful examination of the student's breathing under various conditions. Unemotional propositional speech, conversation, oral reading to self and to audience, and public speaking should be provided for such study. Whenever possible, an objective record should be made of the breathing. Vital capacity measurements may be made by the school nurse. Care should be taken to discount the breathing abnormalities produced by emotional states, since they are to be eradicated not through breath control but

FIG. 8. Apparatus used in recording breathing. *From left to right:* pneumograph, polygraph, experimenter's signal key.

through emotional readjustment. This section is concerned with the stereotyped breathing habits that interfere with efficient phonation. If no apparatus is available for the objective recording of breathing, the speech-correction teacher who has been given training in comparing such recordings with her observation of the movements of the thorax and abdomen can rely upon observation alone.

In the past, much stress has been placed upon the necessity for teaching certain types of breathing habits. Thoracic breathing, abdominal breathing, diaphragmatic breathing, and many other more or less meaningless terms have been espoused by various elocution and speech teachers. Gray has shown that it is difficult to isolate specific types of breathing, that all of the so-called types are used by most individuals, and that, if speakers be classified according to their "type of breathing," there will be as many abdominal and thoracic breathers in a group of the worst speakers as in a group of the best speakers. Type of breathing, therefore, does not differentiate between the good and poor voices. One exception to this statement may be mentioned. Clavicular breathing, which involves the raising of the clavicles and the humping up of the shoulders into a strained position, tends to produce unsteadiness and jerky exhalation during speech. Wiksell's experimentation indicates that, in the cases in which breathing was predominantly thoracic, the subjects could hold a tone for a longer time and could get much better control of breathing than the cases in which abdominal breathing was most prominent. In speech correction, little attention is paid to type of breathing in terms of the musculature involved. We are interested only in providing sufficient breath and in teaching efficient habits of controlled exhalation. If the student attains these goals, he may breathe in any way he wishes.

The teaching of new breathing habits. The procedure to be followed in retraining the breathing used in speech is as follows: (1) The student must be made aware of what he is doing wrongly and convinced of the necessity for the formation of new breathing habits during speech attempt. (2) The old habits must be brought up to consciousness, disrupted, and penalized. (3) New habits of breathing must be taught and strengthened. (4) The student must learn to use the new habits consistently.

The best method of attaining the first goal is to have the student watch his breathing during phonation, comparing it with that of the teacher. Two pneumographs working onto the same polygraph will provide the necessary apparatus. Both student and teacher should speak the same sentences in unison.

If this is impossible, the student and teacher should sit before a large mirror in a position that will provide a profile view of both chests. A turn of the head will enable both the teacher and student to watch the rise and fall of the thorax. Sentences should be spoken in unison, the student attempting to control his exhalation synchronously with the teacher's. A yardstick placed across the surfaces of both chests will aid in this observation. Reading material checked according to the amount read per exhalation is convenient. Through these methods, the student will soon come to realize how much more inefficient his breathing is than that of the teacher, and also wherein his breathing differs. A rubber tube attached to a mouthpiece which fits closely about the mouth may be easily contrived, and if this instrument is used during speech and the end of the tube is placed near a candle flame, the student can readily see the effect of any preliminary exhalation which precedes the attempted phonation.

The student should then use the same apparatus during conversation or recitation from memory, but with his eyes closed, seeking meanwhile to sense when his breathing has been faulty. The teacher can watch the apparatus and tell the student whether his judgments have been accurate. He should then seek to duplicate consciously the old habits, and the teacher may imitate them. Through these and many other techniques which may be easily devised, the student becomes aware of the bad breathing habits.

Using reading material previously prepared for breath groupings and using the apparatus and techniques just described, the student will soon adopt methods which are so much more efficient that they appear almost as soon as the old habits are removed. The speech correctionist does not need to teach the new habits, but merely needs to remove the old. The student needs only to imitate a good model and to understand and experience what is meant by smooth, controlled exhalation in order to perform adequately. The real difficulty is experienced in carrying these new habits into normal, everyday speech.

In order to accomplish the latter end, the student should spend some time each day in oral reading, choosing material which is conversational in form. Selections from some of the modern "patter" plays are excellent material. They should be read as normally as possible. Lines can be memorized and used for speech practice. Speech assignments, checking devices, negative practice, penalties, and the use of nucleus situations will

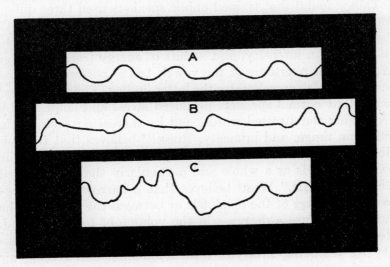

Fig. 9. Three breathing records. *Upper record:* normal silent breathing; *middle record:* breathing during normal speech; *lower record:* breathing during speech of a woman who talked on inhalation. Inspiration is represented by the upward strokes, expiration by the downward. Read from left to right.

enable the student to make the new breathing methods habitual.

Other methods for increasing voice intensity. Other devices which can be used to increase voice intensity are: (1) nasalizing the vowels; (2) finding and using the natural pitch; (3) accompanying vocalization with strong muscular effort, such as clenching the fists; (4) using a loud masking noise to demand greater intensity; (5) changing the openings and shapes of the resonating cavities; (6) using emotional expressions, such as cries of pain, to demonstrate to the student that he possesses adequate intensity; (7) using singing or chanting as the vehicle for louder speech.

Readjustment of resonating cavities. Among the methods for increasing vocal intensity is that which employs readjustment of the resonating cavities.

Talley[5] found that trained public speakers used three different ways of modifying the vowel when they wished to "project" their voices in the audience situation. There was a rise in pitch, an increase in intensity, and a shift of energy from the lower to the higher overtones of the vowel. Laase[6] performed an experiment which corroborates the latter finding. Tiffin and Steer[7] found that normal speakers produced stress and emphasis by prolonging the stressed words, and by increasing their pitch, inflection range, and intensity. Russell[8] believes that the epiglottis and false vocal cords tend to act as filters to "muffle complex sounds as a whole and particularly the high-pitched metallic partials." West[9] believes that a narrow opening between the wings of the epiglottis or between the pillars of the fauces will cause a decrease in the volume of tone produced. Negus[10] demonstrated the importance of resonation to intensity by removing a larynx from an animal and forcing air through its tensed cords. The tone was extremely weak and lacking in quality when compared to the sound normally produced.

These research studies and many others indicate that appropriate adjustment of the resonating cavities can increase

---

[5] Talley, C. H., "A Comparison of Conversational and Audience Types of Speech," *Archives of Speech*, 1937, Volume 2, pages 28–40.

[6] Laase, L. T., "The Effect of Pitch and Intensity on the Quality of Vowels in Speech," *Archives of Speech*, 1937, Volume 2, pages 41–60.

[7] Tiffin, J. and Steer, M. D., "An Experimental Analysis of Emphasis," *Speech Monograph*, 1937, Volume 4, pages 69–74.

[8] Russell, G. O., *Speech and Voice*, New York, Macmillan, 1931, pages 175–176.

[9] West, R., Kennedy, L., and Carr, A., *The Rehabilitation of Speech*, New York, Harper & Brothers, 1937, pages 98–100.

[10] Negus, V. E., *The Mechanism of the Larynx*, St. Louis, C. V. Mosby, 1930, Chapter 11.

the intensity of the voice. Unfortunately, we do not possess exact knowledge of what resonator sizes, shapes, types of tissue, or openings are needed to produce increased intensity. So much individual variation occurs both anatomically and physiologically that no laws of efficient resonation have been formulated. Teachers of public speaking and singing all seem to agree that the resonators must be relaxed and that their orifices or apertures should be as open as possible. They use many vague terms to describe their techniques, which, if they are successful, probably produce the desired results by helping to identify successful performance or by insuring adequate manipulation of the resonating structures. Some of these terms are: "bringing forward the tone," "mouth focus," "voice placement," and "rounded tones." Such terms as "nasal resonance" and "sinus resonance" are probably of the same type.

The speech correctionist seldom uses these vague terms, though we must confess he has few more specific techniques to offer. He demonstrates to the student how resonation can increase intensity with little additional expenditure of energy. He insists that the student use a variety of new resonator openings, shapes, and sizes. He requires the student to experiment with relaxation and tension in the various oral and pharyngeal musculatures, noting the effect upon intensity. The student is asked to increase the loudness of a certain tone as he backs away from the microphone of a recording device so that the record will show no decrease in intensity. He is to increase the intensity by varying the resonators rather than by expending more energy. Similar exercises employ an auditor walking away from the speaker rather than having the speaker withdraw from a phonograph recorder. Asking the student to close his eyes as he performs these exercises will help him to attend to the kinesthetic sensations. He should be asked to describe each successful experience. Thereafter the teacher should use the student's own terminology in identifying the more efficient type of resonation.

Effect on intensity of raising pitch level. Vocal intensity can also be increased by raising the habitual pitch used by the voice case. Scripture[11] quotes an experiment in which a vowel was sung at a constant level of loudness but at varied pitch levels. When the expenditure of air per pitch level was measured, it was found that the air expenditure decreased with rise in pitch. It is a common observation that children's voices "carry" much better than do adults'. While this may be due in part to the concentration of energy within a narrow group of overtones, the higher pitch level is also important. In general, most of the weak intensity cases are using habitual pitches far below their optimal or natural pitch levels. After the latter has been taught, adequate intensity is achieved. Occasionally the student is taught to make his speech more nasal, using humming exercises as the basic technique.

Influence of psychological factors. A lack of adequate intensity is often due to psychological factors. For example:

One individual with a history of prolonged laryngitis, but with a clean bill of health from the physician, claimed that she was afraid to talk loudly because of the pain she had experienced in the past. Something seemed to stop her whenever she decided to talk a little louder. She constantly fingered her throat. She declared that she was losing all her self-respect by worrying about her inability to speak as loudly as she could. Use of a masking noise during one of her conferences demonstrated to her that she could speak loudly without discomfort. Under strong clinical pressure, she did make the attempt, but the inhibition was automatic.

When a masking noise is used with one of these cases, it should be increased very gradually, and then, as the case adjusts the intensity level of speech to the new level, it should be shut off suddenly during his conversation. One of the author's cases was "cured" when he suddenly emerged from a noisy factory and found himself shouting. Vocalization accompanied by strong muscular effort often produces a stronger voice. Cries of pain or warning may often prove to the individual that his difficulty in speaking loudly is not insurmountable.

[11] Scripture, E. W., *The Elements of Experimental Phonetics*, New York, Scribner's, 1902, page 221.

Singing and chanting in unison with a large group will often accomplish the same purpose, especially if the group, at a secret signal from the clinician, suddenly stops. Mental hygiene and an insight into the nature of traumatic experiences usually precede this type of therapy.

Aphonia. Aphonia, or the complete loss of voice, is usually due to overstrain, organic defects, or emotional causes. If the cause is overstrain, rest and silence, or, at the best, whispered speech, should be prescribed. Occasionally the case is required to use a different pitch level when his voice begins to return. If the disorder is due to pathology, medical and surgical care is necessary. If it is due to emotional conflicts, psychiatric treatment (or the type of treatment discussed under readjustment methods) should be administered. In any case, if voice retraining is used, it is merely an accessory tool.

Suggestion is frequently used with hysterical aphonias. Physicians often use a faradic current or ammonia inhalation or massage as the culminating procedures in a period of treatment marked by complete cessation of speech attempt and strong cumulative suggestion. In many instances, coughing is used to demonstrate to the patient that voice exists. Persons who have once had such aphonia are likely to have it again unless the cause is removed. In some instances, when the cause cannot be discovered, a relapse is prevented by having the individual perform some simple vocal ritual each day, such as prolonging each of the vowels for ten seconds.

Some quotations from an article by Sokolowsky and Junkermann (35) will illustrate some of the methods for treating hysterical aphonia:

First, we administered breathing exercises in connection with a systematic speech and voice retraining . . . (using a humming breathing; speech attempt while "pressing together the hands of a nurse standing behind him";) . . . By means of this phonetic re-education we succeeded in restoring the voice to about 60 per cent of our aphonics, a rather meager result considering the relatively tiresome treatment which sometimes lasted several weeks.

Induced by the publications of Muck and his extraordinary results we then tried his method—the introduction of a pellet or small ball into the larynx between the vocal cords, in order to bring about a sensation of being suffocated which superinduced a cry of fright. We have to confess that our own results with Muck's ball were not very encouraging.

As soon as the anamnesis pointed to a psychogenic aphonia and the laryngoscopic mirror confirmed this assumption a short remark such as, "You will be all right quite soon," or, "You will be getting your voice back quite soon," was made. After that the patient was not permitted, so to speak, to "collect his wits." All manipulations such as setting the head in proper position and pulling out the tongue were carried out as quickly as possible, and accompanied by short, crisp and somewhat commanding words. Then followed the deep introduction of the mirror and the attempt to obtain a vocal retching reaction. After this was accomplished, it was brought into the consciousness of the patient with short, crisp remarks, such as "Here we are," "Now your voice is back," or "Do you hear your voice?" After that it required but relatively little effort (the mirror, of course, remaining continually in the throat) to elicit from the patient the unpleasant gag-reminding but nevertheless audible "ah."

Indistinct utterance. Indistinct speech is so frequently confused with intensity voice disorders that it will be discussed in this section. Many individuals possessing this type of speech phonate with sufficient intensity to be heard, but their intelligibility is affected by improper rate, indefinite articulation, and unprecise resonance. These individuals are frequently asked by their auditors to speak more loudly. When this is done, the intelligibility is often decreased still further, owing to the masking of the high-frequency consonant sounds by the lower tones of the vowels. Fletcher[12] concludes from his experiments that consonants are generally harder to recognize correctly than vowels, and that *th*, *f*, *v*, and *z* are the most difficult to perceive at weak intensities. He also demonstrates that a small improvement in articulation produces a great improvement in intelligibility: "If the articulation shows an improvement of from 5 to 10 per cent, the intelligibility will show an improvement of from 20 to 38 per cent."

---

[12] Fletcher, H., *Speech and Hearing*, New York, D. Van Nostrand, 1929, pages 266–289.

These indistinct speakers are therefore taught to emphasize their consonants. The four continuants mentioned above as being responsible for most of the distortion are prolonged. The student is further taught to produce them with a more energetic airflow and a tenser lip or tongue. Since other research studies indicate that the stop consonants *p, b, t, d, k,* and *g* are among the least powerful of all speech sounds, these are also singled out for special attention. Sudden, precise, and energetic closures and openings are taught. At first it is wise to use prescored material in which only one or two of these sounds are underlined. Speech assignments and nuclei situations will carry the new attack into normal speech. Improving such general considerations as the student's posture, neatness, and self-respect often facilitates this more specific therapy.

The Treatment of Disorders of Voice Quality

These disorders are the most common of all voice defects. They include excess nasality, denasality, throatiness, harshness, and all the other descriptive terms which may be used to denote peculiarities of timbre. Only when these peculiarities are sufficiently noticeable to interfere with communication and call attention to themselves can they be considered voice disorders. An infinite range of voice quality variations is found in so-called normal speakers. Excess nasality is probably the most common of these disorders. Cleft-palate speech involves both a phonatory and an articulatory disorder, and the phonatory abnormality is that of hypernasality. The treatment of this disorder employs the techniques sketched both for hypernasality and for articulation, but, because it also requires specialized methods, it is not specifically described in this section.

Tests for voice quality. Disorders of voice quality, with the exception of nasality and denasality, have always been difficult to classify because of the multidimensional nature of timbre. Pitch and intensity are fairly linear functions. One hears high, or low or loud or soft tones. But voice quality (timbre) is based upon a large number of overtones whose contribution to the auditory sensation depends upon their number and the frequency and intensity of each. Hence there is no clear-cut variant which we can perceive. The terms we use to designate voice quality are as numerous as adjectives. Most of them are confused and inaccurate. Few of them mean the same to one person as to another. Nevertheless, within limits, such a classification is of some value and is included in the examinations given below. A laryngoscopic examination is usually needed, and a phono-photographic recording may be recommended. The amount of tension in the laryngeal, pharyngeal, and velar musculature should be noted. The natural and habitual pitches should be recorded to determine if pitch is a factor. The following items should also be administered.

1. Check adjectives which best describe defective voice quality: hoarse, husky, strident, guttural, breathy, throaty, noisy, pectoral, nasal, denasal.

2. Make an auditory analysis to determine which vowels are most defective. All vowels are seldom equally bad, and usually only a few need remedial work. Begin by having the subject read until you can be certain to identify the peculiar timbre responsible for the voice disorder. Then have the subject prolong each of the isolated vowels for about five seconds. Check those that are obviously abnormal, making a recheck to determine which of the vowels are most defective. After completing this, go through the articulation test sentences and words which deal with the vowels, underlining all those most defective. Note also whether the defective quality exists all through the prolonged vowel or merely at its initiation, and whether or not it seems to be affected by the consonants which precede and follow it.

3. Make a similar analysis for nasality disorders. With these, one can use a cold mirror held horizontally and placed with the mirror side up beneath the nostrils, but above the mouth. If clouding occurs on the mirror, the vowel has been nasalized. The same test may be used by placing the fingers on each side of the bridge of the nose and determining nasality by the vibration. When using the words of the articulation test, be sure to substitute others for those containing the *m*, *n*, and *ng* sounds. Note whether nasality is produced on certain vowels when no nasal air is discharged.

4. Once the two or three most defective sounds have been discovered, make a phonetic placement analysis to determine position

of lips, jaws, tongue, and velum. Insist upon other methods of producing the same vowel (with tongue and lips in different positions), and note variations in quality.

5. Study the effect of pitch change on voice quality. Use isolated vowels at many different pitch levels, and also use continuous speech.

6. Repeat the preceding test, using variations in intensity.

7. Study the effect of relaxation, both general and specific, on voice quality. Use the vocalized yawn for the worst vowels.

8. Determine the quality of whispered vowels. Is it better than that of phonated ones? If so, try to make gradual transition from whisper through stage whisper to phonation, without letting peculiarity come in.

9. Study the effect of distraction and imitation of other voices.

Sequence of treatment. Although special devices are used for certain of these disorders, the treatment for most of them involves the same general sequence. This sequence is as follows: (1) Make an analysis of the voice to determine which vowels or continuant consonants are most abnormal in their voice quality. (2) The student must learn to recognize the unpleasant voice quality whenever it occurs in his speech. (3) Through the use of certain techniques, the student must learn to produce the correct quality on isolated vowels. (4) This new voice quality must be strengthened. (5) The student should learn to use the new quality consistently. In the following paragraphs, we shall use the disorder of hypernasality to illustrate the type of treatment to be administered.

Recognition of defective quality. In order that the student may learn to recognize the unpleasant voice quality whenever it occurs in his speech, the vowels that are least defective should be used. The teacher should imitate these vowels as the student produces them, and then repeat them, using excess nasality. The student will readily recognize the difference. He should be required to produce these vowels first normally and then with excess nasality, carefully noting the difference. Lightly placed thumb and forefinger on each side of the septum, or the use of the cold mirror placed under the nostrils, will provide an accessory check of the presence of the hypernasality. The student should then listen to the teacher's production of his worst vowel, with and without nasality. If difficulty is experienced in recognizing this, the student can correlate his auditory judgments with the visual and tactual sensations received from the use of the mirror and finger-septum contact. Requiring him to close and open his eyes during alternate productions of the vowels as the teacher uses the mirror under her nostrils will soon provide adequate discrimination.

After some of this training has been successfully completed, the teacher should read a passage in which certain vowels are underlined and are purposely nasalized. The student should listen carefully, checking on a copy of the passage all vowels in which he hears the unpleasant quality. Many of the games and exercises used in the ear training of articulatory cases can be modified to teach the student better discrimination and identification of the good and bad voice qualities. Although at first the teacher will need to exaggerate the hypernasality, she should endeavor to decrease it gradually until the student is skilled in detecting even a slight amount of it. After this has been done, the student should read and reread a certain paragraph, making judgments after each word as to whether or not excess nasality occurred. These judgments may be checked by the teacher, and the percentage of correct judgments ascertained. This procedure will serve as a motivating device. The student may also be required to repeat series of words or isolated vowels, using the mirror under his nostrils and making his judgment of normal or nasal voice quality before opening his eyes to observe the clouding or nonclouding of the mirror. Much home practice of this sort can be used.

Producing good voice quality. In most of the disorders of voice quality, it is advisable to work with the worst vowel first when the student attempts to produce clear and adequate phonation. Thus, in the nasality case, the vowel on which the student shows the worst hypernasality is singled out for his first trials. An exception to this policy is found in the cleft-palate and other organic disabilities, wherein one must often use the easier sounds first. Very little intensity should be used in the first attempts, and every type of available reinforcement should be employed. The hypernasality case should use warming-up exercises, such as yawning, puffing out the cheeks, blowing balloons, and other methods, to insure firm closure of the nasopharynx by the velum. Many of these exercises are given in the references. Care should be taken to prevent the student from constricting the nares during these performances. The student should use the mirror under the nostrils and the finger-septum contact to notice the first signs of nasal phonation. Often, a larger mouth opening or a slightly different tongue placement will help to keep the old habits from returning. As in the articulatory disorders, the actual attempt should be preceded by a review of the ear-training exercises. The teacher should use discrimination stimulation, giving the incorrectly nasalized vowel and then the normally phonated vowel several times before requesting the student to make his first attempt. If this preliminary work has been carried out thoroughly, little difficulty will be experienced, and vowels relatively free from excess nasality will be phonated.

Strengthening new voice quality. After this vowel has been produced correctly, the student should attempt to maintain and prolong it, paying a great deal of attention to the "feel" and the sound of it. The student must be cautioned to keep out all hypertension. Without changing facial, mouth, or body positions, he should then cease phonation, take a deep breath, and attempt to produce it again. Series of alternate phonations and silences should be produced on each exhalation. Whenever the vowel becomes too nasal, the student should be given a rest and the entire procedure of preliminary exercises repeated. Through careful work of this kind, the student will soon learn to produce the vowel correctly whenever he wishes. It is frequently necessary to insist upon sudden initiation of the vowel, using signal practice, in order to insure nasality-free vocalization at the very first instant of phonation. Often the student will fall into this error, making the old adjustments first, then changing to the new as the vowel is continued. This is fatal to the swift production needed in speech.

Although the worst vowel is the one first chosen for remedial work because of its contribution to better speech and because its successful production will influence the production of other defective vowels, we use the easiest consonant and vowel combinations in strengthening the new adjustments. The vowel should be practiced alone until it can be produced satisfactorily and consistently without the preliminary preparation. It is then wise to practice nonsense syllables in which the consonant follows the vowel (*ob*, *op*), then those in which the vowel follows the consonant (*bo*, *po*), and finally those in which consonants both precede and follow the vowel (*bop*, *pob*). The first consonants used in these combinations should be the plosives *p*, *b*, *t*, *d*, *k*, and *g*, then the sibilants *s*, *z*, and *sh*, then the continuants *f*, *v*, *l*, and *r*, and finally the nasals *m*, *n*, and *ng*. Such a sequence will be found to be most effective. Familiar words can be used as well as nonsense syllables without encountering much difficulty.

Making the new quality habitual. After the student has successfully mastered the majority of the above exercises, he can be required to read from copy carefully prepared to indicate his difficult sounds. Symbols and underlining can serve to teach him to reject the old mechanics prior to speech attempt and to prepare for adequate phonation. They may also be used to indicate the words on which the student should use negative practice. In voice disorders of all kinds, it is necessary to use a great deal of this negative practice, for the consciousness of faulty phonation will soon be lost unless frequently reinforced. As soon as the student has fairly good control of an isolated vowel, a nonsense syllable, or a familiar word, he should phonate it incorrectly to heighten the contrast. A brief illustration of such copy is as follows:

```
          *                        #              *
O/n this joyful occasio/n Alice was sitting o/n
```

#
the back of the sa/me white swa/n.
*

Key to symbols: / Be sure to separate vowel from consonant!
                       * A difficult sound for you. Be careful!
                       # Use negative practice on this sound.
                       — Prolong this vowel.

During the early stages of treatment, it is wise to use the same reading or memorized material over and over again until the student has attained a rather good awareness of the sounds which are likely to require more care. Often it is wise to prolong the vowel presenting difficulty and, for a time, to separate the vowel from the more difficult consonants such as the *m* or *n*. Assimilation nasality, or the carrying over of the nasality legitimately used in producing or preparing for the *m*, *n*, and *ng* sounds, often demands the use of signal practice to insure clean-cut transitions. After the student has mastered the prepared reading material he may progress to unscored reading, then to careful conversation with the speech correctionist, and finally to speech in outside situations. Speech assignments, checking devices, negative practice, penalties, and nucleus situations will make it possible for the student to attain complete mastery of his vocalization.

Other voice-quality disorders and methods of therapy. Hoarseness, huskiness, throatiness, and all the other odd types of voice quality are frequently due to hypertension, emotional conflicts, overstrain, and organic defects; the treatment for these conditions has already been discussed. The student should become familiar with the references dealing with these aspects of the disorders.

When these other disorders of voice quality are due to functional causes such as imitation or improper habits of voice production, the same sequence of ear training should be used, although the accessory devices used for nasality cannot be employed. Phonograph recordings will enable the student to study the voice quality in a manner that can be obtained by no other method. These recordings may be used continuously during treatment, and the teacher may record her own voice quality to provide comparison with the student's. Whenever the student is required to listen to his own voice, the voice recorder should be used, as it saves a great deal of time. However, through intensive and well-planned training, the same results may be obtained without this apparatus.

When the voice is pectoral, guttural, or throaty, it is often necessary to show the student that it is possible to articulate the vowels in other than his habitual manner. The opening of the mouth may be widened, and increased in vertical dimension, or made with lips protruded. The tongue placement may be varied greatly during the maintenance of one vowel. The student should be required to vary these positions and the tenseness of the walls of the mouth and throat. These exercises will demonstrate that differences in quality can be produced, and often much better timbre will result. It is frequently necessary to teach a new manner of vowel articulation in order to get the desired quality. When denasality is due to habits formed during adenoidal and catarrhal childhood, voice re-training is necessary. The student should be required to snort the vowels and to work for nasalization of all speech. Humming exercises and the use of the mirror and finger-septum contact will usually produce the desired result. Different pitch levels will also produce better quality. The procedures for strengthening and habituating the new quality are similar to those used for hypernasality.

Throatiness. The throaty quality of voice, when due to functional causes, is one of the most difficult to change. It is occasionally the result of lowering the habitual pitch level, especially when a falsetto was previously used. When the constrictor muscles of the pharynx are hyperactive, the choked, throaty voice is frequently found. Many of the individuals with such voice quality depress their chins against their necks when the throatiness is most apparent. Tension of the extrinsic laryngeal and pharyngeal musculature is usually present. The speech defective seems to be speaking as he prepares to swallow. The treatment of throatiness usually consists of the following techniques: (1) raising the habitual pitch level three or four semitones; (2) insisting upon a very erect posture and eliminating the tendency to depress the chin through penalties, checking devices, and negative practice; (3) using chanting and singing exercises to reduce the excess tension and silent semiovert rehearsals of sentences prior to utterance; (4) preceding utterance by flipping the tongue up and down in the mouth cavity so as to prevent the incipient swallowing movements from occurring, thereby breaking up the old pattern of vocalization; (5) using vocalized sighing to produce some vowel free from throatiness and thereafter using this vowel to "key" all vocalization in nucleus situations. This vowel can be phonated between sentences and between phrases in the same manner used by many normal speakers when they are at a loss for words.

Guttural voices. Some individuals are encountered whose voices probably merit the adjective *guttural* rather than *throaty*. The terminology is no doubt somewhat dependent upon sex differences or pitch, since a voice which would be termed *throaty* in a woman is called *guttural* when it occurs in a male. A distinction is sometimes made in terms of the mechanics of phonation, guttural voices being due to partial vibration of the false vocal cords in addition to the normal activity of the true cords. Constriction of the pharynx seems to occur in both types of voice, and the treatment is the same for both.

Harsh voices. Harsh, piercing, or rasping voices seem to be accompanied by this false vocal-cord vibration. Voelker[13] describes one form of the disorder as characterized by "a rattling, rumbling, cracking or ticker-like substitute for phonation." These extra vibrations range from six to thirty per second. Normal speakers often show this voice quality when grunting or in moments of indecision. It may be easily produced when vocalizing on inhalation. Voelker recommends breath training, speech with yawning, and vocalized sighing. The student must

[13] Voelker, C. H., "Phoniatry in Dysphemia Ventricularis," *Annals of Otology, Rhinology and Laryngology*, 1935, Volume 44, page 471.

learn to hear these vibrations in his own speech before any therapy will be successful. Russell[14] describes the strident, piercing voice as primarily due to raising the larynx up under the hyoid. He describes the subsequent tension as follows:

As the voice begins to get strident and blatant, one sees the red-surfaced muscles which lie above the vocal cords begin to form a tense channel and press upon the vocal cords themselves. This pressure is brought about primarily by the ventricular bands. . . . Consequently, but a very small strip of the glottal lip is left free to vibrate. The resultant is that the edge is pushed up and these edges are forced to close together in cymbal-like fashion.

Treatment for this disorder is similar to that for guttural and throaty voices except that, in addition, the student is taught to recognize the raising of the larynx. This can be done by observation in a mirror and by feeling the notch between the thyroid and the hyoid with the forefinger.

Imitation as a clinical device. All functional voice disorders respond to direct imitation as a form of therapy. The model set for the speech defective should contrast as much as possible with the former voice defect. Thus, nasality cases are required to imitate denasality, weak voices simulate models who have excess loudness, and so on. Other characteristics of the persons used as models should also be imitated. A throaty voice defective may be asked to imitate some person who has a thin, twangy voice, not only in his speech, but also in his manner of walking, posture, gesturing, and nervous movements. It is also useful to employ a phonograph recording of some opposite type of voice, playing it over and over and requiring the student to say the same sentences in unison with the record. Other recordings may be used in which the model repeats each sentence twice, with a pause after each one to permit the student to repeat the same words, thereby enhancing the likelihood of more perfect imitation.

It must always be remembered that voice disorders become

[14] Russell, G. O., "Physiological Causes of Guttural and Piercing Deaf Voices," *Oralism and Auralism*, July, 1929.

such intimate parts of the personalities of their possessors that they are not eradicated easily. The student must be allowed to become accustomed to the new voice, and this process should be a gradual one. He should not be asked to use the new type of voice in all situations, after he has first acquired its mastery. Nucleus situations should be designated and gradually extended so they will ultimately include all of his speech experiences. He should voluntarily practice his new type of voice in public speaking and in other emotionally loaded situations.

Hoarse voice. The adjective *hoarse,* like most of those used for voice disorders, is somewhat vague. It is frequently but not always accompanied by huskiness or breathiness. Frequently produced by laryngitis, it often persists long after the infection or inflammation has disappeared. Many boys develop a hoarse voice just before puberty in their effort to imitate the voice quality of an adult male and it disappears with the laryngeal change. It also is often found in athletes as a result of their strenuous efforts which entail excessive closure of the glottis. Any great muscular effort requires a firm and rigid thorax and this requires a closure not only of the true but often of the false vocal cords. A hoarse voice can also be produced by phonation with the false vocal cords. It is usually low in pitch. Moser (29) has even used this voice in order to lower the habitual pitch. The false-vocal-cord or ventricular voice is not only hoarse but harsh. Voelker (42) describes it very well:

The voice is apt to sound rough and crackling. The more chronic the use of this vicarious sound source, the more unpleasant the sound. . . . Ventricular voice is apt to be weak, and it is this weakness which causes the patient to seek attention of the physician of the speech clinic. The complaint of phonasthenia (weak voice) seems strange, since ventricular phonation is related to the explosive physiological functions in which the sound, if it is produced at all, as in coughing, sneezing, thoracic fixation or grunting, has considerable volume and carrying power. In fact, an actor was once trained in it to save his vocal cord voice through the long rehearsals and extended performances. That roar was completely adequate to fill the auditorium and even had the lion's ventriloquial effect in that it seemed to come from everywhere. Patients coming to clinics for ventricular hoarseness or phonasthenia regularly complain of clearing mucus from the throat and of hacking and coughing.

With respect to the last observation it is interesting that Allen and Peterson (18) found that the habitual use of a falsetto voice produced an inflammation of the vocal cords rather than the inflammation producing the vocal defect. Voelker (42) has the following to say about the causes of ventricular phonation:

One patient complained of dropping his voice at the end of sentences, and it was found that he did not lower his vocal cord pitch but actually stopped using his vocal cords at the end of the sentence and substituted for them a ventricular vibration. An actor, with an excellent stage voice, complained of hoarseness only in conversation. It was found that in intimate and quiet conversation he used a ventricular voice to "save for his art" his stage voice. A youth was criticized by his parents for having a high and squeaky voice and acquired ventricular phonia in order to lower his voice to a normal pitch. Thus, instead of lowering his voice to a normal pitch, of perhaps 150 cycles, he lowered it to one of between 48 and 57 cycles. A similar case was found in which a man 31 years old, who had a deaf wife, became self-conscious about his yelling and outside his home developed phonation with the ventricular bands to subdue his voice. A college student raised the pitch of his voice to read aloud or to recite but used a ventricular tone in conversation. Sometimes it is found in careless conversation only. A 5-year-old boy was kidded by his playmates for having a high voice, and he lowered it by acquiring a ventricular voice. An 18-year-old youth, with a eunuchoid quality, substituted ventricular phonation for his weak and strident vocal cord voice and thought his new hoarse voice gave the impression of masculine virility.

Thus far we have tried to outline the general methods of treating pitch, quality and intensity disorders as though they were usually separate and discrete problems. Actually, in many cases all three of these aspects may be faulty. Often, by working on the pitch we can alter the intensity; by working on the quality, either of the other two characteristics of phonation can be affected. Pitch, intensity, quality, all three of these are so closely bound together, that sometimes more progress can be made by working with one of them which is not the prime difficulty.

Similarly, certain of the common causes of voice disorders can produce difficulties in any of the three aspects of phonation. Laryngeal inflammation causes a lower voice, a weaker voice and a hoarse one. We therefore provide a section of this chapter dealing with these causes and their amelioration.

Need for medical co-operation in diagnosis. Many voice disorders are medical problems, and the speech correctionist must always keep this in mind. Much harm can be done by administering vocal training to a case whose disorder is due to active pathology or organic abnormalities. Whenever the case exhibits a chronic hoarseness, huskiness, or breathiness, it is essential that a specialist make an examination before the speech correctionist does any remedial work. Whenever the voice disorder follows a severe injury or illness, the physician must be consulted. Whenever the voice disorder accompanies such symptoms as extreme lassitude, extreme tenseness or activity, spasticity, or conditions of ill health, no speech-correction work should be done without medical approval. Moreover, voice is one of the most sensitive indices of mental health, and, whenever the voice disorder seems to be merely a part of a pronounced psychoneurotic condition, the psychiatrist should be consulted. The speech correctionist is favorably situated to contact many cases which the medical profession would never see, and he should always seize the opportunity to get co-operation from it. Unfortunately, laryngoscopic examinations by a specialist are rather costly, but they should be made whenever possible. Voice disorders demand more medical co-operation than do any other disorders.

Of course, many voice cases are functional, and the physician will readily advise speech-correction procedures for them. Other cases demand retraining even after the pathology or abnormality has been taken care of through medical or surgical therapy. Habits grow up about voice, even as they do about articulation. Generally speaking, the speech-correction teacher will do most of her work with cases of *nasality (including cleft palate), denasality, throaty, guttural, or harsh voices, monotones or peculiar inflections, high-pitched or falsetto voices, and weak or aphonic voices.*

Methods for removing the causes of the voice disorders and for minimizing their effects. The physician will take care of the eradication of most of the remediable organic causes for voice disorders. The speech correctionist should know enough about these causes to appreciate what has been done or could be done so that he can refer the case to the proper specialist and can modify the treatment according to his recommendations. He should also know whether the condition is likely to return. Since most of this information is rather technical and is available in other texts, the student is advised to use the special references given at the end of the chapter. The speech-correction teacher can do much to aid in building good habits of body hygiene, thereby preventing the development of foci of infection. Most cases of denasality and hoarseness can be helped by the institution of a careful routine of cleanliness and care of nose, mouth, and throat.

Hearing loss. When the voice defect is associated with a hearing loss, the teacher should take advantage of every opportunity to become familiar with the operation and use of hearing aids. She should refer the student to a lip-reading teacher, who will not only aid in the perception of speech but also help to clarify the various vowel positions through phonetic placement. Attention to kinesthesia, and the tying up of intensity and pitch levels and fluctuations with bodily movements, can do a great deal to compensate for the hearing loss, especially if the loss is not one of long standing.

Delayed sexual development. Another cause of voice disorders is lack of physiological or psychological sexual development, which produces the shrill high pitch termed juvenile or eunuchoid voice. Gilkinson[15] points out that his research findings corroborate the generally accepted idea that people are inclined to judge masculinity in terms of the speaking voice. When other secondary sex characteristics are also lacking, the speech correctionist should refer the case to the physician, who may prescribe hormonal treatment or other measures. Schicker[16] reports successful lowering of pitch in three of five cases as a result of administering testicular extracts. On the other hand, Crews[17] demonstrates how such techniques as silence, suggestion, relaxed vocal sighing, and mental hygiene can solve the same problem when the causes are psychological.

Puberty. The teacher should be able to recognize the symptoms of change of voice in early adolescents, and she can do much to minimize the emotional accompaniment which usually occurs. Education of parents, teachers, and associates of such children is often necessary, since many "boy sopranos" become voice cases if their mistaken parents or teachers seek to perpetuate the former pitch levels. Often the child can be taught to control the fluctuations by relaxation and the use of accessory movements such as head and body gesturing. The elimination of undue excitement and the common speech conflicts is always important at this time.

The speech problem of the man who has persisted in retaining his boy's voice is a very serious one, since many social penalties are commonly placed upon such symptoms. West (43) in an excellent article describes other effects of puberty on voice:

In many cases the young person continues to use the prepubescent voice after the larynx has matured. With the boy this means that he will talk in a falsetto. It is often difficult indeed after he has employed this falsetto for many months to persuade him to use his nor-

---

[15] Gilkinson, H., "The Relationship Between Psychological and Physical Measures of Masculinity," *Genetic Psychology Monographs*, 1937, Vol. 19, pages 105–154.

[16] Schicker, H., "Die Eunuchoide Stimme und Ihre Hormonale Behandlung," *Arch. Gest. Phon.*, 1938, Vol. 2, pages 161–175.

[17] Crews, L., "A Case of Juvenile Voice," *Proceedings of the American Speech Correction Association*, 1936, Vol. 6, pages 142–149.

mal low-pitched voice. The social problems presented in this change are difficult to meet. In the girl the change is not so much in the structure of the larynx as in the linings of the pharyngeal resonators. The quality of the voice normally changes with the change in the texture of these surfaces. However, many young women, having accustomed their ears to that quality that the voice showed before puberty, strive to continue it. The effort to produce this quality in spite of the change of resonator produces a tense and unpleasant vocal timbre.

Sluggish articulators. Many voice cases without organic defect have palates, tongues, lips, and jaws which are rather sluggish in their speech activity, and many other cases adopt fixed habits of speech in which the above-mentioned structures make but minimal movements. Nasality and a "mushy, hot-potato-in-mouth" quality often result from such habits, and, therefore, the habits require modification. The general outline of treatment for these cases is as follows: (1) phonograph recording of voice and other techniques to promote self-hearing; (2) comparison with other individuals in the habitual use of the same structures (this may be carried out through testing the comparative abilities to make a certain number of tongue-palatal contacts per second, or through observation of self and model in a mirror while speaking in unison); (3) the use of swallowing, chewing, coughing, and similar biological movement sequences to promote speed of the articulators; (4) babbling practice while relaxed; (5) specific exercises in sudden initiation, repetition, or rhythmic timing of velar occlusion, tongue-teeth contacts, jaw openings, and so on; (6) exaggerated articulation of the vowels, compensating for error; (7) normal speech assignments; (8) negative practice. Many exercises for accomplishing these goals will be found in the references or may easily be invented.

Strain. One of the most frequent causes of voice disorders is overuse and strain of the voice. While the best therapy for this condition is to take care of it before it occurs—that is, to use preventive rather than remedial methods—it presents a very serious handicap when it does occur. Parents of children who show an especially prevalent tendency toward becoming very hoarse or dysphonic after strenuous play should be informed of the probable consequences and urged to do what they can to prevent the screaming and shrieking which seems to be such a large part of American childhood. During the period of huskiness or hoarseness following overstrain, it is necessary to prescribe and enforce whispered speech, which should consist of relaxed whispering rather than the tense, strained, aspirate quality frequently heard. The child should be prevented from engaging in any further strained vocalization during the period of recovery. While some voices seem able to withstand any amount of abuse, the majority of them definitely cannot, and certain voices need positive protection.

Individuals whose occupations demand a great deal of public speaking often misuse their vocal apparatus in several ways, especially when there is great competition for speech or attention. They use too high a pitch or too nasal a quality. They draw up the thyroid to a position directly underneath the hyoid bone, thereby producing a rather high-pitched and strident tone. Some of them, especially the announcers, hawkers, and newsboys, acquire habits of maintaining a constant pitch with a minimum of inflections. Others get stereotyped inflections so marked that they call attention to themselves and interfere with communication. Occupational voices, such as the "schoolma'am's voice" and "clergyman's tone," frequently result. Most of these conditions are readily cleared up through information as to the causes and the other possible vocal methods available to these speakers. Where the causes result in an actual voice disorder, that disorder may be removed by the methods to be described in the next sections.

When poor pitch discrimination, the use of an unnatural pitch level, or the presence of bad breathing habits are the causes of the voice disorder, remedial measures are necessary. The habits must be broken, and new ones must be built up.

Imitation. A very common cause of voice disorders is imitation. Most children ape the mannerisms of all individuals for whom they have respect, affection, or hero-worship. This imitation is a form of identifying oneself with the person imitated. Unfortunately, it often causes the child to acquire the disabilities of the model. The child usually progresses through a series of such identifications as he matures, and so the bad effects of any single identification are usually canceled. Education of the parents or associates of the child will prevent any pathological fixation resulting from encouragement of such imitation. The best method to use in eradicating the influence of imitation is to bring the mannerisms up to consciousness with consequent insight into the mechanism involved. The child should be required to imitate the model in a very conscious manner, listening to the pitch, intensity, and quality thereby produced. Burlesquing and exaggerating the traits imitated often eradicate them. Good-natured and humorous penalties help a great deal. Other models should be imitated, especially in situations in which the student is somewhat insecure. Even when these habits are of long standing, such techniques are very useful.

Hypertension. Another common cause of voice disorders is the presence of excess tension in the vocal apparatus. The laryngeal valve is one of the first structures of the body to reflect any general tenseness. This is clearly demonstrated in the emotional states of fear, excitement, and rage. The popular expressions, "My heart was in my mouth" (globus hystericus), and "I was scared speechless," indicate the validity of this observation. Readiness for emergency action demands the holding of the breath with a resultant firm closure of the vocal cords, and tenseness is merely a synonym for such readiness. Moreover, excess tension causes constriction of the soft surfaces of the resonating cavities and difficulty in performing the quick transitions needed in speech. All of these factors produce symptoms of defective pitch, intensity, and voice quality.

The usual cause of this hypertension is insecurity and maladjustment. Feelings of inadequacy in a social situation always provoke tenseness, and, when this sense of inadequacy permeates the majority of the individual's life situations, a general and almost permanent hypertension results. Only through mental-hygiene methods and readjustment can such a problem be solved. Voice training will always be useless until such a cause is eliminated. Occasionally, however, hypertension becomes such a habitual associate of certain specific speech situations, such as the telephone or public speaking, that it persists long after the original insecurity has disappeared. It often becomes localized in certain structures, such as the throat or the tongue. In these instances, relaxation exercises are helpful and necessary.

Methods for relaxation. Many exercises and systems of relaxation have been invented and are in widespread use. The student should familiarize himself with these methods as they are described in the references given at the end of the chapter. Those by Jacobson are especially recommended. In general, the sequence is usually as follows: (1) The student is required to assume a position which requires a minimum of muscular contraction in order to maintain his posture. This is frequently accompanied by strong suggestions by the teacher of quiescence, peacefulness, freedom, and limpness. Biological functions such as yawning or stretching are used as reinforcing devices. Sleep and hypnoidal states, however, should be guarded against, for what is desired is conscious relaxation. (2) After the student has attained a rather consistent state of general relaxation, the teacher, speaking and moving slowly, should move the student's arm up and down or from side to side, requiring the student to remain entirely passive and without resisting the movement. This will give the student some of the sensations of the type of kinesthesia desired. (3) After this has been done successfully, the same procedure should be repeated with the exception that the student resists the movement while maintaining a passive and fairly complete state of relaxation with the rest of his body. The resistance should not be complete but yielding, resulting finally in thorough relaxation of the structure moved. Differential tension produced through the resistance should be gradually changed to differential relaxation. These techniques should then be repeated in an easy sitting and standing posture. (4) After the student has learned to employ the techniques consistently with his arms or legs, he should attempt a similar tensing and relaxing of the lips, jaw, tongue, palate, throat, and larynx, always seeking to identify, perpetuate, and produce the sensations which mean relaxation. Frequently, these sensations seem to be of a negative variety to the subject—that is, they appear when he seems to be "letting go" or "becoming limp." They consist of "not doing" something, of "not making" some contraction. (5) Speech activity should be attempted first in a very effortless whisper, taking place on the regular expiration of silent breathing, without permitting any alteration in the regularity of the preceding inspiration. It should proceed through gradual stages, often employing a quiet yawning to produce the effortless vocalization desired. It should always be accompanied by the "feel" of relaxation in the structures of the laryngeal and articulatory musculature. (6) Beginning first with reading, repetitive, or memorized material when alone with the teacher, the student progresses to simple propositional speech, such as that involved in retelling stories or incidents. Then other people are included within the speech situation, and, finally, question-and-answer techniques are used. (7) The student is required to go, with the teacher as an observer, into speech situations which will produce mild emotional states. In these he attempts to speak while still maintaining both a general and localized relaxation. From this point, he should be required to keep a diary or daily check of situations in which he failed to carry out his new technique, and frequent checkups should be maintained.

Emotional maladjustment. Some authorities state that the most common of all causes of voice disorders is maladjustment. It is certainly true that a great many voice cases present personality problems and give a history of profound emotional conflicts. This is due, in part, to the influence of emotion upon intonation. The cries of animals and infants and the speech of primitive man demonstrate conclusively that one of the fundamental expressions of emotional states is that of phonation. Pitch level, inflection, quality, and intensity all show the influence of emotion. The long training required by actors in the perfection of their art, a training which frequently demands the artificial creation of an emotional state, shows this relationship. The phonatory aspect of speech always tends to reflect the attitude of the person speaking.

In view of these observations, it is not difficult to understand why emotional conflicts and maladjustment will produce voice defects. Aphonia, the complete loss of vocalized speech, is frequently hysterical. Too high a pitch level, nasality, and a harsh or strident voice quality are often due to the individual's desire to attack or dominate the group which makes him insecure. Individuals who tend to retreat or escape from unpleasant reality or social rejection often exhibit monotones or stereotyped inflections. Such symptoms are due to the desire to guard against the group's awareness of the emotion being experienced by their victim. And, as we said in the last section, a sense of inadequacy in any situation results in hypertension, which itself can cause disorders in all the three aspects of speech. When such factors cause the peculiar voice, it is often necessary for the speech-correction teacher to help the individual solve his emotional conflicts.

Whenever possible, the speech correctionist should enlist the co-operation of the school psychologist, the parents, and the classroom teacher. Occasionally it will be necessary to refer the case to a psychiatrist or psychoeducational clinic. It must always be remembered that the solution of mental conflicts involves a great deal of responsibility for the teacher. Amateur experimentation with human lives is detestable. Nevertheless, parents and teachers are constantly being compelled to help the child solve his emotional problems, and the speech correctionist must often aid them. If he thoroughly realizes his limitations and adopts the attitude of an assistant rather than that of a Dr. Freud, he may be of inestimable value. Most persons beset with emotional conflicts need some assistance and guidance, even if it be no more than the presence of a human ear into which they can pour their troubles. If this ear belongs to a person with some background in mental hygiene and abnormal psychology, and some experience in self-improvement and adjustment, a well-planned remedial program will soon be devised and initiated. Suggestions for the treatment of maladjustment were given in Chapter 4.

The causes of voice disorders which have been mentioned are the most common ones which the speech correctionist will meet. Every effort should be made to discover and remove them and their influences. Voice disorders, more so than any other disorder, require the diagnosis and removal of etiological factors. Treatment of the symptoms is often necessary, but voice retraining is usually doomed to failure unless the reasons for the defect are eliminated.

Illustrative Case Report

The case was a young man, aged 25 years, who had suffered infantile paralysis at thirteen, and as a result could only walk through the use of crutches. He seemed remarkably well adjusted to his physical handicap but was extremely concerned and maladjusted about his speech defect, a high-pitched falsetto voice. His history prior to the illness had little significance for prognosis or treatment. Thereafter he had developed withdrawal reactions ranging from fantasy to isolating himself on the farm of one of his father's tenants. He refused to attend high school after his Junior year. This reaction was the direct result of a remark he had overheard which cast aspersion on his masculinity. He came to the clinic reluctantly and without hope.

Examination disclosed normal secondary sex characteristics, vocal cords of normal length and texture, superior intelligence and hearing, musical talent, and marked introversion. Analysis of the voice demonstrated the following: excellent pitch discrimination and placement within his range; normal inflection and singing ability; a pitch range of nine semitones from D above middle C to $G\sharp$ with a habitual pitch of F. All of his tones, both sung or spoken, possessed the falsetto quality. He could yodel occasionally at higher pitches than those given. In speaking he habitually drew the larynx upward and backward as in swallowing. This reflex did occur frequently both prior to speech attempt and within his sentences. The omohyoid muscle was excessively contracted and resulted in a peculiar shoulder posture. He usually spoke with the chin lowered. All of the extrinsic throat muscles were highly tensed. No breathing abnormalities showed up in the polygraphic record.

Phonographic recording of the voice and the use of a hearing aid which amplified his own voice were used to help him formulate the problem to be solved and information was given him concerning the etiology and therapy for falsetto voice. Then he was asked to lie down on a cot with his head hanging backward over the edge. In this position he was asked to whisper a prolonged *ee* (*i*) vowel, sustaining it as long as possible. We then asked him to produce the same sound in the same way but "to sigh it softly but aloud." The pitch produced was *G* below middle *C*, and he was so surprised that he sat up, so tense that we terminated the conference, instructing him not to do any practice by himself. The next day the same procedure was performed, this time after preliminary relaxation and cautions to remain that way. We were able to produce all the vowels and voiced continuant sounds both in isolation and in nonsense syllables.

The next day we used short phrases and sentences first uttered in a monotone at a pitch level of *A* below middle *C*, then with inflections. No failure was experienced but at the end of the practice period he expressed doubts concerning his ability to speak "in a man's voice" with his head held normally. In our next session we raised the head slowly until it was level with the cot, without losing the lower pitch level. We suggested that he try the same technique by himself at home when lying on his bed. When he returned the next day he was speaking normally at a pitch level of *A* below middle *C*, and he reported that he had "slipped" into the falsetto only three times, during excitement. He complained, however, that he felt strange and uncomfortable "as though there was a stranger using my mouth." We then gave him a play to read with parts for a small child and a father. He used the old falsetto for the child's role and the new deep voice for the father's. Within a week he had become accustomed to the new voice and a year later was entirely recovered.

References

1. Allen, B. and Peterson, G. E., "Laryngeal Inflammation in a Case of Falsetto," *Journal of Speech Disorders*, 1942, Volume 7, pages 175–178.

T-F: A falsetto voice is usually psychogenic in origin.

T-F: Inflammation of the vocal cords is more often the result of a vocal disorder than its cause.

Essay: How can lowering the pitch decrease the tension?

2. Bangs, J. L., and Freidinger, A. A., "A Case of Hysterical Dysphonia in an Adult," *Journal of Speech and Hearing Disorders,* 1950, Volume 15, pages 316–323.

T-F: The patient was placed on silence for four weeks prior to therapy.

T-F: The symptomatic therapy was also a psychotherapy.

Essay: Describe the therapy with this case.

3. Bangs, J. L., and Freidinger, A. A., "Diagnosis and Treatment of a Case of Hysterical Aphonia in a Thirteen-year-old Girl," *Journal of Speech and Hearing Disorders,* 1949, Volume 14, pages 312–317.

T-F: The girl had whispered for five years before getting therapy.

T-F: The girl was taught the phonetic alphabet.

Essay: Describe the treatment of this case.

4. Babcock, M., "Speech Therapy for Certain Vocal Disorders," *Journal of Laryngology and Otolaryngology,* 1942, Volume 57, pages 101–112.

Treatment for aphonia and weak voices is included in this article.

5. Bartholomew, W. T., "The Paradox of Voice Teaching," *Journal of the Acoustical Society of America,* 1940, Volume 11, pages 446–450.

The author criticizes some of the directions given by voice and speech teachers about relaxing the throat, placing the voice, and "getting the voice out of the throat."

6. Berry, M., and Eisenson, J., *The Defective in Speech,* New York, F. S. Crofts, 1942, pages 148–176.

A general discussion of the nature, causes, and treatment of voice disorders. Exercises are given for each of the main voice defects.

7. Crews, L., "A Case of Juvenile Voice," *Proceedings of the American Speech Correction Association,* 1936, Volume 6, pages 142–149.

The description of the treatment of a youth with a child's voice.

8. Curry, R., *The Mechanism of the Human Voice,* New York, Longmans Green, 1940.

Perhaps the best reference on the function of phonation to date. The anatomy, physiology, and physics of the voice are treated thoroughly and scientifically. The chapter, "Disorders of the Voice," is an excellent one.

9. Curry, T., "Hoarseness and Voice Change in Male Adolescents," *Journal of Speech and Hearing Disorders,* 1949, Volume 14, pages 23–25.

T-F: Hoarseness and huskiness are quite characteristic of more than half of male children from 10 to 14 years, according to author.

T-F: According to Froeschels, adolescent hoarseness is not organic.

10. Curry, T., "Voice Breaks and Pathological Larynx Conditions," *Journal of Speech Disorders*, 1948, Volume 13, pages 356–358.

T-F: Voice breaks in pitch can occur before puberty.

T-F: Voice breaks can be upward as well as downward in pitch.

Essay: Describe two of the cases cited.

11. Duncan, M. H., "Personality Adjustment Techniques in Voice Therapy," *Journal of Speech Disorders*, 1947, Volume 12, pages 161–167.

An account of group therapy from the mental hygiene point of view. Some typical cases are presented.

12. Fairbanks, G., *Practical Voice Practice*, New York, Harper & Brothers, 1944.

Exercise material for voice retraining is provided. There is an excellent section on changing the pitch and another on rate control and phrasing.

13. Fairbanks, G., "Recent Experimental Investigations of Vocal Pitch in Speech," *Journal of the Acoustical Society of America*, 1940, Volume 11, pages 457–466.

A summary of unpublished investigations in voice. Natural pitch of superior male speakers is C below middle C; for superior female speakers, $G\sharp$ below middle C. Other similar data.

14. Fairbanks, G., *Practical Voice Practice*, New York, F. S. Crofts, 1944.

Methods for determining the natural pitch of the voice are described and exercises and drill material for changing the pitch are given.

15. Fletcher, H., *Speech and Hearing*, New York, D. Van Nostrand, 1929, pages 266–289.

This section of the book lists the audibility characteristics of the various speech sounds.

16. Froeschels, E., and Jellinek, A., *Practice of Voice and Speech Therapy*, Boston, Expression Co., 1941, pages 248 *ff.*

A description and theoretical justification of the chewing method for producing relaxed voices.

17. Gilkinson, H., "A Study of the Relationship Between Psychological and Physical Measures of Masculinity," *Genetic Psychology Monographs*, 1937, Volume 19, pages 105–154.

This study gives methods for determining the habitual pitch levels, with an account of the reliability of the measures.

18. Glauber, I. P., "Speech Characteristics of Psychoneurotic Patients," *Journal of Speech Disorders*, 1944, Volume 9, pages 18–30.

Case presentations of psychoneurotic patients demonstrate that the voice of such patients is often affected.

19. Harrington, R., "A Study of the Mechanism of Velopharyngeal Closure," *Journal of Speech Disorders*, 1944, Volume 9, pages 325–345.

A technical but excellent description of how the soft palate is controlled.

20. Henrikson, E. H., and Thaler, M., "Assumptions and Their Relation to the Use of Speech Drills," *Quarterly Journal of Speech*, Volume 31, 1945, pages 229–230.

T-F: Two drills are better than one drill.

T-F: Most nasality is due to carelessness.

Essay: What is the essence of the argument put forth by these authors?

21. Holmes, F. L. D., *A Handbook of Voice and Diction*, New York, F. S. Crofts, 1940.

Exercises in relaxation, in getting the optimal pitch, in flexibility of pitch and intensity, and in voice quality retraining are given.

22. Huber, M. W., and Kopp, A. E., *The Practice of Speech Correction in the Medical Clinic*, Boston, Expression Co., 1942.

Treats the more rare varieties of abnormal voice such as: vicarious voice; hoarseness; adenoidal speech; and dysphonias of functional origin.

23. Hultzen, L. S., "Apparatus for Demonstrating Nasality," *Journal of Speech Disorders*, 1942, Volume 7, pages 5–7.

Describes a contact microphone to fit on the nose and thereby to help self-hearing and ear training.

24. Jacobson, E., *Progressive Relaxation*, Chicago, University of Chicago Press, 1938.

A practical clinical discussion of the method of progressive relaxation in which the person is trained to reduce or completely eliminate muscular tension. A long bibliography is given.

25. Judson, L., and Weaver, A. T., *Voice Science*, New York, F. S. Crofts, 1941.

The anatomy, physiology, and physics of voice are described in detail. The examination technique for observing the larynx is clearly presented.

26. Loebell, H., "Voice and Speech Disorders in the German Army," *Quarterly Journal of Speech*, 1944, Volume 30, pages 259–261.

T-F: Overexertion can cause aphonia.

T-F: Unless the patient continues to use his new voice he will become hoarse again.

Essay: What kinds of treatment were used for these disorders?

27. Mithoefer, W., "Simple Treatment for Defects of Singing and Speaking Voice," *Archives of Otolaryngology*, 1941, Volume 31, pages 16–22.

The author recommends the use of a faradic current of electricity as part of the treatment for aphonia and dysphonia.

28. Moser, H. M., "Diagnostic and Clinical Procedures in Rhinolalia," *Journal of Speech Disorders*, 1942, Volume 7, pages 1–4.

Describes twelve methods, mechanical and otherwise, which will aid a case in lifting his soft palate, or in strengthening it.

29. Moser, H. M., "Symposium on Unique Cases of Speech Disorders; Presentation of a Case," 1942, Volume 7, pages 173–174.

The author describes the use of ventricular phonation as a device to lower the habitual pitch of the voice.

30. Peacher, G., "Contact Ulcer of the Larynx: A Clinical Study of Vocal Reeducation, Part III," *Journal of Speech Disorders*, 1947, Volume 12, pages 179–190.

T-F: The ulcer healed as a result of speech therapy.

T-F: Surgery plus silence is the most effective method for aphonia.

Essay: Describe the vocal therapy advocated.

31. Pronovost, W., "Research Contributions to Voice Improvement," *Journal of Speech Disorders*, 1942, Volume 7, pages 313–318.

The results of recent investigations in voice are summarized and their implications for vocal therapy are presented. There are good suggestions for breathiness, increasing the pitch range, and improving the quality.

32. Root, A. R., "The Pitch Factor in Speech; A Survey," *Quarterly Journal of Speech*, 1930, Volume 16, pages 320–335.

A survey of the historical concepts of pitch and pitch changes, with a summary of recent experimental investigations in the field. A long bibliography is included.

33. Scripture, E. W., *The Elements of Experimental Phonetics*, New York, Scribner's, 1902.

This old classic is still the source of many novel ideas regarding voice. The section on overtone production is especially worth reading.

34. Snidecor, J. C., "The Pitch and Duration Characteristics of Superior Female Speakers During Oral Reading," *Journal of Speech and Hearing Disorders*, 1951, Volume 16, pages 44–52.

T-F: We can speak at a lower pitch level than we can sing.

T-F: Female pitch levels for adults are 2/3 of an octave higher than those for males.

Essay: How many different vowels are there in the Rainbow passage?

35. Sokolowsky, R. R., and Junkermann, E. B., "War Aphonia," *Journal of Speech Disorders*, 1944, Volume 9, pages 193–208.

The nature and treatment of aphonia. The various methods for shocking the patient into vocalization are described.

36. Stanley, D., *Your Voice*, New York, Pitman, 1945.

This book should be read by the student with a skeptical eye, but the language used is the language of most teachers of singing.

37. Strother, C. R., "The Vocal Consequences of Various Surgical Procedures for Relief of Bilateral Recurrent Nerve Paralysis of the Larynx," *Journal of Speech Disorders*, 1940, Volume 5, pages 121–127.

Do not do any speech training with bilateral paralysis of vocal cords or patient may die. Describes a new operation which restores abduction of cords and then permits speech therapy.

38. Thorne, K., " 'Client Centered' Therapy for Voice and Personality Cases," *Journal of Speech Disorders*, 1947, Volume 12, pages 314–318.

Recommends and describes the counseling interview as psychotherapy.

39. Van Dusen, C. R., "A Laboratory Study of the Metallic Voice," *Journal of Speech Disorders*, 1941, Volume 6, pages 137–140.

A description of the auditory characteristics of the harsh "metallic" voice. The fundamental and lower overtones are more prominent in the metallic voice.

40. Vennard, W., *Singing: The Mechanism and the Technic*, Ann Arbor, Edwards Brothers, 1949.

An excellent little book on voice training from the point of view of the singing instructor.

41. Voelker, C. H., "Frequency of Hoarseness Due to Phonation with the Thyro-arytenoid Lips," *Archives Otolaryngology*, 1942, Volume 36, pages 71–76.

Vocalization with the false vocal cords frequently produces hoarse voices.

42. Voelker, C. H., "Phoniatry in Dysphonia Ventricularis," *Annals of Otology, Rhinology, and Laryngology*, 1935, Volume 44, pages 471–472.

Describes the unpleasant voice quality as "a rattling, tumbling, cracking or ticker-like substitution for phonation." Outlines the treatment.

43. West, R., "The Function of the Speech Pathologists in Studying Cases of Dysphonia," *Journal of Speech Disorders*, 1938, Volume 3, pages 81–84.

Brief discussion of the duties of a speech correctionist in diagnosing and treating functional speech disorders.

44. West, R., Kennedy, L., and Carr, A., *The Rehabilitation of Speech*, Harper & Brothers, New York, (revised edition), 1947.

Chapters 6 and 7 concern the various disorders of voice and should be read by all students of speech therapy.

45. Wiksell, W. A., "An Experimental Analysis of Respiration in Relation to the Intensity of Vocal Tones in Speech," *State University of Louisiana Studies*, 1936, Volume 27, pages 37–51, 99–164.

An analysis of the relation between vocal tone and types of breathing, vocal capacity, and chest expansion.

46. Williamson, A. B., "Diagnosis and Treatment of Eighty-Four Cases of Nasality," *Quarterly Journal of Speech*, 1944, Volume 30, pages 471–479.

T-F: Rhinolalia clausa is synonymous with denasality.

T-F: Rhinolalia aperta requires a cleft or sluggish velum.

Essay: Describe the type of therapy used.

47. Williamson, A. B., "Diagnosis and Treatment of Seventy-Two Cases of Hoarse Voice," *Quarterly Journal of Speech*, 1945, Volume 31, pages 189–202.

T-F: Hoarseness is produced by laryngeal inflammation primarily.

T-F: Speech therapists should receive medical clearance before accepting voice cases showing hoarseness.

Essay: Evaluate the author's argument.

48. Wyatt, G., "Voice Disorders and Personality Conflicts," *Mental Hygiene*, 1941, Volume 25, pages 237–250.

The emotional causes of voice disorders are discussed.

9. Stuttering

A severely handicapped adult stutterer is not a pleasant sight. Not even to the stutterer himself. This is what one such person wrote shortly after he had observed his symptoms in a mirror for the first time:

He was horrible—that person in the mirror. He choked, panted, twisted his face. The lips protruded quiveringly in an impossible struggle to vomit the word. The glazed eyes denied all contact with the outside world. The tongue fought viciously to prevent any air from escaping even as the chest and belly heaved to blast it out. Finally when it seemed the face would blow apart, a contorted head jerk broke the agony and the word exploded. What was the word? My name—just my own name.

The normal speaking individual is surprised and appalled by such a stutterer. He finds it incredible that speech which flows so easily and automatically from his own mouth should require such an effort from another's. Surely there must be some grave and deep abnormality here. The suddenness, the grotesqueness, are too mysteriously peculiar to be ignored. The listener recoils from such monstrousness, or he laughs or pities, even as men have done for a thousand years when confronted by gross deformity. To each of us there is threat when another human runs amok.

Fortunately, all stutterers are not so severe. Indeed, no single stutterer is always or consistently so handicapped. Though stutterers spend their lives in a restless quest for some healer who can give them free speech, the great majority of them, oddly enough, have more fluency than they have stuttering if the total number of words spoken are evaluated in this way. Often, immediately after a severe blocking they may utter two or three sentences with complete ease. At certain times, or in certain situations they may have no difficulty at all. We worked with one case who usually stuttered on the word "two," but never on the words "to" or "too," even though all are uttered in exactly the same way. How shall we understand this mysterious disorder? Where shall we find the "impediment"?

Many people have tried to find the answers to these questions. Many have been sure that they knew the answer to the stuttering problem, but the honest speech therapist knows that he is still confronted with a disorder which retains much of its age-old mystery. Most of the past and present explanations contain some truth; none of them is entirely satisfactory. Many beginning students are so disturbed when they discover such a state of affairs that they tend to lose interest in the subject. But there is to be found a similar mystery in many of the other disorders that afflict mankind—heart disease, tooth decay, asthma and cancer, to name only a few. If there are conflicting theories concerning the nature of stuttering, there is also the ever-present fact that stutterers are with us, needing help. And we can do much to help them.

So far as stuttering is concerned, speech correction is at present in the era of "authorities" just as medicine was before Pasteur's discovery of bacterial agents in disease. Some of those early medical authorities were able and wise physicians. They had made some very keen and valid observations concerning diseases. In some instances they discovered the cure for the disease long before they knew its nature. For example, the witch doctors of native tribes on the Malay Peninsula diagnosed diabetes by putting specimens of urine near ant hills, and, when the ants were attracted, prescribed certain food taboos which helped their patients cut down on sugar intake. The results were excellent, but the theories which they used to justify their diagnosis and prescription were, to say the least, confused and inaccurate. Stutterers have been helped by many different methods of treatment based on many conflicting theories. In this text we shall endeavor to present the nature and treatment of stuttering in the light of our present knowledge. There is much that we do not know about stuttering, yet we know enough to help the majority of our cases.

In Chapter 2 we defined stuttering as the disorder characterized by blockings, prolongations, or repetitions of words, syllables, sounds, or mouth postures, all of which (together with the contortions or devices used to avoid, postpone, disguise, start, or release the speech abnormality) produce interruptions and breaks in the rhythmic flow of speech. This is admittedly more of a description than a definition, and it indicates the complexity of the disorder. In its mildest form, its possessor is often entirely unaware of the interruptions. In very severe stutterers, the interruptions are accompanied by contortions so grotesque that they almost resemble spastic and epileptic seizures. In adult stutterers, an almost infinite variety of stuttering symptoms may be found, although in young children, when the disorder first tends to manifest itself, the symptoms are largely confined to the above-mentioned repetitions and prolongations. These seem to be the only symptoms common to all stutterers.

Stuttering is no respecter of persons. It afflicts king and beggar, savant and ignoramus, Hebrew and Hottentot, virtuous and sinful, and all other categories you might choose. Moses himself is said to have stuttered, and we know that King Charles I, Charles Lamb, and Charles Darwin (to select but three of the millions of people who have experienced this disorder) were likewise afflicted. There are approximately 1,400,-000 stutterers in the United States alone, and one of every one hundred children is destined to suffer from this abnormality.

It is obvious that so universal and dramatic a disorder should provoke many attempts to cure it or alleviate its distress, and the history of these attempts comprises a large share of the history of speech correction. Witchcraft, the surgeon's knife, appliances for the tongue, drugs, hypnotism, psychoanalysis, arm swinging, and a host of other devices and methods have been employed, and a few "cures" seem to be obtained by any method, no matter how grotesque. Naturally, the charlatans and quacks have flourished in so fertile a field, victimizing many thousands of stutterers every year. The medical profession, however, has largely ignored stutterers, and only in the last few years have the scientists concerned themselves with this urgent problem. Much of the research that has been carried out has been sterile, resulting in a large number of antagonistic theories whose proposers have spent more time in defending their theories than in testing to discover more pertinent facts about the abnormality.

Much of the mystery of stuttering is due to the tendency of investigators to confine their observation to the adult case, with little regard for the development of the disorder. The research on children who stutter has been meager, but it at least enables us to see the dim outlines of a consistent pattern of growth.

The Origins of Stuttering

Stuttering begins in early childhood in the vast majority of cases, usually between the ages of two and four years of age, the period of speech development during which the child is mastering his fluency skills. Sometimes it begins dramatically and suddenly:

One of our cases began to stutter severely on Christmas morning, repeating sounds and syllables, hesitating, and prolonging vowel sounds so markedly that he was referred to us that very afternoon. We had seen the child the week before and had noticed no speech abnormality, nor had his parents, according to their report. He spoke normally that morning until he asked the question "Dih-dih-dih-dih-dih-didn't I g . . . ggg . . . ge . . . get a-a-a-anything fr . . . om mmmmmmy Da . . . da . . . daddy?" The father was not present, having been on a business trip, and he had expected to return that afternoon, bringing his presents with him. However, he was delayed for three more days, and his return did not allay the problem. Subsequent exploration revealed that the child felt profoundly rejected by his busy father.

Much more frequently, however, it begins so gradually that few parents can date its onset with any degree of certainty. Most parents expect a certain amount of non-fluency of children this young and tend to ignore it. As Davis (46) has shown, all children show a marked amount of repetition in their speech, of sounds, syllables, words and phrases. When a child is constantly trying to verbalize new experiences, competing with adults for communication, attempting to imitate their complex sentences, trying to speak under extreme emotion, hunting for the proper words with meager vocabularies, putting half-formed thoughts into the grammatical and syntactical patterns of acceptable English, hesitations are bound to occur. The need to speak, the need to impose a newly discovered ego on a busy adult world, the extreme urgency of the demand for expression are very potent at this period. Most children run a gauntlet when they try to talk, beset and belabored by fluency-disruptors from every direction. The majority of children pass through unscathed, but some fall by the wayside. They become the stutterers.

What distinguishes these children from those who become fluent? There are several explanations. They may be children whose frustration tolerance is low. They may be children whose speech environments are excessively loaded with fluency disruptors. They may be children whose basic fluency skills are inadequate. They may be children whose parents react to their normal non-fluency by anxiety or penalty. They may be children to whom broken speech has become the outward expression of a deep emotional conflict. Or the child may be the victim of a combination of several of these factors.

We have already considered an example of the onset of stuttering emerging from a background of emotional conflict. Let us look at some of the other origins.

Jimmy, aged 4, was in most respects a rather ordinary normal child. But he differed markedly from other children his age in his outstanding inability to tolerate frustration. This was not inborn, but the result of poor handling by his parents, his uncle and his older sister. The whole family loved to tease each other, to play practical jokes, to upset apple carts and egos. Even as a baby, Jimmy was teased with the bottle being held tantalizingly to the lips, or withdrawn, or waved from side to side. The adults liked to pretend to drop him; they put obstacles in the way of his crawling; they greatly enjoyed seeing him become purple with rage. At the age of two he was holding his breath until his face became blue. Toilet training was slow and his family interpreted his occasionally urinary lapses upon those who held him as a sign of his family-belongingness. As is obvious from the foregoing description, a good amount of hidden hostility permeated the entire family living, but it appeared only in joking and teasing forms. The approved culture pattern was to be a good sport, to be able to take it and dish it out.

Jimmy, however, never quite managed to adopt these values. He fought back; he threw temper tantrums; he kicked and bit and howled. They called him a poor sport and, since they despised poor sports, they worked hard to toughen him to their teasing. He had spoken well and without any non-fluency until his fourth birthday when his sister began to kid him about his pronunciation of words beginning with the *s* blends which he had not mastered.

At this point they gave him, for the first time, a nickname "Twaberry Bwonde" since his hair was that color and he pronounced the words in that way. He reacted by going berserk, and so more teasing occurred, this time focused primarily on speech. The sister learned that he would tend to make more articulatory errors by interrupting him, finishing his sentences or hurrying, and she went to work. Within one week he was stuttering severely, though in a repetitive fashion. Two weeks later, he was showing facial contortions and severe struggling in breathing. At this point the parents became alarmed and brought the child to the speech therapist.

Although the parents and family changed their policies and all teasing was eliminated, the stuttering persisted. It was not until a lot of release therapy through play and until a course of training in frustration tolerance was instituted that first the struggle, and later the repetitions subsided and disappeared.

The above case study illustrates three of the situations out of which stuttering emerges: the low frustration tolerance, the presence of excessive fluency disruptors, and a basic emotional insecurity which became focused on speech.

Ricky, aged 5, illustrates another source of stuttering, one which Johnson has vivified by his statement that "Stuttering begins, not in the child's mouth but in the parent's ear." We first met the child at the age of three. He was brought to us by his mother, a former college speech teacher. She was tense and anxious about the boy, claiming that he was beginning to stutter. In three hours of observation, play, and parent conversation, we were unable to find anything but an occasional repetition of a phrase or whole word, usually under conditions of word choice which would have made any adult hesitate. Each time one of these occurred, she would roll her eyes or tug at our sleeves to point out the stuttering. Knowing that stuttering is intermittent, we even introduced some experimental stress, hurrying the child, interrupting, rejecting his statements, and averting our attention. He was remarkably fluent, much more so than most children of his age.

Recognizing the mother's anxiety, and being as careful as possible, we tried to reassure and educate her concerning the prevalence of repetition and hesitation in most children's speech. We made available some parental counseling to help her face her own problems, but she refused to participate. Said she, "You're just like everyone else. Every doctor and speech therapist I've taken Ricky to has said the same thing. You can't fool a child's own mother. He's stuttering and you know it."

A year later, she brought the child back to the clinic, and sure enough he was stuttering with all the abnormality of an adult. "See!" she said triumphantly, "I told you he was a stutterer all the time."

Rigmor Knutsen, a Danish speech therapist, said to us, "In Denmark we find a great many children who begin to stutter after the speech therapist has treated them for their delayed speech. Do you not also find this true?" We answered that we had known several cases who bore out her observation and told her about Carlene.

Carlene, at four, had no intelligible speech. She used a few vowels and grunts with her gestures to make her wants known. She was referred to us by the psychological clinic who had found her IQ on the performance tests to be so low that they were considering suggesting commitment to a state school for the feeble minded. By imitating her behavior until she imitated us we were able to go about getting her to produce almost all of the isolated speech sounds. By avoiding all requests to name objects, and through the use of self talk and parallel talking, we evoked enough vocalized and whispered words to accept her for therapy. At the end of three months of daily work, she was speaking in short phrases and retests in the psychological clinic showed her to be of normal intelligence. Her parents were very proud of her achievement, but during the summer vacation, they worked too hard upon her speech production and she began to stutter very markedly. Advised to give up all therapy, the parents co-operated willingly and within two more months the symptoms disappeared completely. The burden of trying to master her articulation and fluency skills had been too great. It was interesting that she regressed to simpler phrases and sentences as the stuttering disappeared, and for a time her articulation became worse.

Many children who do not have delayed speech go through a similar period of non-fluency when, urged by parental approvals, they try to master the adult patterns of speech too quickly. It is a long step from the single word utterance of the one-year-old to the multiple-word phrases and sentences of adult speech. Children who try to dance before they have learned to walk trip themselves, and the same thing occurs in speech. We tend to think of penalties as being provocative of stuttering.

Excessive approvals at the wrong times can create such a demand as to produce speech hesitation as well. Many children from happy homes can start to stutter in this way.

Even when the demands of the parents for fluency are not excessive, certain children appear to be stuttering-prone. The hereditary factor has been noted in many researches, and although some of the predisposition toward stuttering may be a matter of the social inheritance of speech anxieties as Gray (66) has indicated, yet Nelson (12) showed that even when the children had no contact with their stuttering parents, the orphans who stuttered had more stuttering in their background than did the normal speaking orphans.

Even when there is no history of stuttering in the family, some children seem ill-equipped to handle the intricate timing of muscular coordinations which fluent speech requires. The utterance of a single word is a marvel of precise timing of breathing, phonation and articulation. Just as some children are superbly coordinated, so also are there the awkward ones. If a thousand children were measured in terms of their ability to move their tongues, mouths, vocal cords or breathing muscles in a complicated sequence, we would find as many dubs at one end of the distribution as we find verbal athletes at the

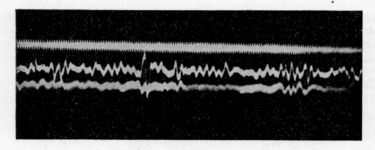

Fig. 10. Action current record showing unequal reception of nervous impulses in the paired masseter muscles during the stuttering act. *Upper line:* time in thousandths of a second; *middle line:* action currents in right masseter; *lower line:* action currents in left masseter.

other. If the environmental pressures or emotional loading of communication were held constant, those of the tangled tongue would be likely to show more hesitations, repetitions and interruptions than would the verbal athletes. A certain amount of stuttering no doubt comes from this source. Let us look at such a child.

John was four and a half years old when we examined him. Although his parents brought him to us because of the excessive repetitions and prolongations that intermittently filled his speech, it was apparent that his difficulty was not confined to that function. He was poorly coordinated in many ways whenever he tried to do something swiftly. He fell more frequently. He could not clap his hands rhythmically. He could not keep time to the simplest tunes by tapping or body swaying. The task of rolling a ball across the floor by pushing it with both hands was impossible, although he could throw it with one hand fairly well. While sitting down, he could not raise both feet off the floor at the same time. He could not hit two keys on a piano simultaneously when he used both forefingers. On the Wellman tracing path test, he could draw fairly well with either hand, but when he held the pencil in both, he was helpless. He was entirely unaware of his stuttering and it appeared quite automatic and unconscious. What was more interesting was his normal speech. The latter was full of hesitations, pauses and fixed posturings. When he repeated in unison with us simple sentences at a very slow rate, he spoke perfectly, but when we increased the speed just a little he showed much non-fluency under the same conditions. He could move and speak smoothly at a very slow tempo, but the slightest hurrying or other disruptive pressure caused incoordination and blockings. His hand preference was generally in favor of the right hand, but he did many things with the left and often showed ambivalence in deciding which to use. Although there was no evidence of cerebral palsy or history of brain injury, the general pattern of poorly timed movements was so clear as to have some superficial resemblance to that disorder.

Stuttering then has a multiple origin. It can emerge out of backgrounds of emotional conflict, low frustration tolerance, a speech environment filled with fluency disruptors, a poorly timed dysphemia, parental labeling of the normal non-fluencies as abnormal, and from the stress felt by most children if, driven by their parents, they try too swiftly to master the art of talking in phrases and sentences. Of all these factors, the last is probably the most common source of stuttering. Our culture stresses the acquisition of adult forms of speech at too early an age and at the same time it provides no adequate methods of teaching the child to be fluent. Moreover, the age of fluency acquisition comes at the very period that prohibitions and taboos of every kind begin to be felt by the child. It is not surprising that more boys than girls stutter when we consider that the female child matures faster than the male. And it is not surprising that there are more than a million children of school age who stutter in this country. The real astonishment comes when we find so many more children running the gauntlet of

cultural ignorance and pressure and coming out safely with
fluent speech. Most children are amazingly tough.

Primary Stuttering

Thus far we have been using the term "stuttering" for the
repetitions, prolongations, hesitations and other forms of non-
fluency. Are we not, then, doing exactly what some parents do
when they label the normal non-fluencies by such a stigma
word? Johnson (84) and others of the semantic school prefer
to reserve the word stuttering for the advanced stages of the
disorder. They claim that all non-fluency is normal until the
person begins to fear it or struggle with it. Only then does it
become abnormal and deserve the term "stuttering." They
argue that if all the conditions surrounding the moment of
hesitation or repetition were known, it would be a perfectly
natural response of a normally functioning human being. Unfortunately our culture does not agree. Unlike the Indians (see
Johnson) *we* have a word for excessive repetitions, prolongations or breaks in the fluency of speech and we call it stuttering.
Perhaps we shouldn't use it, but we do. To try to tell a culture
it is thinking or talking incorrectly is to try to sweep back
the ocean with a broom. If a boy is saying "Mmmummy,
ca . . . ca . . . ca . . . ca . . . can I-I-I-I- I gggggo tuh-to th---e
st-st-stu-store wwwwith y-you?" it is terribly difficult to convince his mother that she and her husband and their friends
and his teacher are all wrong, and that he is not stuttering
at all but merely non-fluent. We in this book prefer to achieve
the same purposes by using the term "primary stuttering."

What then is "primary stuttering"? Glasner and Vermilyea
(64) questioned 171 therapists and their co-workers and found
that though much variability occurred, the great majority of
them used the phrase to designate repetitions, hesitations and
prolongations in speech without awareness or anxiety and without reactions of struggle or avoidance. We would insist that
in addition to this descriptive catalogue of behavior we also

employ the concept of variation. Only when this behavior is
so prevalent that it exceeds the normal amount of such non-
fluency should we make such a diagnosis. Similarly, since these
symptoms vary markedly with the amount of emotion being
expressed, and also with the amount of communicative conflict (interruptions, hurrying, listener inattention, etc.), we
would reserve the term primary stuttering for that which appears under conditions in which most of us would expect little
non-fluency to occur. In other words, we are deliberately adopt-
ing the cultural norms of fluency as our criterion. If a child
repeats, hesitates or is non-fluent so frequently that his speech
calls attention to itself and markedly interferes with communication, then our society tends to call him a stutterer and so
do we. However, if these symptoms comprise the total of his
abnormality and occur automatically and without evidence of
self-awareness, avoidance or struggle, and they appear in situations where most children are fluent, then we would insist that
he be diagnosed as a *primary stutterer* and treated as such. This
treatment, as we shall see, is aimed toward maintaining the
lack of awareness and anxiety, toward the removal of all factors which tend to disrupt smoothness of utterance, toward the
providing of experiences in fluency and toward strengthening
the child's resistance to those pressures which precipitate stuttering.

We have talked about the symptoms of primary stuttering
as though they were merely excessive amounts of the same type
of non-fluencies which all people have, adults and children
alike. While we do maintain this frequency factor, we also wish
to call attention to a qualitative aspect of the behavior our
culture tends to label as stuttering. The man on the street tends
to make a distinction between the fumbling repetitions of whole
words, sentences or phrases, repetitions which are felt by him
to be a normal frailty of communication in a competitive world,
and the more rapid, automatic repetitions of a single sound or
syllable. Davis's research, which has been quoted extensively
in support of the thesis that primary stuttering is merely nor-

mal non-fluency under stress, found that all children showed repetitions in their speech. But when her data are broken down into syllable, whole word and phrase categories, the repetition which the normal children had was in 90 per cent of the cases the repetition of whole words or phrases, not of a syllable or sound. As her own experiment also showed, the only stutterer in the group had a much greater proportion of syllable repetition, a finding which agrees with our own observations. The normal speaking child will say, "Mommy, may I--may--may I go with you?" but the stutterer will ask the question in this way: "Mmmm-mom-mommy, m-may I guh-guh-guh-go go wi-wi-with yyyyyyou?" The researches of Froeschels (58), Voelker (162), and Egland[1] also indicate that while the stutterer has difficulty in uttering his words, the nonstuttering child shows most of his hesitancy in completing his thought.

Primary stuttering is too useful a concept to discard. By employing it we avoid much difficulty and even danger. Parents of a child with excessive non-fluency are hard to reassure. They have had too much experience with "pooh-pooh therapy." They have been told long before not to worry, that of course the child would outgrow it. Even in those instances where they do accept the therapist's interpretation that the repetitions and hesitations are normal, they and the child live among friends, teachers and classmates who do not. Moreover such reassurance tends at other times to let them surrender all responsibility for altering the unfortunate conditions. They continue to heckle, interrupt, accuse, question, demand and reject. We find it wiser to say to them, "Yes, your child is stuttering, but it's a different kind of stuttering. Fortunately, he is still in the primary stage of the disorder, and with your help we should be able to help him master the fluency skills he needs. He has a little more non-fluency than the average child, but we should be able to reduce it."

---

[1] Egland, G., "An Analysis of Repetitions and Prolongations in the Speech of Young Children," State University of Iowa, Unpublished Master's Thesis, 1938.

"Outgrowing" stuttering, the term so frequently applied to the gradual disappearance of the handicap, is really a matter of maturation. The first symptoms appear when the child is in a state of developmental confusion. He is learning to speak while he is also giving his attention to the acquisition of walking and many other motor skills. His environment bombards him with hundreds of stimuli, and he responds to all of them, having learned experimentally no process of selection. Many simultaneous reactions, therefore, tend to create a nervous instability, which is often evidenced in an instability in the operation of the speech mechanism. As the process of maturation proceeds, the child learns his motor skills, and, when they become automatic, he does not need to concentrate upon them. He also learns to select stimuli from the barrage thrust upon him, and consequently much confusion disappears. He learns to erect barriers against environmental excitement and does not respond to all disturbances. Thus the child's entire mechanism becomes more stable, and, with increasing stability, the speech blocks often vanish. However, they disappear only if, during this period of instability, the child has not become aware of them as a definite handicap. If he can be prevented from reacting to his stuttering, he will develop none of the tricks for hiding blocks or for making speech attempts easier. Thus he will be spared the abnormal communication which these habitual tricks and techniques ultimately bring. Treatment of the young primary stutterer consists primarily of prevention.

This prevention is accomplished chiefly through the education and co-operation of the parents and teachers. It can truthfully be said that the way to treat a young stutterer in the primary stage is to let him alone and treat his parents and teachers. Nothing must be done to call his disorder to his attention or to point it out to him as an abnormality that he must eradicate. Such techniques only serve to develop awareness of the abnormality and subsequent sensitivity concerning it. But much can be done in the home and school to keep him from developing the useless and handicapping secondary symptoms. The most important remedial methods for helping a young primary stutterer follow.

First, and of the greatest importance, all speech conflicts must be removed. Whenever a child in the first phase of stuttering experiences a speech block, some attendant pressure exists which precipitates that interruption. Therefore, his experiences and his environment must be analyzed to determine what these pressures are. One satisfactory way of making this analysis is to keep a list of all words on which blocks occur, the situations in which they are found, and the possible pressure that caused them. Parents often go just this far—they determine the pressure, and then do nothing about it. It is not enough to recognize the precipitating factors; definite steps must be taken to remove or minimize them. Some of the common speech conflicts which should be checked and removed are: interrupting the child; talking for the child whenever communicative difficulty is evident; suggesting other methods of talking which you think will make speech easier for him (such as talking slowly, taking a deep breath before words, thinking what he will say before he starts to talk, substituting another word for one on which trouble occurs, and so forth); ridiculing the child whenever blocks appear; requiring oral confession of guilt (whereby emotionality becomes attached to the speech act); too high speech standards in the home or school; penalizing or punishing the child when abnormality occurs (such as telling him to remain silent until he can say the word correctly); requiring the child to talk when he is fatigued or excited; attempting to make the child hurry when he is talking slowly; and forcing the child to "show off" by speaking pieces or reading to strangers when he is unwilling to do it. Each of these may seem of minor importance, but each is a potential force for increasing the number of primary blocks and for developing subsequent secondary reactions.

Second, the child must be kept in as good a physical condition as is possible. A stutterer needs more rest than the average child. We have mentioned that stuttering seems to come in waves of increased frequency and severity. Periods of good speech alternate with bad periods. When the stuttering is at the height of a frequency wave, fatigue will greatly increase the actual number of blocks, and, when stuttering is at the bottom of that wave, fatigue will precipitate blocks which otherwise would not occur. The child must also have a well-balanced diet, and all sources of physical infection or irritation should be removed. He must have as much physical stability as it is possible for him to attain.

Third, the child must have a pleasant home situation. All possible family conflicts should be cleared. This will be very difficult for some parents to accomplish, for a child reacts to implied attitudes, even though those attitudes are not discussed openly before him. Any implication of them reflects in his emotional adjustments, and anything so vital to the child's future welfare should be well worth any difficulty of accomplishment. In some homes, too, the tempo of living is so fast that it creates instability in the child. The members of the family act impetuously and under great tension, and the child will naturally acquire the same type of reactions. A stuttering child needs a home life devoid of such tension and full of calm activity, and this is another problem for his parents to solve as soon as they can. Use of a good routine is a very effective way of destroying nervous, useless activity in a home and of supplying much-needed stability. Finally, the rest of the family should accept the child's stuttering unemotionally as his particular way of talking.

Fourth, the parents and teachers must learn not to react emotionally to the child's stuttering blocks. Because of the principle of empathic response previously discussed in this text, the reactions of others to the abnormality will help to determine the stutterer's own reactions. If you are surprised, embarrassed, or impatient, he will become aware that his communication is not normal and will react likewise. If you tell him to hurry, to say words over and say them correctly, or if you say

words for him because you don't want to wait for him or because you don't want others to see his handicap, he will become
confused and ashamed and will begin to struggle and force in
an attempt to speak normally. If you blush or seem embarrassed when he has difficulty in the presence of others, he will
realize that there is something about his speech which makes
others uncomfortable. One of the greatest needs in stuttering
therapy is to train others in nonreaction to the speech block.
Even though it be painful, the normal individual should discipline himself to look the stutterer directly in the eye while
he is talking, to show no signs of impatience, and to make no
attempt to help him speak. These attempts to help a stutterer
talk only develop feelings of inadequacy and dependence in
him. Understanding one's own emotional reactions, and a
course of self-discipline in reacting intelligently rather than
emotionally to one's personal problems, will greatly facilitate
the development of nonreacting attitudes toward those who
have more obvious differences. When the primary stutterer
repeats and prolongs, the parents should wait quietly for the
blocks to pass, and the stutterer should feel that he has all
the time in the world to finish the sentence.

Fifth, the parents and teachers should seek to cancel all the
child's unpleasant memories or experiences of stuttering. One
of the best ways of doing this is to distract his attention to
something else immediately after a block occurs, so that the
block will not linger in his consciousness. Another way is to
have the parents and teachers fake a stuttering block occasionally when talking to the child, so that he will not think such
speech is peculiar only to him. Still another valuable technique
is to manipulate the conversation so that the child can successfully say words with which he previously experienced difficulty,
so that the final memory will be one of normal utterance of
those words. If forcing begins to appear in the speech, the parents can show the child that he made the word difficult by
"pushing it out," and that they, too, would experience the same
difficulty if they forced the words out as they uttered them.

Great care should be taken to erase memories of speech difficulty, for if a stutterer retains impressions of unpleasantness, he will build up fears of such occurrences in the future.

Sixth, try to establish favorable speech conditions in the school and on the playground. The teacher can help the classroom situation to a great degree if she ignores the stuttering and refuses to react to it, for she determines the attitude of many of the children. She should tactfully explain to the other children in the room that the stutterer just has a different way of talking, that it is only temporary, and that he will get over it sooner if they all give him plenty of time to talk and pay no attention to the different kind of speech. She should encourage the child to recite, and should never call attention to any evidence of speech abnormality in the recitation. The classroom situation can be made much more favorable if all other problems are settled in an unemotional way. If the teacher is easily provoked to anger, easily embarrassed, and shows her own emotionality often, it will be much more difficult to establish a nonemotional attitude in the children. If the stutterer is teased on the playground, the teacher should discuss that problem with the other children, attempting to solve it not by threats or punishment, but by the explanation that all of the others have differences, too, and that they will actually harm the stutterer if they taunt him because of his different speech. The attitude in the school is of vital importance, because children can be ruthless in their attitude toward a handicap. But a wise teacher can create an understanding attitude of acceptance and unemotionality, even though she may be unable to recognize the actual techniques with which it is accomplished.

Seventh, the child should be given as many ideal speech situations as possible. He can strengthen his normal speech by exercising it. Let him tell stories, recite verses, and read aloud in situations in which there is no pressure or tension. Let him have the responsibility, and do not interrupt or correct him. Encourage him to talk in family situations in which there is no tension—at the dinner table or in informal recitals of his day's activity. Have the other children in the family, or the parents, play speech games with him which emphasize slow, distinct speaking and rhythmic speech. Little dramatizations of stories can be arranged in the home, in which the stutterer is given parts which call for slow, smooth speech. Above all, the child should not be placed on exhibition. He should be encouraged to volunteer in informal situations, and should be accepted as part of the group when there is no attendant speech tension. It is usually unwise to place a young primary stutterer in any speech-correction class, as it only tends to point out his abnormality. Treatment of the young primary stutterer is always indirect. On those days when few blocks occur, he should be stimulated to speak as much as possible. On the days when he has a great deal of trouble, he should be so handled that he talks very little.

Eighth, insist upon unilaterality in most of the child's activities. Let him determine his own hand preference and eliminate all effort to change this preference. When the child is able to write easily, teach him to talk and write at the same time, using the technique described in the next sections of this chapter. Give him many new one-handed skills and do not permit him to engage in such activities as typing or piano-playing.

Ninth, train the child to perform temporal patterns with the paired musculatures. The parent and teacher can play little games in which the child beats out simple rhythms. Thus the parent can tap out a simple iambic rhythm, or play it on one piano key, while the child claps his hands, or kicks with both feet, or protrudes his tongue, or blows through a straw into water. The old nursery game of "pattycake" is an excellent device. Various rhythms may be used. Both limbs and both of each pair of speech structures must act simultaneously in similar or mirrored ways.

Tenth, increase the child's personality assets in every way and decrease his liabilities. The solution of his emotional conflicts and behavior problems will often reflect itself in better speech. Many a primary stutterer has been "cured" by giving him mastery of new skills and greater social adequacy.

Eleventh, if it is impossible to keep the child from being dubbed a stutterer and penalized because of his speech difference, it is wise to tell him that he does indeed have some hesitations and repetitions in his speech, but that these are not at all serious, that he will probably outgrow them, and that almost every person has them. The parent and teacher may point out those that occur in their own speech or they may occasionally fake a few of them so that the child will attach no importance to them. If he is being teased about the disorder, he should be taught to admit it casually by saying, "Sure, I stutter a little. Everybody does. What of it?" Most teasing stops when confronted by such an attitude.

It is also possible to stop much of the teasing by calling in the ringleader of the group doing the teasing and informing him of the consequences of his actions. For some odd reason, teasing usually stops when it is realized that it leaves a permanent effect. If the ringleader is also given the responsibility for preventing any playground teasing, he will usually co-operate enthusiastically.

Desensitization therapy. Most of the techniques mentioned earlier have required the speech therapist to play a relatively passive role so far as the case was concerned. His function was, through counseling and planning, to alter the child's environmental influences so that they would contribute toward fluency rather than interfere, to provide release and supportive psychotherapy.

Recently, a new form of active therapy for primary stutterers has been developed [2] which bears great promise of overcoming some of the greatest difficulties in treating primary stutterers. Most primary stutterers respond favorably to a co-

---

[2] The author owes his initial interest in this therapy and subsequent experimentation with it to George O. Egland, who first brought the concept to his attention.

ordinated program of the type we have described, but there are
some who become worse as the environmental pressures are removed, and there are many whose parents and teachers cannot
be persuaded to change their unfortunate policies. What can
we do with these children? Give up the case and blame the
failure on the child's peculiar constitution or the parent's guilt?
No, there is another alternative, if we can toughen the child,
build up his tolerance to stress, and create callouses against the
hecklings, rejections or impatience. Human beings learn to
adapt to extreme noise levels, to incredible heat and cold. The
housefly can even eat DDT and like it. Should we not try some
desensitization, just as the physician gives the shots for hay-
fever? Instead of lowering the fluency disruptors at home while
being unable to do anything about them on the school playground, should we not train our stuttering child to be able to
tolerate them without breakdown. As we indicated earlier,
some children shift downward their thresholds of speech breakdown as soon as the parents decrease their home pressures.
This just makes such a child all the more helpless outside the
home.

At any rate, this is what the speech therapist does. He first
establishes a social relationship with the child in which the latter does not realize that he is doing any speech therapy. They
may be setting up a toy railroad on the floor or participating
in any other similar activity. The speech therapist then works
to achieve a basal fluency level on the part of the child. This
may in rare cases have to begin with grunts or interjections,
but usually it consists of simple statements of fact, requests,
observations, etc. The therapist, as he works, thinks aloud in
snatches of self talk, commenting on his activity. Soon the
child will begin to do the same, and by appropriately altering
the communicative conditions, and his own manner, the therapist gets the child to speaking with complete fluency. In the
primary stutterer, this is not too difficult. Then, once the basal
fluency level has been *felt* by the child, the therapist begins

gradually to inject into the situation increasing amounts of those factors which tend to precipitate repetitions and non-fluency in that particular child. He may, for instance, begin gradually to hurry him, faster and faster. *But*, and this is vitally important, the therapist stops putting on the pressure and returns to the basal fluency level as soon as he sees the first signs of *impending* non-fluency. How can he tell? Experience and training will help, but we have found usually, that just before the non-fluencies appear, the child's mobility begins to decrease—he freezes, or his general body movements become jerkier, or the tempo of his speech changes. There are other signs peculiar to each child, and a little experimentation will help the therapist know when to stop putting on the pressure just before the stuttering appears.

As soon as the therapist returns to the basal fluency level, he again begins slowly to turn up the heat, to hurry the child a little faster, to avert his gaze more often, or whatever he happens to be trying to toughen the child against. Then an interesting thing occurs. The child can take more pressure the second time than he could the first. The increment is very marked. But again, the first signs of approaching stuttering appear, and again the therapist goes down to the original basal fluency level. Most children do not seem to profit from more than four of these cycles per therapy session, since the tolerance gain decreases somewhat with each subsequent "push." It should be made clear, that throughout this training, the child never does stutter, if the therapist has been skillful. What he feels, probably, is that he is being fluent-under-pressure. Fluency becomes associated with the feeling of being hurried. Perhaps this is why there is a remarkable transfer. The effects of this toughening to stress are not confined to the speech therapist. The child seems to be able to stay fluent even when his father keeps interrupting him. This technique, for lack of a better term, we can call *desensitization therapy*. We have found it very useful.

Case Study of a Primary Stutterer

At the time of examination Tommy Buckton was four years old. An only child, reared in a prosperous but childless section of the city, he presented the picture of unhappy forced maturity. His manners were adult. His conversation during our first meeting concerned electricity, badminton, and brontosauri as well as the more normal interests of his age. He insisted from the first on demonstrating his knowledge. He could say the ABC's; he could print his name and several other words; he could sing; he owned a typewriter; he had built a bridge "with very little assistance." He had "eighty-three dollars in the bank" and three war bonds. He "collected paper match folders." He had gone to the cafeteria all by himself and had paid for his own meal. He uttered these statements of his prowess politely and almost as though defining his status as an adult individual was obvious but necessary.

Unfortunately, the effect of precocity was marred by frequent repetitions of initial syllables of his long words, and by prolongations of the first sound or vowels of the short words. He seemed to be entirely unaware of these symptoms. They did not alter the swift, tense flow of his sentences. No forcing was apparent even when a syllable was repeated ten or twelve times. No eye-shift or avoidance mechanisms were present. The primary symptoms were especially prevalent at the beginning of sentences after a pause. They also occurred when he was interrupted or misunderstood or corrected. No breathing abnormalities were present. His articulation was perfect. He was thoroughly right handed. When he was asked to keep time to the rhythm record, he did unusually well, but was very much upset because he made errors on the more difficult series. He stuttered much more when trying to give excuses for these errors.

The interview with the mother disclosed that the child's father had stuttered as a boy, and that the paternal grandfather had stuttered until his death. The child had never seen this grandfather, however. Two severe illnesses had occurred during the boy's second year, and he had begun to stutter rather gradually "just before his third birthday" and "about the time he recovered from the last siege of pneumonia." The parents had not been concerned about the boy's hesitations and repetitions at first, ascribing them to his "lowered vitality" and to the fact "that all children go through some of this hesitating." The periods of non-fluency alternated with others of speech "so good that we were sure he was going to be a lawyer when he grew up." The mother was the first to become concerned about his symptoms and the first to label it "stuttering." This diagnosis was made after an old school friend of the mother's had visited their home for several days and had brought along her son of about the same age as Tommy. During this entire visit, Tommy's speech was "terribly broken." He "repeated all over the place. He could hardly say anything without trying eight or nine times." According to the mother, he did not play well with his visitor. He clung to his playthings and refused to share them. He continually asked how long the visitors were going to stay. He constantly interrupted his mother's conversations with her friend. "All in all, he was just a terrible child. We couldn't understand it because he's generally so well behaved."

It was difficult to get the mother to give us a clear picture of the subsequent behavior. She used such phrases as "He began to resent our leaving him, although we had always done so before without provoking any tears or protests." "It finally got to the point where my husband and I could not talk to each other at the table without his constant interruptions." "He grew more and more demanding of my attention." "When our maid left and Mrs. Brown came, he resented her efforts to discipline or manage him. He wasn't particularly mean; he just refused to co-operate or just ignored her." "He always stuttered much more when he knew we were going to leave him in her charge for an evening or a week end."

An interview with the father helped to clarify the picture somewhat. "My wife hates housework or the responsibility of a home. She wants to be always on the go. Quite a club woman. She doesn't know how to handle the kid, and admits it in front of him. Not that he's hard to handle either. But she gets excited and upset and the boy seems to feel it. She's got a lot worse since Tom began to stutter, and we've had a little trouble about it. I can't reason with her, and you'll find you can't either. So far as his stuttering is concerned, I'm not worried. I had a little myself when I was young, and he'll get over it all right. But she gets rattled about it and would drag him all over the place trying to get him examined."

We visited the home one late afternoon and stayed for dinner to observe the conditions there. Two very important facts came to light. First, the parents both treated the child exactly as though he were an adult. Their demands upon him for social conformity were far out of line. They also devoted much of the attention they gave to the boy to evoking exhibition of the intellectual sort. They displayed his interest in prehistoric animals, his ability to play a tune on the grand piano, his anagram blocks. The boy obviously enjoyed their approval of his intellectual prowess. Second, the dominant method used for discipline was a threat of leaving him. For instance, the mother asked him to wash his hands, a request he ignored. Whereupon, she stated that if he did not do so immediately, she, his father, and their guest would refuse to eat with him. "We shall probably have to eat downtown again, Tommy." Tommy hastily washed his hands. The mother boasted that this technique plus the isolation was always effective. "We have never had any real difficulty with Tommy ourselves, but Mrs. Brown finds him very difficult at times." The boy was well behaved, according to her criteria.

The boy showed many of the repetitions on the long words during his exhibitionism and his interruptions at the table. The father ignored them, but the mother always stopped and became tense and nervous. Several times she supplied the word the boy was attempting to say. He showed no reaction.

Treatment began with five one-hour interviews with the mother. In them we were able to lead her to see that the boy was being forced to attain verbal and social achievements far beyond his natural capacities. She also attained insight into the destructive effect of her methods of discipline and her reactions to his stuttering. In addition, she began to understand that she was resenting the child's interference with her own desires and comfort, and that she was rejecting her responsibilities as a mother.

In order to provide sufficient motivation for the change which had to be made in the child's environment we had her observe a class of very severe adult stutterers who told of their unhappy experiences. She left the class very much shaken but determined to do anything that would keep her child from having to undergo such a handicap. We then gave her some material to read on the nature and treatment of primary stuttering and asked her to discuss the whole problem with her husband, but to accept full responsibility herself for its solution.

We then suggested the following: (1) Eliminate the demand for speech exhibition of any kind. (Throw away the book of Brontosauri, and so on.) (2) Ignore all forms of exhibitionism or react to them with perfunctory interest. (3) Familiarize herself, through visits to pre-schools and kindergartens, with the interests and behavior patterns of other children of Tommy's age and then expect no more of him. (4) Make arrangements to have him play with other children of his own age occasionally and to enter pre-school within three months. (5) Dismiss Mrs. Brown and adopt the role of the perfect intelligent mother for three months. (6) Cease threatening to leave the boy, and curtail drastically those activities which required her to leave him even for a few hours. (7) Give the boy a lot of obvious affection and "babying" and spend several hours a day in playing with him. The play activities should be those of other children his age, and with physical or mechanical or exploratory play predominating. The former emphasis on intellectual activities should be gradually decreased. (8) The parents should speak to the child in short simple sentences without being obvious about it. Long or unfamiliar words should be avoided. The speech in the home should be quiet and unhurried. (9) When Tommy had one of his fluent periods he should be stimulated to speak a great deal. On his bad days, he should have little necessity to speak at all. (10) All disturbing influences such as confession of guilt, interruption, confusion, misunderstanding, should be minimized as much as possible. (11) All attempts at correction or finishing his troublesome words should be eliminated. The parents should look at him calmly and wait for him to say the word. He should feel no necessity for hurry. The mother should train herself to remain relaxed when he is stuttering. (12) Use a good deal of speech play. Echo games, rhythmic vocalization, relaxed speech, and other relatively easy forms of speech activity were demonstrated to the mother and she was asked to try some each day.

The mother was then given a set of blanks with headings for each of the above twelve items on each, and she was urged to make a daily report to us of her efforts to solve the problem by filling out the blanks. We also arranged for a weekly conference to iron out any difficulties which did arise. Somewhat to our surprise, the mother was very conscientious and did an excellent job.

The stuttering symptoms gradually disappeared. The periods of fluency became longer and the bad periods much shorter. Within six months the boy was in nursery school and no symptoms were ever noted there. The mother, interestingly enough, was more grateful for the change in her own personality and life than she was for the boy's release. The father laughed at the whole program and said, "I told you he would outgrow it just like I did."

Transitional Stuttering

If we could get all of our cases in the stage of primary stuttering, we would be fortunate indeed. But many parents never bring their children to the speech therapist until the disorder has progressed to the struggling phase of its development. They begin to get concerned when the child begins to show a new kind of behavior invading the simple bouncing repetitions of syllables or easy prolongations of an articulatory posture. The child begins to force and to struggle, and he shows signs of distress.

He also shows another new bit of behavior: the *stuttering tremor*. It comes from the tension and from the fixed articulatory postures. The formerly easy repetitions now begin to end in these tight closures, which show their tension in a fast vibration we call a tremor. The lips, for example, in uttering the word "paper" are pressed tightly together when a series of repetitive syllables fails to result in communication or brings a parental scowl. The child says, "puh-puh-puhpuhpuh-pppppp . . . aper." In the struggling which takes place the lips are highly tensed. This of course prevents the breath from getting past this articulatory dam. The more tense the stutterer becomes, the tighter the lips are pressed until finally a sudden localized burst of tension sets into motion a vibrating tremor. Like the *intention tremor* or the *athetoid tremor* of brain injured individuals, the stuttering tremor creates in its possessor a vivid feeling of inability and frustration. He feels blocked. His lips seemed locked by some mysterious force over which he has no control. His response to the awareness of tremor is to increase the tension, which only speeds up the tremor, or to make a sudden jerky movement of the structures involved. If this movement is out of phase with the tremor, he often finds release and the word is uttered. If it is in phase, then he bounces right back into his tremor and the same impasse of self defeating struggle. These tremors are devastating experiences for most stutterers. To them, they seem as threatening as a sudden inability to move an arm would seem to us. The loss of one's power to control one's limbs or mouth can produce anxiety very quickly, and it does so in the stutterer. Some stutterers begin to avoid feared words because of the penalties society inflicts upon abnormality, as we shall see in the next section. But many others develop their first fears and withdrawals as a result of experiencing tremors.

During this transitional period the stutterer begins to spend his energies, not only in trying to utter the word but also in escaping from the tremors. He begins to battle himself. Many of the spasmodic, bizarre contortions that mark the adult stutterer were originally movements that in the random struggle by chance happened to precede release from tremor. Whatever is done just before an escape from punishment becomes strongly reinforced.

We have been describing the transitional stage of stuttering development in terms of the appearance of these features: the growing awareness that his speech has something socially unpleasant about it, an increasing feeling of communicative frustration, the changing of the automatic easy repetitions into slower but highly tensed prolongations, the growth of stuttering tremors and the development of fixated interrupter movements amid the random strugglings. All of these are to be found in the normally progressive course of the disorder. But it must be made clear that few children march in a straight line from primary, through transitional into secondary stuttering. During the transitional stage the struggling is not always present. Much of the abnormality is still repetitive, unconscious and automatic. The child only occasionally shows awareness or evidence of frustration. But these instances become more frequent as time goes on, and no therapy is available. At first the child may struggle hard with marked facial contortions in the throes of his frustration to say what he wants to say, and yet show very little awareness of these contortions. He just doesn't seem to notice it until other people bring it to his attention in an unpleasant way or until the stuttering tremors force him to recognize that his speech is different.

In transitional stuttering as in primary stuttering, the broken fluency comes in waves of frequency. The child still has a few days or even weeks when it seems to disappear completely. His awareness of abnormality, his struggling, his tremors also show a similar ebb and flow. Although he is in greater danger than is the primary stutterer, he has still not reached the point of no return. The disorder can still reverse its course and wind back through excessive non-fluency into normal speech. Only when the stutterer begins to fear words and speaking situations does the danger become critical, and the disorder a self-perpetuating one. Some cases, especially those who begin to stutter later in life or those who are strongly penalized, show an almost immediate shift from primary into secondary stuttering. But most children go through this transitional stage.

Treatment of transitional stuttering. The treatment of children in this stage follows much the same course as that used in the treatment of primary stuttering. We must increase the essential emotional security, remove the environmental pressures that tend to disrupt speech, and increase the amount of fluent speech which he experiences. Every effort should be made to prevent traumatic experiences with other children or adults who might tend to penalize or label the disorder. By creating a permissive environment in which the non-fluency has little unpleasantness, much can be done to help the child regain his former automaticity of repetition. The wise parent will find ways of distracting the child so that the struggling will not be remembered with any vividness. Some parents have increased their own non-fluency, reacting to it with casualness and noncommittal acceptance. One of them used to pretend to stutter a little now and then, commenting, "I sure got tangled up on that, didn't I? What I meant to say was. . . ." It is also wise to provide plenty of opportunity for release psychotherapy, for ventilation of the frustration. Let them show their anger. Help them discharge it.

If teasing has reared its ugly head and the child does come home crying or unpleasantly puzzled by the rejecting behavior of his playmates, the situation should be faced rather than avoided. Here is a mother's report:

Jack came home today at recess. He was crying and upset because some of the other kindergarten children had called him "stutter-box." And they had mocked him and laughed at him. He asked me what was a stutter-box and for a moment I was completely panicky though I hope I hid the feelings from him. I comforted him and then told him that everybody, including big people, sometimes got tangled up in their mouths when they tried to talk too fast or were mixed up about what they wanted to say. Stutter-box was just a way of kidding another person about getting tangled up in talking. I told him to listen for the same thing in the other kids and to tease them back. Later on that day he caught me once and called me a stutter-box. We laughed over it, and I think he's forgotten all about it today. I hope I did right. I just didn't know what to do.

As in the treatment of primary stuttering, it is possible for the speech therapist to do some direct therapy if the child can be kept unaware of the purpose of their interaction. This therapy involves the determination of basal fluency levels and the judicious insertion of stress into the communicative situation. In working with the transitional stutterer, however, it is wiser to use the first appearance of tension in the repetitions or postural fixations as the cue to return to the basal level. As in primary stuttering, we try to harden the case to the factors that precipitate his non-fluency, but in transitional stuttering we keep putting on the stress (the interruptions, impatience, hurry, etc.) even though the repetitions begin to appear. But we stop short, and return to our basal fluency level, just before the tension, forcing, or tremors show themselves. By this technique, it is possible to bring the child back to a condition where there may be many of the primary symptoms, but little or no struggle reactions.

Secondary Stuttering

In the early days of the airplane, we heard much of the *point of no return*. This phrase referred to that point on a transoceanic flight where the supply of gas was no longer sufficient to enable the pilot to fly back to his starting base. In the development of stuttering there is a crudely similar point of no return. It comes with the fixing of situation and word fears. When a case shows marked fears of speaking situations, when he fears certain speech sounds or avoids certain words, the disorder has taken a definite turn for the worse. Many children with marked primary stuttering symptoms, and even quite a few who are struggling in the transitional stage, seem to be able to unravel their speech problems and find perfectly normal speech. They respond readily to indirect therapy of the type we have described. Some of these children show a spontaneous recovery without specific speech therapy even of the indirect kind, as their environments become more favorable or their ego status improves. But once a stutterer begins to objectify his difficulty, to scrutinize approaching situations and words with anxiety, this favorable prognosis is no longer present. The disorder becomes self-perpetuating.

How does this happen? What is the method by which the disorder becomes self-reinforcing? These are tough questions and there are many possible answers. Some authorities insist that a neurotic *need for stuttering* is created once the case becomes aware that his symptoms can help him as well as hurt him. They say that often the stuttering serves as an acceptable excuse, as a defense against the exorbitant demands of conscience or culture. Most stutterers reject this explanation, but some secondary gain from stuttering is often to be found, in the adult case at least.

How situation and word fears precipitate stuttering. More immediate and probably more important, is the fact that the fear of stuttering, like most fears, creates its own hesitancy and tension and ambivalence. These factors are the very ones which create non-fluency in the normal speaker, and they have a more potent effect on the stutterer's speech. Very often, too, feelings of guilt may create the disturbed emotions so disruptive of fluency.

The fact that I am Chinese is very important in my stuttering. We are trained from infancy never to do anything which would cause our families to lose face. I cannot tell you how strong this need is, but maybe you can understand by my telling you how I cut off part of my tongue when I stuttered in front of my father when I was only five. I almost bled to death. I don't think at all about my own trouble, only about what a disgrace I am to my family. I fear stuttering more than anyone I have every known. I am even afraid to talk to myself sometimes. I sleep on my face so I will not speak in my sleep. And the more I think about it, the more I stutter. The more I try to hide it or avoid it, the worse it gets. . . .

The emotions generated during the approach to a feared situation or word are far more powerful than most non-stutterers would be likely to suspect. One of our cases with a normal pulse rate of 74 beats per minute found an increase to 87 as he dialed a phone number, a rate of 114 at the moment his listener said "hello", and a final peak of 123 as he attempted his first speech. Intense feelings of panic, frustration and self-disgust become clustered about the act of talking, and they are bound to interfere with the smoothness of the functioning. Thus, the fear of stuttering produces more stuttering.

Approach-avoidance conflicts. Another way of explaining how non-fluency can be increased by word fear is that based on the concept of the approach-avoidance conflict. Suppose the stutterer wants to order a cup of coffee. He starts out: "I would like a cup of. . . ." At this moment, he suddenly becomes highly aware that on the next word his face may become repulsively contorted, that he may find himself frustrated in a long, tremorous prolongation of a tightly pressed back-tongue posture, that his listener may be startled or irritated. Instantly, he feels pulled forward by the need to complete his communication and he feels a strong urge to utter the word "coffee" as quickly as possible. But at the same time, the expected unpleasantness pulls him backward. A tug-of-war ensues. Sometimes, when neither force is strong enough to win, oscillation occurs and repetitions, hesitations, retrials, and half-hearted speech attempts reflect the equality of the two competing urges.

To speak or not to speak, that is the stutterer's vital question. At times the struggle shows itself in a complete impasse. The urge to attempt the word "coffee," and the fear of the subsequent abnormality counteract each other to such an extent that the person's mouth is immobilized, frozen in a fixed grimace. Thus, either repetitive (clonic) or prolonged (tonic) symptoms may be created by adding fear to the forward flowing process of communication. Fear is the refrigerant that always congeals action. It inhibits. And when one's fluent utterance is suddenly frozen by fear, hesitancies are bound to occur.

It is for this reason that we speak of secondary stuttering as being a disorder infinitely more dangerous and difficult than either primary or transitional stuttering.

The vicious circle. Not only is word-fear able to beget stuttering symptoms; it almost seems to be able to reproduce itself. When words or situations are perceived as being full of unpleasantness, the stutterer tends to avoid them. He not only becomes more hesitant in his speech, but also in his general behavior. He escapes from the approach-avoidance misery by refusing to talk, or by using a synonym instead of the word that scares him, or by putting off the speech attempt as long as possible. But the future fear is increased by each successful avoidance. Here is an excerpt from a stutterer's autobiography:

For years I ducked *k* and *g* words. They were my "Jonah" sounds. They always made me stutter. So I just wouldn't use them. There are lots of ways a stutterer has of hiding his running away from the words he can't say and I knew all of them and used them. But then, when I was fifteen, my folks moved to Kenmore Street in Greenwood and I had to give my address using the feared sounds. I would avoid all I could but there are some times when you can't and you just have to say it. Well, I stuttered harder and longer and more awful on that Kenmore word than any other I've ever said. And even now I'm more afraid of *k* words than of any other. I think it's because I backed away from them so long.

What happens is this: the successful avoidance causes some anxiety reduction. Then, when a similar situation presents itself, the need to avoid is even stronger due to the preceding reinforcement. But now, no avoidance is possible. The conflict becomes even greater. And so several vicious circles (or rather spirals) are set into motion. The more one stutters, the more he fears certain words and situations. The more he fears, the more he stutters. The more he stutters, the harder he struggles. The more he struggles, the more penalties he receives, and the greater becomes his fear. The more he fears, the more he avoids; and the more he avoids speech, the more he fears speaking. And so the stutterer becomes caught in the tangled ropes of his own knotting. Once stuttering creates fear, and this fear, more fear and more stuttering, the disorder can exist on a self-sustaining basis. It can maintain and perpetuate itself even though the original causes may long since have lost all effectiveness and importance. Predisposing or precipitating causes have little importance, once the chain reaction gets going. Perhaps it is for this reason that deep psychotherapy has had but meager success with stuttering. Once stuttering becomes not only a response but also a stimulus, it must be attacked directly.

How the stuttering symptoms are reinforced. There is another basic concept which must be understood by those who wish to help the secondary stutterer. It is this very significant fact: the contortions, tremors, and other unpleasant abnormalities which cause the stutterer so much distress are terminated by the utterance of the word. No matter what silly gyrations his mouth goes through, finally the word comes out. When it does, the panicky fear belonging to that word subsides. In essence, what the stutterer does then is to make a very serious error of judgment. He attributes his release to the struggle and the abnormality. He says, "I squeezed my eyes and then the word came out. If I want to have any future word come out, I'll have to squeeze my eyes."

When any bit of behavior in a punishment situation is followed by release from punishment, it gets powerful reinforcement and strengthening. The stutterer is like the cat in a puzzle-box who happens to look under its left leg at the moment its tail hits the lever that opens the cage. The cat will tend to assume the same head position when it is put back in the cage.

In most cases, the actual release from blocking is due to the fact that the stutterer has had sufficient abnormality to satisfy his morbid expectation. Once the fear is satisfied, the tension subsides and with it, the tremor. The word can now be uttered. If, at this instant, the stutterer by chance happens to gasp for breath, he will tend to feel he must gasp henceforth. The release has rewarded the behavior which preceded it. Why do secondary stutterers show such an amazing variety of bizarre symptoms? The only ones they have in common are repetitions and prolongations. All others are diverse. We would account for this variety in terms of the reinforcement given certain items of struggle behavior occurring at the moment of release. Anxiety reduction is a powerful conditioner. So also is the escape from punishment. Both of these powerful reinforcers play an important part in secondary stuttering. They create new symptoms and they help to perpetuate the disorder. Therapy must be so designed as to prevent them from doing their foul work. They cannot be ignored.

How the fears of stuttering develop. By fear we mean the expectation or anticipation of unpleasantness. The unpleasantness in stuttering can be (1) the experience of frustration, of being unable to communicate, of being unable to move a tongue or lip out of its tremor; of being unable to inhibit facial contortions or abnormal sounds; or (2) it can be the unpleasantness of feeling rejected by one's associates, of being on the receiving end of social penalties, of finding one's speech attempts greeted by anxiety, impatience, pity or laughter.

Most texts on stuttering stress the fears but ignore the importance of the frustrations which are equally vivid parts of the stuttering experience. The intermittent nature of stuttering makes it all the more unpleasant.

If I were blind, I could get used to it and learn to make the best of a bad situation. If I were deaf, I could learn to read lips and face the fact that I could never hear again. If I had no arms, I could finally learn to feed myself with my toes or let others feed me. But I'm a stutterer only part-time. Sometimes I talk as well as the best speaker on earth. Then again, boom! I'm stuck, helpless, petrified in the mouth. The next moment I'm normal again. It drives you crazy and you can't ever adjust to it.

The inability to move or control a part of the body is profoundly disturbing. It has some death-threat in it. If suddenly you could no longer raise your arm, you would find yourself terribly frightened. You would struggle and be afraid. You would know frustration of a peculiarly vivid kind. The stutterer feels the same way when he finds his jaws frozen in a tremor or his tongue stuck quiveringly to the roof of the mouth.

This temporary inability to move the speech muscles can be explained in many ways: as a manifestation of a latent dysphemia; as a conditioned inhibition; or as a moment of emotional blankness. It may be merely symptomatic of a chronic speech hesitancy which has been practiced so often that it has become habitual. It may be only the result of simultaneous and opposing desires to speak and to remain silent. But introspectively, the dominant feature of the stuttering experience is the feeling of being "blocked" in the forward flow of speech. As one stutterer said:

What happens is that I can't go on. I can't complete the word I want to say. I'm stuck. I either hang there struggling on a consonant or find my mouth repeating the same syllable over and o er again like a broken record. Sometimes I'm talking great guns when bang! I'm hung up higher than a kite. Something seems to freeze my tongue or throat shut or else it turns it over to an automatic repeater.

In our first chapter we described some of the ways our society reacts to the person handicapped in speech. In it we traced the historical progress from attitudes of rejection, through humor and pity to the more modern policy of retraining and re-education. The stutterer knows all these reactions and more, too. Here are some excerpts from autobiographies:

What hit me worse of all and something I've never forgot or forgiven was how the parents of other kids would yank them away from me when they would hear me stutter. They wouldn't let me come in their yard to play. They told me to go home and stutter somewhere else. They didn't want their kid to get infected.

.   .   .

Elsie was the worst. She was always teasing me, calling me "stutter-cat" or "stumble-tongue" or mocking me. She was so slick at it that hardly anyone but me noticed it. She'd say it as she went by my desk, under her breath, so only I got it. I could have killed her if I hadn't been so hurt and helpless. And I couldn't hit her, because boys can't hit girls, not even out on the playground.

.   .   .

Whenever I'd stutter, Dad would slump down behind his paper, or if he didn't have any, he'd just look away and pretend to think. Sometimes, he'd just drum on the table with his fingers or hum an absent-minded little tune, as though to say, "I'm not listening so it doesn't count." He never teased me or said anything about my stuttering. No one did. It was as unmentionable as Sex. My father as a small town minister believed in letting sleeping dogs lie. I grew up feeling that stuttering was somehow pretty sinful.

. . .

My nick-name was "Spit-it-out-Joe" or "Spitty" for short. I got it from my third grade teacher, an impatient, agressive old dame who couldn't bear to hear me block. Every time I did, she'd yelp, "Spit it out, Joe!" and the kids picked it up and I've carried the tag for years. I still have dreams of killing the old hag."

. . .

My mother only did one thing when I stuttered. She held her breath. She never teased me, punished me or seemed embarrased. Her lovely face was always serene. But she held her breath. She was entirely patient, sweet and understanding. She gave me the feeling that she was proud of me and was completely confident that everything would turn out all right. But she held her breath every time I stuttered. That breath-holding sometimes sounded louder than thunder to me.

It is from experiences such as these that most young stutterers begin to expect unpleasantness in the act of speaking. This expectation may at first be specifically focused on a single word, the one on which the unpleasantness occurred. Or it may start with a more general fear of a certain situation, such as talking over the telephone, or speaking to a hard-of-hearing grandmother. Stuttering fears are of two main types: situation fears and word fears.

Word fears. The first word fears arise from two main sources: (1) from words which are remembered because of the severe frustration or vivid penalties experienced when uttering them, and (2) from words which because of their frequent use under stress accumulate more stuttering memories upon them.

The question words have always been hard for me to say, ever since I can remember. What? Where? When? Why? How? My folks were always so busy. I always had to interrupt something important they were doing. They either answered without paying any real attention so I had to say it again, or else they told me not to bother them, or they told me to stop asking so many questions.

.   .   .

My own name is my hardest word. Too many big people have asked me, "What is your name, sonny?" I've had to say it too many times when I got into trouble. I've said it so often and stuttered on it so often that I almost think it should be spelled with more than one *t*, like T-T-T-Tommy.

.   .   .

I believe I remember the very first time I stuttered or at least it was the first time I ever noticed it. I was in the second grade, in the third row, last seat. The teacher asked me several simple *times* problems in multiplication, and I stuttered and she got irritated and asked me something simpler until finally she said, "Okay, dummy, how much is two and two?" and I couldn't say, "Four." I've been afraid of that number and of all *f* words ever since.

These fears, starting from such simple instances, grow swiftly. Often their growth almost seems malignant, constantly invading new areas of one's mental life. A child begins by first fearing the word, "paper." He has had an unpleasant experience in uttering it. He sees it approaching, and expects some more unpleasantness, either frustration or penalty. He finds more difficulty. Soon he is fearing many *p* words besides "paper." He recognizes "pay" and "penny" as hard words to say. Then the fear generalizes or becomes fastened to other features of the stuttering experience. It spreads to other words having similar visual, acoustic, kinesthetic, tactual, or semantic features.

The visual transfer, for example, may be in terms of spelling cues. Because of his fear of *p* words, he may see the word "pneumonia" as dreaded, even though the actual utterance begins with a nasal sound. Or, to illustrate the acoustic transfer, he may come to fear the *k*, *ch*, and *t* sounds because they, like the *p*, are ejected with a puff of air. Or tactually and kinesthetically, he may soon be fearing all the other lip sounds, starting with the *b*, then spreading to the *w*, *m*, and even the *f* and *v* sounds. The spread of fear can take several directions. The following example illustrates how the cues precipitating fear of stuttering can spread semantically.

I had never, so far as I remember, had any real trouble on words beginning with a *w*. Oh, I might have had some, I suppose, but generally I considered them easy sounds to say. And I had very frequently used the word, "well", as a sort of handle, saying it as a kind of way to get started. Sometimes, of course, I might have to say it three or four times before the next word came out, but, anyway, I could always say "well." It was a handy trick to cover up and postpone. Then one day I had an experience which ruined that word for me forever. To this day, "well" is a very hard word for me to speak without stuttering, and it all happened because of that one experience. It happened like this. I was in a grocery store, asking for five pork chops, and I got blocked in saying the name of the meat. It was a long one with hard sticking in my throat and I kept trying to break it by saying "well." I must have used too many of them because a man behind me impatiently shouted, "Well, well? You aren't well, young lady. Get out of here and go home to bed. You're sick. Not well, sick! Do you hear, sick!' I fled without the pork chops, but I can never use the word in the sense of healthy without blocking completely. I sometimes can use it as a starter, but if I happen to think of it as the antonym of "sick," I block on it immediately.

Situation fears. We have been describing the stutterer's conflicting urges to utter and to avoid the utterance of a given word. Shall he or shan't he attempt it? He scrutinizes the word for cues which might indicate danger, for resemblances to other words formerly provocative of great unpleasantness. The same sort of process occurs on the situation level. Sheehan (138) puts the matter as follows:

At the *situation* level there is a parallel conflict between entering and not entering a feared situation. The stutterer's behavior toward using the telephone, reciting in class, or introducing himself to strangers illustrates this conflict. Many situations which demand speech hold enough threat to produce a competing desire to hold back.

Often in word fears there occurs an actual rehearsal of some of the expected abnormality. Breathing records show that even prior to speech attempt the stutterer's silent breathing often goes through the same peculiar pattern that he shows when actually stuttering (151). In situation fears this is not the case. Situation fears are more vague, more generalized, more focused on the *attitudes* of the listener and the stutterer than upon the *behavior*. Situation fears can range in intensity all the way from uncertainty to complete panic. We have known stutterers to faint and fall to the floor in their anticipation of a speaking situation. The fear fluctuates in intensity from moment to moment. It is often set off by the stutterer's recognition of certain features of an approaching speech situation as similar to those of earlier situations in which he met great penalty or frustration. Stutterers learn to scan an approaching speaking situation with all the concentration of a burglar looking over a prospective bank. Like word fears, situation fears generalize. They may begin from a simple recognition on the part of the child that he was having much difficulty in talking to a certain storekeeper. Remembering this, he may begin to fear speaking in any store; or to take another tack, he might begin to fear talking to all strange men, or to mention still another, he might fear having to relay any message given him by his mother. Situation fears are like word fears in another way, too. Avoidance increases them greatly. The more the stutterer runs away from a given speaking situation, the more terrifying it becomes.

Both situation and word fears can serve as *maintaining* causes of the disorder. By constantly reinforcing them by avoidance, the stutterer keeps his stuttering "hot." Any therapy worthy of the name must have as one of its basic aims the elimination of this avoidance. Stuttering begins to break down and disappear as soon as the stutterer ceases his constant reinforcing.

How reactions to fear or experience of stuttering become habitual symptoms. Expectancy devices are of four major types:

those of avoidance, those that postpone the speech attempt, those that are used as "starters" to terminate the postponement and initiate the speech attempt, and, finally, those of antiexpectancy. A number of examples for each of these reactions are given in the section on examination procedures for stuttering at the end of this chapter. It is often difficult for the nonstutterer to realize that much of the abnormality he witnesses in examining a stutterer is due to the latter's efforts to avoid unpleasantness. The desire to avoid stuttering may lead to such jargon as "To what price has the price of tomatoes increased to today?" when the stutterer merely wished to say "How much are your tomatoes?" Dodging difficult words and speech situations becomes almost a matter of second nature to the stutterer. He prefers to seem ignorant rather than to expose his disability when called upon in school. He develops such a facility at using synonyms that he often sounds like an excerpt from a thesaurus. He will walk a mile to avoid using a telephone. And the tragedy of this avoidance is that it increases the fear and insecurity, makes the stutterer more hesitant, and doubles his burden.

Procrastination as a reaction to approaching unpleasantness is an ordinary human trait, and the stutterer has more than his share of the weakness. We have worked with stutterers whose entire overt abnormality consisted of the filibustering repetition of words and phrases preceding the dreaded word. They never had any difficulty on the word itself, but their efforts to postpone the speech attempt until they felt they could say the word produced an incredible amount of abnormality. One of them said, "My name is . . . my name is . . . my . . . my . . . my name is . . . my name . . . name . . . name . . . what I mean is, uh . . . uh . . . my name is Jack Olson." Others will merely pause in tense silence for what seems to them like hours before blurting out the word. Others disguise the postponement by pretending to think, by licking their lips, by saying "um" or "er." Postponement as a habitual approach to feared words creates an anxiety and a fundamental hesitancy which in themselves are precipitative of more stuttering.

Stutterers also use many tricks to start the speech attempt after postponement has grown painfully long. They time this moment of speech attempt with a sudden gesture, or eye-blink, or jaw-jerk, or other movement. They return to the beginning of the sentence and race through the words preceding the feared word in hope that their momentum will "ride them over their stoppages." They insert words, phrases, or sounds that they can say, so that the likelihood of blocking will be lessened. One of our stutterers hissed before every feared word, "because I get started with the *s* sound which I can nearly always make." Another used the phrase "Let me see" as a magic incantation. He would utter things like this: "My name is LemeseePeter Slack." Another, whose last name was Ranney, always passed as O'Ranney, since she used the "oh" as a habitual device to get started. Starters are responsible for many of the bizarre symptoms of stuttering, since they become habituated and involuntary. Thus, the taking of a deep breath prior to speech attempt may finally become a sequence of horrible gasping.

The antiexpectancy devices are used to prevent or minimize word fears from dominating the attention of the stutterer. Thus, one of our cases laughed constantly, even when saying the alphabet or asking central for a phone number or buying a package of cigarettes. He had found that, by assuming an attitude incompatible with fear, he was able to be more fluent. Yet he was one of the most morose individuals we have ever met. Other stutterers adopt a sing-song style, or a monotone, or a very soft, whispered speech so that all words are made so much alike that no one will be dreaded. Needless to say, all these tricks fail to provide more than temporary relief, and all of them are vicious because they augment the fear in the long run.

In addition to these reactions to fear, we find the release reactions which occur after the stutterer has experienced the actual block. In general, there are only two main types of release symptoms: (1) those with which the word is completed in some manner after the block occurs, and (2) those which involve a cessation of the speech attempt and a retrial. Among the observable release devices of the first type are: to continue the word with increased force or tension on the speech muscles, to interrupt prolongation and finish the word, to continue with a changed voice pitch, to stop briefly and finish the word, and to continue with speech on inhalation. In the second class we find these reactions: to stop at the feeling of block and try the entire word again, to stop and use some starting device on the retrial, to stop and use a distraction, to stop and assume a confident behavior, to stop and postpone the new attempt for a time, to stop and avoid the word, and to stop and wait until almost all breath is gone, subsequently saying the word on residual air.

Tremors and interrupter devices. The tremors which we described under the topic of transitional stuttering are very prevalent in secondary stuttering. In some stutterers several structures will be vibrating at the same time—the lips, the jaw, and the diaphragm, and often at different rates. The case attempts to free himself from the tremor by increasing the tension or by using some interrupter device similar to the starter tricks he has used to initiate speech attempt after prolonged postponement. He tries to wrench himself out of the frozen vibration of the tremor by sheer force. Even as he closes the articulatory door of the tongue or lips and holds it tightly shut, he strives to blow it open with a blast of air from below. When the opposing forces are equal, nothing happens except the quivering of the muscles. Oddly enough, no stutterer tries to open the speech doors voluntarily; he must break them down with a surge of power. As in transitional stuttering, the random struggling often results in out-of-phase movements of the vibrating structures which cause a release from tremor and make possible the utterance of the word. One stutterer may squeeze his eyes shut; another will jerk his whole trunk; another may suck air in through his nostrils. These peculiar reactions have become habituated through their chance presence at the moment of tremor release. The anxiety reduction, the freedom from punishment gives them their compulsive strength. The stutterer comes to feel that only through using them can he ever escape from the dreadful feeling of inability which the tremor creates in him. Even when they do not give release, he will try them over again, sniffing, not once, but twenty and thirty times in his desperate effort to free himself from the mysterious closure that his opposing efforts have produced. There are easier ways to terminate tremors than these, but few stutterers ever find them without the aid of a therapist.

Examination procedures for stutterers. It is vitally important that the initial examination of the stutterer be both systematically and carefully performed. The case history should be thorough, and every source of important information should be exploited. The case himself should be interviewed and explored at length. All data bearing on dysphemic, emotional, or developmental etiology should be carefully evaluated. The stutterer's basic attitudes of attack or withdrawal, both in terms of speech defect and other liabilities, must be determined. The history of his secondary symptoms (see the special case history for stuttering in the Appendix) is often of great importance to therapy, since the latest symptoms often yield most quickly to therapy. The symptoms themselves, together with the characteristic communicative conditions under which they occur, must be identified. The breathing abnormalities, if present, should be noted. The areas of great tension should be located, and since the struggle to speak often begins in one area, such as the lips, and spread to other areas, the directions of this tension-irradiation should be observed. Since stutterers frequently block the vocal airway at the vocal cords, velum, hard palate, teeth, or lips by excessively hard contacts, the location of these hard contacts must be found. The cues that set off fear of speech situations and "Jonah" words should be analyzed. Finally, the history of the stutterer's attempts to free himself from his impediment must be disclosed. It is usually unwise to use methods of therapy which have previously failed.

If the above description of the stutterer's examination seems somewhat vague, the following instructions, which were given to guide a beginning student in her first examination of a child who stuttered, may prove more specific:

While the child is in the playroom, interview the mother. You need not investigate the predisposing or precipitating causes of his disorder at this time since you will have ample opportunity to do so in later interviews, but you should try to get (1) the *child's attitude* toward his problem; (2) the *parent's attitude* toward the disorder; (3) some indication of *how the child might respond* to your examination procedures; (4) some of his *interests and experiences* about which he might be willing to talk. Then ask the mother to go with you back to the playroom and tell her to let the child know she is right in the next room and will be through in a little while. As the mother does so, be sure to talk with her in a friendly manner so as to establish a relationship. If necessary, have her introduce you as the play-room teacher.

Let the child have the opportunity to size you up while you straighten up the room or do a few other things of the same sort. Get acquainted with him in an unhurried manner by making some statements about the play materials available in the room. Show him how some of the toys work. Keep talking, but demand no answers. As soon as you can, get out the materials for the (5) *Wellman Tracing Path Test* and, as you illustrate, tell him to see how well he can draw between the lines. Go directly from this to the (6) *Durost Asterisk Test*, and then to the (7) *Vertical Board Test of Laterality*. These tests seem to fascinate almost all children, and we doubt you will have much difficulty in this regard. Use the toy gun to determine (8) *eyedness* and throughout the examination observe his (9) *hand preference*. Watch him carefully for signs of negativism or fatigue, and temporarily shift to play activity whenever they occur. Then ask him if he would like to see you write with your stomach. Take him into the laboratory and hook yourself up to the polygraph and make a breathing record. Be sure to talk as you do so. Then (10) make a *breathing record* of him. If possible, go directly from this to the making of a (11) *phonograph record*. Ask him to count to ten, but then ask him some questions such as: "Your mother tells me you have an older brother. What is his name?" Try to get a transcription of a few blockings and watch his reactions closely. Then play the phonograph record of the rhythms used to test diadochokinesis. After you demonstrate, ask him to keep time to the sounds by (12) *biting*, (13) *panting*, and (14) *tongue protrusion*. If this seems too difficult for him, use the metronome to give a rhythmic stimulus of a simpler sort. Watch for extra movements, flutterings, tonic contractions, and, of course, sheer inability.

Take him back to the playroom and let him choose his own activities for a time. By sharing one of them, initiate a conversation which should continue long enough to give you a pretty good idea concerning the presence of (15) *primary symptoms*, their number per word, their tempo, and whether or not they are accompanied by tension or awareness. Note any evidence of struggle or avoidance. If he does seem to be a primary stutterer without awareness, or struggle, or avoidance, introduce some pressure factors such as interruption, hurry, impatience, misunderstanding, strong demand for a certain specific answer, or disregard, etc. Note (16) which of these *disturbing influences* seem to produce the most symptoms. Get him to talk about his home, parents, brothers and sisters, friends, enemies, schoolmates and teachers, punishments, achievements. Note (17) any *certain topics of conversation* which produce the most symptoms. If you are still certain he is a primary stutterer, take him back to the waiting room and begin to take a careful case history.

If you are certain he is aware of his symptoms, and does struggle or avoid in his efforts to prevent or minimize his stuttering, engage him in enough further conversation to enable you to make a careful symptom analysis. This should include (18) *avoidance* devices or habits, (19) *postponement* tricks, (20) *starters*, and (21) *antiexpectancy* devices.

If the child is so adept at avoiding or postponing that he shows few true blockings, ask him to say (quickly! and loudly!) such words as "BANANA-BANANA-BANANA" or his father's full name pronounced in similar fashion. Then try to analyze his stuttering to determine where the (22) major areas of *forcing* and *hard contacts* seem to be. Also note the (23) presence and location of *tremors* of the lips or tongue. Check to see whether (24) *false-vocal-cord phonation* occurs on the vowels during stuttering. Determine (25) the *manner of release* from blocking in terms of retrials, interrupter devices, or tension decreases. On what sounds did he place his mouth in position to utter the sound before actually making a speech attempt upon it? These we call (26) preformation.

Either through frank discussion of his problem, or through observation, try to determine what (27) *words or sounds* seemed most feared or stuttered upon. On which ones did he have the longest or most severe blockings? If possible, ask him what types of speaking seem most difficult or dreaded. To whom does he have most trouble speaking? Check home, school, play, or work activities to locate the (28) *feared situations*.

Observe (29) his *post-spasm reactions* and attitudes toward his speech difficulty. If possible, get him to tell you what unpleasant experiences he has had with stuttering. Find out from the child, if you can, how his parents or teachers or playmates tease, punish, or otherwise react to his blocks. Finally, discuss with him what (30) *methods* have been used to help him overcome his stuttering and what he thought of them.

Record the results of your examination in terms of the 30 items numbered above. Then take a careful case history from the mother and summarize the information thereby procured under the following headings: (31) *predisposing causes;* (32) *precipitating causes;* (33) *maintaining causes;* (34) *manner of development*, including changes in symptomatology and growth of anxiety and frustrations; (35) the boy's major *assets and liabilities*, and his characteristic *reactions to penalty and approval;* (36) *environmental factors* which tend to perpetuate the disorder, with some estimate concerning their possibility of removal; (37) environmental factors indicating a good *prognosis;* and (38) *suggestions* concerning therapy.

In order to familiarize the student with some of the examinations mentioned in the above description of testing procedures, we are describing some of them in greater detail.

Laterality tests. Much research has recently pointed out the effect on speech of a shift of handedness or of confused sidedness or laterality. Reliable histories of shift of handedness are difficult to procure because of the lapse of time, the effects of imitation, and the reluctance of parents to confess such a causal factor. Therefore, it is necessary to use laterality tests to determine whether or not confused laterality is a contributing or essential cause of the child's speech disorder. The speech disorders usually so affected are stuttering and delayed speech. Unfortunately, most of our measures of sidedness are either tests of speed, strength, and accuracy, or expressions of hand preference, all of which are the features most susceptible to environmental influence and training. A few tests of so-called native-sidedness do exist, and, although crude, they are used in a battery together with the other measures to determine if laterality is a causal factor. Tests of speed, strength, and accuracy are most important diagnostically when they demonstrate ambidexterity or favor the usually nonpreferred hand. Many tests may be used for measuring these three factors, but the three most convenient and adequately standardized are the Wellman Tracing Path[1] test for accuracy, the Durost Asterisk Test[2] for speed, and the Smedley Dynamometer Test[3] for strength. All of these tests must be administered in such a fashion as to reduce distortions due to training. Each of them is taken first with the nonpreferred hand, next with the preferred hand, then again with the preferred hand, and last, with the nonpreferred hand. The scores should be averaged and expressed as fractions—the numerator representing the average accuracy of the right hand, the denominator, that of the left. Directions for administering the first two of these tests are given in their respective forms. Directions for the dynamometer test are simply to hold the dynamometer at full arm's length and apply the pressure. Scores should be recorded on a special test form similar to that given at the end of this chapter.

The most valid and reliable hand-preference questionnaire is the one standardized by C. J. Hull.[4] It requests the student to indicate if the right, left, or either hand performs the activity when hammering, cutting with scissors, distributing cards, spinning a top, winding a watch, using a toothbrush, sharpening a pencil, writing, drawing pictures, throwing, and using a tennis racket. She expressed her results in terms of a handedness index computed according to the formula: $R + 1/2E \div N = Index$.

Tests of so-called native-sidedness include: eyedness, convergence, strength, thumbedness, footedness, and the vertical

---

[1] Wellman, B. L., "The Development of Motor Coördinations in Young Children," *University of Iowa Studies in Child Welfare*, 1926, Volume 3, pages 1–93.

[2] Durost, W. M., "The Development of a Battery of Objective Tests of Manual Laterality," *Genetic Psychology Monograph*, 1934, Volume 16, pages 4–237.

[3] Whipple, G. M., *Manual of Mental and Physical Tests*, Baltimore, Warwick and York, Inc., 1924.

[4] Hull, C. J., "A Reliable Hand Preference Questionnaire," *Journal of Experimental Education*, 1936, Volume 4, No. 3, pages 287–290.

board or critical-angle board tests, the last mentioned being the most reliable and best standardized. Eyedness may be tested by providing the subject with a paper cone, the large end of which the subject is requested to place to his face as he looks through the cone to view the experimenter's eye. The cone prevents the use of both eyes at any one time, and the one used is termed the dominant eye. The experimenter should give

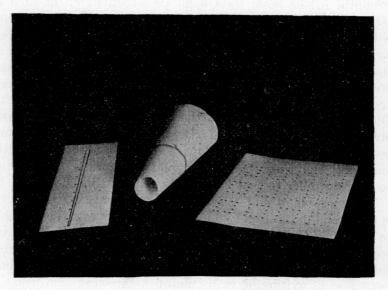

Fig. 11. The cone used for testing eyedness, and the asterisk and tracing path tests of laterality.

at least ten trials as he moves about. Convergence strength is tested by requiring the subject to focus his eyes on the end of a lead pencil as the experimenter slowly brings the pencil in perpendicularly to the bridge of the subject's nose. The experimenter records which eye fails to "break" or swing outward. This eye is termed the dominant eye in convergence. At least ten trials should be recorded. Thumbedness is easily determined by requiring the subject to clasp his hands, interlocking the fingers in the usual fashion. The dominant thumb is that which is on top. Footedness may be determined by standing the subject with his back to the wall and asking him to kick the wall three times very quickly. The reliability of all of these measures is somewhat doubtful, but they are useful in indicating a general tendency in favor of one or the other side.

Vertical board test of laterality. This test consists essentially in simultaneous writing with both hands, one on each side of an upright vertical board. The patterns used are of three types.

Fig. 12. A student being given the vertical board test of laterality. Bimanual stylus, visual pattern, and kinesthetic pattern are also shown.

The first is the kinesthetic, consisting of a pattern learned while blindfolded by tracing with a bimanual stylus. The pattern itself is a deep spiral groove cut into a flat board or cardboard. The examiner places the point of the bimanual stylus in the center of the spiral and, during the first trial, helps guide it as the blindfolded subject traces it. Four trials without guidance are then required; the pattern is withdrawn, and the subject uses the stylus to draw the pattern on the table top. If the subject does not draw a good pattern, he is required to take more practice trials until he does. He is then asked to draw the same pattern reduced to one fourth its original size on the table top. If this is successful, he discards the stylus, takes a pencil in each hand and, at command, draws the patterns, as swiftly as he can, simultaneously with both hands on opposite sides of the vertical board. Three such drawings are required, and other patterns may be used (160). A simple, two-handed stylus may be contrived by thrusting a pencil through the centers of two 4-by-1-inch strips of thick cardboard, separating them by about three inches, and using the projections of the upper strip as handholds and those of the lower as a means of steadying the forefingers. A large sheet of paper folded over the top of the vertical board will provide a permanent record of the performance; on each side, the hand with which the pattern was written correctly should be indicated. The second pattern is a visual pattern, held up above the examiner's head so as to prevent the subject from watching both his hands and the pattern at the same time. No blindfold is used, and the subject is instructed to follow the pattern with his eyes as he draws it with his hands on the vertical board. The third, or script pattern, consists of the drawing of a word spoken to the subject, who is again blindfolded. Typical visual patterns are asymmetrical figures with the first stroke being made vertically. Good words for the script pattern are: *boy*, *catch*, *dog*. The subject should make clear patterns and should begin instantly at command, drawing simultaneously with both hands *as fast as he can*. The nondominant hand will produce mirroring in all of these tests, while the dominant hand will draw the pattern correctly. In case of poor co-operation, a new pattern should be used. Keep the subject in ignorance of the fact that the test is a handedness test. If the subject mirrors with the hand normally preferred, the results tend to indicate confused laterality. Left-handed people mirror with the right hand; right-handed people do the opposite; ambidextrous individuals either mirror with both hands or do not mirror at all.

Diadochokinesis and rhythmokinesis. These two polysyllabic verbal monstrosities are terms used to refer to the stutterer's ability to move the speech musculatures rhythmically and rapidly. What we actually measure is the stutterer's ability to protrude or lift the tongue, or move his jaw, or pant with speed and accuracy. Some stutterers, who can coordinate a hand or a leg with extreme facility, are very awkward in moving the paired speech muscles with precision or speed. Their tongues are protruded not rhythmically but clumsily. They show trem-

FIG. 13. Testing diadochokinesis.

ors, flutterings, and extra movements or even cessation of all movement. Some stutterers when tested react to the above experiences by saying that they "blocked" or stuttered in these silent activities (80). Certainly tonic and clonic reactions are very evident. Not all stutterers show these malcoordinations (148). Our task in this testing is to discover whether the stutterer being examined is one of those who does.

A good deal of complicated apparatus has been used to test

the stutterer's diadochokinesis, but we have found that a phonograph recording of a series of rhythmic sound stimuli is adequate to permit us to detect those stutterers who are grossly defective. The record is made by having a trained musician tap out a series of musical notes, arranged in rhythmic patterns. The first pattern consists of a fairly slow but regular series of notes evenly spaced: * * * * * * * * * * * *. The next four patterns are similar in form but are produced at increasing speeds. Then more complex rhythms are introduced as stimulus patterns, and in successive trials they are produced at different speeds. Some of the patterns we use may be represented visually in this way:

```
** * *    ** * *    ** * *
*  ***    *  ***  * ***
* ** *    *  ** *  *  ** *
```

The instructions for administering this test are simple. We say to the person we are examining:

In the record which I will play for you, you will hear some musical notes. Your task is to click your teeth together (*or pant, or protrude the tongue*) in time to the music. Listen to the music until you hear how it is arranged, and then start keeping time. Try to do it as exactly as possible. Now watch me do it first and then we'll let you try.

Since some individuals find a little difficulty in understanding what is desired, it is always wise to use a practice session or two. As indicated above, the stutterer should perform these patterns at different speeds, since different persons have different optimal motor tempos. With small children we employ only the simple, regular patterns.

In recording the results of the test, we are interested primarily in the extreme variations from the performances of the average child, and since each homemade record will vary in this regard, normal individuals must be tested to determine such crude norms. Yet, so marked are the broken rhythms, blockings, and tremors of certain stutterers that the abnormality is obvious. We usually give the jaw-bite first, then the panting, and finally the tongue-protrusion.

Breathing. Whenever possible, it is wise to record the breathing patterns during the stuttering blocks. Kymograph or polygraph records can often demonstrate symptoms which are difficult (though not impossible) to detect by careful observation. The breathing of a stutterer often reflects his efforts and struggles to break the hard contacts of the tongue, lips, or vocal cords, which are so characteristic of secondary stuttering. It also can demonstrate the presence of fear in the form of a suspension of silent breathing or a slowness of inhalation. When simultaneous records of thoracic and abdominal breathing are made, the stutterer often shows that his chest cavity is expanding or inhaling at the same time that his abdomen is contracting in the effort to speak. Tremors of the breathing musculature are also noticeable in some cases. In others, the stutterer's attempts to interrupt his blocks or to time the speech attempt will be reflected in sudden inhalations or gasps. One of the most common of secondary symptoms is the stutterer's attempt to speak on residual air. He exhales suddenly and much more thoroughly than during normal speech and then makes the speech attempt on the very "end of his breath."

In adults, stereotyped and consistent patterns of breathing abnormality are found, and these are occasionally rehearsed prior to speech attempt. Many stuttering blocks do not manifest themselves in any respiratory irregularity. The breathing disturbances in stuttering are probably the result of the vocal struggle rather than its cause. Devices such as an initiatory gasp, used deliberately for timing the speech attempt on a feared word, produce many of the above symptoms. The use of breathing exercises in the treatment of stuttering has been generally discarded by most clinicians.

Symptom analysis. This part of the stuttering examination is of great importance and must never be slighted. Much of the abnormality of stuttering consists of habitual reactions associated with the fear or block, and these must be carefully identified. This is frequently more difficult than might be expected. Severe secondary stutterers often have a whole series of devices or habitual approaches to the speech attempt on a feared word. Some of these devices seem to be reserved for conditions of extreme panic and only make their appearance under that condition. The first examination seldom provokes the entire gamut of secondary symptoms. We therefore provide the adult stutterer with a check list of these symptoms so that he can supplement our observation. In examining a stutterer, however, we must be careful to test him under conditions of stress in order to get a true picture of the manner in which he approaches a hard word or attempts to release himself from the blocking. Phonograph recording, telephoning, speaking before an audience, paraphrasing, narrating anecdotes about unpleasant stuttering experiences, all can be used to provoke severe enough symptoms to permit diagnosis. The general classes of symptoms which must be checked are: symptoms of avoidance, postponement, "starters," anti-expectancy, release, and the postspasm reactions. These can be underlined on a stuttering history blank as they are noticed, or written on a special blank provided for the purpose. Special notation should be made of the symptoms that appear most frequently.

1. *Symptoms of avoidance.* Some of the means by which a stutterer may avoid a feared word are: giving up the speech attempt altogether, substituting a different word for the one feared, changing the order of the words (circumlocution), waiting for help on the word, pretending to have to think, and using very condensed or telegrammic speech.

2. *Symptoms of postponement.* Stutterers often postpone the attempt on a feared word either because their fear is so great that they feel there is no possibility that they can say it at the moment, or because they feel that they may say it without any difficulty if they wait for a few seconds. Some of the techniques which they use to accomplish such a delay are: pausing, using accessory vocalization (such as saying "a . . . a . . . a . . . ," "why," or "er" before a word), repeating preceding words, repeating preceding sounds, prolonging the last part of the preceding word, repeating entire phrases preceding the feared

word, or slowing down the rate at which the preceding words are spoken. Here the stutterer is avoiding the feared word in time, though he does not intend to avoid it completely.

3. *Symptoms of starting.* Stutterers sometimes feel that most of their difficulty comes when they are attempting to start a word and that, if they can just start it some way, they will be able to say it successfully. Some of the more common types of these starting devices are: use of a starting word, sound, or phrase (such as "um," "well," or "you see"), use of some particular stereotyped movement just before the word is attempted (such as a body jerk, throat clearing, swallowing, or eye blink), repetition of preceding phrases at increased rate (sometimes called "getting a running start"), suddenly changed pitch of the voice, suddenly changed intensity of the voice, suddenly increased tension, suddenly decreased tension, and use of some movement to time the actual moment of speech attempt (and not before that moment, as was suggested in the above technique), such as tapping the foot, blinking the eyes, or jerking the head.

4. *Symptoms of anti-expectancy.* The relationship of fear to stuttering is so great that stutterers often feel that if they could destroy the fear of approaching words, they would be able to say them without difficulty. The three major ways of doing this are: using a kind of speech in which no word stands out enough to be feared, filling the mind with other things so that the expectancy of stuttering is kept out (distraction), and assuming an evident attitude of self-confidence. In the first-mentioned class, we find these types of devices: use of a monotone, slow and deliberate speech, singsong speech, very rapid speech, and slurred speech. In the second class, we find: unnatural speech which demands strict attention, voluntary movements of the body which serve as a distraction, visualization of words, a sequence of breathing or vocalization patterns, and overattentiveness to phonetic drill positions. In the third class, among those devices which are used to attain self-confidence, we may see: assumption of aggressive, belligerent, or clowning

behavior, whispered rehearsal, compensatory behavior of various kinds, and the use of coughing, or some such obvious activity, to prove to the stutterer that he is still able to control his speech organs. ‹

5. *Symptoms of release.* After a stutterer finds himself in a block, he does certain things to release it. Some of these more commonly used techniques of release are: to stop immediately and try again on the same word, to pause when the block is felt and then to finish the rest of the word, to stop and postpone a new attempt for some time, to stop and wait until almost all breath is gone and then to say the word on residual air, to stop and assume a confident behavior (to change the attitude), to continue the word and increase the tension, to continue the word and change the pitch of the voice, and to change the pattern of breathing by speaking the rest of the word on inhalation.

Sequences. While discovering what secondary symptoms are manifested, notations must be made of the sequences in which these symptoms occur. Does the stutterer follow a stereotyped pattern? Does he always pause first before a feared word, then start it by swallowing? Or does he usually postpone the attempt on a feared word by repeating the preceding word, and, if that fails, by repeating the whole preceding phrase? Does he try to release a spasm first by forcing, and, if that fails, does he attempt a release through stopping and starting again? Most stutterers follow some definite sequence in the secondary symptoms which they utilize in the attempt to speak. Sometimes a sequence will contain four or five secondary reactions. Many of these patterns have become very strong through their continued use, and the definite sequence must be recognized before any work can be done upon its disintegration.

The clinician must familiarize himself with evidences of these secondary symptoms in the speech of the stutterers whom he examines. It is also desirable to find out what methods for the alleviation or cure of the speech defect have been suggested to the stutterer and have been tried subsequently by him. (Examples of such suggested methods are: talking slowly.

swinging the arm when talking, taking a deep breath before feared words, using monotone, stopping and starting the speech attempt again, and so on.) Since there is often a positive relationship between these tricks and the spasm pattern which the stutterer has developed, the development of the reactions must be clarified for him.

Cues—specific expectancy. After a symptom diagnosis has been made of the stutterer, one must discover, through questioning, what the cues are which set off the actual stuttering block. For every stutterer who is aware of his speech difference, certain features of communicative material stand out as being invested with stuttering threat. These words, or parts of words, which stand out are the centers and subcenters of the configuration of communication. Some of the stuttering landmarks in a sentence upon which word fear is experienced are: the first words in a sentence, the last words in a sentence, the unfamiliar word, the word which is difficult to pronounce, and the inexact word. Often the accented syllables also serve as cues which arouse specific fear of a certain part of a word. In addition to the cues that are dependent upon the actual content of the communicative material, there are the more artificial cues which arise from the stuttering experience of the individual. If special sounds or words have been stuttered upon sufficiently enough and vividly enough in the past to leave an indelible impression upon the stutterer, they, too, may subsequently set off specific fear of stuttering. The clinician must find which of these cues is responsible for precipitating specific fears in the stutterer.

General expectancy. In addition to discovering the cues which set off specific expectancy in the stutterer, the situation, or general fears must be found. Does the stutterer have blocks when talking or reading aloud when alone? Does he stutter when he sings or whispers? Which people in the home situation are the most difficult? Are there playground or business situations which are greatly feared? What situations does he avoid? Does he avoid the use of the telephone? What situations does he recall as having been very unpleasant because of his stuttering?

Prior to entering a feared situation, does he rehearse what he is going to say or does he visualize himself stuttering? How does he attempt to change a feared speech situation so that he will have less trouble? Does he brood over speech failures? Is his characteristic reaction to a feared situation one of retreat or one of attack? Is he prone to have reactions of absolute panic? Question the stutterer as to each of the above.

Request the stutterer to give examples of any of the following penalties which have been inflicted upon him. Which are most common?

The penalties are of three types: social, sexual, and economic. All of these penalties are expressed through audience behavior. Some of the most common audience reactions that fall under the category of social penalties are:

1. Attack by, or rejection from, a social group.
2. Underestimation of stutterer's intelligence.
3. Expression of dislike, discomfort, anger, irritation, disgust, or impatience.
4. Expression of amusement.
5. Interruption, anticipation, or thwarting of communication.
6. Ridicule.
7. Pity and tolerance.

The most common sexual penalty is rejection of companionship by members of the opposite sex.

Economic penalties which are interpreted from audience reactions are:

1. Peremptory rejection of application for employment.
2. Unwillingness to place stutterer in a position of responsibility.
3. Overprotection.
4. Demand for speech improvement under threat of losing economic security.
5. Impatience with communication limitation.

Attitude toward stuttering. After the specific and general fears have been determined, the clinician must discover the general attitude of the stutterer toward his speech handicap. Does he obviously suffer whenever he has a spasm? Is he able to watch one of his blocks? Does he accept his defect optimistically or does he have a pessimistic view of life because of it? The following simple tests may be given, during which the tester notes the reaction of the stutterer. (1) Ask the stutterer to imitate one of his blocks, looking in the mirror as he does it. (2) Ask the stutterer to relate some incident concerning his speech, and see whether or not he is able to look at you during a block. (3) Bring a stranger into the room, and see whether or not the stutterer will speak to him when asked a question. Did he look at the stranger?

In addition to these observations, it is well to ask the individual to answer a few such questions as: (1) Do you think there is any advantage in being a stutterer? (2) Does stuttering make it difficult or embarrassing for you to buy something in a store? (3) Is the average person as friendly with a stutterer as he is with a normal speaker? (4) Does stuttering make it difficult for you to keep friends? (5) Are you ashamed of your stuttering? (6) Does your stuttering make life seem worthless to you? (7) Would you rather be blind than stutter?— Ask the same question substituting deaf, fat, having a large birthmark on face, and feeble-minded, for first handicap. The obvious reactions of the stutterer to these questions, combined with his reactions to other tests and his blocks in general, will give quite an adequate picture of his attitude toward his speech difference.

CASE REPORT OF A SECONDARY STUTTERER

Name: Mrs. M. S.   *Age:* 39   *Speech Defect:* Stuttering

Ruth X was born May 24th, 1902. Her father, aged 32 at her birth, was a severe stutterer, his disorder "resulting from black diphtheria when a boy." [3] Her mother, aged 31 at Ruth's birth, had no speech defect but was in "poor health" during most of Ruth's childhood. A brother, two years older than Ruth, also stuttered severely from the "beginning of speech" and had a "mental condition" (probably amentia) resulting from rickets. The maternal grandmother, who

---

[3] Words in quotation marks are case's own.

lived with the family for several years during Ruth's childhood, showed symptoms of senile amentia.

The mother's health was "fair" during pregnancy, but she had a "bad fall" during the last months. Instruments were used during delivery, but no injuries were reported and the baby is said to have nursed readily. She was breast-fed and her rate of growth was normal. Ruth reported that the illnesses prior to onset of stuttering at "about seven or eight years" were "tonsillitis, whooping cough, enlarged glands, and thyroid trouble." She could give no further details. No attempts were made to change the child's handedness and there was no left handedness in her immediate family. She began to speak at "the normal age" and at first is said to have spoken without stuttering.

She had few fights with her childhood playmates. She described herself as a follower rather than a leader. Preferred girl playmates, one of whom has remained a close chum. She said her parents declared her to be a very shy, nervous, good child. Items of questionnaire which she checked as occurring *occasionally* in childhood were constipation, thumb-sucking, strong fears, selfishness, lying, and jealousy. She was not athletic, having always been "rather awkward and poorly coordinated."

She lived, during her childhood and school life, in a large city. The parents rented their home but were described as being in "comfortable circumstances." The father was a skilled laborer and the family had no major financial conflicts. He was very religious, somewhat irritable, and insisted upon strict obedience. A certain amount of family friction existed (reason unknown) and the parents quarreled in front of the children, but Ruth reports that the "family spats made both parents very unhappy" and "did not last very long at a time." She said she liked her mother best "because she was not so strict."

In school, her progress was uneventful except that at eight years of age, due to typhoid fever and an appendectomy, she failed the second grade. She was an average student, liking school and her teachers, none of whom seemed to have penalized her stuttering. She did some oral reading and reciting in the early grades, but soon was freed from recitation during the rest of her school life. She graduated from high school at eighteen. No speech correction was available during this period.

After her graduation from high school, she did housework at home and helped with the neighbors' children. She took some night school courses, one in speech which gave her no relief, but was unable to gain employment. At the age of twenty she had diphtheria resulting in "heart trouble" for several years. It has since disappeared. At twenty-five a severe attack of influenza left her with a "bad sinus infection" which she has had ever since. She was in ill health during much of her twenties. She had two operations for hemorrhoids and at thirty a hysterectomy was performed. At thirty-two she had spinal meningitis and was bedridden for a year. When she was thirty-five she married a World War veteran seven years her senior, who had been divorced. They have lived happily and she says that he is very kind and understanding. He is a foundry core-maker by trade, but for the last three years has been on WPA. Her mother died two years ago, followed by her father a year later. Ruth reacted to this by a "nervous breakdown," from which she has since "recovered." Ruth's parents left them a little farm, and they live there and are paying off the mortgage.

Her stuttering, she said, was first noticed in the family by herself, about seven years of age, during a school recitation. She described it as consisting of "easy, quick repetitions of the first sound or letter of the word." At first it seemed to be confined to "no particular words or sounds," but often seemed "located at the beginning of the sentence." She declared that "at first they surprised me and weren't awfully unpleasant, but now, Oh, my!" These symptoms were not like those of her father who had long "sticky blocks in his throat," but they increased in frequency and by the time she entered high school long tonic prolonged blocks appeared. She could account for the onset of her stuttering only in terms of heredity. She stuttered no more at home or on the playground than at school. She used the following words to describe her changing reactions to her stuttering: "First I was indifferent, then surprised; then it made me mad, and then I began to get scared and to avoid talking." She said that school recitations, errands, speaking to clerks, and meeting strange people were her first feared situations. Conversation with her father became very difficult for he always "looked embarrassed and seemed to hate to see me stutter."

Other conditions which have continued to increase the frequency of her blocks are: excitement, fatigue, asking questions, interrupting and giving directions. She has always "stuttered more to people she knows well than to strangers." She reacts to interruption or help on her hard words by anger and frustration. She described her physiological reactions as "heart thumping, flushing, tension, and gasping." She has never known any periods of free speech as long as a day since she began to stutter, and the disorder has gradually but progressively become more of a handicap in that the blocking increased in frequency, duration, and abnormality.

At the present time, under conditions of even casual conversation, communication is very difficult. The following may describe a common symptom complex: She begins to vibrate her right hand up and down patting her knee very rapidly as she prepares for the attempt on the feared word. Then she swings both arms upward in jerky arcs, saying "eeyah-ohah" as a starting ritual. With the arm jerk and the ejaculations she used a rapid lip quiver or jaw jerk as she makes a sudden attempt to utter the word. Usually this fails several times, and she repeats the routine with increasing force until finally the word is forced out. Occasionally, the arm jerks are reinforced with bodily movements so intense that we have seen her throw herself out of a chair.

The characteristic symptoms are those above described, but occasionally she will attempt to use a slow rhythmic, measured rate of syllable utterance for a time. This usually fails, and then she resorts to the familiar struggle. Still more rare is an infrequent automatic repetition or smooth easy prolongation. The breathing record shows opposition between thorax and abdomen, and a rapid abdominal tremor coincident with the arm and finger jerks. She frequently attempts speech on residual air, and employs great gasps to free herself from the speech interruption.

The arm-swinging symptom is a recent addition, not having occurred until three years ago, and at present it is the most hated feature of her "curse." It began as a deliberate device to time the moment of speech attempt. She had attended a commercial stuttering school in Detroit where they were able to give her a little temporary relief by using a hand-swinging movement to time the moment of speech attempt. Although she had never been able to employ the trick with any marked degree of success, save when reading to herself, she decided that the "muscular reinforcement" of the hand-swinging must have had some value. She, therefore, drilled herself in making the speech attempt upon the feared word the moment she raised her right hand to touch her hair. At first the device seemed to work, but soon it became habitual, automatic, and now she cannot prevent its occurrence.

She is very emotional since this symptom has arisen and gets morbid. She cries easily. Once she has attempted a word she seldom gives up until it has been uttered. She does not substitute easier words very often because there are few she does not fear. Other devices are used to postpone speech attempt and still others to minimize the fear of words (monotone, whispered rehearsal, swallowing to prove to self she still has control of speech organs, assumed humorous attitudes). At the present time she has had no therapy at our clinic, having had but two appointments thus far which were used for examination and case study. She plans to come to the clinic for remedial work soon after the beginning of the year.

Her attitude toward therapy is that of desperation—the grasping of straws—no great hope or confidence that she will conquer handicap. Specific methods to release herself from stuttering blocks which she has tried herself and violently rejects are:

1. Stop and start over.
2. Talk slowly.
3. Talk swiftly.
4. Talk in a low voice.
5. Stop and take a deep breath.
6. Use a vowel to start the word.
7. Placing the tongue in certain position.
8. Talk on tail end of breath.
9. Talking with objects in mouth.
10. Opening mouth before attempting speech.
11. Rhythmic speech.
12. Timing the moment of speaking with some other movement.
13. Relaxation.
14. Distractions.
15. Body jerks.

The Treatment of Secondary Stuttering

Theories of stuttering. At one time, the poor student of speech therapy had to be able to describe fifteen different theories concerning the nature and treatment of secondary stuttering, and there were others they might have included in their study. While there is still disagreement and confusion among therapists with respect to their explanations of this disorder, the arguments are not so strident, and large areas of mutual thinking prevail. Formerly, there tended to be various schools each holding a definite and rigid theoretical dogma. Modern research has made available new sources of information. Cooler heads have examined the evidence again and have been able to reconcile opposing points of view. Probably the most important factor was the giving up of the belief in a *single cause* for stuttering. The *fallacy of the single cause* has been responsible for confusion in many fields, and it certainly caused plenty of difficulty in speech correction.

Most of the disagreement still remaining clusters about the origin of the symptoms. The *neurotic* theory of stuttering considers the symptoms to be merely the outward evidence of deep-seated emotional conflict. Travis (149), for example, says:[4]

> . . . stuttering is a defense created with extraordinary skill and designed to prevent anxiety from developing when certain impulses of which the stutterer dares not become aware, threaten to expose themselves.

Dunlap (53) has this to say of the stutterer: "Sometimes he is in constant fear lest he inadvertently reveal something he would his elders did not hear," and this same author placed great stress on the stutterers' repression of profane or filthy words or thoughts. Coriat (44), a psychoanalyst, puts the belief in these words:

> When a stammerer attempts to talk, the mouth movements are the persistence into maturity of the original sucking, and biting lip-nipple activities of infancy. . . .

In essence, the neurotic theory of stuttering claims that the approach-avoidance conflict is a basic one, and it insists that speech therapy devoted solely to the eradication of the symptom has no utility. If speech therapy is to be successful, it must also be a psychotherapy.

We are pretty sure that some stutterers have this type of causation. Some of our cases cannot be reasonably understood in any other way. These are in the marked minority, however. In them the stuttering is symptomatic of a primary neurosis. But there are many more stutterers in whom the neurosis, if any, is secondary. The stutterer develops the stuttering he has acquired from other sources into a defense mechanism. As one of our cases said, "Sure, I get some good out of it. If I have to stutter, I might as well use it to dodge some of the pain of living. It's not good for anything else." Most normal people are neurotic some of the time, and so are most stutterers, in this sense. A few, however, have compulsive symptoms which can only be understood in terms of psychopathology. In them, the stuttering starts in a neurosis and remains in one.

---

[4] Page 93.

Another theory which refuses to give up the ghost is that which explains the stutterer's problem in terms of a constitutional difference or predisposition. Stutterers are said to have dysphemia. By the term *dysphemia* we refer to an underlying neuromuscular condition which reflects itself peripherally in nervous impulses that are poorly timed in their arrival in the paired speech musculatures. Travis (147) has shown that during the stuttering block the action currents (which accompany nervous impulses from the brain) do not appear simultaneously. This may indicate a lack of cerebral dominance, according to his theory, or merely the disruption of coordination which results from emotional upheaval in the central nervous system. Most coordinations break down under great stress of fear or insecurity, and the coordinations of speech have always been known to reflect emotional blockings. The importance of the concept of dysphemia is that it explains the stutterer's speech interruptions in terms of a nervous system which breaks down *relatively easily* in its integration of the flow of nervous impulses to the paired peripheral muscles. In order to lift the jaw, for instance, nervous impulses must arrive simultaneously in the paired muscles of each side. In some stutterers these arrival times are disrupted; they are not synchronized. It is very difficult to lift a jaw or a wheelbarrow by one handle. The dysphemic individual is able to time his speech coordinations pretty well as long as the coordinating centers in the brain are not being bedeviled by emotional reactions and their back-flow of visceral sensations. He can talk pretty well when calm and unexcited. But his thresholds of resistance to emotional disturbance are low. His coordinations break down under relatively little stress. We have all known pianists and golfers who could play excellently by themselves but whose coordinations were pitifully inadequate to the demands of concert or tournament pressures. The dysphemic person is thought to be neurologically differentiated from other persons in what Gutzmann speaks of as "a weakness of the central coordinating system."

It may well be true that the term *dysphemia* is merely a

cloak for our ignorance, yet there are many evidences that such a condition exists in certain individuals. Chief among these are research findings which indicate that (1) the tendency to stutter seems to be inherited; (2) the stutterer is often more poorly coordinated in swift or rhythmic movements of the speech musculatures during silence; (3) the stutterer exhibits metabolic and biochemical differences; (4) the stutterer frequently shows confusion in handedness and other peripheral signs of central laterality; (5) the brain waves of stutterers differ from those of nonstutterers. These research findings are not entirely conclusive, since other investigations have challenged their accuracy; yet when we consider that among the groups of stutterers tested there must have been many whose stuttering was of neurotic or developmental origin, the positive findings seem to have increased significance.

Many phrases other than dysphemia have been used to indicate that stutterers are neurologically differentiated from nonstutterers. Some of these are: "neuropathic diathesis," "lack of a sufficient margin of cerebral dominance," "constitutional incoordination," and "nervous instability." Greene (67), for instance, says:

The stutterer is psychobiologically a variant. Whatever the exact nature of the underlying inferiority—and as yet we do not know—it appears to be an hereditary factor that predisposes the individual to emotional instability and disorganization in general, and to stuttering speech in particular.

Hahn (70), whose text summarizes the current views concerning the theories and therapies of stuttering, declares:

Most authorities view stuttering as the result of a malfunctioning nervous system, and contend that in the early or primary periods of onset the central nervous system has not reached a maturation point sufficient to withstand certain shocks, childhood diseases, ego competitiveness or malnutrition. These and other "trigger" causes affect the nervous system, and speech, dependent so much on finely adjusted muscle groups under brain leadership, naturally is affected.

Again, as in our discussion of the neurotic theory, we wish to state our belief that some few cases seem to acquire stuttering from a background of dysphemia. In a thousand children, there are bound to be a few poorly timed ones at one extreme of the distribution. They will be bound to have more non-fluence than the verbal athletes at the other extreme. Their speech will probably break down under less pressure than will the great majority of children. If we think of stuttering as having a multiple causation, we can easily accept this as one of the sources. If among our cases we find one who is thoroughly disjointed in his general non-speech coordinations, with a history of stuttering in the family, mixed handedness, poor diadochokinesis, we feel that he should perhaps have special training both in improving his timing, decreasing his tempo of speech and living, and in building his barriers against the speech disruptors to which he seems especially vulnerable.

A third theory, the *semantic theory*, views stuttering as the product of poor diagnosis on the part of the parent who mislabeled and misinterpreted the normal hesitations of beginning speech to mean stuttering. According to Johnson (85), the chief exponent of this theory, the stutterer himself makes a similar misjudgment. He accepts the falsely based stigma, and then proceeds to react to the label as though it were a fact. He begins to avoid the figments of his distorted imagination; he "hesitates to hesitate" and most of his habitual symptoms are the product of this concern. He battles an abstraction, and so, of course, the battle is in vain. Somehow, the stutterer must learn to think straight, to stop fighting the windmills of speech. He must face his fears and learn to tolerate non-fluency. This is Johnson's statement of the theory (84):

In a fundamental sense, stuttering is not a speech defect at all, although excessive nonfluency might sometimes be so regarded. Stuttering is an evaluational disorder. It is what results when normal nonfluency is evaluated as something to be feared and avoided; it is, outwardly, what the stutterer does in an attempt to avoid non-fluency. On such a basis his reluctance to speak at all, his shyness, his excessive caution in speaking, his great effort to speak perfectly, which shows up in his facial grimaces, bodily contortions and strained vocalizations—all this, which is what we call stuttering, becomes understandable when viewed as avoidance reactions, reactions designed to avoid the nonfluency which the individual has learned to fear and dread and expect.

Speech therapy becomes a matter of changing the stutterer's attitudes toward his speech and toward his environment. With many of these implications we agree. The stutterer must learn to think straight. He must decrease his need to avoid. He must increase the need to approach. He must do a lot of reality testing. He must face his fears and revise his non-fluency reactions. Many stutterers seem to fit the pattern of this explanation. The influence of social penalty and social stigma in producing the morbidity of stuttering is quite apparent in most cases. If to this etiological concept is added the role of communicative frustration as an equally potent original cause, we would agree that the large majority of stutterers have such an onset. We also feel that most stutterers require new attitudes toward their speech problem and toward themselves. However, we feel that stuttering is more than a simple approach-avoidance conflict, that it is also an avoidance-avoidance conflict, with important dynamics focused on escaping from the stuttering tremor.

A fourth major view of stuttering can be called the *conflict reinforcement* theory of stuttering. It treats the disorder from the viewpoint of modern learning theory. The primary symptoms are seen as the result of competitive and opposing urges to speak and not to speak. When these tendencies are approximately equal, oscillations and fixations in behavior occur. These are the repetitions and prolongations of the primary symptoms. The conflicting urges may come from many sources. The child may want to speak but may not know what to say or how to say it. He may need to speak at a time when he thinks his listener is not listening or does not want to hear him. He may have the urge to say something "evil" which may receive penalty. He may want to speak like big people, yet not have the fluency or articulatory skills to keep the flow going. He may have an urge to express himself at a time when he feels ambivalent. The lag of a clumsy tongue may oppose a strong need to talk quickly. Any of these and many other situations could produce the opposing forces. All this theory considers is what results when the urge to speak finds a contrary urge not to do so.

Secondary stuttering is viewed in much the same way, except that now, with the increased awareness of the stigma, the need to avoid the noxious behavior has become much stronger. Since communication is essential to our culture, and few stutterers can afford to give up speaking, the new conflict is even more powerful than before. With the development of fear and anxiety, the oscillatory and fixation symptoms serve as fear reducers. By this we mean that the stutterer has in advance of the speech attempt on a feared word a certain expectation of unpleasant abnormality. Milisen and Van Riper (49) showed that the stutterer is able to predict the duration of his blockings in a general way. If he does expect a long blocking, only a long blocking will satisfy that fear, and only when the expectation has been met will the tension level begin to subside. Only when this tension level subsides can the stutterer escape automatically from his tremor.

But most stutterers want to hurry the process. They do not want their expected block to run its course. Once they have begun the actual speech attempt and find themselves in tremor, they are caught in a new kind of conflict, an avoidance-avoidance conflict. Here they are beset by three alternatives, all unpleasant. They can stop everything and be silent, but this silence is painful, too. They can continue their frustrating tremors, but these are as unpleasant as silence. Or they can begin to struggle, to jerk, force, twist and turn in their efforts to break the tremor, and these contortions bring much social penalty. What usually happens is that the first two alternatives, silence and tremor frustration, become more and more unpleasant as time goes on, and so they repel the stutterer away from themselves into the clutches of the random struggle. Either this happens or the interruption and abnormality have lasted long enough to satisfy the expectation and the tremor dies out with the tension decay. One of the worst features of the struggle response is that the interrupter devices become strongly reinforced by the sudden reduction of anxiety and punishment which come with the utterance of the word. It is obvious that the author has a preference for this last theory, so briefly sketched here. He feels that it enables all of the other theories and causes and symptoms to be brought into the same tent. It offers suggestions for therapy which are far greater than those provided by the other ways of looking at stuttering. In the following sections of this chapter will be found many techniques directly based upon the principles stated.

The various methods for treating secondary stuttering. From our consideration of all of these points of view, the student would be likely to expect that an equally wide variety of therapeutic methods would be available. Oddly enough, this is not the case. When the actual therapies now in use are scrutinized, one is impressed not by the differences but by the similarities of the methods used. Terminologies, emphases and theoretical justifications differ, but the activity remains the same. This rather curious agreement is even more evident when we examine the subgoals set up for the stutterer. No matter to what theory they subscribe, all therapists attempt to reduce the stutterer's fears, forcings, and inadequate social behavior. All speech correctionists carry out some etiological therapy, depending on the theory of causation to which they subscribe or on the causal factors present in any given case; and this part of the therapy differs widely. However, few clinicians actually working with stutterers confine their efforts to eliminating the causes. All of them work with symptoms—with the situation and word fears and with the repetitions, prolongations, facial contortions, and other typical stuttering reactions. There seem to be two major schools of thought in terms of actual therapy.

One school of speech correctionists, numbering among its adherents many of the older workers in the field, attempts to teach the stutterer methods for *avoiding* or preventing *fear* and *occurrence* of stuttering blocks. It aims to eliminate the emotional factors which precipitate the symptoms. The stutterer is urged to believe in the theory advanced by the clinician, and nothing is left undone to convince him he can be cured. Strong clinical suggestion and even hypnosis are used to strengthen his confidence in the remedial techniques. Routine breathing and vocalization exercises and rituals are employed. Through the use of distractions of all kinds, the fear of stuttering is kept from consciousness. Gestures, head movements, and other forms of muscular reinforcement are used as starters. Strange methods of vocalization—preceding all consonants by a vowel, sing-song speech, the "octave-twist," stereotyped rhythms of stress or phrasing, slurring of the consonants, and many other similar devices—are used to keep the fear from becoming potent enough to precipitate stuttering. Every effort is made to get the stutterer to forget his fears and symptoms. He is urged to consider himself a normal speaker. By the use of speech situations and types of communication arranged according to graduated levels of difficulty, his confidence is nursed along until it becomes sufficient to enable him to speak without fear or stuttering at each successive level. Group techniques help to decrease the fear and increase the suggestion.

In most cases, this type of treatment produces immediate release from fear and stuttering. The stutterer believes that at last a miracle has happened. Hesitantly he applies the formula and lo! it seems to work. His confidence grows by leaps and bounds, and, as it does, his fears decrease. He writes his clinician a glowing letter of praise and thankfulness and departs for his home. Occasionally, his new speech fluency continues for the rest of his life. Whenever fears arise, and they are inevitable, he applies the formulas given to him by the speech correctionist. If the environmental pressures are not too great, and novelty, suggestion, and faith are still effective, the formulas successfully dispel the fear. He realizes that he can still speak without stuttering.

Unfortunately, like most of the devices the stutterers themselves have invented, the formula devices soon become habitual and relatively unconscious. When this happens, they no longer are able to take the place of fear in the stutterer's mind, and relapse usually occurs. Giving the stutterer a period of free speech does not solve his problem if, and when, fear returns. Nevertheless, in the safe haven of the speech clinic, where belief and novelty are important factors and both group and clinical suggestions are everywhere, the stutterer finds great relief. Under such conditions, few stutterers experience much trouble, but unfortunately, such conditions do not exist in ordinary life. When the stutterer returns to his home or former environment, or meets situations which remind him of past failures, there is no one around to tell him that his fears and blocks are mere bugaboos which will disappear if he follows the formula. Life is not made up of easy speech situations or optimal conditions for communication. He finds that he cannot remain relaxed when he applies for a position. He finds it impossible to remain permanently unemotional. The self-confidence, so carefully and painstakingly nurtured by the speech correctionist, collapses like a house of cards. The formula suddenly seems to have lost its charm. Faith crumbles. The stuttering returns in all its viciousness, often with greater frequency and severity than before. The stutterer attempts to relax, but fear and panic prevent relaxation. He starts his arm swing, or "octave twist," or whatnot, and finds that suddenly it does not keep out the blocks. After repeated failure, he finally gives up and resumes his hunt for a new miracle worker to cast out his "stuttering devil." Meanwhile, the speech correctionist has new stutterers to whom the formula may be taught.

The second major school of speech correctionists is relatively young. While most of the devices used by the other school have been employed for centuries, those of the new school have evolved in the last ten or twenty years. Although its adherents quarrel among themselves about the etiology of stuttering and fail to agree with regard to the nature of the primary symptoms, they all doubt that the secondary stutterer can ever entirely free himself from fears of certain situations and certain words. They feel that an individual who has developed habits of avoidance, postponement, timing, and disguise as reactions to the fear of stuttering will never break those habits merely by experiencing a period of free speech. They doubt that faith in any formula will eliminate the fear in the majority of stutterers. They feel that the effects of suggestion and situation are temporary, and that self-confidence is affected by too many other factors to render it a permanent foundation for fear-free speech. In other words, this school believes that it is impossible to keep out all fears or occurrences of stuttering blocks for any great length of time, and that no abnormal form of rhythm or utterance will provide permanent relief.

The adherents of this school point out that it is possible to modify the form of the stutterer's speech abnormality without preventing its occurrence. They call attention to the wide variation in secondary symptoms found in different stutterers as a sign of the fact that it is possible to stutter in many different ways. They claim that it is possible to stutter with a minimum of abnormality and interruption and that, when this is done, the fear of stuttering and most of the blocks disappear. They insist that most of the abnormality and interruption is produced by the stutterer's conscious or habitual devices to avoid, minimize, disguise, or release himself from the blocks he feels. They believe that these devices can be disrupted and eradicated. They attempt to use the fear of stuttering as a signal to warn the stutterer to modify and control the form of any symptoms which might ensue, and as a signal to adopt new preparatory sets which can prevent the occurrence of the old secondary symptoms. They insist that the stutterer acquire an objective attitude toward his speech difference—that he admit its existence and refuse to pose as a normal speaker, but that

he control his fears and blocks so that only a minimum of interruption and abnormality will occur. They feel that such an attitude so diminishes the social penalties placed upon the disorder
that the fear of stuttering is greatly reduced. They declare that
these principles not only will decrease the duration and severity
of the individual blocks but that those blocks will diminish in
number. Fluency and release from fear are thus considered to
be by-products of *controlled stuttering* rather than the results of
avoided stuttering. The adherents of this school argue that their
methods provide security for the stutterer when fears or blocks
do reoccur. We may summarize the point of view by saying
that this school teaches the stutterer not to keep out or avoid
his blocks and fears, but to control them so that they can occur
with a minimum of interference to communication.

Outline of treatment for modifying the form of stuttering. It is
probably obvious that the author belongs to the latter school.
The method for treating the secondary stutterer, which will be
described in this text, points its therapy at the following goals:
(1) Decrease the practices that reinforce the strength of
the stuttering reaction. (2) Help the stutterer solve as many
of his emotional conflicts as possible and change, if we can, the
environmental conditions which tend to keep him a fundamentally hesitant person. (3) Decrease the fears and malattitudes
by teaching the stutterer to admit and accept his stuttering as
a temporary problem which must be faced and conquered.
(4) Modify and lessen the severity of the stuttering blocks by
eliminating the secondary symptoms of stuttering. (5) Teach
the stutterer not to avoid fears or blocks, but to use them in
learning how to stutter in an easy, effortless fashion, with a
minimum of interruption or abnormality. With this therapy it
usually takes longer to achieve speech free from blockings, but
relapse is much less frequent, and the stutterer always has a
method for controlling his fears and stuttering reactions if they
do return.

The treatment of the secondary stutterer is largely carried
out through individual conferences with the speech correction-

ist, through the use of carefully prepared speech assignments, and through co-operative projects involving groups of stutterers. Like all speech defectives, each stutterer presents an individual problem and must be treated as such. Certain individuals require much more work on one phase of the treatment than do others. Personality readjustment such as that sketched in Chapter 4 is frequently necessary. Adequate motivation is important, for this treatment makes such a strong demand on the individual that perfunctory co-operation dooms it to immediate defeat. It is usually wise to let the student see the exact sequence of the treatment so that he may appreciate the importance of attaining the subgoals in order to attain the final goal of free speech.

Therapy is carried out through a series of successive periods or levels, each of which involves the use of new subgoals and techniques. The techniques, however, overlap, and those of prior levels continue throughout all later ones. Thus the assignments and projects of the second stage include not only the new techniques specific to that level but also all those used in the first stage. New subgoals and new techniques are added to, not substituted for, former ones. During the work on each of these levels, the speech correctionist should use every effort to prevent speech fluency due to the influence of suggestion or attitudes of self-confidence. These factors are too unstable to be relied upon for permanent relief. Instead, all clinical emphasis should be placed upon the attainment of good mental hygiene, the ability to disrupt the old habitual reactions of avoidance or release, and the ability to control the form of speech abnormality. Speech free from all stuttering is a by-product and an end-product, not the immediate goal. Stress is not placed on the absence of stuttering blocks or fears, but upon those blocks and fears that are controlled. The student is encouraged to stutter, but to stutter without the old abnormalities of emotion and behavior.

The first goal of therapy. Our first task is to help the stutterer to *stop reinforcing his stuttering.* Few therapists or cases realize how hard stutterers labor to maintain the strength of the symptoms. To the dispassionate but alert observer, the effort and time spent in strengthening the very thing from which the sufferer wishes to be freed appear incredible. As we have previously mentioned, the stutterer keeps his fear "hot" by avoiding or postponing feared words and situations. To dodge a little temporary unpleasantness, the case does things which create fear enough to cause him ten times the unpleasantness he has avoided. Somehow, the therapist must get the stutterer to tackle his feared words, to enter directly into the situations in which he fears stuttering may occur. The case must learn that stuttering fear is similar to the mythical hoop snake which will chase you if you run away, but which flees itself if you march up to confront it. The case must, for the time being, be willing to stutter openly without recoiling from his blockings, without struggling to yank himself out of his tremors. The therapist must help to increase the approach drive and decrease the avoidance urge, if the basic conflict is to find solution. The case must be trained to perceive approaching feared words as opportunities to stutter freely and thereby to eliminate many of the most distressing symptoms—those that are used to avoid the speech attempt or to interrupt the tremors. Most of the worst features of stuttering are those reactions which attempt to restrain, to time speech attempts, to force or to hide. Fluent stuttering eliminates most of them and at the same time decreases much of the fear.

Eliminating avoidance. No stutterer will ever stop avoiding words or situations unless the punishment received in facing them is somehow countered by reward. The therapist must provide that reward. In part, the reward consists of the approval of the therapist and the other cases. Our culture always penalizes the person who runs away or dodges his fears. We are taught to admire the stripling who throws a punch at a bully even though he takes a bad beating. Though far from stoic, we respect the person who can stand up to pain. These cultural values can be mobilized by the therapist.

Many stutterers are full of self-revulsion, hating themselves for their "cowardice" and intricate maneuverings of avoidance. Once they find in the therapist a person who can look at their contortions without laughter, impatience, rejection or pity, they experience a great relief and release. They begin to test the therapist's permissiveness. They try out on her all the most horrible contortions they can muster, and if the therapist accepts these offerings with eager clinical interest but no penalty, the case, often for the first time, can make a tentative attempt to expose his stuttering without disguise, recoil or struggle. Once the case realizes that the therapist can accept him as he is, he finds enough basic security to enable him to experiment with his stuttering, to explore this horrible area of the self. He learns that his feared words become opportunities to get acquainted with himself. Instead of being revolted, he becomes interested.

Stutterers can be willing to give up their avoidances if they see this as a necessary step in achieving the final goal of fluent stuttering. All of us can endure temporary discomfort if we can see that it is necessary to our future happiness. Any subgoal takes on the attractiveness of the final goal if the relationship is clear. If the stutterer realizes that avoidance is a barrier to any further progress in speech, he will be more likely to give it up. The therapist should help the case understand why the avoidance is harmful, how it creates symptoms as well as more fear. It is difficult to be rational when one is afraid, but it is also possible to become afraid of a consequence even worse than temporary stuttering—namely, the termination of treatment. Therapists must be patient but there is little hope for the case who continually reinforces his fears by consistent avoidance. The case must understand this.

Much avoidance can be eliminated if the therapist will herself demonstrate that she can tolerate stuttering. If she will have the case serve as an observer as she enters a store and stutters voluntarily yet calmly, it always makes a vivid impression. The sight of another person jumping a ditch, entering a feared situation, or touching a wire which may be electrified, is tremendously reassuring. The more the case can identify himself with the therapist, the greater will be the potency of setting such an example. The stutterer must learn that the stove is not as hot as he thinks, that stuttering can be tolerated.

Stutterers can also learn to approach rather than avoid their moments of stuttering by reason of their curiosity. Most cases are bewildered and mystified by their disorder. They simply cannot understand it. It doesn't make any more sense to them than it does to others. Under the guidance of a wise therapist, they can begin to explore this behavior, to become vitally interested in it. Feared words become opportunities to learn more about themselves as well as their mysterious symptoms. We have known stutterers to want to stutter so much for this purpose that they were unable to do so.

Many cases have avoided and postponed so often and so long that the responses are almost automatic. They can scan a series of synonyms and pick the safest one in the fraction of a second, often without missing a syllable. It is very necessary that they get these avoidance reactions under voluntary control if they are to decrease and eliminate them. The therapist often requires the case to report all the different varieties experienced, or to describe in writing each instance of avoidance within a given period of time. By becoming highly conscious of them, by observing them in oneself and in other stutterers, the reactions can be controlled. A conscience against using such tricks can be built up, even when no penalties upon avoidance are employed. Progress in giving up avoidance is always slow, but it can be made sure.

Finally, the stutterer should be encouraged to stutter as much as possible during this first stage of therapy. He should talk more than he ever has done. Often therapists require that the case collect as many as five hundred or a thousand stutterings per day, or a lesser amount per hour. This "bath of stuttering" has certain cleansing powers, and it certainly does counteract the old tendency to avoid every word or situation in which stuttering might occur.

Through structuring the therapy situation in these ways, much of the strength in the avoidance drive can be reduced. With its reduction comes relief, both in frequency and severity of symptoms. The intensive study of the stuttering and of the self begins to help the stutterer to come to grips with his problem, to see it differently. He no longer sees it as a mysterious curse. He begins to feel some responsibility for his behavior. Instead of surrendering to his impulses to flee the scene of the crime, he tends to look at what he has done when stuttering. He begins to test reality, to see how his listeners really do react, to experiment with his own blockings. He begins to see that there might be other types of stuttering available to him, types that are much less painful and frustrating. Instead of surrendering all control to the blind struggling, avoidance and escape reactions, he begins to fight for some mastery over self. But most important of all, he has reduced the amount of fear reinforcement. He no longer spends most of his energy keeping his fears alive and potent. Instead of building up the fears, he now works to tear them down.

The basic method in accomplishing these ends is the collection of stuttering experiences. The stutterer goes forth to seek his fears and his blockings. He uses them for analysis. The actual moments of stuttering, together with the pre-spasm and post-spasm periods, comprise the stuff of therapy. Here is where the changes occur. Here is where the individual confronts himself, faces his fears, strives for self-mastery and accepts the responsibility for his behavior. Therapy for the secondary stutterer consists of a large number of these stutterings studied and examined in a permissive atmosphere so that changes in the stuttering may occur.

Group, individual, and self-therapy. Most therapists prefer to use a combination of group therapy, individual therapy, and self-therapy. The case needs the support of the group. Often

he can see and understand behavior in another stutterer long
before he can recognize it in himself. The other stutterers also
serve as mirrors in which he can see himself. Partial insights
when shared can become complete. The group of stutterers
creates an optimal atmosphere where the cases can experiment
with their own stuttering without feeling too much penalty.
But group therapy seldom is sufficient by itself. The case needs
individual help from his personal therapist. He needs to identify himself with an individual who is adequate, who can be
trusted, who has more strength and understanding than either
he or his fellow stutterers. He needs someone to share his defeats and triumphs privately. But even when we add this to
the group therapy, we still do not have enough. The stutterer
must from the beginning accept much of the responsibility for
healing himself. He must organize, perform, and report a good
many activities designed to make progress toward the attainment of his goals. Self-therapy is essential.

Preventing symptom reinforcement. We have shown how important avoidance is in strengthening the situation and word
fears of stuttering and why we must reduce that avoidance if
we are to decrease the frequency and severity of the symptoms.
Now we must show how we can solve the other part of the
stutterer's dilemma—the fact that the abnormality becomes
rewarded by the utterance of the word which emerges from that
abnormality. Unless we can prevent stuttering from reinforcing
itself, unless we can break up the self-perpetuating mechanism
by which it continues to exist, all our work in eliminating avoidance will fail. Stuttering keeps itself going by two methods:
(1) the avoidance trick breeds the fear, and (2) the release from
punishment, frustration and anxiety (which comes with the
final utterance) reinforces the abnormal behavior which immediately preceded it. We must attack the second reinforcer
as well as the first.

The therapist who merely attempts to get the case to speak
without stuttering during the therapy session does little to
weaken the old responses. They merely lie latent and hidden,

ready to emerge growling as soon as the case leaves his verbal bodyguard. We must not merely inhibit the symptoms; we must not just repress them. Instead we must break them up if we want to weaken them. We must, through pull-outs and canceling, keep the symptoms from strengthening the stuttering through escape from unpleasantness. We must make sure that repression does not create more trouble than it prevents. We must keep avoidance from reinforcing the fears. We must devise a therapy which will help the stutterer accept the responsibility for his behavior, recognize his frailties, and confront the revelations of his inner self, honestly and objectively. A therapy such as we outline here at least provides a framework for an all-out attack on the problem of stuttering.

Cancellation techniques. Ordinarily the conclusion of an act of stuttering produces a reduction of fear and an escape from frustration. It frees the stutterer to proceed with his communication. Even though he immediately falls into another blocking, he at least escapes from fixation on the word that he had dreaded. This momentary feeling of relief has reinforcement value. It keeps the symptoms at full strength.

The *post-spasm period* is most important in therapy. This is the Achilles' heel of the disorder. To attempt to alter or control the pre-stuttering period is too difficult because of the intense fear. To attempt to modify the stuttering *immediately* by working on it during its compulsive course is similarly onerous. But in the period immediately following the stuttering we have our most favorable point of therapeutic attack. If we can do something constructive at this time, we can prevent repression from doing its evil work. This post-spasm period is the best time for clear-thinking analysis of the stuttering behavior, for contact with the self. If we can use the post-spasm period to contrast the maladaptive symptoms which have just occurred with a more efficient, less destructive form of non-fluency, then we will have attacked the disorder at its most vulnerable spot. Finally, and of greatest importance, by inserting a deliberate, voluntary bit of discriminating behavior at this moment, we prevent the symptoms from being reinforced by the feeling of relief. Before the stutterer is free to continue with the remainder of his utterance, he must still go through the process of cancellation. Only the cancellation sets him free from communicative frustration. Therefore, it will be the cancellation that gets the greatest reinforcement from this source.

It must be made clear that our goal is the modification and weakening of the old symptom pattern and the creation of a competitive and substitute form of fluent stuttering. Therefore, after the stutterer has paused and analyzed the stuttering which has just occurred he then speaks the word again. But this second time he tries to stutter on it differently. He does not attempt to say it normally, even if he can do so. If necessary, he must utter the word using some pseudo-stuttering of a non-struggling, continuously moving variety. We ask him merely to stutter again with as little abnormality as possible, to stutter "in the direction of zero," to modify his old characteristic symptoms in terms of a more efficient utterance. Many different sub-projects can be devised under the general classification of cancellation. We can do various things during the pause; we can try different forms of fluent stuttering when we attempt the word again. In this post-spasm period we have at our disposal the optimal conditions for discrimination, for learning and unlearning. We cannot afford to ignore this opportunity for therapy.

To illustrate a few of the uses to which cancellation techniques can be put, we list the following procedures: (Note: the word "block" is used because most stutterers seem to prefer it to designate an occurrence of the stuttering act.)

1. Have the old block. Pause and repeat the block openly but with no sound. Try the word again, but hit it differently. After the cancellation, estimate whether you duplicated the old block during the pause, and whether you succeeded in changing it when you said it the second time, and if the pause was obvious.

2. Have the old block. Pause, and during the pause repeat the old block silently. Decide which part of the old block you are going to leave out, and try the word again leaving out the part decided on.

3. Have the old block, pause and duplicate the old block silently. Plan to try the word again using a slow, controlled repetition of the first sound, and rehearse this silently during the pause. Try the word again.

4. Have the old block. Pause and repeat it silently, then rehearse it with a tremor that diminishes in amplitude and frequency before release.

5. Have the old block. Pause and plan to *stutter* very slowly on the word when you try it again.

6. Have the old block. During the pause, identify one feature of it that you will prolong when you say it again.

7. Have the old block. Prolong the pause until your listener gets restless or interrupts, then stutter easily and calmly on the same word before continuing.

8. Have the old block. During the pause, try to identify the articulatory contact or posture that served as a trigger to set off the tremor. On the cancellation, prolong this trigger posture without going into tremor.

9. Have the old block. Pause long enough to observe your listener's reaction to your stuttering. On the cancellation, stutter as calmly as you can until his reaction changes.

10. Have the old block. During the pause, try to plan a form of stuttering so effortless and fluent that your listener will not be affected in the least. Then make the attempt.

11. Have the old block. Pause, duplicate the old block silently, then try to make the cancellation as a slow movement response rather than a fixation.

These are only a few illustrations of the variations possible in therapy. The therapist should always insist that the case stutter his way entirely through the word before pausing and canceling. If this is not done, the whole technique will merely become a postponement trick. He should always keep in mind that this canceling is of no value in itself. Only insofar as it helps the stutterer face his problem before the eyes of the world, only as it prevents repression and relief-reward, only when the new attempt shows the stutterer that he can find a fluent way of stuttering will cancellation be a therapeutic tool.

Repression elimination. When cancellation is used, the anxiety and the frustration do not entirely subside the moment the jaw jerk ends in utterance. The stutterer still cannot run ver-

bally away from the scene of his fluency crime. He is compelled
to confront his behavior rather than repress it. Most secondary
stutterers do a great deal of this repression. They detach themselves from the abnormality of their mouths. This is natural
enough since the experience is so punishing, but the detachment
and the repression are the very things that make the stutterer
feel his symptoms are compulsive and uncontrollable. When he
reacts by canceling, he throws away a stuttering breeder-
reaction and acquires behavior which permits problem solving.

Breaking up the stereotype of the symptoms. Many casual ob-
servers of the stuttering act make the mistake of considering
it merely random struggle. This might perhaps be the case
early in the disorder's history, but in most secondary stutterers
the stuttering behavior is highly organized. What we see is no
disintegration but an abnormal *integration* of speech. So exact
and similar are many of the stutterer's blockings that occasional breathing records of one stuttering act can be placed over
those of another such act with perfect matching. Much variation in terms of duration may occur; many stutterers have
several "spasm patterns" which they try out in turn when very
afraid; but most secondary stutterers have characteristic stuttering patterns as distinctive as their fingerprints. This similarity we call stereotypy, and much of the strength of stuttering
depends upon it. By training the stutterer to vary the kind of
stuttering he has learned, it is possible to weaken it. In unity
there is strength, in disunity, decay. Our task in therapy is to
break up the unity of the symptom organization. Once the
stutterer begins to vary his symptoms in the direction of less
abnormality but more fluency, the old symptoms no longer
become stronger with each new moment of stuttering.

How pull-outs can prevent symptom reinforcement. Stuttering
symptoms will not get reinforced by anxiety reduction or
punishment-escape if we can train the case to insert some controlled behavior between the old symptoms and the final utterance of the word. If the case can get voluntary control of the
stuttering before he speaks the word that is giving him trouble,

it will be the voluntary rather than the involuntary behavior which will be strengthened. If the release from stuttering emerges immediately from the tremor or the struggling contortions, these will be the things reinforced. But when, *during the blocking*, the stutterer strives to control, to slow down and damp out the tremors (instead of using a compulsive jerk or surge of tension) it will be the control which will get the strengthening. If, during the stuttering, the case works to modify and vary the symptoms in the direction of less abnormality, this modifying activity will get the reinforcement. Is not our therapeutic goal the strengthening of the stutterer's ability to control his speech behavior?

Usually it is wise to give the stutterer some thorough training in cancellation prior to the training in pulling out of blocks. In many cases, the stutterer begins to pull out of his tremors and other struggling symptoms as soon as he gets enough experience in modifying his stuttering in the post-spasm period. Conditioned responses always tend to move forward in time. Instead of waiting until the stuttering has run its automatic course, the case starts to take charge during the spasm-period. However, in most cases it is better to wait until the cancellation has been well established.

Often the first control possible to the stutterer during his blocking is that of magnifying or intensifying what is occurring. The therapist asks the stutterer to try to make the stuttering worse, to press harder, to jerk further, to exaggerate the tremors, to prolong the fixations, to hurry the repetitions. This is often the first modification possible. The next control is that which calls for the fixation or "freezing" of one of the spasmodic movements involved. At a sudden signal by the therapist, the stutterer must freeze in the stuttering posture being exhibited at the moment and maintain it purposefully until released by the therapist. Different types of release reactions are practiced: quick ones, slow ones, weak ones, strong ones, etc. Next the tremors are modified in every possible way, but with emphasis on slowing down the frequency and decreasing the amplitude.

Then the trigger postures are modified both in terms of location and tension. The stutterer comes to realize that no human can utter the first sound of the word "keep" with his lips tightly closed. And so he begins to modify this, to open the lips gradually, to experiment with looser contacts, to determine how much tension focused on a certain area is required to set off a tremor. He often, during this period, learns to set off the tremors deliberately, to throw himself into what he calls "real blockings." By learning how he set off the tremors, he also learns how to control them. There are many times when the case suddenly realizes that he is attempting to utter a word while holding his breath or inhaling. At this time, the pull-out will involve bringing in voiced or unvoiced air-flow. The case should move gradually from the uncontrolled to the controlled behavior. He should not stop the first and then make a new attempt. Transition, not substitution, is needed. No word can be uttered in the abnormal fashion attempted by the stutterer. Instead of floundering around until by chance or satiation the correct articulatory and phonatory set-up is made available, the stutterer wrestles with his stuttering apparatus and makes it conform to the phonetic requirements of the word.

It is very essential that the stutterer do this psychic wrestling. He who has felt helplessly unable to control his speech organs will not feel that he has won any mastery over them unless he has fought for that mastery. This is the age-old battle for responsibility for one's behavior which every neurotic must win. Pull-outs provide a favorable battlefield. The stutterer must modify the old reactions, rather than inhibit them and substitute new ones. The transitions should be gradual, not sudden; visible, not hidden. Our culture respects and rewards the person who fights for self-control, as the stutterer discovers to his great surprise.

No stutterer will win every battle, of course. At first, he will lose many more than he wins. He may try to get control, almost achieve it, then surrender to the old struggling. The wise therapist will predict this and accept it as entirely natural. She will know that one true success is worth a thousand failures. So vividly rewarding is the single instance of controlling the uncontrollable, the case makes giant strides as soon as one appears. At times, when failures are too prevalent, the case can still cancel and get something good out of the occurrence of stuttering. However, progress, though uneven, always seems to take place, and soon the stutterer has learned to get control much more quickly than before. Very soon, he finds some new rewards. He is now able to stutter so briefly and so unabnormally that his social penalties begin to decrease. With them disappear the fears. And so we find a marked lessening in both frequency and severity of stuttering. At this point the therapist must be careful to go slowly, to restrain progress rather than hasten it. The new reactions must be strengthened a good deal in order to have them permanently usable. The well known "flight into health" is to be found in speech therapy as well as in psychiatric practice. When the stutterer realizes that he has some control over the severity of his symptoms, the frequency may decrease almost to zero and thereby prevent strengthening of the new tools. It is not unusual also to find that the quicker pull-outs soon move forward in time and become preparatory sets. These can often prevent the occurrence of any abnormality, and some pseudo-stuttering should always be prescribed if this occurs too soon or too often.

The new type of stuttering should be one of short duration and little abnormality, in either vocalization or associated movement. The previous goals and methods are still part of the therapy. Assignments are given daily to reinforce and review them. But in this third period, instead of negatively trying to eliminate and reject old reactions, the stutterer attempts to learn a new reaction, a new way of stuttering. Since old habitual reactions are also broken by substitution of new ones, this therapy serves a double purpose. It also reinforces the mental-hygiene aspect of the therapy, since stutterers will not be nearly so likely to avoid, disguise, or develop emotional maladjustment about stuttering which does not thwart or socially penalize them. It tends to shave the reactions to stuttering to a minimum, leaving little to handicap them. In every sense of the word, the stutterer can afford to stutter. Both the primary and secondary reactions which form so large a share of the handicap are usually eliminated. When this happens, the fears

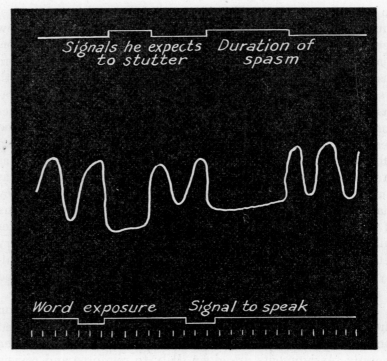

Fig. 14. Breathing record showing evidence of preparatory set to stutter on residual air.

of words and situations largely disappear, since one cannot be afraid of that which is not unpleasant. Indeed, when the stutterer learns that it is possible to stutter in a way which carries no thwarting or social penalty, his successful control of the blockings is actually pleasant.

We may outline our methods for teaching the stutterer to

stutter easily and effortlessly as follows: He must learn to (1) *react to the fear of stuttering by rehearsing the old spasm pattern and then rejecting it;* (2) *assume a new preparatory set to start the speech attempt from a state of rest, to prepare the second sound of the word, to make the first sound with loose contacts or relaxed positions, to make the first sound as a movement, and to make a gradual but voluntary shift from one sound to the next without retrial.*

We train our stutterers to recognize the old preparatory set, and then to reject it in favor of an alternative plan of attack. They are taught to rehearse the old abnormality consciously (they will anyway!) and then to reject it. Then they specifically plan to "hit the word in a new way." This new preparatory set has three dominant features: (1) to make the speech attempt from a state of articulatory quiescence rather than from a highly tensed musculature; (2) to initiate air flow—or voice flow—simultaneously with the speech attempt; (3) to make the feared sound of the word as a relaxed but highly voluntary *movement* leading directly into the succeeding sound.

It is apparent that what we have described is in essence merely a description of a speech attempt such as a nonstutterer might make. Each of the three features characterizes every normal utterance of a word. Stutterers attempt their nonfeared words in this selfsame manner. But when they expect stuttering, they attack the word in a totally different fashion. They create a focus of tension in the tongue, lips, or throat long before they start the word. Instead of initiating movements, they assume articulatory positions. For example:

When I've got to say my name, Mary, in a hard situation, I know just what's going to happen. My lips are going to clamp together suddenly, and I'll keep them glued there until the block is over and the word comes out. I don't make a sound and there isn't a breath of air stirring, although I'm squeezing in with my abdomen as hard as possible to make the air burst open my lips.

My tongue is up in the back when I make a *k* sound at the beginning of a hard word. It's stationary back there, but I'm pushing hard with it, trying to bore a hole through the roof of my mouth. The speech bottle is corked tight. I ought to have sense enough to open the cork, but all I do is press on the bottle down below. Sometimes if I struggle hard enough, put all my effort into one sudden push, I can break the blockade and out comes the word, but usually the more I push with my stomach, the tighter I press my tongue.

I knew I would have to thank my hostess at the end of the party, and, believe it or not, I had my tongue between my teeth in a tight *th* sound for ten minutes before I gathered enough nerve to approach her. The inevitable happened, and there I stood with my tongue still in its tooth-vise, frozen and motionless. All I could think of was: "A zombie, I. The living dead!"

In all of these descriptions, we can notice the production of a fixed articulatory position rather than the starting of a movement. We can also observe that these stutterers are attempting to produce the sound that is feared rather than the whole word. They are not trying to start a movement sequence. The *m*, the *k*, and the *th* are so feared that they dominate the whole experience. It is because of this morbid focus of attention that the stutterer is often unable to profit from releases that do occur. Often the "Mary" will emerge as "Mmuh-mmmuh-mary." This behavior may be explained as due to the stutterer's fear of the isolated *m* or *muh* sound. The schwa vowel (ə) in a non-sense syllable is always used when the consonant is perceived as isolated. Hence the use of *kuh* or *puh* to represent the isolated *k* and *p*. The stutterer attempts feared words only in terms of their feared sounds. Thus, he thinks he is having a great deal of trouble on the *s* sound of the word *stutter* even though he produces it as *sssssssss-stutter*. To sum up these observations, the stutterer attempts his feared words much differently than his nonfeared words: because of his fear, he plans, and tries to produce, isolated sounds rather than total words; he attempts these sounds as though they were fixed, static positions instead of the flowing movements they should be; he uses these positions to constrict and block off the flow of air or voice, and then struggles to break the hard contacts above by excessive air pressure from below.

Our task, then, is to teach our stutterers to attempt their

feared words exactly as they do their nonfeared ones. It is folly to expect them to do so at command, when they have such long-practiced abnormal methods of word attack. Instead, we must provide them with enough experiences in attacking feared words with the lips or tongue held loosely and quietly. We must help them find out that it is possible to "keep the mouth in motion" even when attempting the feared sound of a feared word. We must enable them to learn that it is possible to start a feared p word, for example, without pressing the lips together with compulsive force. Once they learn how short and effortless their blocks are when the air flow and speech attempt are made simultaneously, we have little need to motivate our stutterers. Once they learn how much easier it is to loosen the tongue in its contact with the palate than to blow it down with a sudden blast of air, they will try to find ways of approaching their feared words and releasing themselves from their blockings.

Despite the wide variety of ways of stuttering, it is difficult to convince any one case that he can stutter in other and easier ways. We must get him to experiment with his own stuttering. Our task is to suggest alternative approaches or methods of release that will tend to decrease the abnormality and interruption. We must also provide him with opportunities to stutter in these new ways and guide him in the learning process. For this part of the therapy is not only unlearning; it is learning as well. There will be failures, of course. The old familiar habits are strong; the new ones are vague, weak, and ill-formed. But failures are always necessary to learning. If we consider them analytically and understand their nature, the new skills will be bound to improve. It is vital however, that the attempts to learn to stutter without hard contacts, without tension, without preformation, be carried out in feared situations. The stutterer will learn much faster under these conditions, since a few unexpected successes will contribute more to learning than the familiar failures. Actually, all that the stutterer really needs to solve his problem are enough fears and moments of stuttering to experiment upon, and the idea that it is possible to stutter easily and effortlessly. If he will then vary his approach to the feared words, his symptoms also will vary. We have known stutterers who got to work by themselves, with no more clinical help than the statements in this paragraph, and learned to stutter so easily and effortlessly that the largest share of the handicap was eliminated. They were not cured. They continued to have what they called stuttering blocks, but the latter did not interfere with communication or provoke social penalties. This is no small achievement. The difficulties are great, especially when the stutterer works alone and without guidance. But it is possible to stutter in many ways, and one of those ways is with a minimum of interruption or abnormality.

In some clinics stutterers are deliberately taught a new way of stuttering, a new "spasm pattern." Two of these ways are in common use: (1) the voluntary repetition of the first sound or syllable of the word ("voluntary stuttering," or the "bounce" pattern) and (2) effortless prolongation of the first sound or syllable. Johnson (84) describes these two patterns thus:

. . . the non-fluency pattern is adopted and used *instead* of stuttering. Probably a simple repetition, like "tha-tha-tha-this" is most preferable, partly because it was just such behavior as this which was first diagnosed as stuttering and needs, therefore, to be re-evaluated as normal and acceptable. However, a simple, effortless prolongation of the first sounds of words will, in some cases, prove satisfactory, although considerable practice is required in prolonging the *p* and *t*. Also, care must be exercised lest the prolonging become a complete stoppage reaction, which would be merely another way of stuttering.

Bryngelson (80) recommends that the "voluntary stuttering" (repetition pattern) be first taught in reading and speaking before the mirror, but then extended to all activities. Johnson (84) likewise uses this mirror practice, but he also says:

If a dictaphone, or better, a mirrorphone is available, it is helpful to record one's speech, using the new repetition pattern and then listen to it over and over again, in order to become thoroughly accustomed to it and to learn to do it as smoothly and effortlessly as possible.

Gradually, then, the stutterer should introduce this pattern of non-fluency into his everyday speech, trying it out first in the easier situations and then introducing it in more and more difficult situations. He should employ it whenever he would otherwise stutter and he should also feign it liberally in saying certain words on which he would not otherwise stutter.

Another quotation may help to illustrate the teaching of these stuttering substitutes. Travis (149) says:

> With the idea that he is not to hide his stuttering, he is trained not only to change his mental set toward the defect but to stutter in a forward flowing, easy "bouncy" pattern, as in "ba-ba-ba-ball." The purpose of the bouncy type of stuttering and of the objective viewpoint is to lessen the tension and strain on the speech organs, to overcome individual objectionable habits accompanying the spasm, to free the person of fear, dread, or shame, and to promote physical and mental adjustment to the stuttering. After the bouncy pattern is perfected, the smooth pattern, in which the spasm is translated, is encouraged, the effort being to develop forward, flowing vocalization without repetition.

We do not advocate the use of either of these patterns as a substitute for the old stuttering abnormality. We doubt very much that any person will ever be entirely willing to "bounce" his syllabic way through life. A stutterer may be able to accept such a "method of stuttering" or such a "type of non-fluency" for the time being, while he is in the speech clinic, but in the crucial speech situations of normal existence, he must be able to stutter with much less conspicuousness than either voluntary repetition or prolongation can provide. If it is possible to approach feared words so that they sound like "th-th-th-th-this" or "llllllllllike" that, why not go one step farther, and find out how to utter them *like th*is." We can see no virtue in the demonstration of abnormality as such, if it is possible to stutter without it. Clinicians no doubt have insisted on some demonstrable repetitive or prolonged abnormality in order to keep the stutterer from falling into his old avoidances. But there are many dangers in the use of these patterns, too. The bounce can, and usually does, turn into a postponement trick. On a mildly feared word the stutterer will repeat the first syllable three times; on a badly feared word eight or ten times. Moreover, the sheer repetition of a sound has nothing to do with the necessity for making a transition to the second (or next) sound of the feared word. One might as well say "tra-la-la-la-boy" as to say "ba-ba-ba-boy." Stutterers often bounce fluently until they start the actual speech attempt. Then they go into the old contortion, or resignedly start bouncing again. The same criticisms may be leveled against the use of the smooth-prolongation pattern.

The above criticisms are not meant to imply that we do not use voluntary stuttering or smooth prolongation in our therapy for stutterers. We use both types. But we use them primarily as mental-hygiene and teaching devices. We feel that the "bounce" or repetitive form of pseudo-stuttering is one of the best agents for teaching the stutterer to face his problem as a problem rather than a curse. It is tolerated by society much more than is his old gasping, grunting, horrible abnormality. The stutterer who looks his listener in the eye and voluntarily repeats the first syllables of his feared words in a calm and effortless fashion becomes a totally different person so far as his speech defect is concerned. Instead of the random struggling or the craven hesitant approach to the attempt of feared words, we find purposive integrated speech attempts. The stutterer can learn to re-evaluate his disorder through the use of these forms of pseudo-stuttering. We use these forms of pseudo-stuttering, then, in attaining the following goals: (1) to teach the stutterer to attack the feared word without hesitancy; (2) to teach him to begin the word with its first sound instead of prefacing the speech attempt with a ritual of gasping, mouth opening, tongue protrusion, or other unnecessary movement; (3) to help him experience a symptomatology different from his old form, and one which is socially and personally preferable; (4) to give him a form of speech behavior which will enable him to say to the world, "Yes, I stutter. It's my problem, and I am attempting to solve it. I'm not emotional about it and you need not be upset either"; (5) to keep his speech on a highly voluntary level.

We ask our stutterers to use these forms of pseudo-stuttering first on nonfeared words but in feared situations. In this way, the mental hygiene value of the technique is especially effective. After the stutterer has learned to use the bounce or effortless prolongation calmly and with excellent attitudes, we then ask him to attempt his most-feared words in the same manner. Often the stutterer experiences great surprise when a badly feared word emerges as an easy, effortless repetition or prolongation rather than as the old contortion he had expected. A few of these experiences will teach him the usefulness of altering his preparatory sets prior to speech attempt. They will help him to realize that he can stutter in a much less abnormal fashion.

It is at this point that we start teaching the stutterer to attempt his feared words by starting the air flow simultaneously with the movement sequence necessary to the production of the word. We continue to use the bounce and the effortless prolongation, but only as evidence of good mental hygiene. Thus:

Whenever anyone compliments you on your fluency or freedom from stuttering be sure to say something like this: "I have d-d-d-done pretty wwwwwell so far, but I sti-sti-still am working on it." Then, when you meet that person in the future you will not be tempted to avoid or postpone in order to keep his good opinion. You ought to know by this time that those tricks only increase the fear and will sooner or later precipitate more trouble. After all, you are still working on your problem, so demonstrate it by using some calm pseudo-stuttering.

We teach our stutterers to continue to use these patterns whenever they are tempted to hide or disguise or avoid their stuttering. They are taught to employ them on nonfeared words at the first sign of panic. But we do not think it necessary to use them as approaches to feared words. As we have said, they are likely to be used as postponement devices, and their duration is likely to be proportional to the fear. As a mental-hygiene or teaching device they are excellent. As a method of stuttering they leave much to be desired.

Teaching the speech attempt from a state of rest. In teaching the stutterer to attack his feared words so as to produce a minimum of interruption and abnormality, we direct his efforts so that they bear on only one feature of the preparatory set at a time. Our first goal is to teach the stutterer that it is possible to make the speech attempt from a state of rest, even though he is full of fear and certain that he will stutter. Thus, we ask him to hunt for a feared situation and a feared word. We point out to him the fact that formerly he would make the speech attempt on this word from a highly tensed speech musculature. From our past study of his symptoms, we point out just what area seems to be the most tense—the lips, the tongue, and so on. We ask him to keep this area, this focus of tension, as relaxed as possible. He may become as strained as he wishes in any other area, but the focus area, wherever it may be, must be kept loose during the moment of speech attempt.

Relaxation has been used in treating stuttering for a hundred years, but we feel that it has been wrongly used. The stutterer usually has been asked to remain generally relaxed, to become limp, to "play rag doll." Such a condition helps to prevent the struggle reactions so characteristic of severe stuttering, to avoid hard contacts and tension tremors. But the demands of normal existence prevent an individual from existing in a flaccid state. Fears, sudden challenges, insecurity will all set off sudden involuntary tension states. To ask the stutterer to remain entirely relaxed is to ask him to have no fear of stuttering.

It is possible, however, as the work of Jacobson has shown, to use some differential relaxation *especially when no major voluntary activity is being performed.* We do not ask the stutterer to maintain an attitude of general bodily relaxation while uttering his feared words. We merely ask him to keep his lips loose until he actually makes the speech attempt on such a word as "please." Or we suggest that he experiment to see

whether he can keep from tightening his tongue (if that is the
focus of tension) until he starts to say such a word as "look."
In other words, the stutterer must learn to make his speech
attempts from a state of resting speech musculatures. We say,
in effect: "Stutter or not on this word, but make the speech
attempt without getting your mouth all tightened up. Keep
your mouth and throat loose until you actually begin the word.
You must learn to start feared words as you do nonfeared
words. Why tie yourself up in a knot of tension before you even
start?"

This, then, is our first goal in learning to stutter with a minimum of effort and abnormality. We insist that the stutterer
confine his efforts to its attainment until he has demonstrated
his ability to make the speech attempt from a state of rest in
eight or nine very feared situations and on feared words. We
do not judge this ability in terms of its resultant effect on
speech. For the time being, we do not care whether or not he
stutters badly after he makes the speech attempt. But we do
want him to learn to start the feared words without preliminary
tension. By doing so, he is destroying the old preparatory sets,
since one of their dominant features is this selfsame preliminary
hypertension.

*Starting the air flow or voice flow simultaneously with speech
attempt.* If you will watch any severe stutterer carefully during
his blocks, you will notice how often he places his mouth in
position for the first sound of a word before starting the vocalization or air flow. Voiced consonants such as *b* are produced
as "puh"; the words beginning with *v* are pronounced with a
prolonged or intermittent *f;* the mouth formations for the vowels are produced long before the voice begins. These symptoms
probably arose originally from the stutterer's desire to hide his
blocks, to suffer their tensions and struggles in silence. But
their effect is a baleful one. They break up the precise timing
which characterizes normal speech. The speech attempt is made
fractionally: first the position is assumed, and second, the air
flow or voice flow is started. This process of *preformation* is a

secondary symptom. We have never observed it in primary stutterers. It occurs as a part of the stutterer's characteristic windup for his speech attempt on a feared word. It engenders much of his difficulty "in getting started." It facilitates tremors and spasms of the glottis, or false-vocal-cord occlusion, or ventricular phonation. Stutterers must be taught to replace this preformation by carefully initiating the air flow or voice flow with speech attempt. In producing a voiced plosive, such as begins the word *goat*, the stutterer must learn to start the vocalcord vibration simultaneously with the raising of the back of the tongue. In producing a word like *shoot*, the voiceless air flow is timed to coincide with the movements which comprise the (*sh*-) phoneme. The stutterer must learn to do this under conditions of fear. Even when he is afraid he "will get stuck" he must learn how to time the voice and the tongue movement simultaneously. It is not difficult, since he does it regularly when uttering *g* words which he does not fear. A few experiences in attacking feared words in this way not only enable him to reject the preformation of which he was formerly unaware, but also teach him that air flow and speech attempt can be accomplished simultaneously, even when afraid.

Teaching the speech attempt as a voluntary movement sequence. It is interesting that three eminent authorities in the field of speech correction, Froeschels (60), Despert (48), and Robbins (131) with totally different clinical backgrounds, all advocate the use of "speech-chewing" or "breath-chewing" as a technique for eliminating stuttering. They have different reasons for attributing its efficacy, however. One of them uses it to induce relaxation; another, to free the person from a childhood emotional conflict based on the eating-speaking situation. We feel that if chewing-speaking exercises have any value it must lie in the fact that during chewing the mouth is continually in motion. The stutterer who chews as he speaks his feared words will not attempt them in terms of their first sounds alone. He will not assume a fixed position of the tongue or jaws or lips while "chewing" out his words. He will not make such hard contacts or tense positions of the articulators. All these values are good, but they may be achieved directly and much more "normally."

The stutterer must prepare himself to make initial or feared sounds of a feared word as a movement. This entails some training in perception. Stutterers, like everyone else, tend to think of sounds as alphabetic letters, as fixed entities. They think of the *f* sound as the sound produced by assuming the position of lip-biting and then blowing out the air. When this sound is carefully observed, however, in its natural habitat, that is, within words, the sound is produced by a continuous upward and downward movement of the lower lip and jaw. The movement never stops when the lip strokes the upper teeth. The contacts are so loose as scarcely to deserve the name. The movement then flows into sound. From this description we see the three criteria of a dynamic speech attempt: (1) the mouth must be kept in motion; (2) the contacts must be light, lest the movement be interrupted; and (3) the succeeding sound must be prepared for in mouth and mind so that the movement may have direction.

In teaching the stutterer to accomplish these ends, we dwell on only one of them at a time. For example, we ask him to make a prewritten phone call, and have him underline one word on which he expects to stutter badly. We ask him to rehearse aloud the old preparatory set to assume a fixed position, and then to reject it. He then attempts the word from a state of rest, but endeavors to keep his lips, tongue, or jaws moving slowly and voluntarily as they produce the succession of sounds that make up the word. The movements should be flowing rather than suddenly jerked. Once they are begun they should not cease until the word has been uttered.

The contacts should be made lightly and dynamically rather than statically. They should be brushed or stroked rather than pressed. One of the best uses of the smooth-prolongation pattern previously described is to teach the stutterer that it is possible to make these light contacts even when a plosive such as the *k* or *p* are prolonged. However, we urge the stutterer to use this effortless prolongation only to learn what loose contacts are. Once he understands, he must use the prolongation only for purposes of good mental hygiene. In attempting feared words, he should use the light contacts merely as part of the flowing movement sequence.

At this point it should be said that the use of light contacts prevents the stutterer from building up the hypertension and struggle which mark the use of hard contacts. Tremors require tight contacts or tense muscles in order to function, and so they also are prevented. Since the air-way is not being blocked off by glued lips or a cleaving tongue, the stutterer need not strive to blast the obstacle away by sheer force of breath. The use of light contacts and loose constrictions also facilitates the ability to attempt the word as a sequence of uninterrupted movements. In most stutterers, the movements which they do begin are interrupted whenever hard contacts occur. Keep the contacts light and the movement flows on unimpeded.

Finally, the movements must have direction. Most stutterers fail to realize that in stuttering it is not the sounds that are faulty but the transitions between sounds. Even after long struggle, the first syllable of the word *baby* may emerge as *bbbbbbbbbuh* (bʌ), rather than *bbbbbbbbba-* (be). The stutterer may find himself prolonging the same sound interminably or repeating it like a broken record. Why continue to make a sound when you have already produced it? The answer to this question is that the stutterer's attention is so focused on the one feared sound that he never thinks of the sound that should succeed it. He seldom thinks of the *oy* in the word *boy*, because he is too engrossed in breaking the barricade of his lips. We know that stutterers can be taught to reconfigure their feared words so as to give direction to their movements. In teaching the stutterers to keep the movement flowing in the direction of the succeeding sound, we often ask them to form this second sound prior to speech attempt, or to plan to emphasize it slightly. We must do something to break the stutterer's habit-

ual tendency to stop and fixate at one point in his movement
sequence. By making sure that the mouth keeps moving in the
direction of the succeeding sound, we prevent the false releases
(*ssspuh-spoon*) and the fixation on a single articulatory position.

The above description of the process of making a speech
attempt so as to minimize the interruption or abnormality may
seem far too complicated for the average stutterer. We have
had to be analytical in describing it, but actually the process
is one which every stutterer practices every time he utters a
word without stuttering on it. We all time the moment of
speech attempt with air flow or voice flow; we produce sequen-
tial movements rather than static positions when we say a
word; we use light contacts and fairly relaxed musculatures
when we speak. The stutterer has always used these methods—
but not on his feared words. When uttering the latter, he does
all the wrong things: tensing the muscles prior to speech attempt; assuming fixed positions with hard contacts; failing to
time his air flow with the speech attempt; and trying to say
the word as though it consisted of one isolated sound. Each of
these reactions creates a great deal of abnormality and interruption. They constitute much of the stutterer's burden. If he
can be shown that it is possible to approach a feared word in
the fashion that he approaches a nonfeared word, much of his
abnormality would disappear. We are sure that this can be
done and with much less difficulty than might be expected
from the description of the procedures sketched above. After
all, we are merely teaching him to do consciously what he has
usually done unconsciously. It might be objected that teaching
the stutterer to do these things would tend to make him too
conscious of his mechanics, too concerned with details. If a
stutterer has to go through such a rigmarole of preparation on
every feared word, will he not prefer the well-worn grooves of
his abnormality? An old ache is, after all, easier to bear than
a new one. To this we would heartily agree, were it not that
the new preparatory sets become habituated very swiftly *if*

they are taught under emotional conditions and that they result in greatly improved fluency. Relatively few successful experiences are required. If one had to go through life alertly scrutinizing every word, rejecting old reactions and specifically preparing new ones, this therapy would be worthless. But the new preparatory sets soon become stronger than the old, and the moment a word is perceived as feared, they come into play. The stutterer's speech seems to handle itself. Almost unconsciously and without preformation, he makes the speech attempt from a state of rest and utters the word as a sequence of movements. We have observed stutterers using these preparatory sets without realizing that they were doing so. If some of these movements lag a little, the abnormality and interruption are slight. Any stutterer can afford to stutter in this way.

As soon as the stutterer has gained through experience a knowledge of how to attack his feared words through the substitution of new and better preparatory sets, he is sent out into normal situations involving much speech to perfect his new skills. He is asked to keep a success-failure ratio; to present an analysis of his failures and a program for their eventual conquest. When he finds himself stuttering in his old way, he attempts to bring his symptoms under control before effecting a release. He does not stop and start over again, nor attempt to jerk himself out of his hard contacts and tremors. Instead he continues the speech attempt but in a more intelligent fashion, by loosening his contacts, decreasing the tensions, bringing in the air flow or voice, and starting the movement into the second sound. Finally, after the word has been spoken, he arranges to "cancel" the failure by pausing deliberately and speaking the word again with better preparation, and, last of all, by using the word in another sentence as soon as possible. Thus the stutterer always has the possibility of making some speech progress. If his preparatory sets are still too weak and the old spasm results, he can still bring his blocks under voluntary control. If he does not manage this, he can cancel. Only when he does nothing at all about his stuttering will he fail to gain some benefit from his fears or blocks. Few stutterers will be able to persist in their blind struggling spasms if they are exposed to as thoroughgoing a therapy as we have outlined in this chapter.

References

The literature on stuttering is so scattered and the titles of the articles are so misleading that the beginning student in speech correction often feels utterly helpless in attempting to understand the problem. The various points of view are often conflicting. One authority declares one thing; another rejects it in favor of his own pet theory. So far as stuttering is concerned, speech correction is in the same state that medicine was before Pasteur's discovery of bacteria. Fortunately, some research has been done, but it has not been conclusive. We are therefore providing the student with brief abstracts of most of the important work done in this field. He may thereby be spared some of the confusion which bedevils the beginner who tries to understand stuttering.

1. Abbott, J. A., "Repressed Hostility as a Factor in Adult Stuttering," *Journal of Speech Disorders*, 1947, Volume 12, pages 428–430.

Some of the stutterer's reluctance to give up his symptoms is due to the hostility release he gets from them. Psychotherapy is needed.

2. Ainsworth, S., "Integrating Theories of Stuttering," *Journal of Speech Disorders*, 1945, Volume 10, pages 205–210.

The author attempts to sort all the theories of stuttering into three classes: the dysphemic, the developmental, and the neurotic. Opposing points of view are contrasted.

3. Ainsworth, S., "Present Trends in the Treatment of Stuttering," *Journal of Exceptional Children*, 1949, Volume 16, pages 41–43.

A clear presentation of the five main goals of therapy.

4. Ammons, R., and Johnson, W., "Studies in the Psychology of Stuttering: XVII. The Construction and Application of a Test of Attitude Toward Stuttering," *Journal of Speech Disorders*, 1944, Volume 9, pages 39–49.

The test is described and shown to be important in determining how morbid a stutterer feels about his speech defect.

5. Anderson, J., and Whealdon, M. L., "A Study of the Blood Group Distribution Among Stutterers," *Journal of Speech Disorders*, 1941, Volume 6, pages 23–28.

No differences between stutterers and nonstutterers.

6. Backus, O. L., "Incidence of Stuttering Among the Deaf," *Annals of Oto-rhino-laryngology*, 1938, Volume 47, pages 632–635.

There were 55 stutterers in schools for the deaf; six were congenitally deaf.

7. Barbara, D. A., "A Psychosomatic Approach to Problems of Stuttering in Psychotics," *The American Journal of Psychiatry*, 1946, Volume 103, pages 188–195.

The psychotics in a state hospital for the insane demonstrated that their stuttering at least was completely psychogenic.

8. Barber, V., "Studies in the Psychology of Stuttering: XV. Chorus Reading as a Distraction in Stuttering," *Journal of Speech Disorders*, 1939, Volume 4, pages 371–383.

When stutterers read in unison they do not stutter as much. Reading the same material is easier than when the co-reader reads different material.

9. Belgum, D., "Stuttering," *Hygeia*, 1944, Volume 22, pages 346–347; 391.

Therapy at the University of Minnesota Speech Clinic is described by a case.

10. Bender, J. F., "Do You Know Someone Who Stutters?" *Scientific Monthly*, 1944, Volume 59, pages 221–224.

Describes two different types of treatment used by the same clinician. Emphasizes the importance of rapport between stutterer and clinician.

11. Bender, J. F., "The Prophylaxis of Stuttering," *The Nervous Child*, 1943, Volume 2, pages 181–198.

An excellent summary of the nature of stuttering, with a fine discussion of its prevention.

12. Bender, J. F., *The Personality Structure of Stuttering*, New York, Pitman, 1939.

Summary of concepts of stuttering; research on stuttering; the stuttering personality. A good source book for the findings of experiments on the personalities of stutterers.

13. Bender, J. F., and Kleinfeld, V. M., *Principles and Practices of Speech Correction*, New York, Pitman, 1938.

Fifteen of the various theories concerning the nature of stuttering are clearly presented.

14. Berman, A. B., and Train, G. J., "A Genetic Approach to the Problem of Stuttering," *Journal of Nervous and Mental Diseases*, 1940, Volume 91, pages 580–590.

The nature of the stuttering "inheritance" does not follow Mendelian laws.

15. Berry, M. F., "A Common Denominator in Twinning and Stuttering," *Journal of Speech Disorders*, 1938, Volume 3, pages 51–57.

Stuttering, twinning, and left-handedness are produced by the same generic factors.

16. Berry, M. F., "A Study of the Medical Histories of Stuttering Children," *Speech Monographs*, 1939, Volume 5, pages 97–114.

More diseases of the nervous system among stutterers: encephalitis, etc.

17. Bilto, E. W., "A Comparative Study of Certain Physical Abilities of Children with Speech Defects and Children with Normal Speech," *Journal of Speech Disorders*, 1941, Volume 6, pages 187–203.

Both stutterers and articulation cases are inferior to normal speakers in large bodily coordinations.

18. Blanton, S., and M. G., *For Stutterers*, New York, D. Appleton-Century, 1936.

A book based on the thesis that stuttering originates in emotional disturbances and is maintained by them. Emotional patterns, theories of stuttering, theories of treatment, and suggestions for parents, teachers, and stutterers are discussed.

19. Bloodstein, O. N., "Conditions under which Stuttering is Reduced or Absent," *Journal of Speech Disorders*, 1949, Volume 14, pages 295–302.

A survey of the literature to demonstrate those ameliorating environmental or communicative conditions which reduce frequency of stuttering.

20. Bluemel, C. S., "Primary and Secondary Stammering," *Proceedings of the American Speech Correction Association*, 1932, Volume 2, pages 91–102.

A good description of the development of stuttering, how to treat the primary form, and how to prevent the secondary form.

21. Bluemel, C. S., *Stammering and Allied Disorders*, New York, Macmillan, 1935.

A consideration of primary and secondary stammering and other speech defects from the viewpoint of Pavlov's theory of conditioning and inhibition. Other theories of stammering are reviewed, and some of the author's own therapeutic suggestions are given.

22. Boome, E. J., and Richardson, M. A., *The Nature and Treatment of Stuttering*, New York, Dutton, 1932.

23. Brown, F. W., "The Permanent Cure of Stuttering," *Mental Hygiene*, 1933, Volume 17, pages 266–277.

Personality problems of stutterers must be solved before permanent cure.

24. Brown, S. F., "The Loci of Stutterings in the Speech Sequence," *Journal of Speech Disorders*, 1945, Volume 10, pages 181–192.

The author summarizes the results of other studies concerning the word cues which the stutterer interprets as threatening stuttering or which produce it. Stutterers have more difficulty on certain words than on others, on words beginning a sentence than on other words, on longer words than on shorter, on accented syl ables than on those unaccented, and on meaningful material than on nonsense material containing the same words.

25. Brown, S. F., and Hull, H. C., "A Study of Some Social Attitudes of a Group of 59 Stutterers," *Journal of Speech Disorders*, 1942, Volume 7, pages 323–324.

Stutterers are more poorly adjusted in social situations.

26. Brown, S. F., and Shulman, E. E., "Intra-muscular Pressure in Stutterers and Non-stutterers," *Speech Monographs*, 1940, Volume 7, pages 67–74.

Stutterers are not any more tense than normal speakers. Relaxation therapy is not advisable in an etiological sense.

27. Bryngelson, B., "A Study of Laterality of Stutterers and Normal Speakers," *Journal of Social Psychology*, 1940, Volume 11, pages 151–155.

Seventy-eight stutterers were matched with nonstutterers. Group differences in confused or shifted laterality were found to be statistically significant.

28. Bryngelson, B., "Prognosis of Stuttering," *Journal of Speech Disorders*, 1941, Volume 6, pages 121–123.

Good prognosis for therapy requires: intelligence, determination, self-discipline, a good home life, youth, and good health.

29. Bryngelson, B., "Psychologic Factors in the Management of the Exceptional Child," *Journal of Exceptional Children*, 1938, Volume 5, pages 65–67.

The teacher's function in helping the stutterer to adjust to his speech difference is clearly presented.

30. Bryngelson, B., "Psychological Problems in Stuttering," *Mental Hygiene*, 1937, Volume 21, pages 631–639.

Outlines psychological and speech therapy. Recommends "voluntary stuttering."

31. Bryngelson, B., "Stuttering and Personality Development," *The Nervous Child*, 1943, Volume 2, pages 162–171.

Describes some of the parental methods which produce secondary stuttering and maladjustment. Describes the "objective attitude toward stuttering."

32. Bryngelson, B., Chapman, M. E., and Hansen, O. K., *Know Yourself—A Workbook for Those Who Stutter*, Minneapolis, Burgess, 1944, page 53.

A series of discussions and projects which progressively help the stutterer to understand his problem and to solve it. Useful in public-school work.

33. Bryngelson, B., and Clark, T. B., "Left-Handedness and Stuttering," *Journal of Heredity*, 1933, Volume 24, pages 387–390.

The results of this study seemed to indicate that left-handedness is a sex-limited characteristic, most often transmitted from the male through the female and back to the male.

34. Bryngelson, B., and Rutherford, B., "A Comparative Study of Laterality of Stutterers and Non-Stutterers," *Journal of Speech Disorders*, 1937, Volume 2, pages 15–16.

A study of the handedness history of 74 stutterers and 74 non-stutterers, showing 4 times as much ambidexterity and 8 times as much shifting in the stuttering group.

35. Bullen, A. K., "A Cross-Cultural Approach to the Problem of Stuttering," *Child Development*, 1945, Volume 16, pages 1–88.

Comparison of different cultures in terms of the factors that produce stuttering.

36. Bullwinkle, B. A., "Methods and Outcome of Treatment of Stutterers in a Child Guidance Clinic," *Smith College Studies of Social Work*, 1933, pages 107–138.

The seven cases who showed no improvement were shy, sensitive, mother-attached, and rejected.

37. Buckholtz, C. A., "Indigenous Confidence for Stutterers," *Quarterly Journal of Speech*, 1933, Volume 20, pages 60–64.

Build up the stutterer's confidence by any means and you solve his problem.

38. Burkhart, E. J., "History and Present Status of the Correction of Stuttering," M. A. Thesis, Unpublished, Marquette University, 1941.

There seems to be a wide divergence in theories of stuttering but a great similarity in the methods used for treating it.

39. Carhart, R., "An Experimental Evaluation of Suggestion Relaxation," *Speech Monographs*, 1943, Volume 10, pages 29–40.

Simple instructions to relax are better than suggestion relaxation, but there is no carry-over into life situations involving speech.

40. Carhart, R., "The Two-Room Technique in the Treatment of Stuttering," *Journal of Speech Disorders*, 1941, Volume 6, pages 105–112.

Building up of confidence through use of a trick microphone connection.

41. Clark, R. M., "Supplementary Techniques to Use with Secondary Stutterers," *Journal of Speech and Hearing Disorders*, 1948, Volume 13, pages 131–134.

Group therapy and non-directive counseling and written autobiographies are recommended.

42. Cobb, S., and Cole, E. N., "Stuttering," *Physiological Review*, 1939, Volume 19, pages 49–62.

A summary of neurological findings on stutterers to indicate that the disorder may be due to a variation in cerebral structure.

43. Cooper, C. A., "Discussion on the Relationship Between Speech Disorders and Personality Defects in Children, and How Stuttering May Unfavorably Affect Children's Personality Development," *Journal of Pediatrics*, 1942, Volume 21, pages 418–421.

Parents are likely to overvalue the importance of the speech defect and to underestimate the importance of the personality conflicts which produce or result from stuttering.

44. Coriat, I. H., "The Psychoanalytic Conception of Stuttering," *The Nervous Child*, 1943, Volume 2, pages 167–171.

"Stammerers are narcissistic infants who have compulsively retained the original equivalents of nursing and biting." Exposition and some illustration.

45. Cypreason, L., "Group Therapy for Adult Stutterers," *Journal of Speech and Hearing Disorders*, 1948, Volume 13, pages 313–319.

Describes the plans and procedures of such therapy.

46. Davis, D. M., "The Relation of Repetitions in the Speech of Young Children to Certain Measures of Language Maturity and Situational Factors," *Journal of Speech Disorders*, 1940, Volume 5, pages 235–246.

The author examined children 2, 3, and 4 years old. Repetition of words and phrases decreased with age; syllable repetitions did not. Four syllable repetitions per thousand words; 14 word repetitions per thousand; 24 phrase repetitions per thousand. Boys had more syllable repetitions than girls. These were normal-speaking children.

47. Daniels, E. M., "An Analysis of the Relation Between Handedness and Stuttering with Special Reference to the Orton-Travis Theory of Cerebral Dominance," *Journal of Speech Disorders*, 1940, Volume 5, pages 309–326.

No evidence was found that shift of handedness, or ambidexterity or left-handedness, produces stuttering.

48. Despert, J. L., "A Therapeutic Approach to the Problem of Stuttering in Children," *The Nervous Child*, 1943, Volume 2, pages 134–147.

Two cases of stuttering children are intensively explored and treated by psychiatric and speech therapy. Advocates "chewing" of speech.

49. Douglass, L. C., "A Study of Bilaterally Recorded Electroencephalograms of Adult Stutterers," *Journal of Experimental Psychology*, 1943, Volume 32, pages 247–265.

Bilateral occipital blocking is significantly greater in stutterers during stuttering.

50. Douglass, E., and Quarrington, B., "The Differentiation of Interiorized and Exteriorized Secondary Stuttering," *Journal of Speech and Hearing Disorders*, 1952, Volume 17, pages 377–385.

A very important classification of stuttering in terms of the individual's reactions to his disorder. The importance of avoidance devices in the shaping of the basic personality problem is described.

51. Dow, C. W., "Stuttering: A Tentative Outline of an Hypothesis and Therapy," *Journal of Speech Disorders*, 1941, Volume 6, pages 40–45.

Teaches his cases to form the speech sounds voluntarily and in proper sequence without forcing.

52. Duncan, M. H., "Home Adjustment of Stutterers vs. Non-stutterers," *Journal of Speech and Hearing Disorders*, 1949, Volume 14, pages 255–259.

Using the Bell Adjustment Inventory, stutterers demonstrated a feeling that their homes lacked sufficient love and understanding.

53. Dunlap, K., "Stammering: Its Nature, Etiology and Therapy," *Journal of Comparative Psychology*, 1944, Volume 37, pages 187–202.

Tension and frustration are the predisposing cause of stuttering. Emotional shock precipitates the disorder.

54. Fink, W. H., and Bryngelson, B., "The Relation of Strabismus to Right or Left Sidedness," *Transactions of the American Academy of Ophthalmology and Otolaryngology*, 1934, pages 3–12.

Strabismus, left-handedness, and stuttering seem to be associated.

55. Fletcher, J. M., *The Problem of Stuttering*, New York, Longmans, Green, 1928.

Includes the classification of speech defects, statistical data on stuttering, various theories of the causes of stuttering, physiological symptoms of stuttering, explanation of the author's belief that stuttering is a morbid social maladjustment, and suggested environmental therapy.

56. Fogerty, E., *Stammering*, New York, Greenberg, 1936.

Advocates removal of emotional causes, use of breathing exercises, suggestion, and relaxation.

57. Freestone, N. W., "A Brain-wave Interpretation of Stuttering," *Quarterly Journal of Speech*, 1942, Volume 28, pages 466–468.

Stutterers had more alpha waves and larger waves than did normals. The author's discussion of the findings and their interpretation is especially worth while.

58. Froeschels, E., "A Study of the Symptomatology of Stuttering," *Monatschrift für Ohrenheil*, 1921, Volume 55, page 1109.

Describes the sequence of development as follows: 1. nonforced repetitions, normal tempo; 2. nonforced repetitions, irregular tempo; 3. forced repetitions, normal tempo; 4. forced repetitions, irregular tempo; 5. forced repetitions, abnormally fast; 6. forced repetitions, abnormally fast, then inhibited; 7. forced repetitions, abnormally fast, then inhibited and slowed down; 8. slow repetitions, obviously postponement devices.

59. Froeschels, E., "Differences in the Symptomatology in the United States and in Europe," *Journal of Speech Disorders*, 1941, Volume 6, pages 45–46.

American stutterers are more skeptical and need a belief in an organic cause. They develop secondary symptoms more readily.

60. Froeschels, E., "Pathology and Therapy of Stuttering," *The Nervous Child*, 1942, Volume 2, pages 146–161.

Discusses other methods of therapy, and recommends his own "chewing speech."

61. Froeschels, E., "Stuttering and Nystagmus," *Monatschrift für Ohrenheil*, 1915, Volume 49, pages 161–167.

This old reference expresses the author's present views but more clearly. "A speech act in its normal course is suddenly interrupted through lack of an idea or word or through a psychological repression such as embarrassment, fright or great joy." "If during the period of initial stuttering, the child is not made conscious of it through incorrect educational methods or fearful attitudes in some person over him, this initial stuttering vanishes as soon as the stream of thought becomes more regular and vocabulary is available."

62. Gifford, H. M., *How to Overcome Stammering*, New York, Prentice-Hall, Inc., 1940.

Stuttering considered as a symptom of an emotional conflict and treated as such by correcting the maladjustment and using suggestion and relaxation.

63. Glasner, P., "Personality Characteristics and Emotional Problems in Stutterers Under the Age of Five," *Journal of Speech and Hearing Disorders*, 1949, Volume 14, pages 135–138.

Points out that many of these children were not merely victims of non-fluency penalizing, but troubled children with definite parental and home problems.

64. Glasner, P. J., and Vermilyea, F. D., "An Investigation of the Definition and Use of the Term 'Primary Stuttering,'" *Journal of Speech and Hearing Disorders*, 1953, Volume 18, pages 161–167.

Although there are objections to the use of the term, most therapists find it useful.

65. Gottlober, A. B., *Understanding Stuttering*, New York, Grune and Stratton, 1953.

An undocumented compendium of information, advice and anecdotes about stuttering.

66. Gray, M., "The X Family: A Clinical and Laboratory Study of a 'Stuttering' Family," *Journal of Speech Disorders*, 1940, Volume 5, pages 343–348.

Two branches of a stuttering family were studied. One branch was "stuttering conscious." The other was not. In the first family branch 40 per cent stuttered; in the other, only 6 per cent did.

67. Greene, J. S., "Stuttering: What About It?" *Proceedings of the American Speech Correction Association*, 1931, Volume 1, pages 165–176.

Declares strongly against using distractions. Maintains that they only work temporarily and that in the long run they harm the stutterer more than they help him.

68. Greene, J. S., and Small, S. M., "Psychosomatic Factors in Stuttering," *Medical Clinics of North America*, 1944, Volume 28, pages 615–628.

From 30 to 40 per cent had Rorschach indications of marked emotional instability.

69. Hahn, E. F., "A Study of the Effect of Remedial Treatment on the Frequency of Stuttering in Oral Reading," *Journal of Speech Disorders*, 1941, Volume 6, pages 29–38.

Outlines a treatment which involves: relaxation, breathy tone, silent recall of how the sound was made, beginning with simple material and proceeding to complex, conscious phrasing, prolonging the vowels, rate control, beginning with easy and going gradually into difficult situations, building up confidence, carrying fluency into outside situations, and using some psychotherapy.

70. Hahn, E. F., *Stuttering: Significant Theories and Therapies*, Stanford University: Stanford University Press, 1943.

Probably the best compendium of the theories and treatments of stuttering available to the student.

71. Harle, M., "Dynamic Interpretation and Treatment of Acute

Stuttering in a Young Child," *American Journal of Orthopsychiatry*, 1946, Volume 15, pages 156–162.

Describes a play-by-play account of psychotherapy with a young girl who stuttered severely.

72. Heilpern, E., "A Case of Stuttering," *Psychoanalytic Quarterly*, 1941, Volume 10, pages 95–115.

A summary of a case of stuttering due to "oral eroticism."

73. Heltman, H., *First Aids for Stutterers*, Boston, Expression Co., 1943.

Well-written description of the nature of stuttering, the theories of its cause, and its prevention. The author also discusses self-help for the stutterer, stuttering in the school, and speech hygiene.

74. Heltman, H., "History of Recurrent Stuttering in a 25-Year-Old Post-graduate College Student," *Journal of Speech Disorders*, 1941, Volume 6, pages 49–50.

Eighteen years of intermittent stuttering; frequent relapse; final cure.

75. Heltman, H., "Psycho-social Phenomena of Stuttering and Their Etiological and Therapeutic Implications," *Journal of Social Psychology*, 1938, Volume 9, pages 79–96.

Hesitation and repetition are common to most, if not all, children during the years of developing speech; and this may be due to an inadequate vocabulary or to general confusion. "But whatever the cause, if the physical aspects of this lack of fluency in childhood were observed in adults it would be diagnosed as stuttering."

76. Hill, H., "An Interbehavioral Analysis of Several Aspects of Stuttering," *Journal of General Psychology*, 1945, Volume 32, pages 289–316.

Stuttering as emotional blocking of the speech sequences. The article is stimulating but not for the beginning student, since it is couched in Kantorian terminology.

77. Hill, H., "Stuttering: I. A Critical Review and Evaluation of Biochemical Investigations," *Journal of Speech Disorders*, 1944, Volume 9, pages 245–261.

An excellent and critical summary of most of these investigations.

78. Hill, H., "Stuttering: A Review and Integration of Physiological Data," *Journal of Speech Disorders*, 1944, Volume 9, pages 289–324.

The physiological data reviewed in this summary of investigations include researches on: breathing, blood pressure and other cardiovascular changes, tonus and tetanus, reflexes, eye movements and pupilary changes.

79. Hogewind, F., "Medical Treatment of Stuttering," *Journal of Speech Disorders*, 1940, Volume 5, pages 203–208.

Stutterers present symptoms of somatic as well as psychogenic disorders.

80. Honig, P., "The Stutterer Acts It Out," *Journal of Speech Disorders*, 1947, Volume 12, pages 105–109.

Psychodrama as an aid to psychotherapy is presented.

81. Hunsley, Y. L., "Disintegration in the Speech Musculature of Stutterers During the Production of a Non-vocal Temporal Pattern," *Psychological Monographs*, 1937, Volume 49, Number 1, pages 32–49.

Stutterers who tried to follow a rhythmic pattern of clicks by biting, tongue protruding, and panting were inferior in these skills to normals.

82. Johnson, W., "An Open Letter to the Mother of a Stuttering Child, *2* in *Speech Handicapped School Children*, New York, Harper & Brothers, 1948, pages 443–451.

Parental information given in the form of a letter.

83. Johnson, W., *Because I Stutter*, New York, D. Appleton-Century, 1930.

Written on the basis of the author's own experiences and deals particularly with the effect of the stutterer's experiences upon the development of his personality.

84. Johnson, W., "The Indians Have No Word for It: I. Stuttering in Children," *Quarterly Journal of Speech*, 1944, Volume 30, pages 330–337.

One of the best articles to put in the hands of the parents of a primary stutterer. The treatment of primary stuttering or non-fluency is described.

85. Johnson, W., "The Indians Have No Word for It: II. Stuttering in Adults," *Quarterly Journal of Speech*, 1944, Volume 30, pages 456–465.

A very clear and very interesting application of semantics to stuttering. Recommends the voluntary bounce pattern, the disregard of the cues that set off fear, and the attempt to reduce stuttering to hesitant speech.

86. Johnson, W., "The Treatment of Stuttering," *Journal of Speech Disorders*, 1939, Volume 3, pages 170–171.

Recommends using various methods, and tolerance for the points of view and therapies used by other clinicians.

87. Johnson, W., and Cooley, W. H., "The Relationship Between Frequency and Duration of Moments of Stuttering," *Journal of Speech Disorders*, 1945, Volume 10, pages 35–38.

Neither frequency of stuttering nor duration of stuttering can by themselves be regarded as the true measure of severity.

88. Johnson, W., Darley, F. L., and Spriestersbach, D. C., *Diag-*

nostic Manual in Speech Correction, New York, Harper & Brothers, 1952.

Procedures for examining a stutterer are given.

89. Johnson, W., and Duke, L., "Change of Handedness Associated with Onset or Disappearance of Stuttering," *Journal of Experimental Education*, Dec., 1935, Volume 4, No. 2.

Case studies illustrating the effect of a shift of handedness on the onset or the disappearance of stuttering.

90. Johnson, W., Knott, J., Webster, M. J., Larson, R. P., Solomon, A., Sinn, A., Millsapps, L., and Rosen, L., "Studies in the Psychology of Stuttering," *Journal of Speech Disorders*, 1937, Volume 2, Studies 1–7.

A series of seven studies showing: 1. That moments of stuttering are distributed in a nonrandom order among words spoken. 2. Eighty-eight per cent of the words on which stuttering was expected were stuttered upon. 3. When a cue which had been associated with a difficult situation was introduced into a situation previously considered "easy," the stuttering increased significantly in the latter situation. 4. Expectation of stuttering need not operate on a highly conscious level. 5. Stuttering is reduced 98 per cent when expectation of stuttering is eliminated. 6. When words previously stuttered upon in a passage were omitted, future stuttering occurred on words closely associated with those omitted. 7. The use of changes of speech patterns serves as a distraction which decreases the frequency of spasms.

91. Johnson, W. (and others), "A Study of the Onset and Development of Stuttering," *Journal of Speech Disorders*, 1942, Volume 7, pages 251–257.

Careful summaries of case histories show that in some cases stuttering develops after the diagnosis. Summarizes the developmental factors present and finds few differences between stutterers and a group of matched normal children.

92. Kamm, B., "Resistance Problems," *Bulletin of the Meninger Clinic*, 1938, Volume 2, pages 161–171.

A stutterer fights the efforts of those who try to help him. Sabotage in the clinic.

93. Karlin, I. N., "A Psychosomatic Theory of Stuttering," *Journal of Speech Disorders*, 1947, Volume 12, pages 319–322.

Stuttering is the result of both organic and psychogenic factors. Parents should reduce stress during the period of myelinization of the speech areas of the brain.

94. Kemble, R. P., "Constructive Use of the Ending of Treatment," *American Journal of Orthopsychiatry*, 1941, Volume 11, pages 684–691.

Some excellent suggestions about how to end treatment.

95. Kimmell, H., "Studies in the Psychology of Stuttering: The Nature and Effect of a Stutterer's Avoidance Reactions," *Journal of Speech Disorders*, 1938, Volume 3, pages 95–100.

Autobiographies from 39 stutterers were examined to determine the kinds of avoidance reactions shown by stutterers and the effect these had on their adjustment.

96. Klingbell, G. M., "The Historical Background of the Modern Speech Clinic: Stuttering and Stammering," *Journal of Speech Disorders*, 1939, Volume 4, pages 115–131.

Short descriptions of the theories and treatments of stuttering from ancient times to the present.

97. Knott, J. R. and Johnson, W., "The Factor of Attention in Relation to the Moment of Stuttering," *Journal of Genetic Psychology*, 1936, Volume 48, pages 479–480.

The stronger the attention to stuttering, the more stuttering; the greater the need to avoid, the more frequent the stuttering.

98. Knutson, T. A., "Oral Recitation Problems of Stutterers," *Elementary School Journal*, 1939, Volume 39, pages 604–608.

Practices of teachers in calling on stutterers to recite are listed and recommendations are given.

99. Knutson, T. A., "What the Classroom Teacher Can Do for Stutterers," *Quarterly Journal of Speech*, 1940, Volume 26, pages 207–212.

Outlines classroom policies and information the classroom teacher should possess about speech defects.

100. Kopp, G. A., "Treatment of Stuttering," *Journal of Speech Disorders*, 1939, Volume 4, pages 166–168.

A famous passage on "No one has ever cured an adult stutterer."

101. Kopp, H., "The Relationship of Stuttering to Motor Disturbances," *The Nervous Child*, 1943, Volume 2, pages 107–116.

Oseretzky's tests on 450 stutterers reveals that stuttering "is not a psychologic but a neurologic disorder characterized by a profound disturbance of the motor function."

102. Kosh, Z. H., "Integrated Course for Stutterers and Voice Defectives," *Quarterly Journal of Speech*, 1941, Volume 27, pages 97–104.

Used a "charm school" approach to treatment of high-school girls.

103. Krausz, E. O., "Is Stuttering Primarily a Speech Disorder?" *Journal of Speech Disorders*, 1940, Volume 5, pages 227–231.

Stuttering is not a speech disorder but a negative compulsive behavior focusing on the social aspect of speech.

104. Krout, M. H., "Emotional Factors in the Etiology of Stut-

tering," *Journal of Abnormal and Social Psychology*, 1936, Volume 31, pages 174–181.

Three college stutterers have their emotional conflicts analyzed.

105. Kruzman, M., "Psychosomatic Study of Fifty Stuttering Children," *American Journal of Orthopsychiatry*, 1946, Volume 16, pages 127–133.

Stuttering seems to show responses similar to those of obsessive-compulsive neurosis.

106. Lane, R. R., "Suggestions for Handling Young Stutterers," *Elementary School Journal*, 1944, Volume 44, pages 416–419.

Policies for classroom teachers. Do's and Don'ts.

107. Lassers, L., *Eight Keys to Normal Speech and Child Adjustment*, Leon Lassers, 2855 Thirty Fourth Ave., San Franscisco, California.

Material for parents and teachers. Much better than most available sources.

108. Lemert, E. M., *Social Pathology*, New York, McGraw-Hill, 1951, Chapter 6, "Speech Defects and the Speech Defective."

The author, a sociologist, examines the problem of stuttering from the point of view of cultural anthropology.

109. Lemert, E. M., "Some Indians Who Stutter," *Journal of Speech and Hearing Disorders*, 1952, Volume 18, pages 168–174.

The cultural attitudes of the coastal Indians toward stuttering as an unpleasant and amusing difference are described.

110. Lemert, E. M., and Van Riper, C., "The Use of Psychodrama in the Treatment of Speech Defects," *Sociometry*, 1944, Volume 7, pages 190–195.

Psychodrama, phonographic recordings of stutterer's experiences, and other dramatic devices are used in psychotherapy for stutterers.

111. Levbarg, J. J., "Hypnosis—Treatment Used on a Stammerer with Marked Mental Disturbance," *Eye, Ear, Nose and Throat Monthly*, 1941, Volume 20, pages 55–56; 60.

Hypnosis was used to explore conflicts and to reduce the fear and blocks.

112. Lindsley, D. B., "Bilateral Differences in Brain Potentials from the Two Cerebral Hemispheres in Relation to Laterality and Stuttering," *Journal of Experimental Psychology*, 1940, Volume 26, pages 211–225.

More blocking and unsynchronized brain waves in stutterers than in normals.

113. Louttit, C. M., *Clinical Psychology*, New York, Harper & Brothers, 1936, pages 446–450.

Two very interesting case studies showing psychotherapy.

114. Maddox, J., "The Role of Visual Cues in the Precipitation of Stuttering," *Proceedings of the American Speech Correction Association*, 1938, Volume 8, pages 49–51.

An experimental study showing that the frequency of stuttering was increased when the stutterer observed himself in a mirror when reading aloud.

115. Meltzer, H., "Personality Differences Between Stuttering and Non-stuttering Children as Indicated by the Rorschach Test," *Journal of Psychology*, 1944, Volume 17, pages 39–59.

Fifty cases of each group were tested with Rorschach. "In practically all factors which implicate emotional instability the scores of stuttering children exceed those of the control group."

116. Milisen, R., "Frequency of Stuttering with Anticipation of Stuttering Controlled," *Proceedings of the American Speech Correction Association*, 1938, Volume 8, pages 44–46.

A study concluding that the median stutterer was unable to predict more than 61 per cent of his spasms, and that the occurrence of spasms tends to bring an increase in spasm frequency.

117. Milisen, R., and Johnson, W., "A Comparative Study of Stutterers, Former Stutterers and Normal Speakers Whose Handedness Has Been Changed," *Archives of Speech*, 1936, Volume 1, pages 61–86.

A study of causes, age of onset, and causes of the disappearance, showing the average onset of stuttering at the age of three, and 40 per cent outgrowing stuttering before eight years of age.

118. Milisen, R., and Van Riper, C., "A Study of the Predicted Duration of the Stutterer's Blocks as Related to Their Actual Duration," *Journal of Speech Disorders*, 1939, Volume 4, pages 339–345.

The stutterer can successfully predict the duration of his stuttering blocks.

119. Moncour, J. P., "Environmental Factors Differentiating Stuttering Children from Non-stuttering Children," *Speech Monographs*, 1951, Volume 18, pages 312–325.

Stuttering children had more over-protection, domination, inconsistent discipline, sibling rivalry and other similar emotional factors in their home environments than did matched normal children.

120. Nelson, S. E., "Personal Contact as a Factor in the Transfer of Stuttering," *Human Biology*, 1939, Volume 11, pages 393–418.

Personal contact or imitation must be only a slight factor in causing stuttering to run in families.

121. Nelson, S. E., "The Role of Heredity in Stuttering," *Journal of Pediatrics*, 1939, Volume 14, pages 642–654.

The author compared 204 stutterers with equal number of non-stutterers and found much more stuttering in the families of the former.

122. Obermann, C. E., "Steps in Overcoming Stuttering," *The Nation's Schools*, 1942, Volume 30, pages 37–39.

Some very practical suggestions are given for treating secondary stuttering.

123. Owen, T., and Stemmerman, P., "Electric Convulsive Therapy in Stammering," *American Journal of Psychiatry*, Volume 104, 1947, pages 410–413.

The case history of a girl stammerer who was given such treatments with favorable but not conclusive results is provided.

124. Peters, C., "Public Speaking; A Therapeutic Procedure," *Quarterly Journal of Speech*, 1933, Volume 20, pages 64–67.

Helps to break up bad breathing habits and build good mental hygiene.

125. Pitrelli, F. R., "Psychosomatic and Rorschach Aspects of Stuttering," Psychiatric Quarterly, 1948, Volume 23, pages 175–194.

Compared non-psychotic and psychotic stutterers with psychotics who had formerly been stutterers. Etiology felt to be psychogenic.

126. Pittenger, K., "A Study of the Duration of the Temporal Intervals Between Successive Moments of Stuttering," *Journal of Speech Disorders*, 1940, Volume 5, pages 333–341.

Stuttering does not occur in cyclic patterns. There are no rhythms of occurrence.

127. Porter, H. v. K., "Studies in the Psychology of Stuttering: XIV. Stuttering Phenomena in Relation to Size and Personnel of Audience," *Journal of Speech Disorders*, 1939, Volume 4, pages 323–333.

There is a significant increase in the frequency of stuttering with increase in the number of auditors up to four. A close agreement exists between actual stuttering and its anticipation.

128. *Proceedings, American Speech Correction Association*, "A Symposium on Stuttering," 1931, Volume 1.

A collection of the papers on the treatment of stuttering presented by 28 speech correctionists at the national convention. Various techniques of visual treatment, psychological, breath control, mental hygiene, psychoanalysis, and cerebral dominance therapy are discussed and explained.

129. Rheinberger, M. B., Karlin, I. W., and Bergman, A. B., "Electroencephalographic and Laterality Studies of Stuttering and Non-stuttering Children," *The Nervous Child*, 1943, Volume 2, pages 117–133.

The authors compared ten stutterers with ten nonstutterers and found no differences in brain waves, but the nonstutterers were more unilateral.

130. Richardson, L. H., "The Personality of Stutterers," *Psychological Monographs*, 1944, Volume 56, No. 7, pages 1–41.

Stutterers are more depressed, introvertive. Several tests were given.

131. Robbins, S. D., "Distraction in Stuttering," *Proceedings of the American Speech Correction Association*, 1932, Volume 2, pages 103–110.

A very comprehensive study of distraction as a device for eliminating the fear and the occurrence of stuttering. Recommends its use.

132. Robbins, S. D., "Relative Attention Paid to Vowels and Consonants by Stammerers and Normal Speakers," *Proceedings of the American Speech Correction Association*, 1936, Volume 6, pages 7–23.

The conclusions from a study comparing the most prominent letter, the most prominent-looking letter, the most prominent-sounding letter, and the most prominent-feeling letter of stammerers and normals.

133. Rotter, J. B., "The Nature and Treatment of Stuttering: A Clinical Approach," *Journal of Abnormal and Social Psychology*, 1944.

Case histories are presented to show that stuttering cannot be understood apart from the environmental and emotional conditions under which it occurs. Eliminate the cause, not the symptoms.

134. Scarborough, H. E., "A Quantitative and Qualitative Analysis of the Electroencephalograms of Stutterers and Non-stutterers," *Journal of Experimental Psychology*, 1943, Volume 32, pages 156–167.

No differences between 20 normal speakers and 20 stutterers.

135. Schuell, H., "Working with Parents of Stuttering Children," *Journal of Speech and Hearing Disorders*, 1949, Volume 14, pages 251–254.

The organization and aims of three interviews with such parents are described in detail as a supplementary way of aiding the speech therapy.

136. Schultz, D. A., "A Study of Non-Directive Counseling as Applied to Adult Stutterers," *Journal of Speech Disorders*, 1947, Volume 12, pages 421–427.

Found differences in the responses of stutterers and psychoneurotics, but methodology is open to question.

137. Sheehan, J. G., "The Modification of Stuttering Through Non-reinforcement," *Journal of Abnormal and Social Psychology*, 1951, Volume 46, pages 51–63.

When stuttering brings no release from tension it is not reinforced.

138. Sheehan, J. G., "Theory and Treatment of Stuttering as an

Approach-Avoidance Conflict," *Journal of Psychology,* 1953, Volume 36, pages 27–49.

The author discusses the evidence for stuttering as a result of an approach-avoidance conflict at various levels, and applies the anxiety reduction hypothesis as explanatory of the persistence of stuttering.

139. Solomon, M., "Stuttering as an Emotional and Personality Disorder," *Journal of Speech Disorders,* 1939, Volume 4, pages 347–357.

Stuttering is the reflection in speech of a struggle to get some equilibrium during social interaction. The stutterer is one who lives in a relatively constant stage of emotional strain and whose speech breaks down under this pressure.

140. Solomon, M., "Stuttering, Emotion, and the Struggle for Equilibrium," *Proceedings of the American Speech Correction Association,* 1936, Volume 6, pages 221–239.

One of the clearest descriptions of the way a stutterer feels about his stuttering, the development of the secondary symptoms of avoidance and struggle, and the fears and shames which accompany the disorder.

141. Spadino, E. J., "Writing and Laterality Characteristics of Stuttering Children," *Columbia University Teachers College Contributions to Education,* Number 837, New York, 1941.

Few, if any, differences between stutterers and nonstutterers.

142. Spring, W. J., "Words and Masses: A Pictorial Contribution to the Psychology of Stuttering," *Psychoanalytic Quarterly,* 1935, Volume 4, pages 244–258.

The verbal and painting activities of a young boy are analyzed to clarify the reasons for his mother-hatred.

143. Steer, M. D., and Johnson, W., "An Objective Study of the Relationship Between Psychological Factors and the Severity of Stuttering," *Journal of Abnormal Psychology,* 1936, Volume 31, pages 36–46.

An objective study of the frequency of stuttering as related to different speaking situations.

144. Strother, C., "A Study of the Extent of Dyssynergia Occurring During Stuttering Spasm," *Psychological Monograph,* 1937, Volume 49, pages 108–128.

A study of action-current, breathing, and eye-movement abnormalities during the overt stuttering spasm. Among other conclusions, it was found that no one type of abnormality always occurred on all of the blocks.

145. Strother, C. R., and Kriegman, L. S., "Diadochokinesis in

Stutterers and Non-stutterers," *Journal of Speech Disorders*, 1943, Volume 8, pages 323–335.

A review of other studies of diadochokinesis and an experiment showing no essential differences between stutterers and nonstutterers.

146. Strother, C. R., "Rhythmokinesis in Stutterers and Non-stutterers," *Journal of Speech Disorders*, 1944, Volume 9, pages 239–244.

No differences were found between the two groups.

147. Travis, L. E., "Dissociation of the Homologous Muscle Function in Stuttering," *Archives of Neurology and Psychiatry*, 1934, Volume 31, pages 127–131.

Action currents were taken from masseter muscles of stutterers and normal speakers during stuttering and during free speech. In general, the currents were identical in normal speech, and in stuttering those of one masseter muscle were much different from the action currents of the other.

148. Travis, L. E., *Speech Pathology*, New York, D. Appleton-Century, 1931.

Reviews the earlier research on dysphemia from the point of view of cerebral dominance.

149. Travis, L. E., "The Need for Stuttering," *Journal of Speech Disorders*, 1940, Volume 5, pages 193–202.

The need for stuttering must be removed or barriers built, or the integration ability of the stutterer must be augmented so that the need will not be felt.

150. Usher, R. D., "A Case of Stammering," *International Journal of Psycho-Analysis*, 1944, Volume 25, pages 61–70.

In rather difficult terminology, the case of a stutterer whose symptoms concealed unjustified fears, depression, and anxiety.

151. Van Riper, C., "A Study of the Thoracic Breathing of Stutterers During Expectancy and Occurrence of Stuttering Spasm," *Journal of Speech Disorders*, 1936, Volume 1, pages 61–72.

A study of stutterer's breathing during expectancy and actual block, showing that there is generally a high correspondence and that some stutterers present constant breathing abnormalities.

152. Van Riper, C., "Do You Stutter," *Atlantic Monthly*, 1939, Volume 164, pages 601–609.

A popular history of the treatment of stuttering and the quest for a stuttering cure.

153. Van Riper, C., *Stuttering*, The National Society for Crippled Children and Adults, 11 S. La Salle St., Chicago, 1948.

Material for the intelligent parent and teacher, representing the general areas of agreement on this controversial disorder.

154. Van Riper, C., "The Growth of the Stuttering Spasm," *Quarterly Journal of Speech*, 1937, Volume 23, pages 70–73.

An article showing the difference between the primary stuttering blocks of children who have just begun to stutter and the elaborate superstructure of habit reactions present in secondary stuttering blocks. A description of how these secondary reactions are built up is given.

155. Van Riper, C., "The Influence of Empathic Response on the Frequency of Stuttering," *Psychological Monograph*, 1937, Volume 49, No. 1, pages 244–246.

Stutterers were asked to repeat words pronounced by another stutterer, and the results showed that stutterers had more blocks upon words which the pronouncer stuttered upon than on the words which the pronouncer said with no difficulty.

156. Van Riper, C., "The Effect of Penalty Upon Frequency of Stuttering," *Journal of Genetic Psychology*, 1937, Volume 50, pages 193–195.

A study to investigate the relationship of expected or felt penalty to the actual number of spasms, showing that a positive relationship exists.

157. Van Riper, C., "The Preparatory Set in Stuttering," *Journal of Speech Disorders*, 1937, Volume 2, pages 149–154.

An outline of symptomatic therapy for stutterers, describing the preparatory set, and designed to tear down the old preparatory sets toward feared words, with a subsequent substitution of new sets for the old.

158. Van Riper, C., "The Quantitative Measurement of Laterality," *Journal of Experimental Psychology*, 1935, Volume 18, pages 372–382.

A description of a laterality test employing the simultaneous drawing of patterns on two writing boards which can be converged at varying angles. The angle at which one hand produced mirrored patterning was shown to differentiate between thoroughly right- or left-handed and ambidextrous groups. Stutterers were shown to have a high degree of ambilaterality.

159. Van Riper, C., "To the Stutterer as He Begins His Speech Therapy," *Journal of Speech and Hearing Disorders*, 1949, Volume 14, pages 303–306.

An outline of the therapy for secondary stuttering and the general attitudes required of clinician and case.

160. Voelker, C. H., "A New Therapy for Spasmophemia on Gestalt Principles," *Archives Pediatrics*, 1942, Volume 69, pages 657–662.

Rather difficult to understand but results are said to be excellent.

161. Voelker, C. H., "The Visualization Treatment of Spasmophemia," *Medical Record*, 1935, pages 142, 272.

The greater the visualization of the words, the more he fears them and the more he stutters.

162. Voelker, C. H., "A Preliminary Investigation for a Normative Study of Fluency; A Clinical Index to the Severity of Stuttering," *American Journal of Orthopsychiatry*, 1944, Volume 14, pages 285–294.

The differences in the types of fluency break between stutterers and normal speakers. The former had more prolongations, syllable and word repetitions. The average normal-speaking child had no syllabic repetitions per one hundred words.

163. Wedberg, C. F., *The Stutterer Speaks*, Redlands, Calif., Valley Fine Arts Press, 1937.

An autobiographical account of how one stutterer "cured" himself.

164. West, R., "A Neurological Test for Stutterers," *Journal of Neurology and Psychopathology*, 1929, Volume 10, pages 114–118.

A test using jaw-brow movements in repetitive acts, showing stutterers inferior to normals in such neuromuscular coordinations.

165. West, R., "The Pathology of Stuttering," *The Nervous Child*, 1943, Volume 2, pages 96–106.

An interesting summary of the problem of stuttering with little theoretical bias. Lists 13 facts which any theory of stuttering must take into account.

166. Whitten, I. E., "Therapies Used for Stuttering: A Report of the Author's Own Case," *Quarterly Journal of Speech*, 1938, Volume 24, pages 227–233.

A very interesting account of how preliminary psychiatric therapy was followed by successful speech therapy.

167. Will, N., "A Six-month Report on the Personality Development of a Thirteen Year Old Stuttering Boy," *Quarterly Journal of Speech*, 1944, Volume 30, pages 88–95.

The interrelationship of speech and psychotherapy is clearly shown in this case report.

168. Wischner, G. J., "Stuttering Behavior and Learning: A Preliminary Theoretical Formulation," *Journal of Speech and Hearing Disorders*, 1950, Volume 15, pages 324–335.

Presents the basic theory of stuttering in terms of learning.

10.   Cleft-Palate Speech

ᒐᒐᒐᒐᒐᒐᒐᒐᒐᒐᒐᒐᒐᒐᒐᒐᒐᒐᒐᒐᒐᒐᒐᒐᒐᒐ

No individual works very long in the field of speech therapy
without being confronted by the odd honking snort of cleft-
palate speech. The disorder presents both articulatory and
voice problems. Usually we find in the lalling type of utterance
many unusual substitutions such as a glottal plosive (similar
to a tiny cough) for the normally plosive sounds *k* or *t*. Many
of the voiced consonants are characterized by excessive nasal
resonance or nasal emission. The fricative sounds *s, z, f, v, ch*
and others are often accompanied by an audible nasal air leak.
The vowels are generally produced with too much nasality, and
husky, breathy or hoarse qualities of the voice are frequently
found. This picture, of course, represents the extreme in the
severity scale. Some individuals may have little more than a
nasal lisp and some noticeable nasality on a few vowels. But
the acoustic image of cleft-palate speech is distinctive and unmistakable. Once they have heard it, few students ever have
difficulty distinguishing it.

Causes. Although the most common cause of this type of
speech disorder is an actual cleft or gap in the roof of the mouth,
this is not always the case. The soft palate or velum may be
paralyzed or sluggish as a result of diphtheria or polio or some
other severe illness. When this "back door to the nasal caverns"
is unable to close sufficiently or quickly enough, part of the

air flow and sound may travel through those chambers and emerge from the front doors, the nostrils. This we call nasal emission. At other times, no nasal air flow may take place, but the nasal chambers will still reverberate and echo in a fashion our culture finds unpleasant. This is the phenomenon of excessive nasality, the whine we hear on the vowels and voiced consonants.

How is this excessive nasal resonance produced? We are not entirely sure in all cases. We are not even sure that the peculiar whining quality we call nasality does require a reverberating nasal cavity and an open back door. We do know that, generally, when the opening to the nasal cavity is too wide as compared with the opening into the mouth cavity, then nasality appears. Researchers have found that a rubber tube with an opening greater than six millimeters, when passed through the nose and back down into the throat will produce a nasal tone. If a smaller tube is used the speech seems oral in quality. But we have seen a few cases of wide open clefts in the soft and hard palates who spoke with little or no nasality. Though they seemed to use a different type of tongue positioning and a wider mouth opening, their speech was entirely adequate. McDonald and Baker (20) explain this and other related peculiarities by stating that most nasality is due to the placement of the back of the tongue. When the rear portion of the tongue is retracted too far or carried too high and the jaw opening is lessened, the individual creates new resonating cavities in the throat and mouth which in turn create the nasal tones. Such a tongue position would also tend to direct the air flow upwards, and if the nasopharyngeal port is more open than necessary, the air and sound might emerge through those passageways. Buck (7) has independently investigated the same problem, however, and his research fails to corroborate the belief in an abnormally high or retracted tongue position as characteristic of people with cleft palate speech. It is quite possible that different individuals manage to create the same excessive nasality in different ways, and both explanations—an excessive velar opening and a high retracted tongue position—are worth therapeutic consideration. Clinically we have worked to alter both abnormal features for a long time.

Because excessive nasality and nasal emission can be produced without any true organic cause, we find individuals with cleft palate speech as the result of imitation.

In surveying a country school we found seven children all of the same family and with ages ranging from 6 to 15 years, with cleft palate speech. Only one of them, the youngest, had any actual cleft, and it was a divided uvula only. The oldest child, a girl, had the most severely defective speech. All of these children were able to sing without any nasality or nasal emission and their articulation in singing was much better than in speech. They lived on an isolated farm with a mother who had an unrepaired cleft of both palates, the upper gum, and the upper lip. Her speech was severely affected. Therapy progressed very swiftly when they were able to use a hearing aid and a play-back recorder. We found that they could imitate normal speech very readily and that no carry-over of the nasality was present.

A mild type of cleft-palate speech sometimes occurs as a result of the removal of very enlarged adenoids. Many parents tend to blame the surgeon for this unhappy consequence in their belief that he has cut or injured the muscles which narrow the naso-pharynx. While this could possibly be the case, we find more often that the sudden nasal air leak and excessive nasality come because the child is raising his velum to the same level it had attained previously when the adenoids had narrowed the passage. With the adenoidal growths gone, the opening (which before was below the margin necessary to produce nasality) now is large enough to cause defective voice and articulation. Therapy must be focused on teaching the child to make higher and stronger elevations and closures of the soft palate.

We have also examined cases, usually feeble-minded, who possess perfectly normal palates, both in structure and in function, who have so little energy to spend in speech that their drooping palate and inactive tongue are but the reflections of a totally subnormal individual. It takes some work to keep an active velum. Perhaps one reason many children who do have cleft palates are penalized as being feeble-minded is the cultural recognition that there are these cases.

There are said to be some individuals who have what is called "velar insufficiency." This term refers to a soft palate supposedly too small, narrow, or short to cause a complete closing of the naso-pharynx. We have seen several cases who were unable to close this passage and whose palates showed no gross abnormality, but we could not say whether or not the palate was too short. After all, the velum is not a flap or structure like an ear. It is merely a name for the location where many muscles come together and intertwine. Its length or width would be extremely difficult to measure consistently. We feel that most cases of so-called velar insufficiency are merely individuals who have learned to speak using the wrong positions of the tongue or an inaccurate judgment of the amount of naso-pharyngeal closure required for acceptable speech. With most of these cases of velar insufficiency, ear training alone has done wonders. Anderson[1] has this to say:

In these cases it will be observed that even when the palate is fully elevated, there is still a noticeable space between the palate and the posterior pharyngeal wall. This condition may be so pronounced that the individual will sound very much as if he had a cleft palate.

However, as we have indicated before, most of the research shows that complete closure is not required. Hixon (14), Harrington (13), and Kaltenborn (16) have in their research studies demonstrated that complete closure is the exception rather than the rule. The amount of closure required varies with the particular sound being uttered. Bloomer (6) who was able to peer inside the nasal cavities of patients through surgically created openings in the face which permitted direct observation found that *ee* (i) and *oo* (u) required the highest elevation of the soft palate of any of the vowels, and *zh* (ʒ) and *r* needed the most for the consonants. Williams (27) using X-ray pictures has

---

[1] Quoted by permission of the publishers from Virgil A. Anderson, *Improving the Child's Speech*, New York, Oxford University Press, 1953, page 225.

shown that the vowels *ah* and *œ* require the least closure or elevation.

Cleft palate and cleft lip. Although, as we have been describing, there are other causes for cleft-palate speech, the largest single cause is of course organic in nature. When the floor of the nasal cavity has a rift or hole in it, the mouth and nose tend to function differently in resonation than they do when the floor is intact. The individual with a large cleft in the soft palate, hard palate, upper dental arch, and upper lip is almost doomed to defective speech unless elaborate surgical, prosthetic, dental, psychologic and speech therapy services are devoted to his rehabilitation.

There are many varieties and locations of the clefts. At times only the uvula may be divided into two little prongs with everything else intact and no speech problem. In other cases the cleft may be hidden under the lining of the roof of the mouth and be not much more than a tiny perforation. But more frequently we find very obvious and serious clefts which, according to Veau's classification, are of four types: Type I, Cleft of the velum only; Type II, Cleft of the hard palate and velum; Type III, Cleft of both hard and soft palates plus unilateral clefts in the upper gum and upper lip; and Type IV, Cleft in both hard and soft palates and bilateral clefts in the upper gum and upper lip. (See reference 22 by Morley for illustrations.)

Incidence and causes of clefts. Various estimates of the number of cleft palates have been made available. Oldfield (23) cites the proportion of one cleft in each 600 births in England, and other researchers place the figure slightly higher. Lowry (18) claims that there are 200,000 individuals with clefts in this country alone with 4,600 new ones arriving each year. McDonald (19) says, "Until more studies of the mortality of cleft palate infants are reported or until some actual study of the incidence of cleft palate in the total population is made, the estimate of one cleft palate case per thousand population appears to be defensible."

Although some of the clefts are caused by accidents and injuries after birth, the majority of them are due to failure in embryonic development. During the sixth week of the unborn child's existence the primitive structures of the upper jaw grow very swiftly toward the midline and join those of the nose. From them emerge two shelves which eventually form the palate. The union is practically complete by the ninth week. This is what occurs in most unborn children. But in a few, for reasons we do not entirely know, the timetable has been upset. The two shelves stop growing before they meet. Not only humans but lambs, dogs and goats have been known to be born with clefts. Scientists have been able to produce cleft palates experimentally in rats by depriving the mothers of riboflavin, a vitamin found in large amounts in liver. Some evidence linking calcium deficiencies has also been adduced. But most authorities feel that the failure of the embryonic structures to unite is due to some characteristic carried by the genes. This genetic factor is probably recessive and its operation is not well understood. According to Oldfield (23) 11 per cent of all cleft palate children have similar defects in their immediate families. One parent with a cleft palate has one chance in fifty of having a child with a cleft (21). According to Harkins (13) more whites than Negroes and more males than females have clefts.

Effects of clefts. A cleft palate and lip have profound consequences. From birth onward, the organic difference plays an important part in the individual's life and in his family's. The shock of having a defective child can lead parents to make some grievous errors in child rearing—rejection, overprotection, indulgence—so that the entire personality will be warped even more than the mouth. The social penalties experienced by a cleft-palate child are at least as severe as those felt by the stutterer. Feeding problems confront the new mother immediately. The hare-lip cannot grasp the nipple; the divided upper gum cannot press it; the tongue does not squeeze efficiently; the milk runs out of the nose; swallowing is interfered with; great quantities of air are taken in with tiny droplets of milk. The nipple should be oversized and placed well back in the mouth or the Brophy nipple purchased which has a built in flap to keep the milk in the mouth. Often the openings in the nipple must be widened and then the tongue fails to learn any independent tip action (15). The teeth are commonly displaced when they do erupt and chewing is poorly coordinated. Very often these children, according to Sataloff and Fraser (24), have hearing losses since infections from the mouth can easily go up through the cleft and the Eustachian tube to the middle ear. Colds are frequent and prolonged. Nutrition is often poor and development slowed. It's tough to possess a cleft palate.

It is also difficult for the family financially. Although in many areas it is possible for children with cleft palates to have surgery, prosthedontia and orthodontic services at the expense of the state, this is not always the case, and in any event there are many other obligations such as travel to eat up the family funds. Most children with cleft palates and cleft lips now have their first operation (on the lip) at about the third or fourth month. In a double hare-lip, first one cleft is brought together, then about six weeks later, the other. Often the lip may need another operation at the age of three or four years to loosen it, remove adhesions, or improve the cosmetic appearance.

The surgery for closing the palatal clefts and creating a functional velum is now postponed until the child is from four to seven years of age. Formerly it was performed much earlier, but failures were so frequent and interference with the normal growth processes of the palate and teeth were so apparent that the later date is now preferred by most oral surgeons. Depending upon the nature of the cleft and the training of the surgeon, various operative techniques are employed. The holes must be closed, the bones or the soft tissue overlying them must be brought together without producing scar tissue or shortening or abnormal thickening of the velum. The greatest care must be taken to insure the adequacy of muscle action. Cleft-palate surgery is some of the most intricate ever to be mastered by man. The structural proportions must not only be adequate for the patient at the age of the operation; the surgeon must also have the ability to predict how future growth will affect them. Merely sewing up the tissue in the midline will seldom produce a functional palate. Usually, a flap of tissue from the intact part of the hard palate must be utilized to lengthen and create a flexible velum. This is called the "push-back" operation. Great skill must be used lest scar tissue or structural tensions cause retardation of growth or displacement. In certain difficult cases, a pharyngeal flap operation is performed. In this, tissue from the back wall of the throat is brought forward and anchored to the palate. In this position it acts as a physiological bridge. The patient, by squeezing the flap with his constrictor muscles is able to close the passageway to the nose.

Despite all this careful and ingenious operating, many cases and their parents find disappointment in the surgical result. Only occasionally will surgery by itself produce normal speech even when an adequate palate has been created. By the time the operations have been concluded most of the speech sounds have been learned in a defective fashion. Speech therapy will be required in most cases to activate the new structures in phonation and articulation.

Prosthesis. Another approach to the problem of the cleft palate has come from the field of dentistry. When surgery is impossible or has failed to create an adequate constriction in the naso-pharynx, appliances called "obturators" can be constructed and fitted to the opening. These appliances, made of plastic or certain alloys, usually resemble a dental upper plate with a projection (called the bulb) which fits into the nasopharyngeal opening. This speech appliance is anchored to the teeth by clasps or other forms of retention or in some instances is fitted into the actual cleft of the hard palate. It is made removable for hygienic reasons. Temporary appliances can be made as early as four years of age. The designing and fitting of these appliances requires great skill and judgment and must be done by an expert.

The case is taught, usually by the speech therapist, to

squeeze the bulb with the sphincters of the pharynx first in silence, then in silent inhalation through the mouth, then in tidal in-and-out respiration, then in speech. The first speech sounds, those vowels with wide mouth openings and low tongue positions (such as *ah*), are taught while squeezing the bulb. Next, we work with the other vowels, blending them with those first mastered. Low pitches and intensities are used, and various devices to check the air flow through the mouth are provided. Ear training is essential at this time. We then train our cases to emit voiced air through the mouth as the tongue tip moves independently of the jaw, all this while maintaining some contact with the bulb of the appliance. Then we practice the unvoiced plosives (*p, t, k*), the voiced plosives (*b, d, g*), then the unvoiced and voiced fricatives (*f, s, sh,* and so forth), in that order. These consonants are used first in the final position of syllables using the easiest vowels (*ah* and *ae*) to produce nonsense words such as "ahp" and "app." Then by making "sound sandwiches," *appa, atta,* etc., we can work around to their use in the initial positions *pa, tat,* and *kakka.* We have found that the sibilants *s* and *z* should not be worked with until most of the other sounds are fairly adequate. We prefer to make sure that the patient speaks very little *except during speech therapy* when he first wears the appliance, and we believe in a very intensive training program at this time. Proper speech habits should be taught from the first so that little unlearning will be needed.

Speech therapy after surgery. The aims of therapy are these: (1) to narrow the naso-pharynx by learning to use the repaired structures; (2) to eliminate much of the excessive nasality through ear training and vocal training procedures; (3) to direct the air flow outward through the mouth opening; (4) to eliminate the lalling type of utterance and activate the tonguetip during phonation; (5) to improve the articulation of all of the speech sounds.

Using the new palate. We have several ways of learning to

use the new closure mechanism produced by the surgery. First of all, as Morley (22) points out, we must help the cleft palate case to recognize and identify the functioning of velum he cannot see. Kinesthetic sensations often follow tactual ones and so we use massage for this purpose. The massage should, of course, be demonstrated by the physician and its amount designated. It is begun about five or six weeks after the final operation.

Reducing the nasality. Quite as important as the physiological task of narrowing the back doorway to the nose is the psychological task of enabling the case to identify and vary the amount of nasality heard in his own voice. Few cleft-palate cases have any idea of the important differences the voice will show. The playback of their first recording is usually a profound shock to them and must be carefully cushioned. But they must hear the quality if they are ever to reduce it. As in stuttering, we believe that the best procedure to follow is first to accept, then to analyze, then to vary and finally to reduce the abnormality. Cancellations and pull-outs can be used with cleft palate cases too. Williamson (28) and others have shown that great strides in the elimination of nasality can be accomplished by vocal training alone. Our experience has been similar. Even in cases with large unrepaired clefts we have been able through careful ear training and modification techniques to reduce the excessive nasality even if we could not entirely eliminate it. Many of the methods outlined in the chapter on voice disorders are applicable to cleft palate. As McDonald and Baker (20) say:

[The] aim is to produce clear vowel sounds as nearly identical as possible and free from excessive amounts of nasality. In this way he learns to produce an acceptable series of vowel sounds by concentrating on the development of orality.

Directing the air stream through the mouth. Recently there has been some caustic criticism of blowing exercises in cleft palate therapy, and doubtless some of it has been justified. Too much time has been spent in blowing feathers and too little in blowing speech. Despite the criticism, Bloomer (6) found that the palatal activity in blowing was more similar to that found in non-nasal speech than was swallowing, yawning or any other activity. It is unwise to stress blowing with too great a force, or silent blowing, or blowing without concomitant tongue tip activity, but when these have been taken care of, there still remains a very vital function in blowing: it helps to stress oral emission instead of nasal emission. As Young (29) says: "The center of the child's speech consciousness will be in the nose and will stick there long after the operation." Our aim in blowing exercises is to make the child very much aware of his mouth as a blowing tube, as an orifice. In the following exercises we prefer to have the patient blow *voiced* air through the mouth while the tongue is either slightly protruded past the lips or pointing upward.

Activating the tongue tip. All that is needed to produce the characteristic pattern of cleft-palate speech is to take a laller and ask him to add nasality. Perhaps because the upper part of the mouth was tender and sore for such a long time, or perhaps because the lower jaw is commonly thrust forward much further than the upper so that the usual tongue thrust is inappropriate, or for some other reason, the person with a cleft palate seldom uses his tongue tip with ease. He tends to make most of his anterior contacts and positions with the blade of the tongue. In effect, he lalls. To teach him to use tongue tip thrusts is often difficult. The moment he raises the tip, down comes the palate. We do a good deal of training to prevent this reciprocal function. By lifting the tongue tip during mouth inhalation, during mirror observation of palatal rising, during yawning, and by practice in tongue-sucking and clicking, we get real improvement. Also of importance is the freeing of the tongue from its dependence upon jaw movement. Most cleft-palate cases seldom can lift the tongue independently of the jaw but they can be trained to do so, and the training helps all of the speech.

References

1. Anderson, V. A., *Improving the Child's Speech*, New York, Oxford University Press, 1953, pages 224–233.

T-F: According to the author, obturators are most useful when the cleft is in the hard palate.

T-F: The case should use wide mouth openings in articulation.

Essay: What are some of the methods suggested for distinguishing between nasal and oral resonance?

2. Backus, O. L., *Speech in Education*, New York, Longmans, Green, 1943, pages 173–180.

Gives a description of the disorder, speech involvements, causes, surgical repair, mouth-breathing exercises, articulation therapy, reduction of assimilation nasality, and socialization.

3. Backus, O. L., "Children with Cleft Palate and Cleft Lip," Chapter VI, pages 117–157, in Johnson, W. (editor): *Speech Problems of Children*, New York, Grune and Stratton, 1950.

T-F: Fatalities from cleft palate surgery are extremely rare.

T-F: Cleft palate infants babble as readily as do normal ones.

Essay: What does Backus say about the dentist's role in therapy?

4. Berry, M. F., "Lingual Anomalies Associated with Palatal Clefts," *Journal of Speech and Hearing Disorders*, 1949, Volume 14, pages 359–362.

T-F: In 85 or more per cent of all cases the tongue is not well coordinated.

T-F: There may be clefts in the tongue as well as in the palate.

Essay: Describe the development of the palate in the embryo.

5. Blair, V. P., "Cleft Palate—Its Surgery," *Journal of Speech Disorders*, 1937, Volume 2, pages 195–198.

A brief description of the surgical aims and methods used in repairing palatal clefts.

6. Bloomer, H., "Observations on Palatopharyngeal Movements in Speech and Deglutition," *Journal of Speech and Hearing Disorders*, 1953, Volume 18, pages 230–246.

The author made direct observations of the palatal functioning of two patients through surgically created openings in the face. Marked differences in functioning between swallowing and speaking or blowing were noted. Different sounds produced different elevations of the palate.

7. Buck, M., "Facial Skeletal Measurements and Tongue Carriage in Subjects with Repaired Cleft Palate," *Journal of Speech and Hearing Disorders*, 1953, Volume 18, pages 121–132.

T-F: The upper jaw of cleft palate patients is not as long or wide as those of normal individuals.

T-F: Insufficient mouth opening is characteristic of these cases.

Essay: What doubts does this research create in McDonald and Baker's belief that the nasality is caused by a retracted and poorly positioned tongue?

8. Conway, H., "Combined Use of the Pushback and Pharyngeal Flap Procedures in the Management of Complicated Cases of Cleft Palate," *Oral Surg.*, 1952, Volume 5, pages 133–152.

Recommends and describes the combined operation.

9. Dalrymple, L. H., "Our Child Had a Cleft Palate," *Hygeia*, 1949, Volume 27, pages 186–187, 199–200.

T-F: The child's babbling sounded normal to the mother.

T-F: The child began to react with emotion to her cleft-palate difference before she was five years of age.

Essay: Describe the feeding problems of the child.

10. Eckelmann, D., and Baldridge, P., "Speech Training for the Child with a Cleft Palate," *Journal of Speech Disorders*, 1945, Volume 10, pages 137–148.

An excellent description of actual procedures used for cleft-palate children.

11. Graber, T. M., "Changing Philosophies in Cleft Palate Management," *Journal of Pediatrics*, 1950, Volume 37, pages 400–415.

Formerly, the policy was to operate as early as possible, but X-ray studies have shown that the surgically altered palate grows so much slower than the adjacent structures that increased abnormality is produced. Late operation avoids these unfortunate results.

12. Harkins, C. S., "Rehabilitation of the Cleft Palate Child," *Journal of the Exceptional Child*, 1943, Volume 9, pages 98–106.

A very clear and nontechnical description of modern surgical techniques. Discusses obturators and other prosthetic devices. Stresses speech correction.

13. Harrington, R., "A Study of the Mechanism of Velopharyngeal Closure," *Journal of Speech Disorders*, 1944, Volume 9, pages 325–345.

A thoroughgoing description of the muscle action of the soft palate. It shows some pictures of the palate in a patient whose cheek was opened to show it clearly.

14. Hixon, E., "Orthodontia in Cleft Palate Rehabilitation," *American Association for Cleft Palate Rehabilitation Newsletter*, 1951, Volume 1, pages 2–3.

Describes the need for considering muscle balance and rates of bone growth in cleft palate patients. Orthodontia can prevent regression of upper jaw and help to create a good closure.

15. Huber, M. W., and Kopp, A. E., *The Practice of Speech Correction in the Medical Clinic*, Boston, Expression Co., 1942.

Cleft lip and cleft palate are described carefully and vividly with fine pictorial illustrations. The speech-correction methods are briefly outlined.

16. Kaltenborn, A. L., "An X-ray Study of Velopharyngeal Closure in Nasal and Non-nasal Speakers," *M. A. Thesis, Northwestern University*, 1948.

17. Kantner, C. E., "Diagnosis and Prognosis in Cleft Palate Speech," *Journal of Speech and Hearing Disorders*, 1948, Volume 13, pages 211–222.

T-F: The amount of nasality increases in direct proportion to the size of the cleft.

T-F: The best device for testing nasality is still the human ear.

Essay: Using Kantner's discussion, prepare a comprehensive form for the examination of a cleft-palate patient.

18. Lowry, P. C., "Congenital Cleft Palate," *Dental Survey*, 1952, Volume 28, pages 1678–1689.

A general article describing incidence and various forms of treatment.

19. McDonald, E. T., "The Incidence of Cleft Palate," *American Association for Cleft Palate Rehabilitation Newsletter*, 1951, Volume 1, page 2.

20. McDonald, E. T., and Baker, H. K., "Cleft Palate Speech: An Integration of Research and Clinical Observation," *Journal of Speech and Hearing Disorders*, 1951, Volume 16, pages 9–20.

T-F: The authors feel the tongue is more important than the velum in producing excessive nasality.

T-F: Blowing exercises do little good for cleft-palate cases.

Essay: Summarize the plan of therapy outlined by the authors.

21. McEvith, W. G., "Cleft Lip and Palate and Parental Age," *Plast. and Recons. Surg.*, 1952, pages 77–82.

No effect of parental age on precipitation of cleft palates or lips.

22. Morley, M. E., *Cleft Palate and Speech*, Baltimore, William Wilkins, 1946.

T-F: The author advocates thorough training in blowing.

T-F: The author advocates teaching the speech sounds first in their initial positions, then in the final and then in the medial positions within words.

Essay: How does the author explain the functioning of the palate to a small child?

23. Oldfield, M. C., "Modern Trends in Hare-Lip and Cleft Palate

Surgery with a Review of 500 Cases," *British Journal of Surgery*, 1949, Volume 39, pages 178–194.

An excellent survey of the cleft-palate problem. Claims favorable results in terms of speech training in 90.7% of the cases.

24. Sataloff, J., and Fraser, M., "Hearing Loss in Children with Cleft Palates," *Archives of Otolaryngology*, Chicago, 1952, Volume 55, pages 61–64.

Authors find middle ear pathology and conduction hearing loss in the large majority of cleft-palate patients.

25. Shohara, H. H., "Speech Rehabilitation in a Case of Post-operated Cleft Palate Speech and Malocclusion," *Journal of Speech Disorders*, 1942, Volume 7, pages 381–388.

Palatograms are used to show the development of acceptable speech.

26. Wells, C., "Improving the Speech of the Cleft Palate Child," *Journal of Speech Disorders*, 1945, Volume 10, pages 162–169.

An excellent description of methods.

27. Williams, R. L., "A Serial Radiographic Study of Velopharyngeal Closure and Tongue Positions in Certain Vowel Sounds," *Northwestern University Bulletin*, 1952, Volume 52, pages 9–12.

In the *ah* and *ae* sounds the naso-pharynx is open much further than we would expect in non-nasal speech. For the *u* and *ee* (i) sounds the opening is narrowest. The back wall does not bulge forward.

28. Williamson, A. B., "Diagnosis and Treatment of 84 Cases of Nasality," *Quarterly Journal of Speech*, 1944, Volume 30, pages 471–479.

Exercises to elevate the palate or strengthen it are unnecessary in eliminating hyper-nasality. Voice training can do the job alone.

11. Foreign Dialect

᠁᠁᠁᠁᠁᠁᠁᠁᠁᠁᠁᠁᠁᠁

Every speech therapist is asked to help when classroom teachers are confronted by a non-English-speaking child. Such a child presents many problems in a schoolroom. They are generally frightened, helpless and frustrated. They find such activities as going out to recess or going to the bathroom appallingly mysterious. They make mistakes at which the other children laugh. Often they are bombarded by so many confusing though well-meant conversational efforts by their classmates that they withdraw and pretend to misunderstand even when they know what is being said. You can imagine how a Bulgarian child would feel when he tried to interpret the vertical nodding of the head for the negative sign that it means in his own language. Perhaps the first counsel that the speech therapist should give is: go slowly! Let the child see what is going on. Show him you are friendly but do not make demands upon him. Once a small vocabulary is achieved and it will soon come, in comprehension if not in communication, the speech teaching can commence. The speech therapist has many bits of valuable know-how for the teacher of such a child.

Speech therapists are also often asked to work directly with adults who wish to acquire a better mastery of English than they can pick up by themselves or who wish to eliminate the last traces of a minor accent. These individuals, usually well educated, are a joy to work with. They have strong motivation and make swift progress. The large numbers of foreign students coming to the United States provide another group of prospective cases. These are usually organized into classes and are taught by several individuals—a sociologist who acquaints them with our culture and habits, a rhetoric teacher who helps them with the written English, and the speech teacher who trains them in listening, thinking in English, vocabulary acquisition, pronunciation, stress and inflection. Almost every fair sized community now has evening Americanization classes for the foreign born and the speech therapist is often called upon to help in this worthy project.

English is a difficult language. Those of us who have spoken English since we first learned to talk may find the foregoing statement hard to believe, but ask any foreigner! First of all we possess six English tenses, each with two or three simple, progressive and emphatic forms. Few Americans could give examples to fit them. Our parts of speech have no identifying endings as they do in so many other languages. We say, "He took it hard," and the foreigner trying to understand pulls out handfuls of frustrated hair. "Hard" in this sentence should be spelled and pronounced as "hardly" if it is an adverb, but that would change the whole meaning. There madness lies! We who learned our English at our mothers' knees have never bothered ourselves with consistency. Every rule has so many exceptions that most of them are almost worthless. The stress we place upon our syllables or words is irregular and is difficult to classify intelligently.

We have more idioms than most languages and a very active language is constantly changing. Very strange to foreign ears are many of the sounds we use. Finally, our system of spelling is such a mixed-up mess that most of us master it by rote rather than by rule. So little does it help the foreigner, we sometimes prefer to teach the phonetic alphabet at the same time we teach English.

Treatment of the young non-English-speaking child. When a

non-English-speaking child first comes to school, he should be given a few days to orient himself. If any other student can speak his language, the teacher should inform the child through this interpreter that he should watch the other children and do what they do. He should be told that he will not be asked to talk for a little while, and that if he wants to know the name of anything he should attract the teacher's attention and point to it. If possible, the teacher should learn a few of the foreign words and phrases, so that she can say the child's name and "yes" and "no," can give such directions as "Come," "Find," and "See," and can ask such questions as "What is this?" These familiar words and phrases will eliminate the overwhelming insecurity which usually greets the foreign child upon entering school. For several weeks, the child should not be asked to make any attempts to say English words, but every opportunity should be provided for increasing his comprehension. Pantomime, pointing, and the use of pictures, when preceded by the speaking of his name by the teacher or some other student, often build up this comprehension to a surprising degree. Some teachers designate one of the other pupils to act as a talking dictionary several times a day and to name anything the foreign child dramatizes or to which he points. Such a program will invariably result in spontaneous speech attempts and in imitation. The other children often carry out similar procedures on the playground, and most of the language is acquired through play activity. The teacher should try to have a five- or ten-minute period each day in which she attempts to get the child to hear and produce those speech sounds which the foreign language does not possess or which it uses in a slightly different way. These sounds should be identified with noises made by animals or machines and should be practiced independently of any true speech.

As soon as the child begins to use English speech spontaneously, the teacher can begin to build vocabulary. She should not be too critical of pronunciation at first, but after the child has used the new word five or six times, she should point out the errors in contrast with the correct sounds, using the phonic training mentioned in the preceding paragraph to enable him to correct himself. Each new word should be presented in many different contexts and should be reviewed frequently. In order to prevent too narrow associations, each should be used as soon as possible with other contrasting words, such as opposites or different actions. Sentence words should be the first to be acquired, and some other child may demonstrate their meanings by his actions as the teacher repeats the new word. Pictures of children carrying out commands or directions are also useful. Often, the foreign child seems to make rapid progress by imitating the activity of the other members of a group of children as they respond to the teacher's spoken commands. Articles, prepositions, and abstract words should be introduced much later, and many of them can best be learned through indirect methods. Thus, the foreign child learns the words *on* and *under* by following directions to put objects on or under a given table. The teacher must always remember to use as simple directions as possible, employing one-word sentences and pantomime in the early stages so as not to confuse the child with too many words. She must also realize that the child thinks in the other language and must mentally translate everything said to him, a process which, in the young child, necessitates patient waiting for a response.

Although the average child has a vocabulary of approximately two thousand words before beginning reading, no such amount need be required of the foreign child. In fact, after a small basic vocabulary of fifty or one hundred words has been acquired, the foreign child should be given reading as part of his speech training. The words included in modern elementary readers are probably as basic to language acquisition as any. Pronunciation of the difficult words found in reading should be handled apart from the reading situation if the reading skills are not to be affected. The words that the foreign child mispronounces in oral reading should be noted and corrected later. As soon as some reading skill has been gained, the words of the foreign child's new vocabulary should be reviewed over and over, and incorporated into little stories. He should be encouraged to tell these before the group, and social approval should be given for each little triumph. We doubt that phonetic symbols are of much use in training the young non-English-speaking child; they merely increase the already heavy burden which school places upon him. We feel that any child of ten years or less, if given the proper preliminary help, will acquire normal English speech from his fellow students. Once the process of correct speaking is initiated, imitation seems to take care of even the stress and inflection aspects of the problem, providing that environmental factors do not interfere. The teacher should help the child keep a notebook of his most frequent errors; this can be passed along from teacher to teacher as he progresses through the grades.

Teaching English to Adults

This treatment must accomplish the following things: (1) the student must acquire the words and idioms of a basic English vocabulary, first in terms of comprehension, and second in terms of use; (2) he must learn those English speech sounds which never occur in his native language; (3) he must learn to produce and discriminate between those speech sounds which are common both in his native language and also in English, but which vary in duration, in diphthongization, in nasality, and in other relatively inconspicuous ways; (4) he must learn to hear and produce the characteristic patterns of stress and accent which distinguish the old language from the new; (5) he must learn to hear and produce the characteristic patterns of melody, inflection, and intonation which differ in the two languages; (6) he must learn to recognize the sound substitutions, omissions, and additions which contribute to the foreign quality of his speech; (7) he must learn the forms of sentence structure which differ in the two languages; and, finally, (8) he must learn to think in English.

Vocabulary. According to Fries (9) the first words to be acquired should be those concerned with the immediate language-learning situation, and the first project should be built about this experience. Certain of the words must be function words, such verbs as "speak," "repeat," or "Do!" Others will be positive-negative words such as "Yes" and "No" or "Good!" Then there must be enough "content" words to permit comprehension and conversing. These are the names of things. And we also need words to describe those things—the adjectives. These first words must be made functional. So far as possible, the case should be as active as possible. When the therapist says, "Sit down!" he obeys but repeats the phrase as he does so. This self-talk in English should permeate all of the teaching. Short phrases and sentences should be used to describe what he sees, feels or does. Vocabulary is acquired swiftly in this way.

The word lists by Thorndike or by Buckingham and Dolch will insure economy of effort, since each word is listed according to frequency of use. A study by Hughes gives a list of 660 words used in teaching Spanish-speaking children their first English vocabulary. Whatever word list is used, the teacher and student will need to supplement it with words that are peculiarly useful in the latter's immediate environment. As far as possible, the words should be taught vocally rather than by reading or writing. Phonograph recordings can serve as sound dictionaries, if phonetic transcripts are provided with the records. This method has proved very useful.

Each student finds it helpful to make his own vocabulary recording. After learning a series of words and how to transcribe them phonetically, he and the teacher pronounce them alternately into the microphone of a recording device, pausing for a second after each word. When the record is played back, the student can hear his own pronunciation, then the teacher's, and then is given time to pronounce it again before the next word is spoken. A series of these records, frequently replayed, is a very effective therapeutic device. Foreign-language-speaking students also make special recordings of words they are most likely to mispronounce, saying them both correctly and incorrectly. These dictionaries of error, when replayed daily, soon eradicate the mistakes. The students also are urged to keep notebooks in which they note all usage of familiar words which seems to violate the meanings previously taught.

Errors in producing the English vowels and consonants. No great difficulty will be experienced in teaching the foreign-language individual how to produce sounds that do not occur in his native language. They may be taught by the same methods outlined in the chapter on the treatment of articulatory defects. Probably the greatest obstacle lies in the average teacher's unfamiliarity with the student's language. Fortunately, the omissions, additions, distortions, and substitutions of sounds

AMERICAN SOUNDS ABSENT FROM OR "DISTORTED" IN EUROPEAN LANGUAGES*

Vowels and Diphthongs

	[ɪ]	[æ]	[ɔ]	[ʊ]	[ʌ]	[ə]	[oʊ]	[aʊ]	[eɪ]	[aɪ]	[ɔɪ]	[ju]
French	A†	A		A	A		D†	A	D	A	A	A
Italian	A	A		A	A	A	D		D			A
Spanish	A	A		A	A	A						A
Portuguese	A	A		A	A							A
Rumanian		A			A		D	A	D	A	A	A
Greek	A	A		A	A	A		A	A		A	A
German		A			A		D		D			A
Swedish	A	A	A	A	A		D					A
Norwegian	A	A		A			D	D				A
Danish	A			A	A		D		D	D		A
Russian	A	A		A	A	A	A	A				
Polish	A	A		A	A	A	A		D			
Czech	A	A		A	A	A		A			•	
Finnish				A	A						A	
Hungarian	A	A		A	A	D		D				A

The vowels [*i*], [ɛ], [*a*] and [*u*] are present in all.

---

* Sipin, L., "A Comparative Analysis of the Phonetic Systems of Certain Modern European Languages, with Applications to the Correction of Foreign Dialects," M. A. Thesis, State University of Iowa.

† "A" signifies absent; "D" signifies distorted.

Consonants

	[ŋ]	[r]	[l]	[θ]	[ð]	[z]	[ʃ]	[ʒ]	[h]	[ʍ]	[w]	[tʃ]	[dʒ]
French	A	D	D	A	A				A	A	A	A	A
Italian		D	D	A	A			A		A			
Spanish	A	D	D		A			A	A	A	A		
Portuguese		D	D	A	A				A	A		A	A
Rumanian	A	D	D	A	A				A	A			
Greek	A	D	D				A	A	A	A	A	A	A
German	D	D	D	A	A				A	A			A
Swedish	A	D	D	A	A	A		A	A	A			A
Norwegian		D	D	A	A	A		A	A	A	A		A
Danish		D	D					A	A	A	A		A
Russian	A	D		A	A				A	A	A		A
Polish	A	D		A	A				A	A	A		
Czech	A	D	D	A	A				A	A			A
Finnish	A	D	D	A	A	A	A	A		A	A	A	A
Hungarian	A	D	D	A	A				A	A			

The consonants [m], [n], [p], [t], [k], [f], [v], [s] and [j] are present in all; [b], [d], and [g] are present in all except Greek.

commonly made by each nationality are to be found in most of the standard textbooks in speech correction.

Generally speaking, there are a few consistent substitutions characteristic of the individuals of any one nationality who are attempting to learn English. Some omit the sound entirely; others use some native speech sound similar to the English one; still others give the symbol the foreign equivalent and use the latter in pronunciation. A keen ear can soon detect what the errors are.

It is usually difficult to teach the foreign-language adult to distinguish those characteristics of duration, diphthongization, nasality, and force which differ in the old and new languages. Phonetic training will help him to recognize the natural tendencies in American speech to prolong and to diphthongize the vowels. English vowels are not pure vowels, but are diphthongs or triphthongs. Americans ordinarily use very little lip or jaw movement in articulating their vowels or consonants, and when the foreigner's stop consonants are too plosive or too energetic, they contribute to the foreign accent. Many foreign languages use trilled *r* sounds and produce the *l* with a retracted tongue. Others, notably the French, nasalize many of their vowels and voiced continuant sounds. All of these differences reflect themselves in foreign accent and must be eliminated if the individual is to lose his speech peculiarity. This may be done through discrimination and ear training similar to that used for the voice and articulatory cases. The errors must be brought up to consciousness, the old habits broken, and new habits substituted for them. The use of narrow phonetic transcription, which employs symbols indicative of vowel duration, tongue position, and nasalization, is often effective. Matching techniques, contrast of correct and incorrect sound sequences, practice in drawling and prolonging vowels, reading prescored material, and many other methods are useful in carrying out these aims.

Stress. Foreign-language speakers habitually use those stress patterns and accents which are characteristic of the old language, and often find themselves hopelessly confused by the tremendous variety of syllabic accents found in English. It is usually wise to teach the student two or three rules and then ask him to collect and record exceptions in his notebook. The rules which we have found most useful are:

1. In English, we tend to alternate stressed and unstressed syllables.
2. Words of three or more syllables are accented on the first syllable except when it is a prefix.
3. Compound words are accented on the first syllable.

Melody. Probably the most difficult of all characteristics of foreign speech to eradicate is the old melody pattern of the sentence. Each language has its own system of inflection patterns, and, since they are not usually recorded by symbols, they are relatively unconscious and hence difficult to eliminate. The Swedish individual tends to end his declarative sentences with an upward inflection. If he is to free his English of peculiarity, he must recognize this tendency, reject it, and substitute the down glide which is normal to the new language. Three rules are useful in teaching the principles of English intonation:

1. When you ask a question without using a specific interrogative word such as *what* or *when,* use a rising inflection on the last word.

2. When you finish a thought, use a falling inflection on the last word.

3. For unfinished thoughts, as found in dependent clauses or unfinished commands or statements, use a rising inflection on the word before the pause.

It is difficult to hear inflection patterns unless some motor performance is used to identify and record them. Many systems have been devised for this purpose.

Phonograph recordings are invaluable for this part of the work, and the student should imitate the instructor through a wide range of inflection variations. Phonograph records can be used as models for inflection transcription, and after the technique has been mastered the student can be given his own record to analyze in similar fashion. When the student can hear, analyze, or record the inflections of others, and can read from transcriptions of inflections, he has progressed a long way toward the solution of his problem.

Sentence structure. Errors in sentence structure are usually eliminated through two methods. First, the grammar of both the old and new languages is studied intensively, and all instances of contrast are noted and discussed with the instructor. Other examples of each variant word order are collected. It often helps to practice the English word order in the foreign language, since this seems to vivify the experience. Secondly, the student collects and frequently reviews all phrases and sentences which he considers odd or idiomatic. After checking with the teacher, the student enters speech situations appropriate to the employment of the sentences concerned.

Thinking in English. Enabling the student to think in English may seem an almost hopeless task at times, but, after the preliminary steps have been mastered, penalties can be placed upon translation, and through such devices as oral reading and rapid speech the student actually manages to make the shift. At first, this training in English thinking should be given in very small doses and only under the guidance of the instructor, since much verbal and mental confusion can result from this type of speech conflict. If the thinking in English is carried out entirely in one situation, it tends to produce no such conflict, and later on a gradual spread to other situations occurs. Acquiring perfect English after one is an adult is no easy task, but with patience and intelligent direction it can be accomplished.

References

1. Angus, W., "The Turk's Characteristic Difficulties in Learning English Pronunciation," *Quarterly Journal of Speech*, 1937, Volume 23, pages 238–243.

An excellent illustration of the necessity of comparing the speech sounds of the former language with those of English in planning the treatment for foreign speech.

2. Barker, J. L., "Correcting the Mechanism Causing Most Foreign Brogue," *Journal of Speech Disorders*, 1936, Volume 1, pages 3–12.

Points out that breath interruptions, phrasing, intonation patterns, and other phenomena are very important in teaching the foreigner English.

3. Barker, J. L., "Dynamic Versus Static Phonetics," *Journal of Speech Disorders*, 1940, Volume 5, pages 153–183.

Phonetic placement is a poor method for teaching English speech sounds to French- or Italian-speaking peoples because the transitional movements and sounds are so different in these languages.

4. Clarey, M. E., and Dixson, R. J., *Pronunciation Exercises in English for the Foreign Born*, New York, Regents Publishing Co., 1947.

Drill material, word lists and sentences suitable for foreign speech.

5. Cohen, M., "Methods for Teaching *R* to the German Emigre," *Quarterly Journal of Speech*, 1945, Volume 31, pages 214–216.

The difficulties of untrilling the *R* sound are described and solved.

6. David, B. J., "Teaching Speech to Refugees," *Quarterly Journal of Speech*, 1943, Volume 29, pages 483–484.

Must not concentrate on English articulation, inflection, and intonation alone but on cultural patterns.

7. DeVargas, D., "Teaching 'Mexicans' an English Vocabulary," *Elementary English Review*, 1937, Volume 14, page 31.

A brief description of the reasons for failure in teaching children of Mexican background to speak English. Some suggestions to prevent this failure are cited.

8. Duncan, M. H., "Children with Foreign Accents," *Today's Health*, 1950, Volume 28, pages 28–29, 54–55.

T-F: English uses more unstressed vowels than any other language.

T-F: If a child learns English before the age of five he will have little foreign accent.

Essay: Why does foreign accent persist so strongly in the adult?

9. Fries, C. C., *Teaching and Learning English as a Foreign Language*, Ann Arbor, University of Michigan Press, 1945.

Essay: Score this sentence in terms of the code used by Fries to indicate stress and inflection.

10. Krantz, H. C., Winne, S. C., Lewis, H. M., and Kaapu, M. K., *We Speak: A Handbook for the Bilingual American*, Honolulu, University of Hawaii Press, 1952.

This is by far the best-organized and most comprehensive selection of material for improving the speech of individuals who can speak English but with seriously defective accent, poor syntax, grammar and pronunciation due to the influence of another language.

11. Lynn, K., "Bilingualism in the Southwest," *Quarterly Journal of Speech*, 1945, Volume 31, pages 175–180.

A good survey of the literature on speech for Spanish-speaking children. Articulation errors are analyzed in detail.

12. Mammem, E. W., and Sonkin, R., "A Study of Italian Accent," *Quarterly Journal of Speech*, 1936, Volume 22, pages 1–10.

The errors of Italians who speak English are analyzed and explained. Three characteristic patterns of intonation are also illustrated.

13. Mulder, R. L., "Speech for International Students," *Central States Speech Journal*, 1952, Volume 3, pages 21–27.

An excellent summary of teaching aims and devices for foreign college students. Training in listening, spontaneous selection of words and thinking in English are discussed.

14. Tireman, L. S., *Teaching Spanish Speaking Children*, Albuquerque, University of New Mexico Press, 1951.

T-F: This book is written primarily for the classroom teacher.

T-F: Three new English words a day is a good average.

Essay: What is Tireman's attitude toward vocabulary and pronunciation drill?

15. Twichell, D. Y., "Teaching Speech Improvement in Japan," *Journal of Speech and Hearing Disorders*, 1949, Volume 14, pages 196–201.

T-F: The phonetic alphabet is very useful with Japanese students.

T-F: The Japanese student was difficult to motivate in pronunciation.

Essay: What are the basic articulation errors in English as spoken by the Japanese?

16. Villareal, J. J., "Foreign Dialect," *Bulletin of the National Association of Secondary School Principals*, 1950, Volume 34, pages 66–68.

T-F: It is not possible even with practice to tell the foreign-born person's nationality by the errors he makes in speaking English.

T-F: By the time a child enters High School he should be speaking English without accent if he entered school in the first grade.

Essay: What does the author say about intermediate vowels?

17. Voelker, C. H., "The One Thousand Most Frequently Spoken Words," *Quarterly Journal of Speech*, 1942, Volume 28, pages 189–197.

From other studies, the author compiled a word list, including the 100 most frequently used words, which would be useful as a core vocabulary for foreign-speaking individuals.

12. Cerebral Palsy

⎍⎍⎍⎍⎍⎍⎍⎍⎍⎍⎍⎍⎍⎍⎍⎍⎍⎍⎍⎍⎍⎍⎍⎍

This disorder is important in speech correction, not because of its frequency, but because of the severity of the associated speech defects. The cerebral-palsied child may have defective articulation of the lalling variety, but he also may show pronounced abnormality in voice and fluency. Since the speech correctionist is almost certain to meet some of these individuals and must help them gain effective communication, we shall discuss their problem briefly.

Diagnosis of cerebral palsy is, of course, the province of the physician, but the speech correctionist often meets cases who have never had the benefit of medical diagnosis. To undertake a program of speech rehabilitation without medical examination is not only hazardous but directly violates one of the ethical principles of the American Speech Correction Association. Some of these unfortunate children, because of their drooling, unintelligible speech and uncouth coordinations, are generally regarded as feeble-minded and treated as such. According to research, only about 30 per cent of cerebral-palsied children are feeble-minded, and the other 70 per cent may range all the way upward to genius level. The ordinary intelligence tests, involving speech or coordination, do not adequately measure the spastic's mental ability.

The majority of cerebral-palsy cases are caused by injury to the brain at birth. The trauma may be due to extreme pressures on the skull, causing abnormal molding and cerebral damage. Strangulation by the cord or other causes of cyanosis or oxygen lack may produce destruction of brain tissue. Certain diseases with high fevers such as pneumonia or jaundice can also cause cerebral palsy. Many soldiers with gun-shot wounds in the head developed spastic or athetoid symptoms as well as aphasia.

Although the term *spastic paralysis* has come to be used as the popular designation for all types of cerebral-palsy cases, there seem to be four major varieties: the athetoids, the ataxic, the myasthenic, and the spastic. Usually more than one of these four symptom complexes are found in the same case. According to Phelps the athetoid and spastic varieties make up more than 80 per cent of all cases.

Spasticity itself has been defined as the paralysis due to simultaneous contraction of antagonistic or reciprocal muscle groups accompanied by a definite degree of hypertension or hypertonicity. It is due to a lesion or injury to the pyramidal nerve tracts. The muscles overcontract; they pull too hard and too suddenly. Slight stimuli will set off major contractions. The spastic who tries to move his little finger may jerk not only the hand, but the arm or trunk as well. The spastic may have a characteristic manner of walking—the typical "scissors gait." The hands may be clenched and curled up along the wrists in their extreme contraction, or the whole arm may be drawn upward and backward behind the neck. The spastic tends to contract his chest muscles, thus enlarging the thoracic cavity during the act of speaking (12) and compelling him to compress the abdomen excessively in order to force out some air. He thus may be said to inhale with the thorax at the same time that he exhales with the abdomen. Great tension is thereby produced, which reflects itself in muscular abnormality all over the body. It also shows up in speech in the form of unnatural pauses and gasping and weak or aphonic voice. Many of the "breaks" in the spastic's speech are due to this form of faulty breathing.

Since it is difficult for the spastic to make gradual and smooth movements, the speech is often explosive and blurting. Often the extreme tension which characterizes spasticity will produce contacts so hard as to resemble or engender stuttering symptoms. The sounds involving complex coordinations are of course most usually defective, and the tonguetip sounds which make contact with the upper gum ridge are most difficult. Where there is some facial paralysis, the labial sounds are much more difficult than might be expected. In cases where there are both symptoms of spasticity and athetosis, the articulation is prone to be more distorted than if spasticity alone is present. The diadochokinetic rate of tongue-lifting is a pretty good indication of the number of articulation errors to be found in any one case.

Cerebral-palsy cases are also classified in terms of how much of the body is affected. If one limb is spastic or athetoid, the term *monoplegia* is used; if half the body (right or left) is affected, the word *hemiplegia* designates the condition. *Diplegia* refers to involvement of both upper *or* both lower limbs; *quadriplegia* to spasticity or athetosis in all four limbs. According to Heltman and Peacher (14) the greatest number of articulatory errors are shown in quadriplegia involving combined athetosis and spasticity, and the fewest errors are evidenced in spastic diplegia.

By *athetosis* we refer to the cerebral-palsy cases with marked tremors. In these the injury is to the extrapyramidal nerve tracts. Athetosis may be described as a series of involuntary contractions which affect one muscle after another. These contractions may be fast or slow, large or small. The head may swing around from side to side. The arm may shake rhythmically. The jaw and facial muscles may show a rhythmic contortion or repetitive grimaces. In some athetoids, these movements disappear in sleep or under the influence of alcohol. There seem to be two major types of athetoids, the non-tension type and the tension athetoid, who is often mistaken for a true spastic. The tension athetoids are those who have tried to hold their trembling arms and legs still by using so much tension that it has become habitual. The latter may be distinguished from true spastics by moving their arms against their resistance. The tension-athetoid's arm tends to yield gradually; the spastic's releases with a jerk.

Athetoid speech often tends to become weak in volume. The final sounds of words and final words of phrases are often whispered. A marked tremulo is heard. Monotones are very common, and in the tension athetoids the habitual pitch is near the upper limit of the range. Falsetto voice qualities are not unusual. Another common voice quality is that of hoarseness, especially in the males. Like the true spastics, athetoids make many articulation errors, and the finer the coordinations involved in producing the sound, the more it is likely to be distorted. Tonguetip sounds are especially difficult. Breathing disturbances are common.

Intelligent cerebral-palsied individuals meet so many frustrations during their daily lives that they tend to build emotional handicaps as great as their physical disability. Fears develop about walking, talking, eating, going downstairs, carrying a tray, holding a pencil, and a hundred other daily activities. These often become so intense that they create more tensions and hence more spasticity or athetosis. Thus one girl so feared to lift a coffee cup to her lips that she could not do so without spilling and breaking it, yet she was able to etch delicate tracings on a copper dish.

Many of these children are so pampered and protected by their parents that they never have an opportunity to learn the skills required of them for social living. Their parents are constantly afraid that they will hurt themselves, but as one adult tension athetoid said, "My parents never let me try to ride a bicycle and now at last I've done it. Better to break your neck than your spirit." Many spastics come to a fatalistic attitude of passive acceptance of whatever blows, or kindness, or pity society may give them. Others put up a gallant battle and succeed in creating useful and satisfying lives for themselves.

Speech therapy. Very often the cerebral-palsied child is first presented as a case of delayed speech. These children often do not begin to talk until five or six, but many of them could learn earlier with proper parental teaching. In general, the same procedures used on other delayed-speech cases and in teaching the baby to talk are employed. Imitation must be taught. Sounds must come to have meaning and identity. Words must be taught in terms of their sound sequences and associations. Babbling games using puppets are especially effective in getting a young spastic child to talk. It is especially necessary that the child be praised for all vocalization, since he is likely to fall into a whispered or mere lip-moving type of speech. When possible, the first speech teaching should be done when the child is lying on his back in bed, since the thoracic muscles are not so likely to cause chest expansion as the abdomen is contracting during speech. Phonograph records with singing and speech games are very useful in stimulating these children.

In most cases of cerebral palsy the physiotherapist has done a great deal of work with the child before the speech correctionist is called in. Many of the activities used in physiotherapy can be made more interesting to the child if vocalization is used in conjunction with them. Thus one child whose very spastic left leg was being passively rotated in a whirlpool bath was taught to say "round and round; round and round" as the leg moved. He was unable to say these words at first under any other condition, but soon he had attained the ability to say them anywhere, and the distraction seemed to ease some of the spasticity. General relaxation of the whole body forms a large part of the treatment of the spastic and tension athetoid, and even these exercises may be combined with sighing or yawning on the various vowels. Relaxation of the articulatory or the throat muscles seems to be very difficult for these cases, and we often indirectly attain decreases in the tension of these structures by teaching the child to speak while chewing.

Rhythms of all kinds seem to provide especially favorable media for speech practice, if the rhythms are given at a speed which suits the particular case. In following these rhythms it is not wise to combine speech with muscular movements, because of the nature of the disability. Visual stimuli, such as the rhythmic swinging of a flashlight beam on a wall, are very effective in producing more fluent speech. Tonal stimuli of all kinds are also used. Many cerebral-palsied children can utter polysyllabic words in unison with a recurrent melody whether they sing them or not.

In general, the spastic's articulation disorder is of the lalling type. Most of the sounds that require lifting of the tonguetip are defective. When the *t*, *d*, and *n* sounds are adequate, it will be observed that they are dentalized. The tongue does not make contact with the upper gum ridge but with the back surface of the teeth. Several of these cases were able to acquire good *l* and *r* sounds without any direct teaching. Instead, we taught them to make the *t*, *d*, and *n* sounds against the upper gum ridge, and the tonguetip lifting carried over into the *l* and *r* sounds immediately.

In most of these cases, the essential task is to free the tongue from its tendency to move only in conjunction with the lower jaw. The old traditional tongue exercises have little value, but those that involve the emergence of a finer movement from a gross one (see the tongue exercises in Chapter 7) are very useful. Just as we have been able to teach spastics to pick up a pin by beginning with trunk, arm, and wrist movements, so we can finally teach him to move his tongue tip without closing his mouth.

Phonetic placement methods in the teaching of new sounds are seldom successful. The auditory stimulation and modification of known sounds are much better. Babbling practice has great value in making the new sounds habitual. We have found that it is wise to make a set of phonograph records for each case, which provides them with material appropriate to their level and with which they can speak in unison when alone.

The voice disorders that characterize the cerebral-palsy cases are best treated through relaxation and breathing exercises. In the latter, polygraphic recording of breathing is especially valuable. The child does not pay attention to his chest or abdomen as such but rather to the tracings that come from the polygraph pens. While counting or reciting from memory, he is told to try to produce tracings that resemble those on a chart in front of him. The model is of course a tracing of normal breathing during vocalization. Gradually he attains proficiency in this breath control, and the relief from tension and voice improvement is so marked that he carries the new breathing patterns into his other speech.

Many cerebral-palsy cases inhale much more deeply for speech than for silent breathing. They often exhale most of this air prior to speech attempt or in the utterance of the first syllable, and then strain from that time onward. This practice may often be overcome by asking them to say a few words and then blow out a candle on the same breath. Having the child speak into a tube with a small nozzle fastened to a stand in front of a flame will also help him to learn proper breathing habits without ever becoming too conscious of the muscular movements involved.

The breaks in fluency which are so characteristic of the spastic are often eliminated by this training in breathing. But it is usually wise to teach these children a type of phrasing which will not place too much demand upon them for sustained utterance. The pauses must be much more frequent than those of the normal individual, and they should be slightly longer. Thus the sentence: "Practice about thirty words involving the *s* blends according to the following models" might be spoken as a single unit by an adult normal speaker, but the adult cerebral-palsy case should pause for a new breath at least three of four times during its course. If he trains himself to do so, his fluency will improve; since no untimely gasps for breath will occur, his voice will be less likely to rise in pitch or to be strained, and the final sounds of the words will be better articulated. Spastics frequently omit the puff of their final plosives and use lax vowels and continuant consonants because they run out of breath so easily.

Fluency may be improved also by giving the child training in making smooth transitions between vowels or consecutive consonants. Thus, he is asked to practice shifting gradually rather than suddenly from a prolonged *u* to a prolonged *e* sound. At first, breaks are likely to occur, but they can be greatly improved through practice, and the child's general speech reflects the improvement. The plosives often cause breaks in rhythm because the contacts are made too hard and consequently set up tremors. We have had marked success in treating these errors with the same methods we use for the stutterer's hard contacts. In one case, who always "stuck" on his *p*, *t*, and *k* sounds and showed breaks in his speech, we were able to solve the problem by simply asking him "to keep his mouth in motion" whenever he said a word beginning with these sounds.

It is, of course, necessary to supplement this speech therapy with a great deal of psychotherapy, especially in adult cerebral-palsied individuals. They must be taught an objective attitude toward their disorder. They must whittle down the emotional fraction of their total handicap. They must increase their assets in every way. As fear and shame diminish, the tensions will decrease. In many cases, greater improvement in speech and muscular coordination will come from psychotherapy than from the speech therapy itself.

References

1. Bice, H., and Holder, M., "Group Counseling with Mothers of Children with Cerebral-Palsy," *Journal of Social Casework*, 1949, Volume 30, pages 104–107.

Groups of ten mothers of cerebral-palsied children met and discussed mutual problems. They found gains in information and emotional release.

2. Blum, L., Burgemeister, B., and Lorge, I., "Trends in Estimating the Mental Maturity of the Cerebral Palsied Child," *Journal of Exceptional Children*, 1951, Volume 17, pages 174–177.

These authors suggest the Ammons and Ammons Picture Vocabulary Test and several others as being more appropriate than those commonly used to estimate the intelligence of the cerebral palsied.

3. Carlson, E. R., *Born That Way*, New York, John Day, 1941.

T-F: The author believes that stimulation must be kept low if the cerebral palsied is not to show marked incoordination.

T-F: After coming out of an anesthetic all spasticity may be lost for a period of time.

Essay: What individuals were most important in the author's life and why?

4. Cass, M. T., *Speech Habilitation in Cerebral Palsy*, New York, Columbia University Press, 1951.

T-F: The author stresses relaxation as fundamental to all speech therapy.

T-F: The author advocates tying down the arms if their incoordinations interfere with speech therapy.

Essay: Give a brief summary of the book.

5. Cruickshank, W. M., "Implications of Psychological Studies of Cerebral Palsied Children," *Proceedings of the Second Cerebral Palsy Institute*, 1952, page 34.

Signs of aphasic disturbances found in majority of C.P. children. Perseveration, diassociation, and perception of form were impaired.

6. Fischel, M. K., "The Spastic Child," St. Louis, C. V. Mosby, 1934.

An excellent account of how parents can treat their spastic children. Many illustrations of good mental hygiene and speech and muscle therapy are given.

7. Fouracre, M. H., Jann, G. R., and Martorana, A., "Educational Abilities and Needs of Orthopedically Handicapped Children," *Elementary School Journal*, 1950, Volume 50, pages 331–339.

Sixty-four per cent of the cerebral palsied were below 90 in I.Q.

8. Froeschels, E., "A Contribution to the Pathology and Therapy of Dysarthria Due to Certain Cerebral Lesions," *Journal of Speech Disorders*, 1943, Volume 8, pages 301–320.

Summarizes observations of cerebral-palsied speech in terms of breathing, voice, and articulation. Treatment should not be phonetic but should consist of jaw-shaking, pushing, and chewing while speaking.

9. Gratke, J. M., *Help Them Help Themselves*, Dallas, Texas Society for Crippled Children, 1947.

T-F: Sign-language is recommended for cerebral-palsied children with very severe speech handicaps.

T-F: Do not massage spastic muscles to produce relaxation.

Essay: How did the author help her own son?

10. Hatcher, C. C., "Athetoids Relax and Speak," *Crippled Child*, 1949, Volume 27, pages 14–16.

T-F: Speech therapy is usually not needed by the athetoid.

T-F: Tongue exercises should be used in speech therapy for cerebral palsy.

Essay: What exercises for relaxation are given?

11. Huber, M., "Letter to the Parent of the Cerebral Palsied Child," *Journal of Speech and Hearing Disorders,* 1950, Volume 15, pages 154–158.

T-F: Speech therapy for the cerebral palsied should begin at birth.

T-F: Cerebral-palsied children need much training in listening.

Essay: What suggestions does the author make concerning personality development?

12. Hull, H. C., "A Study of the Respiration of Fourteen Spastic Paralysis Cases During Silence and Speech," *Journal of Speech Disorders,* 1940, Volume 5, pages 275–276.

Breathing is very disordered, and opposition between thorax and abdomen during speech is very common. Abdominal contraction is compensatory.

13. Palmer, M. F., "Speech Disorders in Cerebral Palsy," *Nervous Child,* 1949, Volume 8, pages 193–202.

Rather difficult reading but comprehensive.

14. Peacher, G. M., and Heltman, H. J., "Misarticulation and Diadochokinesis in the Spastic Paralytic," *Journal of Speech Disorders,* 1943, Volume 8, pages 137–145.

Recommends diadochokinetic training. Sonants are faster than surds. Many of the articulation errors may be due to the sluggishness of articulation.

15. Phelps, W. M., "Medical Aspects of Cerebral Palsy," *Proceedings of the Second Cerebral Palsy Institute,* 1952, pages 91–94.

Describes causes and makes the point that you cannot judge prognosis in terms of the evident severity of the symptoms.

16. Pohl, J. F., *Cerebral Palsy,* St. Paul, Bruce Publishing Co., 1950.

T-F: This book deals primarily with school-age children.

T-F: The cerebral dominancy of the cerebral-palsied should be determined.

Essay: According to the author, what are the major types of cerebral palsy?

17. Rutherford, B., *Give Them a Chance to Talk,* Minneapolis, Burgess Publishing Co., 1948.

T-F: The author stresses speech hygiene.

T-F: Breathing exercises are recommended by the author.

Essay: Describe how the author teaches phrasing.

18. Rutherford, B. R., "The Use of Negative Practice in Speech Therapy with Children Handicapped by Cerebral Palsy, Athetoid

Type," *Journal of Speech Disorders*, 1940, Volume 5, pages 259–264.

Many of the undesirable contortions of athetoids are habits and may be removed by therapy. Many examples are given.

19. Snidecor, J. C., "The Speech Correctionist on the Cerebral-Palsy Team," *Journal of Speech and Hearing Disorders*, 1948, Volume 13, pages 67–70.

T-F: The ataxic child needs more direct stimulation than the athetoid.

T-F: 94 per cent of the cerebral-palsied need speech therapy.

Essay: Outline the speech therapy for the cerebral-palsied child as presented by the author.

20. Strother, C., "Realistic Educational Goals for the Cerebral-Palsied Child," *Crippled Child*, 1953, Volume 30, pages 4–7.

The need to study the patterns of the child's abilities and disabilities before working out an educational program is stressed.

21. Westlake, H., "A System for Developing Speech with Cerebral-Palsied Children," *Crippled Child*, 1951, Volume 29, pages 20–21, 29.

T-F: It is wise to reward the involuntary movements related to speech.

T-F: Moto-kinesthetic stimulation is recommended by the author in teaching such a word as "mama."

Essay: Describe the "direct speech training" recommended by the author.

22. Westlake, H., "Muscle Training for Cerebral Palsied Speech Cases," *Journal of Speech and Hearing Disorders*, 1951, Volume 16, pages 103–109.

T-F: It is often wise to put the lower jaw in a head frame so its involuntary movements will not interfere with speech.

T-F: A "confusion motion" is an athetoid tremor.

Essay: What differences in muscle training should be used for the different types of cerebral palsy?

13.   Hearing Problems

பார்

Many children in the public schools suffer from some degree of hearing impairment and this loss is often not recognized by the teacher or the speech correctionist. Because incipient losses are difficult to detect, many teachers attribute behavior and scholastic problems to other causes, and the child is labeled as "withdrawn," "inattentive," or "low intelligence." The number of hard-of-hearing children of school age has been estimated at anywhere from 1,500,000 (15) to 3,000,000 (9). Johnson has estimated that approximately three out of every one hundred school children have hearing losses which are educationally significant and another five per cent have impairments that require medical attention, and may, to some degree, affect speech. He further states that about one per cent of school children require the services of a speech correctionist because of hearing losses (15).

Deaf and Hard-of-Hearing Children

There are two main groups of children with defective hearing: (1) the hard-of-hearing and (2) the deaf. The significant difference between the two groups lies in the area of communication. Hard-of-hearing children are able to understand and use speech and language. These children learn to communicate

503

using the sense of hearing, deficient though it may be. This is the group of children that most teachers and speech correctionists will meet in the public schools. However, there is a trend toward the placement of deaf children in the regular public school classroom. The deaf comprise the second major group of children. The deaf are those that have been deprived of the ability to communicate through speech and language because of the severity of the hearing loss (15). These are the children that must be taught speech.

There is also a differentiation made between the deaf and the deafened. This is made on the basis of the time the hearing loss occurred. The deaf are defined as those whose deafness occurred *before* speech and language were acquired; the deafened are those who became deaf *after* the acquisition of speech and language.

The type and degree of hearing loss the child possesses is of great importance when planning an adequate educational program. The speech therapy must be planned with this information at hand.

There are three types of deafness: (1) The conductive or receptive type of deafness, (2) the perceptive or nerve type, and (3) the mixed type deafness.

Conductive deafness is characterized by poor hearing in the low tones and good hearing in high tones by air conduction, or a uniform hearing loss of moderate proportions. A conductive loss is caused by a pathology of the external or middle ear. With a conductive loss, the auditory nerve is functioning, but the sound is not reaching the inner ear.

A nerve deafness, or perceptive deafness, is characterized by good hearing in the low tones and poor hearing in the high tones. Those suffering from a nerve loss often distort or omit the high frequency sounds, such as *s*. Nerve deafness is caused by a pathology of the inner ear, and as the name indicates, the nerve is not functioning adequately.

The mixed type deafness has elements of both conductive and nerve deafness. There is a loss in the low tones, plus a rather severe loss in the high tones. There is some degeneration of the nerve as well as some blockage of the sound by air in the external or middle ear.

All three types of deafness stem from two causes: (1) congenital deafness and (2) adventitious deafness.

Congenital deafness refers to deafness of a hereditary nature or one due to birth injury. Congenital deafness represents 61 per cent of all deafness.

Adventitious, or acquired, deafness is caused by brain infections, high fever diseases, infections of the ear, injuries to the ear, or otosclerosis. Thirty-nine per cent of all deafness is acquired.

As with many disabilities or deficiencies, prevention's ounce is worth far more than the most expert pound of cure. Discovering children with hearing losses is a prime factor in a hearing conservation program. Authorities in the hearing field recommend compulsory hearing tests once a year in all public schools (9). These tests, known as screening tests, are the only means by which many incipient hearing losses can be discovered. An adequate prevention program is always less costly than a rehabilitation program. Many, but not all, states now require that these screening tests be conducted each year.

Adequate and prompt medical care of hearing losses discovered through the screening process will help eliminate future hearing difficulties. New drugs and medicines developed since 1940 have helped the physician and the otologist to decrease the number and severity of middle ear infections. The once-feared mastoid operation is being performed less and less frequently. Eustachian tonsils, adenoids, and packed wax are just some of the causes of conductive deafness which yield promptly to medical attention.

A comprehensive program of prevention and conservation will still further decrease the number of children requiring the services of speech correctionists. It is to be hoped that fewer and fewer children need go through life with "cotton in their ears." At the present time, however, three per cent or more school children with severe hearing problems now need speech correction, as well as training in listening, instruction in the use of hearing aids, lip-reading (speech reading), and additional instruction in reading and writing (15).

Hearing Tests

All children who exhibit some hearing loss are often called "deaf." When the term "deaf" is thus generalized, it is easy to forget that deafness is a matter of degree. There are several methods by which the degree of deafness may be determined.

A *screening* test is usually the first step in attempting to discover whether or not a child's hearing is normal. In order of increasing reliability, the screening test might be: (1) a watch tick test, (2) a voice test, both whispered speech and conversational speech, (3) a phonograph test, (4) an audiometric sweep test. The screening test is followed by a diagnostic test, if there is a hearing loss evident.

The *diagnostic* test may be any one of several tuning fork tests, as administered by an otologist, or a pure tone audiometric test as performed by a hearing therapist. The audiometric evaluation of the child's hearing, as shown by the audiogram, is of great assistance to the speech correctionist as well as the otologist. The audiogram will show the hearing curve, and will illustrate the kind and degree of hearing loss.

It has been recognized that the audiogram reveals only the child's responses to pure tones, and that his functional hearing may differ to some degree from that shown on the chart. In recent years, speech reception tests have been introduced to test the functional hearing, i.e., the hearing for speech. These tests are known as Speech Reception Threshold Tests (SRT), and are designed to determine the lowest intensity at which 50 per cent of the material is heard. There are also articulation tests which attempt to determine the per cent of words heard and understood (intelligibility) at a given intensity.

After a screening test has revealed a hearing deficiency, the child will be given a pure-tone audiometric examination. The *audiometer* is an instrument designed to determine the threshold of hearing at various frequencies and various intensities. The *audiogram* is the chart upon which the child's responses are recorded.

All sound, from any source, has two fundamental characteristics: frequency and intensity. All studies of hearing are based on these two characteristics (19). Frequency refers to pitch levels, and intensity to degrees of loudness.

A simple comparison may be made between the audiometer and an extended piano keyboard. The frequencies, or number of vibrations or sound waves per second which reach a given point, correspond with the keys of our imaginary piano. The piano key, when struck, is heard at a certain pitch or frequency. The key may be struck softly or loudly, and this is known as intensity, or the strength of the vibrations.

On the audiogram (p. 508), the frequencies are shown horizontally on the bottom of the chart (128, 256, 512, 1024, 2048, 2896, etc.). The intensity, shown vertically, is in decibels (0, 10, 20, 30, 40, etc.). The decibel is often defined as the amount of power necessary to give awareness of difference. A change of the power level of a sound by one decibel is approximately the smallest the ear can detect (6).

As can be seen on the audiogram, 0 decibels is considered to be the normal threshold of hearing. This is the lowest, or faintest level at which the normal ear can just perceive the various tones throughout the frequency range. The other limit of normal hearing is the upper level at which sound becomes so loud that it is felt as a tickling sensation or as pain rather than heard. In the 3,000 cycle range where the ear is most sensitive, the upper threshold is approximately 120 db above the threshold of hearing (19). For those with normal hearing, ordinary conversational speech is heard at approximately 50–60 decibels.

If we were to chart individual hearing curves on the audiogram, those curves falling between 0–15 db would reflect normal hearing; between 15–35 db a slight hearing loss; between

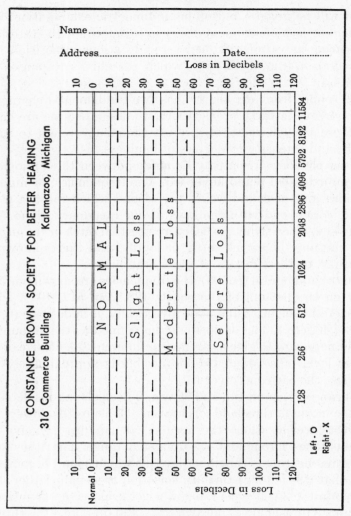

Fig. 15. An example of an audiogram.

35–55 db a moderate loss, and below 55 db a severe hearing loss.

The type of hearing loss can be determined by the hearing curve as seen on the audiogram. A conductive type loss is shown by a curve as follows: a slight or moderate loss in the low tones and normal responses in the high tones; *or* a slight or moderate loss, not to exceed 50 db, in both low and high tones. A nerve type loss is shown by this kind of curve: normal hearing in low tones and dipping down below 50 db in the high tones. The mixed type loss is shown by a slight or moderate loss in the low tones (above 50 db) and dipping down below 50 db in the high tones. As can be seen, 50 db has been arbitrarily defined as the point of differentiation between conductive and nerve type losses.

Using the above formula, the type of hearing loss can be determined from the audiogram. The audiogram will also reveal the degree of loss for the various tones, or frequencies. However, the audiogram tells only half the story. It determines the individual's ability to hear pure tones only. Speech Reception Threshold Tests are needed to determine the individual's functional hearing.

Halowell Davis (2) discusses and gives examples of many of the speech reception tests, including the Spondee, the PB (Phonetically Balanced) Word Lists, and the Continuous Discourse Test. The Spondee Test consists of 42 words, each with two syllables of equal accent, and is used to determine threshold of hearing for speech. The PB Word Lists each contain 50 words, such as "are, bad, bar," and it is an articulation test. The PB Word Lists can be used to help the speech therapist discover which sounds the child hears, and which sounds he misses at various levels of intensity. The Continuous Discourse Test is a threshold test for hearing of continuous speech, and is sometimes referred to as CRI (Cold Running Intelligibility).

The speech correctionist is primarily interested in helping the hard-of-hearing child use and conserve his present hearing to best advantage and to restore any speech sounds which may have been lost. In order to do this, the correctionist must be aware of the power and placement of each sound element on the frequency range. Each speech sound has a different phonetic power. It can easily be seen that those sounds having the most power are the ones which are heard more readily. In a descending scale of power from those sounds which are most powerful to those sounds which are least powerful, they are: (1) pure vowels, (2) semi-vowels, (3) unvoiced fricatives, *sh* and *ch*, (4) stop and fricative consonants, and (5) the least powerful, the unvoiced *th* (ɵ). Fletcher (6) has also charted the relative distribution of speech power into frequency bands. We hear speech sounds at various frequencies, or pitch, and one sound may be heard at more than one frequency. While the speech range is generally considered to be from 500 to 4,000 cycles (512, 1024, and 2048 on the audiogram), speech sounds are actually heard between 200 and 6,400 cycles. For example, the unvoiced *th* (ɵ) and the *s* are very high-frequency sounds. They also have very little power. Therefore, many hard-of-hearing adults and children omit the *s* sound entirely or develop a lateral lisp.

The rapid development and improvement of hearing aids has helped to restore many hard-of-hearing adults to social adequacy, and has aided hard-of-hearing children in the development of adequate speech and language. The latest development, the transistor hearing aid, uses germanium instead of carbon. The transistor is still in the experimental stage but appears to be of great value because of its potentially unlimited power, and because the operating cost is considerably lower than for other types of hearing aids.

A hearing aid is usually recommended when the hearing loss exceeds 30 or 35 decibels. In the twilight area between 15–35 db, lip-reading instruction is recommended for those individuals with a slight loss in this intensity range. When the loss is between 35 and 75 db, a hearing aid is recommended. It is suggested that lip-reading and auditory training be given for those with a loss in this range. If the loss exceeds 75 db, lip-reading is a vital necessity since a hearing aid may be almost useless. Hearing aids are used with those adults who are severely hard-of-hearing to help them monitor their own voices. Hearing aids are also used with severely hard-of-hearing or deaf children if it is felt there will be (1) an improvement in speech and voice,

(2) improvement in hearing, or (3) an improvement in psychological values. Even if only environmental noises can be heard on the hearing aid, this may relieve the child's feeling of isolation.

Lip-reading, or speech reading as it is now known, is recommended for anyone with a hearing loss. For those with rather mild, or very severe losses, it is the only tool which fits the requirements of their loss. For those who have moderate losses, it is an adjunct to the hearing aid.

When the *element* approach to speech reading is used, there is great similarity between it and the ear-training techniques as described in the chapter on the treatment of articulatory disorders. A more visual approach is substituted, but the emphasis remains upon the individual sounds. The sound element is isolated, recognized, and identified both by hearing and by sight. Recognition of the sound is obtained also through the use of nonsense material. The child learns to recognize "puh" on the lips of the teacher, and then the sound is varied to include "poo," "pai," "po," etc. The sound is next used in a clue word, such as "put." The clue word is used in many varying contexts, such as "Put the book on the table," "Put on your coat" and "Put away your pencil." Other clue words are then established, and these words are used in topical material, continuous discourse, and situational speech. Thus, speech reading, as a skill, is developed. It enables a person, regardless of whether or not he possesses normal or impaired hearing, to understand speech by attentively observing the speaker (2). It has come to mean more than merely watching another's lips. It now involves "reading" their expressions, movements, and actions, as well as their lips.

Auditory training with *hard-of-hearing* children has as its purpose the increase in intelligibility of speech and functional hearing. Auditory training with *deaf* children is referred to as acoustic, or auricular training, since the deaf cannot hear speech, with or without an instrument. Acoustic or auricular training has as its purpose, the improvement of the speech of the deaf and the stimulation of the sense of hearing to the degree where the child may recognize pitch, rhythm, inflection, phrasing, and accent.

A short summary of a hearing conservation program might be as follows:

1. Screening test of some kind.
2. Repetition of the screening test when children are the subjects. (This helps to eliminate normal-hearing children who were frightened or confused by the first test.)
3. Individual pure-tone audiometric test.
4. Referral to a clinic to be seen by an otologist.
5. Medical care.
6. Special educational recommendations (includes preferred placement, individual hearing aid, speech reading, auditory training or acoustic training).

Characteristics of Deaf and Hard-of-Hearing Children

As with other physical disabilities, the teacher is likely to wonder if the hard-of-hearing or deaf child in her room is "normal," outside of the known auditory deficiency. The child may exhibit abnormal voice quality, a language deficiency, faulty speech, and a seeming inability to understand, and so it is no wonder that the teacher asks herself if this child has normal intelligence.

When all children with auditory defects are grouped together, a recent study (14) reports that these children fall within the average limits of intelligence when standardized tests are used. Another study (13) found that deaf children, as a distinct group, have an intelligence quotient of 90. Because of the language and speech difficulties, intelligence is more concrete than abstract with the deaf and severely hard-of-hearing. Attempts are being made to develop intelligence tests for deaf children, since tests for normal-hearing children are often tests of abstract intelligence and are based upon language.

The hard-of-hearing children as a group show only a slight educational retardation. It has been pointed out that when hard-of-hearing children are equated with hearing children for intelligence, this slight difference disappears. On the other hand, all surveys conducted on the achievement of deaf children show a severe educational retardation of from three to four years. The resultant educational quotient for the deaf is 70 (15).

There is a wide range of opinions on the degree of personality and social maladjustment attributable to deafness. The current trend is to place even severely hard-of-hearing and deaf children in regular classrooms, or at least in day schools for the deaf. It is thought that the children who attend public day school show less maladjustment than those who are in residential schools for the deaf.

Fiedler (6) feels that the problems of acoustically handicapped children are no different from the problems of hearing children. She states that most problems stem from parent-child relationships, and that there is no direct relationship between the loss of hearing and the development of childhood problems. It is conceded that social or personality problems may be often exaggerated or accentuated by the hearing handicap. However, it is contended that the basic educational needs of deaf and hard-of-hearing children are identical with the needs of all children, hearing or not. These basic needs can best be met for all children in much the same ways in a modern, "child-centered" school.

From this viewpoint, speech is looked upon as a means to aid socialization, not an end in itself. It is pointed out that the profoundly deaf child will never have normal speech. This barrier to communication creates a "built-in" locus of frustration.

Parents of a severely hard-of-hearing or deaf child must become reconciled to the limitation the disability imposes as far as speech is concerned. The child can be taught speech and language but it may never approach the normal speech of hearing children.

Parental reaction to having a physically handicapped child is often one of resentment and guilt. The parents may feel socially stigmatized for having produced a defective child. Rejection or over-protection of the child may result. Both of these reactions delay or damage the child's development. Just as rejection or over-protection create problems in normal hearing children, hard-of-hearing or deaf children have these problems further exaggerated or accentuated by the hearing handicap (21).

The acoustically handicapped child is usually deprived more frequently than normal children of the very important adjustive function of play. The parents fear for the child's safety and try to protect him by isolating him. Levine (12) points out that when sensible adjustment to a child's deafness is made by the parents, the child will react much more normally. However, when the parents are suffering panic reactions themselves, the child's world is further distorted and his precarious balance in it is threatened.

Speech and language come slowly to the deaf child because of the hearing handicap. The slow process of acquiring language through substitute channels means a great retardation in education. The child is dependent upon his teachers for the very wherewithal of the thinking-language process. Deafness imposes a barrier to comprehension. When comprehension is lacking, the appropriate emotional response may be blocked. Emotional development of the deaf child will be affected by this barrier to comprehension. Not until he has a command of language will he have the key to intellectual comprehension (12).

It is not surprising, therefore, to learn that the hard-of-hearing child may feel under constant emotional tension as well. The barrier to comprehension exists for him, even though in a smaller degree. The child with a hearing loss is cast in an indefinite role. He is never able to determine in advance whether or not he will be adequate in any situation. In some situations, where normal hearing is not required, he may function quite adequately. In other situations, he may fail because he has not heard enough, or at all. Since his defect is not obvious, others may misunderstand his speech or actions and think him stupid. The child himself is fearful of misunderstanding and often appears insecure and fearful of making a mistake.

Normal-hearing children are ordinarily equipped with the three fundamentals for learning to talk: (1) The ability to hear and (2) to compare their own word-patterns with those spoken by others, and finally (3) the ability to call the organs of speech into action at the right psychological moment (3). It is obvious that the hard-of-hearing or deaf child is deficient in at least the first two of these three fundamentals. Impaired hearing affects the intelligibility of speech, in that words become proportionately more difficult to understand as the degree of deafness increases.

The hard-of-hearing child inevitably misses, sometimes or always, the sound of certain consonants. The sounds he will miss will depend on the range and degree of the hearing loss. The hard-of-hearing child will imitate the words, or parts of words, that he hears most often and most completely (4). In contrast to this, the deaf or severely hard-of-hearing child has no pattern of language. His world is one of silence or at best, very muted sounds. He cannot express himself through language; he has no words or verbal ideas (18). The John Tracy Clinic, an outstanding clinic for deaf children and their mothers, advocates speech-reading leading to spontaneous speech. After speech has developed, correction of the defective sounds is accomplished through the element approach. The speech correctionist, when adequately trained, can play an important role in bringing speech to the deaf child. She can also be of great assistance to the hard-of-hearing child by helping him to correct his defective articulation, his voice quality, and speech rhythm.

We have been discussing hard-of-hearing and deaf children in whom the auditory defect was known to exist. There are many children in our schools with undetected hearing losses. The teacher and speech correctionist need to know some of the characteristic symptoms of a hearing loss, so that they may help identify those children. These characteristic marks of a hearing loss are (1) verbal direction ignored consistently, (2) close observation of the face of the teacher, (3) consistently turning the head to one side when paying attention to the teacher or another student, (4) apparent and repeated confusions in understanding the speech of others, (5) reading disability, (6) spelling errors, (7) frequent colds with ear discharge, (8) spells of dizziness or head noises. Severe illnesses with high fever may bring about a hearing loss, and the child should be watched upon his return to school for any of the characteristic symptoms, or any sudden change in attitude or behavior. Excessive fatigue during class recitation may indicate that the child is straining to listen and understand. When yearly hearing tests become standard procedure in all schools, the teacher will then be able to recognize and deal with hard-of-hearing children with a much higher degree of success.

Helping the Acoustically Defective Child in School

The classroom teacher and the speech correctionist have a dual role to fill in teaching the hard-of-hearing or deaf child. First, they may be able to help the child make an adequate social adjustment with his classmates. Secondly, they may be able to help the child improve his speech. Both aspects are necessary if the child is to advance educationally and personally.

There are many things that can be done which do not require the expert knowledge of a teacher of the deaf. In helping the hard-of-hearing or deaf child become a part of the group, one must remember that the child himself wants nothing more than to be accepted and to be a part of the group. This may be more important to him than the approbation of the teacher, particularly in the later grades. He will be a figure set apart if he is not subject to the same type of discipline and awarded the same opportunities as the other members of the class. The teacher may adapt and vary the work for him, but she must not over-protect him. If the other children are reciting, she can call upon the hard-of-hearing child for an answer, too. Even giving him a chance to answer a question that requires but a single word will help offset the feeling that he is different, or is being ignored.

If the child wears a hearing aid, he should be given an opportunity to display it as a prized possession to the rest of the class. All children are interested in learning how we hear, and the hard-of-hearing child can demonstrate how his aid works. The teacher can help by explaining its similarity to a telephone. This can be integrated with a unit on communication, or with a unit on health. It is important for all children to know how to take care of their ears.

An interesting experiment might be conducted to show the class how it feels to have a hearing loss. Have the children cover their ears tightly with their hands, and then give them a series of directions in a whisper. These directions might be, "Clap your hands," "Bow your head," "Put up your left hand," and so forth. Another experiment might revolve around playing various children's records at the lowest possible volume, while the children attempt to guess what they are hearing. A third activity would be to have each child listen to the tick of a pocket watch as he moves away from the source of the sound. He is to stop when he can no longer hear the ticking, and a chalk mark is made at that point. This game should enable the children to realize that even among normal hearing individuals, there may be a rather wide range of hearing.

Another classroom activity involves the use of lip-reading. Lip-reading may be correlated with work in phonics by having the children watch the teacher's lips as she forms the sounds silently. Then the children imitate the teacher by forming the sounds with their own lips. Guessing games, such as "What sound do you see now?" can be played. This kind of work helps normal-hearing children become more conscious of sound placement and teaches them to watch closely for visual cues. All kinds of activities can be devised to supplement this kind of lip-reading. The teacher may call roll by silently forming each child's name. The child, upon recognition of his name, raises his hand. Teachers, when first attempting this, are amazed to find that the children become very quiet, each watching intently for his name to appear on the teacher's lips.

Reading, as a means of acquiring information and as a recreational device, is so important to the hard-of-hearing or deaf child that it must be regarded as one of the most important abilities to be gained in school. Oral reading periods should not become "speech" periods as well. When the deaf or hard-of-hearing child is reading for content, he should not have the additional burden of correct enunciation or adequate voice quality to contend with. There are many other periods during the day when speech can be stressed.

In helping the deaf or severely hard-of-hearing child with his speech, the aim is to concentrate on speech *intelligibility*, not on normal speech. With children who have a slight or moderate loss, correction of articulation may be all that is necessary.

The development of individual and group hearing aids has introduced the use of music as a means of building up tolerance for sound. It is also stressed that the repeated hearing of changing pitch, as in recorded nursery and children's song records, will have an effect on the inflection of the child's speaking voice if training is begun early enough (20). A deaf child's voice quality often deteriorates as he grows older, and thus the speech teacher must develop a good phonetic ear to detect incipient voice defects before they become too pronounced (8). While much stress has been laid on voice quality, this author feels that more importance should be attached to corrective work on consonants, vowels, and rhythm. The aim should be toward speech that will enable the person to communicate adequately. It is more important that the deaf person be able to answer and ask questions so that they can be understood than it is for him to develop better voice quality.

Many deaf and hard-of-hearing children speak unintelligibly

because they are trying to imitate verbally what they see in print or what they see on the lips of others. Our language is so unphonetic that even normal-hearing people are often confused. In some instances, the written symbol may represent as many as four different sounds, so it is no wonder that the deaf have difficulty interpreting written words into sound. Acquiring a speaking vocabulary equal to that of the normal hearing child is an almost impossible task for the average deaf child.

Fortunately such an attempt is no longer necessary. It is now possible for the deaf to learn to use a limited vocabulary that will enable them to communicate with no loss of meaning. This system of condensed language is known as Basic English. It consists fundamentally of 850 words with which it is possible to express oneself adequately in the English language. It is the best device we have yet encountered for giving deaf adults communicable speech with a minimum of polysyllabic words. It may serve as a guide in teaching deaf children as well. C. K. Ogden and I. A. Richards have written a number of books that can serve as teaching aids. These include a dictionary that defines about 20,000 words in terms that the average deaf adult can readily understand. The advantages of Basic English for the deaf are: (1) it is a means of giving them adequate verbal communication with a minimum of confusing terms and definitions; (2) it contains only a few words of more than three syllables; (3) once the student has mastered the 850 words he can talk anywhere, anytime, and has no further absolute need to increase his vocabulary; (4) language concepts are acquired along with speech; (5) only a few basic rules need to be learned and these take care of the great majority of changes and exceptions.

Our language presents other difficulties for the hard-of-hearing and deaf who must gain much of their understanding through lip-reading. Many words are homophonous, that is, they look alike on the lips. Such words as "mama," "papa," and "baby" look very much alike. Cognate sounds such as *s* and *z*, *f* and *v*, *p* and *b*, are differentiated only through the use of hearing, rather than the use of sight. There is quite a bit of difference between "I'd like to pat you on the head," and "I'd like to bat you on the head." It is well that the hard-of-hearing person who must decipher this statement can note the speaker's stance and expression, as well as read his lips.

Many speech correctionists have had training in teaching speech and speech reading to the deaf and hard-of-hearing as part of their curriculum. The speech correctionist, in her daily contacts with other teachers, can often suggest procedures which will help the acoustically handicapped children. She can suggest "preferred placement," that is, seating in the classroom which will help the hard-of-hearing child use his available hearing to the best advantage. The speech correctionist can also suggest that if the child does not understand the teacher's directions, these directions be repeated in a different form. If the directions are said again in exactly the same way but in a louder and louder tone, the child may become more and more confused. Both the teacher and the child feel inadequate. When the child does not understand the first time, change the phrasing of the sentence. Often, the same material said differently is immediately grasped (17).

The teacher or speech correctionist need not exaggerate her lip movements. In fact, this is likely to make her lips more difficult to read. She need only speak distinctly and in a moderate tone. It will help the hard-of-hearing child if the light is on the teacher's face. It is suggested that there be approximately a four foot distance between the teacher and the student, and that her face be on a level with that of the child (11). In the teaching of speech reading, words are taught in complete sentence, since the child must learn to recognize words in context. The teacher does not move her head or hands while speaking since movement might distract the child's attention. Bright objects, such as pins or scarves near the teacher's face, may also prove to be distracting during a lip-reading lesson.

Gestures may and should be used in helping the hard-of-hearing or deaf child understand. While using speech rather

than gestures is stressed by many teachers, there are times
when it is more important that the child understand the teacher
and can show that he understands than that he struggle hopelessly with a language structure he has not conquered. The use
of pantomime in place of speech by the acoustically defective
child is usually discouraged, although it persists despite all
restrictions. Since this is so, pantomime should be used as a
basis for developing speech and language. After the child has
acted out a sequence of events, go through the sequence with
him, giving him appropriate clue words for each event. Finally,
have him use speech, with as few gestures as possible, to re-
describe the sequence.

The *element* approach to speech, as used by teachers of the
deaf, is very similar to the ear-training approach used in correcting the speech of normal-hearing children. With the deaf
and hard-of-hearing, the teacher first works for spontaneous
speech. It is only after this is developed to some extent that
speech correction is used. Speech is learned in meaningful
wholes in work and play situations, rather than through im-
posed drill of meaningless isolated sounds (5).

After speech and language have developed, then correction
of isolated sounds can take place. With the child who has a
mild or rather moderate hearing loss and wears a hearing aid,
the ear-training approach may be successfully used since the
child is able to hear the sounds in a rather normal fashion.
With the more severe losses or complete deafness, much of the
actual ear-training must be replaced by a kinesthetic and visual
approach. Sight and touch must replace hearing as the avenue
for learning correct speech sounds. If the child is able to hear
the sound at all, it will be so distorted as to require much effort as regards correct phonetic placement. Speech is usually
taught beginning with the four basic movements of lip-reading:
(1) forward movement of the lips, $\overline{oo}$, (2) backward movement
of the lips, $\bar{e}$, (3) downward movement of the jaw, *ah*, and
(4) upward movement of the jaw. When attempting to teach
nasalized sounds (*m, n, ng*) the finger is placed aside the nose

so that the vibration may be felt. At other times, the child's hand is placed on the teacher's face so that the movement and vibration of the various sounds may be felt. The child watches the teacher and feels the movement and then places his hand on his own face and throat and attempts to imitate what he sees and feels. One of the problems often encountered with deaf and severely hard-of-hearing children is that they will attempt to speak without using any voice. The lip, tongue, and jaw movements which are visible to them will be produced by them, but no sound will be used. A variety of devices must be used to remind them that speech has voice as well as movement.

The teacher and speech correctionist can help the parents of the acoustically handicapped child by passing along various types of information to them. Often the parents of deaf children do not know that the child can be trained in language understanding and speech. This training must be begun very early, and much time can be lost if the parents do not know the proper sources from which help may be obtained. The parents themselves can be educated in the guidance of their children, either by going to specific centers or through correspondence (10).

The John Tracy Clinic in California helps parents by sending correspondence lessons to the mothers of deaf children throughout the country. Competent physicians can be located through the Volta Bureau, Washington, D. C., or through local medical associations. There are usually societies for the hard-of-hearing within reach which may be contacted for other help. These societies can usually suggest the name and address of the nearest clinic for deaf and hard-of-hearing children. The various states have associations for better hearing which are able to offer information and service.

The speech correctionist and regular classroom teacher may find these pamphlets helpful:

1. Tracy, Louise Treadwell, et al., *If You Have a Deaf Child.* Published by the Illinois Annual School for Mothers of Deaf Children, University of Illinois Press, Urbana, Illinois, 1949.
This pamphlet may be obtained from the Division of Education

for Exceptional Children, Office of the Superintendent of Public Instruction, 401 Centennial Building, Springfield, Illinois, or from the Division of Services for Crippled Children, 1105 South 6th Street, Springfield, Illinois.

2. Whitehurst, Mary Wood, *Auditory Training for Children*. Published by Hearing Rehabilitation Center, 645 Madison Avenue, New York 21, New York, 1949.

3. Leavis, Mary Hadnutt, *Beginning Lip Reading*. Published by Mary Hadnutt Leavis, 386 Commonwealth Avenue, Boston 15, Massachusetts.

References

1. American Society for the Hard of Hearing, New Aid and Material for Teaching Lip-Reading, Washington (1537 35th Street NW), 1943, pages 1–169.

A pamphlet which provides grade teachers and trained lip-reading teachers with organized material which has been mathematically tested for lip-readability.

2. Best, Harry, *Deafness and the Deaf in the United States*, New York, Macmillan Company, 1943, pages vii–675.

An encyclopedic book on the deaf which covers the areas of prevention, general condition of the deaf, organizations for the deaf, education, and conclusions.

3. Davis, Halowell, *Hearing and Deafness*, New York, Murray Hill Books, Inc., 1947, pages 474–476.

A standard text concerning hearing problems.

4. Ewing, Irene R., and Ewing, Alex W. G., *The Handicap of Deafness*, New York, Longmans, Green and Company, 1946, Limited American Edition, pages v–327.

A general introduction into the field with special emphasis on "hearing-lip-reading" method.

5. Ewing, Irene R., and Ewing, Alex W. G., *Opportunity and the Deaf Child*, London: University of London Press, Ltd., 1947, pages v–252.

This text concerns itself primarily with deaf children of five years of age and under. It includes a chapter on lip-reading, and on reading and speech in the nursery school.

6. Fiedler, Miriam F., *Deaf Children in a Hearing World*, New York, Ronald Press, 1952, pages 3–320.

This recent book recounts an experimental program conducted at Vassar. It stresses the importance and possibility of including deaf and hard-of-hearing children in schools and programs planned for normal boys and girls.

7. Fletcher, Harvey, *Speech and Hearing*, New York, D. Van Nostrand Company, 1929, pages v–331.

Acoustical Research Director for Bell Telephone Laboratories discusses the perception of speech and music, and the interrelationship between speech, music, and noise.

8. Goldstein, Max A., *Problems of the Deaf*, St. Louis, The Laryngoscope Press, 1933, pages viii–580.

One of the older texts by the former Director of the Central Institute for the Deaf, St. Louis.

9. Haycock, G. Sibley, *The Teaching of Speech*, Washington, D. C., The Volta Bureau, 1942, pages 1–302.

Technical discussion of the principles of connected speech and their application to deaf speakers. Originally issued by the National College of Teachers of the Deaf, London, England.

10. Kessler, Henry H., *Rehabilitation of the Physically Handicapped*, New York, Columbia University Press, 1947, pages viii–274.

This is concerned with a generalized discussion of the problems of the physically handicapped and the principles and practices of rehabilitation.

11. Lassman, Grace Harris, *Language for the Pre-School Deaf Child*, New York, Grune and Stratton, pages vii–263.

Fundamentals of language and speech training, and activities for language development in the nursery school.

12. Leavis, Mary Hadnutt, *Beginning Lip Reading*, Boston, Leavis (386 Commonwealth Avenue), pages 1–53.

A series of lessons and exercises worked out for teachers of the first three grades of public school.

13. Levine, Edna S., "The Deaf," *Psychological Aspects of Physical Disability*, Office of Vocational Rehabilitation, Rehabilitation Service Series No. 211, pages 125–145.

14. McAndrew, Helton, "Rigidity in the Deaf and Blind," *Journal of Social Issues*, Volume IV, Number 4, Fall, 1948, pages 72–77.

15. Myklebust, H., "Clinical Psychology and Children with Impaired Hearing," *Volta Review*, L (February, 1948), page 55.

16. National Society for the Study of Education, *49th Yearbook, Part II—The Education of Exceptional Children*. Chicago, National Society for the Study of Education (5835 Kimball Avenue), pages v–350.

This paper-bound book covers the general concepts and problems underlying special education and discusses the nature and needs of specific handicapped groups.

17. Schachtel, Irving I., *Conserving Our Children's Hearing, Part 1*, Sonotone Corporation, 1948, pages 1–52.

Pamphlet for parents and teachers of children with impaired hearing.

18. Tracy, Louise Treadwell, et al., *If You Have a Deaf Child* (Published for Illinois Annual School for Mothers of Deaf Children), Urbana, University of Illinois Press, 1949, pages 1–134.

19. Watson, Leland A., and Tolan, Thomas, *Hearing Tests and Hearing Measurements*, Baltimore, Waverly Press, 1949, pages v–597.

Text covering interpretation of audiometric data, technical and social aspects of audiometry, hearing aids and advanced audiometry.

20. Whitehurst, Mary Wood, *Auditory Training for Children*, New York, Hearing Rehabilitation Center (645 Madison Avenue), 1949, pages 1–90.

A manual emphasizing graded speech activities with the deaf child. It is an excellent reference for specific suggestions for construction of visual aids to be used with auditory training as well as singing and rhythmic activities.

21. Barker, Roger R., Wright, Beatrice A., and Gonick, Mollie R., *Adjustment to Physical Handicap and Illness, A Survey of the Social Psychology of Physique and Disability* (Bulletin 55, Revised), New York, Social Science Research Council (230 Park Avenue) 1953, pages v–440.

14. The Speech Therapist

This chapter is designed to deal with the nature of speech-correction work and the demands it makes upon those who do it, be they parents, classroom teachers, speech-correction teachers, or members of a speech-clinic staff. Speech correction is re-education, not merely removal of the defect.

Qualifications of the professional speech correctionist. Not only is personality built about differences in speech, but also profound emotional reaction patterns are often associated with these differences. Then, too, re-education frequently demands much of a child in the way of courage, persistence, and applied intelligence. All of these characteristics of the speech-correction situation make certain demands upon the speech correctionist in terms of professional attitudes, academic preparation, personal qualifications, and skill in handling other people.

Speech correction, if it has not as yet attained a professional status, is so steadily achieving one that it behooves all workers in the field to conduct themselves according to a strict code of ethics, to join the American Speech Correction Association, and to keep abreast of the research which is contributing greatly to our knowledge of causes and techniques. The speech correctionist must recognize the delimitation of his field from that of the physician, the psychiatrist, and the orthodontist. He must be prepared to prove his worthiness of their respect and to seek their services whenever necessary.

Principles of professional conduct. Certain principles of professional conduct should be stated. They are: (1) Treat each case as a unique individual, seeking every possible opportunity to increase your knowledge and understanding of him as a person. (2) Refuse to respond emotionally to the speech defective's behavior. Treatment must always be intelligent and purposive. (3) Respect and guard carefully all confidential information. The patient must have perfect confidence in the speech correctionist's intellectual honesty. (4) Draw the line against undue familiarity. Avoid physical contact with the patient. Do not confide in him. Do not show surprise, disapproval, mirth, or annoyance unless you use the expressions for a definite clinical purpose. Refuse to engage in argument or controversy. Conduct yourself so as to increase his respect. (5) Do not practice under false pretenses. Posing always contributes to one's insecurity, and in the intimate relationship which exists in speech correction, poses will soon be detected. (6) Plan your conferences and remedial work. No patient must be permitted to know discouragement because of the teacher's refusal to do her part. If the teacher accepts a case, she accepts the responsibility for doing her utmost. If she contents herself with anything less than her best, she had better do something else. Human handicaps are not to be played with. (7) Maintain a consistent program of self-improvement. (8) Give no promises or guarantees of probable results to the patient or to anyone else. (9) Accept only justifiable remuneration and avoid any taint of exploitation. (10) Treat other workers in the field with respect.

Preparation of speech correctionist. The academic preparation needed by the professional speech-correction teacher is wide and varied. Of the sciences, biology, physiology, anatomy, the physics of sound, biochemistry, general, educational, and abnormal psychology, mental testing, and sociology are the most useful. Foreign languages are valuable, since many foreign-speaking children are referred to the speech-correction teacher. Public-speaking courses provide training for the many talks which the special teachers are called upon to make. Courses in elementary education and the teaching of reading contribute greatly to the solution of the problem of teacher co-operation. Mental- and physical-hygiene courses are of obvious value. Courses in history, literature, and the arts provide a broad background which is always useful in easing human contacts and providing discussion topics. Physical education provides a background for the necessary special orthopedic knowledge required in treating the spastic child and in improving general health. Courses in statistics aid in the evaluation and performance of research. In addition to these general courses, the speech-correction teacher should have thorough training in phonetics, basic voice and speech science, and, finally, in courses in speech correction which cover a thorough survey of the field, diagnosis, examination techniques, and remedial methods, and which provide a great deal of supervised practice in all of these divisions.

To some people speech-correction work is very distasteful, and there seem to be certain personal qualifications which make all the difference between success and failure. In general, the nervous, impatient, high-strung individual does not make a good speech correctionist. Neither does the person who falls into routine, stereotyped methods and remains there contentedly. Successful teachers of speech correction possess the majority of the following traits to a high degree: a sense of humor, patience, curiosity, social poise, ingenuity in inventing and adapting techniques, professional enthusiasm, a sensitive and discriminating hearing, interest in the personalities of others, industriousness, objective attitude toward their own insecurities, calmness, ability to recognize subterfuge and mental mechanisms, and self-respect. Few people, of course, are born so virtuous as the above list of traits might imply, but speech correction puts such a premium upon such characteristics that those who do not possess them try to acquire them as soon as possible. All speech-correction teachers should make a systematic attempt to improve themselves in all of these directions.

Implied in many of the above traits is a skill which is so important that it merits special discussion—the ability to influence, motivate, understand, and control other people. All of us possess some of this ability, but there are few who could not profit from a course of self-training specifically designed to increase it. Such a course would include training in: (1) seeing the other person's point of view; (2) personal adjustment with recognition of one's own mental mechanisms and inadequate reaction patterns; (3) self-discipline; (4) carrying out a long-range program of self-improvement; (5) the study and prediction of human behavior; and (6) controlled experimentation in the field of human relations.

While it is manifestly impossible to give in detail the content of such a course of training without fitting it to the needs of some specific individual, some illustrative assignments may be helpful to a student preparing himself in speech correction.

The beginner in the field of speech correction should make an effort to experience the speech defective's handicap. He should assume a severe stutter, or a lisp, or cleft-palate speech, and enter a few common speech situations. He should stop people on the street and inquire as to the location of certain buildings, using pronounced symptoms of the various speech disorders and noting his own reactions and those of the people to whom he speaks. He should make an attempt to adopt the objective attitude, remaining calm and intelligent in the face of bad audience reactions. He should attempt to make the audience feel more at ease by commenting on his handicap and explaining that he is attempting to get rid of it.

Besides the above methods, he can understand the speech defectives' points of view by reading their autobiographies, by associating with them socially, and by writing descriptions (from the speech defectives' points of view) of situations which are perfectly normal to him. The student preparing himself to do speech correction can train himself in the recognition of his own inadequate reactions to insecurity by holding truth-sessions with his fellow students, in which each member presents the picture of his own personality assets and liabilities, then leaves the room while the other members discuss him, returning to be presented with the composite picture as provided by the discussion. He then verbally accepts or rejects the criticisms and the group co-operates in outlining a campaign of improvement. It is also well to have the student give a verbal and thorough autobiography before some similar congenial group. A month's diary of inadequate behavior reactions or situations in which the student was insecure is effective. Each student should finally present a paper or lecture on the various mental mechanisms, with illustrations of each from his own or his associates' behavior.

Speech correction in the public schools. Speech-correction work is carried out in most schools by the special speech-correction teacher, the elementary classroom teacher, the high-school teacher of speech or English, or an unusually interested principal or superintendent. Without training, many of the latter individuals make woeful mistakes and soon become discouraged. With some training or supervision, however, they do much to eliminate and prevent speech handicaps. The same things may be said about parental speech correction.

The most efficient work is done by the special speech-correction teacher. Her training and freedom from other activities permit this efficiency. When she first enters a school system which has not previously had speech-correction service, she should be given several weeks to survey the various schools and to examine the children who are in need of the help she can give.

Many school systems prefer to have the classroom teachers select the cases with whom the speech-correction teacher is to work. This method is usually not advisable because many classroom teachers are unable to detect the child who skillfully hides his stuttering or pretends to be ignorant rather than attempt to recite. Again, many teachers resent any interruption to their daily schedule, and they either believe the fallacy that all children outgrow their disorder or they minimize its importance. The speech-correction teacher can usually make her survey of a class in the space of an hour and select the cases who should work with her. The classroom teacher should be notified in advance by the principal that the survey is to be carried out so that misunderstanding will not wreck all chance for co-operation. In making this survey, the speech-correction teacher should examine each child individually. A standard, brief articulation test, which includes reading, naming, and propositional speech, should be used. If the school system is so large that this survey would be an all-year task, the teacher should concentrate on three or four schools and confine her activities to them.

After this preliminary survey has been completed, the speech-correction teacher should re-examine the cases found. This second examination should be much more detailed and complete and should follow the type of examination sketched in former chapters. Home calls should be made or the parents should be invited to come to the speech-correction office so that additional information concerning the causes, home conditions, and co-operation may be procured.

It is unwise for the special speech-correction teacher to carry a load of more than one hundred cases. Even this number will necessitate seeing approximately ten cases each hour, since each child should be seen at least twice a week for a speech-correction period of approximately fifteen minutes. Increasing this load merely discourages the teacher, causes her work to become perfunctory, and insures almost certain failure in a large percentage of her cases.

Selection of cases. It is often difficult to keep the case load within the limit that has been recommended, but every effort should be made to do so. This involves selection. Interviews with many speech-correction teachers bring out the principles they follow in order to make this selection most effective. They declare that when selection must be carried out, the first to go are those children with very minor defects—those, for example, who use the vulgar *t* and *d* substitutions for the *th* sounds. Where only one or two sounds are defective and the child can make them correctly when he watches himself, the speech correctionist usually gives some information concerning treatment to the classroom teacher and to the child's parents and lets the child go.

If there still remain many more than the hundred with whom she must work, the speech correctionist eliminates those who have pronounced organic defects, such as adenoids in a case of denasal speech or a very malformed jaw in a child who lisps. These disorders can be corrected by surgical or by orthodontic treatment, and although much can be done by the speech correctionist to teach compensatory movements, the work demands much more time and care than she can afford. Exceptions to this principle, of course, will always exist. Generally speaking, the teacher should select cases who are most likely to profit from her help.

The speech correctionist likewise tries to eliminate those children who have such low intelligence as to make the short periods of treatment relatively useless. School administrators often oppose this, pointing out that the feeble-minded child needs the tool of speech even more than does the normal child; but even though this attitude be accepted, it seems inadvisable to do speech correction with such children unless it can be done thoroughly enough to ensure success. Much more time is needed for them, and the problem should really be handled by the opportunity-room teacher who has had training in speech correction.

If many children in excess of the proper case load still remain, the speech correctionist should confine her efforts to the grades above the kindergarten, since many of the children in the preschool years have not matured sufficiently to acquire certain of the speech sounds. Speech-improvement work should be carried out at these lower levels, but it can be done by the kindergarten teacher.

If still more selection is necessary, the teacher should choose from this group those who show great need and at the same time exhibit good possibilities of improvement. Pronounced emotional conflicts may be referred to the school psychologist or psychiatrist. In any event, the speech correctionist should not wreck her chances of success by taking an immense load of cases. Proper selection according to logical principles will solve this problem.

Organization of speech correction in the public schools. Having selected her cases, the speech-correction teacher's next task is to arrange her appointments. Since there are several sources of difficulty inherent in getting a schedule which interferes as little as possible with the classroom teacher's work, the following suggestions are offered. Classify the cases according to school, grade, type of defect, and probable teaching difficulty. Get the daily schedules of each classroom teacher. Confer with the classroom teacher to determine which periods she would prefer to have her speech-defective children miss. Be sure to avoid the nap, recess, milk-feeding, and writing periods. Do not schedule the period so that the child misses the activity in which he is most deficient. Try to schedule the youngest children for the early morning hours. When several children must come from the same room, try to arrange the scheduling so that they will miss consecutive periods and the disturbance will be minimized.

Although certain children must be taught individually, necessity will demand that approximately ten children must be met each teaching hour if each child is to be seen twice a week. Groups should seldom exceed five children, and in most school systems they average about three. The period should seldom be less than fifteen minutes in duration. The size of the group should vary according to the defects included, and in general it is wise not to use stutterers and articulatory cases in the same group. A larger number of articulatory cases can be handled in a single group than can those of any other type of defect. The younger the children, the larger the group may be. Approximately one fourth of all cases necessitate individual conferences.

Through the principal's office, the classroom teacher can be made to accept the responsibility for sending the child to the speech correctionist at the proper time. Often she writes the child's name and the appointment hour in one corner of the blackboard and insists that the child assume the duty of remembering. When the speech-correction teacher cannot keep her appointments, she usually notifies the principal's office so that the children will not wander aimlessly about the building.

Some school systems feel that the speech-correction work should be carried out in a central place, usually the special building which houses the spastic, deaf, and mentally handicapped children. The school buses bring the children to the speech-correction rooms, but this involves much waiting and waste of time. Another more important objection to such centralization is that, since the speech defective needs little special apparatus for retraining, the work can be done in the child's own school building, thus preventing him from feeling any more peculiar than necessary. Speech correction thereby becomes a subject similar to remedial reading or writing and carries few social penalties. The first aid, nurse's room, library annex, principal's office, or any unused corner which is relatively quiet and free from interruption commonly serves as an adequate place. The speech-correction teacher frequently carries a bag or two of toys, books, and other teaching materials. A special room for speech correction would be preferable, of course, but the service does not need to wait for such space.

Experienced speech-correction teachers often find that one-half day each week should be set aside for office work, home calls, and interviews with classroom teachers. A position of this sort in the public schools entails a great deal of such extra work and is usually considered by any administrator to justify this free period. A series of mimeographed bulletins concerning the nature, causes, and treatment of the various speech defects should be sent out to the parents and teachers. Many speech-correction teachers find that an excellent way of getting classroom-teacher co-operation is to prepare a general outline of the speech-correction program for each child. Copies of this are sent to the parent, principal, and the classroom teacher, and as each major achievement has been attained or a subgoal reached, the classroom teacher is notified. This often results in an independent checking of the child's success in the classroom with a subsequent co-operation that otherwise might not have been forthcoming.

Whenever a child fails to keep an appointment due to illness or some other reason, the speech correctionist may use the opportunity to visit the classroom or to make some sort of written contact with the parent, thus showing her interest in the child. The speech-correction teacher should keep abreast of the major projects going on in the classroom and use the latter to motivate or vary the corrective exercises and at the same time to help the child contribute to the regular classroom work. After the proper rapport has been gained with the classroom teacher, the speech correctionist may occasionally offer to teach some subject such as reading or arithmetic, demonstrating how speech-correction work can be worked into the regular procedure without difficulty. Although many antagonistic and un-co-operative attitudes on the part of classroom teachers are often experienced when speech correction is first begun, they soon disappear if the speech-correction teacher shows an interest in the child and a profound respect for her teaching associates. If she appreciates the power the classroom teacher has to insure or negate her success, she will leave nothing undone in perfecting this relationship. As soon as the work is well initiated, the speech correctionist should invite the principal or classroom teacher to visit one of the speech-correction periods. The speech defective needs to practice his new skills under somewhat emotional conditions in order to insure complete success, and so no concern need be felt for his part. Parents may also be encouraged to make these visits, which produce a respect and co-operation that can be achieved in no other way. Needless to say, they also improve the speech-correction work.

Teachers of speech correction should also consider it a part of their duty to educate the general public as well as the school administration concerning their field. They will be called upon frequently to address parent-teacher meetings, and they should use these opportunities to dispel some of the vast ignorance concerning the causes and treatment of the various speech disorders.

Speech correction and the classroom teacher. Speech-correction teachers often inquire as to the amount of co-operation they can expect from the classroom teacher or parent. The answer is, of course, that they can *expect* real co-operation from very few teachers or parents. Some of the younger teachers, still vibrant with enthusiasm, and some of the older teachers, who have lost their early zest and wish to recapture it, will appreciate a new opportunity to help their students. And there are the real teachers who constantly seek to improve themselves in the knowledge and skills necessary to their profession. Nevertheless, many classroom teachers do not welcome any new opportunity to help their students. As one of them said, "We've got too much opportunity now. We have almost more than we can stand. We have too many students and too little time. Indeed, we are fortunate when we can do what we should to take care of our children as a group." Any unbiased observer will recognize that this objection has evidence to support it. However, if the speech-correction teacher is resourceful and tactful, she can usually convince the large majority of classroom teachers that the child with a speech defect can be helped in his regular subjects without adding appreciably to the teacher's burden.

The speech-correction teacher should be as definite as possible in her suggestions. Thus, one speech-correction teacher who had been offered co-operation by the classroom teacher made the following suggestions:

In your store project, perhaps you can arrange to have Jimmy be the storekeeper. I have taught him how to say the words "six," "seven," and "cents" without lisping, but he often forgets. Perhaps if you will tell him that he must say those three words correctly or lose his turn behind the counter, it will help.

When you have your "telling" period, will you ask Sarah to tell about how we played radio this morning? She is supposed to say "wadio" the first time and then wink at you. After that she should use it correctly.

I understand you are teaching some phonics now. Perhaps Bob can be given a chance to show a little superiority for a change by telling the other children about the *f* and *v* sounds. I will prepare him for this recitation, if you are interested.

Would you mind letting Jimmy and Mary tell their story together tomorrow morning? They have been practicing. I suppose it's really a little play. Concerns the making of soup. It can probably fit into the story period without causing any bother.

John can name and find on the map and tell several things about several strange places that begin with the *k* sound. Some day in Geography when you find a convenient moment, he can interest the class for several minutes. Although this is the sound he fears most, I think he can handle the words without losing his control.

It is obvious from these examples that remedial speech work can really contribute to the interest of classroom activities and that the range of application is very wide. Classwork is primarily useful in making the new speech habits permanent, in recognizing and canceling errors, and in preventing maladjustment. When no speech-correction teacher is available and the classroom teacher must do all the remedial work, she should devote short five- or ten-minute periods during the recess or after school hours to the intensive and individual therapy needed in the beginning stages of treatment. After the child has been taught his new sound, or a method for handling his stuttering, or a new way of phonating, the classroom may be used as a reinforcing agent.

Speech correction in the home. Many of the same observations hold for parental co-operation. The parents can seldom be used in the beginning steps of treatment. They tend to be too hasty, even when they know what to do. The history of past failure in speech teaching tends to handicap them, and too many attitudes inappropriate to the remedial situation are aroused by the parent-child relationship. There are, of course, many parents to whom the above strictures do not apply, and some of them have done excellent remedial speech work, but unfortunately they are in the minority.

Again, when it is necessary that the parent do all the remedial work, it is wise to insist that the preliminary work be done in a special room, such as a bedroom or guest room. This will tend to identify the speech work as demanding different attitudes from those which ordinarily exist between parent and child. Speech periods should be short, well planned, and motivated. Having two ten-minute speech periods each day, always occurring at the same hours, will facilitate the work. If the parent possesses personality traits which tend to interfere with effective training, she should do her utmost to discard them the moment she enters the speech room. If she shows a new personality to the child, the latter will usually adjust to it and much advantage will be gained.

In the majority of cases, it is advisable to have some person other than the parent do the remedial work. If no speech correctionist is available for this purpose, a careful and detailed program of treatment should be outlined by some specialist in the field, and a good teacher persuaded or hired to do the work under his supervision. Frequent reports are necessary if this admittedly makeshift arrangement is the only one possible.

When a teacher trained in speech correction is engaged in the remedial activities, the parents must not delegate all the responsibility to her. Much home co-operation is needed if the treatment is to be efficient. This co-operation can be gained in several ways. Conferences between parents and the speech-correction teacher can clarify the lengthy program usually necessary. Special techniques can be explained, the subgoals outlined, and the amount of expected progress can be estimated. Such conferences also permit the teacher to supervise the homework. Beside these conferences, the teacher should send daily assignments home to the parent. These should be very short, easily understood, and easily carried out. Some actual examples of these assignments follow:

Robert has learned how to do the talking-and-writing technique of which I spoke at our last conference. However, he occasionally says a "th" when writing the "s" symbol. Would you mind helping him as he writes a page of this talking and writing? I'd like to have you encircle every "s" that he mispronounces, and stimulate him with five good clear "s" sounds, before he continues.

Will you please tie this picture of a child making the "f" sound to the door between the kitchen and the dining room, and remind Mary to make the sound every time she goes through?

Will you call one of the chairs in the house the "Make-no-face Chair" and see to it that, whenever your son sits in it and stutters with that facial contortion I pointed out to you in our last conference, he gets up immediately and walks around it, saying "Make no face, make no face, make no face?" If he stutters without the facial contortion, he should be praised even more than if he has no blocks at all, for you remember that at this stage of the treatment we are most interested in getting rid of that one bad symptom. Free speech can come later. And please see to it that he does some speaking from this chair at least three times tomorrow. I would appreciate a note from you describing what happens.

While most intelligent parents welcome these assignments and provide the best of co-operation, it is obvious that other parents could not and would not carry them out. In the latter instance, the problem must be solved at school, using such resources as are available.

Group versus individual techniques. Although, from a consideration of the amount of attention and time to be given, it is better to work with the child individually, nevertheless there are certain advantages to group work which should not be overlooked. The latter provides more natural speech situations; some children are strongly motivated by competition; and speech games are more attractive when carried on in a group.

Since the children within any one group usually possess similar defects, seldom number more than three or four, and fall within a narrow age range, it is possible to employ any of the techniques used in speech correction successfully. When the teacher must give individual attention to any member of the group, she calls the child to her side, and the other members act as an audience, as critics, or carry on some type of seat work.

Some of the more common types of group activities are: listening to the teacher's stories and acting the parts she describes; relaxing; manipulating the speech organs or reciting in unison; echo games; word pointing; identifying categories; imitation activities; guessing games; completion exercises; rhyming; picture naming or describing; answering simple riddles; selecting appropriate sounds or word from a group of words; and matching activities. Any competent teacher will be able to invent many others. Whenever possible, these activities should be linked to the temporary interests and to the projects being carried out in the classroom of the child. Thus, each of the various holidays may be made the theme of the speech-correction project, and the activity characteristic of each season can be modified to provide a motivated vehicle for speech work.

Some children do not respond to group work, and progress much more rapidly when treated individually. With these children, the teacher should seek to effect a strong transference, getting the child to desire her approval more than anything else. Self-competition which will foster very rapid progress can be created on this basis. The teacher should study the child as thoroughly as possible and should adapt her techniques to his interests. When working with older children or adult speech defectives, the speech-assignment method is commonly employed. Since the speech correctionist can seldom spare more than half an hour each day for individual work with any one case, the conference is usually devoted to: (1) the student's report of his experience in carrying out the previous day's assignments; (2) a discussion and analysis of any difficulty that occurred, with suggestions for alternative methods or means of canceling the failures; (3) some supervised retraining; and

(4) the formulation and explanation of the next day's assignments.

The criteria of a good assignment follow: (1) it is directed specifically toward the attainment of a goal which the speech defective understands; (2) it can be performed economically as regards time and effort; (3) it demands no more than the student can be expected to do; (4) it is not vague or general but direct, detailed, and clear; (5) it should permit some objective report. These individual assignments may employ some older friend, parent, or teacher to supervise or assist the child in fulfilling them. Usually the more difficult cases demand this individual type of treatment, but most teachers find it advisable to alternate some group activity with it.

Differences in the treatment of children and adults. In a preceding chapter the speech defective was discussed from the point of view of his developing personality. In later chapters concerning the methods for treating each of the major types of speech defects, modifications of those methods as they pertain to children or adults were described. Nevertheless, the student must be reminded that this text is primarily designed to sketch the principles and basic methods of speech correction and not their specific application. It is doubtful whether any text could possibly hope to describe the great variation of techniques needed in actual remedial work. Each individual must be treated according to his own peculiar characteristics. The submissive or aggressive, the younger or older, the dull or the bright child— each demands his own modifications. With these reservations in mind, it seems advisable to give some general principles in applying the methods of speech correction to children in the age range from four to ten years.

The teacher must provide the motivation in the majority of such cases. Deferred rewards are seldom effective. Concrete symbols of achievement must be used whenever possible, and the teacher must not be too critical. Often the children must be praised for an attempt even though the result is far from satisfactory, for the teacher's praise can become a very important reward and motivation. The teacher should praise success and ignore failure, unless the latter is relatively rare. Whenever too much failure is occurring, vary the activity so that success occurs. Use social approval such as can be gained from other children in the group, from the classmates or regular teacher, or from the parents.

Children can seldom be expected to react to subgoals unless the latter are made ends in themselves. Abstractions of any kind should be avoided. The child needs more help and direction and less logic. Many times any reason seems to be acceptable to him, providing it is simple enough to be understood. Children often seem unable to retain or recall the things taught them from one speech period to another. If the original impression was sufficiently vivid, this failure does not occur. If the teacher prepares the child for the recall by recounting the activities of the preceding period or by giving a short review of them, the child is usually successful.

One very successful public-school teacher of speech correction writes as follows:

I always try to create the attitude that when the child comes to speech class, he comes to work, even though most of our activities approximate play. We always speak of doing *speech work*. Some of my fellow teachers do everything through games, but I believe I get better results my way.

The way I feel or act makes all the difference with little children. If I'm interested, happy, and enthusiastic, I can get them to do anything. Their enthusiasm can easily be worked up. I always try to watch their mood when they first come in, and either fit my activity to that, or else try to modify it. I never make any detailed lesson plans ahead of time. They never work, and some of my best methods have been invented on the spur of the moment. It's fatal to become stereotyped in your speech-correction work. Children sense it immediately. Although it is some trouble, I always make and keep individual notebooks for each child. In this we collect our new sounds and words and record our achievements. This creates self-competition of the best type. On the star page, they often ask me what each star was for, and this certainly seems to motivate them.

I find that I must watch fatigue and shift of attention closely. If I can prevent them during the first two weeks, I never have any further trouble with motivation. The children seldom need to know the reason for any activity; they merely need to share it.

I don't believe that we break old habits in young children. We always build new ones which displace the others. Thus I seldom use penalties of any kind or call attention to errors. Praise and social rewards for success seem more important.

Although I often can find wonderful rationalizations, I know deep in my heard that, whenever I have failed with a young child in getting rid of his defect, it is my fault, not his.

References

1. Ainsworth, S., *Speech Correction Methods*, New York, Prentice-Hall, Inc., 1948.

A book designed for the public school speech therapist, reviewing each of the speech disorders and discussing basic policies of the school administration of special education programs and formulating plans for organizing such a program.

2. Ainsworth, S., "Suggestions for a Successful Speech Correction Program in Public Schools," *Quarterly Journal of Speech*, 1945, Volume 31, pages 471–477.

Many excellent suggestions about public relations, co-operation from the classroom teacher, record keeping, and bulletins.

3. Backus, O. L., *Speech in Education*, New York, Longmans, Green, 1943, pages 89–113.

Relationships with the classroom teacher and parents to achieve better co-operation are sketched in detail.

4. Beasely, J., "Group Therapy in the Field of Speech Correction," *Journal of Exceptional Children*, 1950, Volume 17, pages 102–107.

A summary of the purposes and methods of group therapy as it "should" be carried out in the public schools.

5. Bell, D., and Pross, E. L., "A 'Medicine Bag' for the Speech Correctionist," *Journal of Speech and Hearing Disorders*, 1952, Volume 17, pages 397–400.

Motivational, drill, and activity materials useful in public school speech therapy.

6. Brown, F. M., "A State Auxiliary Program of Speech Correction," *Journal of Speech Disorders*, 1945, Volume 10, pages 133–135.

Describes the working together of a central speech clinic and an itinerant clinic.

7. Chapman, M. E., "The Speech Clinician and the Classroom

Teacher Co-operate in a Speech Correction Program," *Journal of Speech Disorders*, 1942, Volume 7, pages 57–61.

Describes some bulletins used by the speech correctionist to get co-operation from the classroom teacher, and describes the duties of the speech-correction teacher.

8. Dunn, H., "A Speech and Hearing Program for Children in a Rural Area," *Journal of Speech and Hearing Disorders*, 1949, Volume 14, pages 166–170.

Description of such a program in a state with a widely scattered population.

9. Gorman, T., "North Dakota's Clinic on Wheels," *Today's Health*, 1950, Volume 28, pages 22–23, 44.

An account of a speech and hearing clinic operating in a trailer all over the entire state.

10. Houchin, T. D., "Notes on Organizing a Speech Correction Program in the Public Schools," *Journal of Speech and Hearing Disorders*, 1949, Volume 14, pages 53–62.

Probably the best article for the beginning speech therapist who is responsible for organizing a new program in a public school system.

11. Irwin, R. B., *Speech and Hearing Therapy*, New York, Prentice-Hall, Inc., 1953.

A comprehensive treatment of the field of speech therapy in the public schools.

12. Milisen, R., "Introducing Speech Correction into a New School System," *Journal of Speech Disorders*, 1939, Volume 4, pages 241–245.

Outlines the problems often met in introducing speech-correction services for the first time. Many practical suggestions are given.

13. Minneapolis Public Schools, *Speech Correction in Practice*, 1948.

A handbook for speech therapists outlining the organization and methods used in a large metropolitan area.

14. Schuell, H., "Working with Speech Defectives in Public Schools," *Journal of Speech Disorders*, 1939, Volume 4, pages 241–245.

Describes the problems of the speech correctionist in her everyday work, the types of cases, the variety of techniques, and the need for co-operation.

15. Wells, C. G., "Expanding State Speech Correction Services," *Journal of Speech Disorders*, 1945, Volume 10, pages 123–128.

Various plans for providing speech-correction services on a state-wide basis are described and discussed.

16. Young, J. A., "A City and County Speech Re-education Program," *Journal of Speech Disorders*, 1942, Volume 7, pages 51–56.

Describes how a speech-correction service was established in a county which could not afford it.

Appendix. The Case History

⎍⎍⎍⎍⎍⎍⎍⎍⎍⎍⎍⎍⎍⎍⎍⎍⎍⎍⎍⎍⎍⎍⎍⎍⎍⎍⎍

Administering the case history. While the parents or the case himself is usually the source of most of the information, it is generally necessary to interview other associates of the speech defective. Former teachers, the family doctor, welfare investigators, and neighbors or friends may be called upon. The speech defective is often asked to get the co-operation of his former associates in determining the early symptoms or reactions toward his speech defect. These individuals often provide more information than the parents. While the majority of questions should be made as pointed as possible, a few general questions appropriate to the material in each major section should be used. Questions should be phrased so that the influence of suggestion will not prejudice the answer. An exception to this rule, however, is found in the recommendation that delicate questions be asked so as to favor an affirmative answer. Answers should be recorded immediately, and the examiner should master a system of abbreviations or shorthand so that there will be no delay. He should always distinguish in the recording between the person's actual answers and his own interpretation of those answers. The examiner should perfect himself in the art of interrupting irrelevant vocal wanderings and bringing the parent back to the point in question. It is unwise to have the child present during questioning of the parent, and except

545

when the relationship between parents is being studied, it is wiser to question only one at a time. The summary of important case-history findings should be written up as soon as possible.

The case histories given here are phrased in the form of direct questions. This policy was chosen because the text is intended for beginning students in speech correction, and experience has shown the author that such students require this guidance. It must be emphasized repeatedly that each question is merely the first of a series of supplemental queries when the answer indicates that vital information may be forthcoming. No examiner will ask all the questions, nor will he confine himself to them alone.

The case histories which follow are of two types, general and special. The general case history may be considered the device used to procure a picture of the individual's background and physical, mental, personality, and speech development. A shorter form of this history may be obtained by using only the starred items for exploration. Demands upon the teacher's time and the overwhelming case load frequently experienced in public-school work occasionally necessitate this compromise, but the short case history is seldom used except for certain simple types of articulatory or voice cases. In addition to the general case history, the appropriate special case history should be used. Even as the general case history is used for exploration of the person having the speech defect, so the special case history is used to tap the parent's fund of information concerning the causes, development, and consequences of the speech defect itself.

General Case History

Person Interviewed......................... Interviewer....................

Name of Case.................... Date of Birth.............. Sex............

Address.. Telephone Number..............

Rapport..

1. Father
   *Name...
   Age (if dead, date and cause of death)................................
   Handedness.............. Education.............. Occupation...............
   Religion.................. Health.. .... Nationality...............
   *Type of speech defect, if any.......................................
   Type of physical defect, if any.......................................
   Nervous diseases... Excesses (liquor,
   drugs, etc.)...
   Marital history (separation, divorce, previous marriage, etc.)
   ....
   ....
   Attitude toward child's defect.. ....

2. Mother
   *Name...
   Age (if dead, date and cause of death)................................
   Handedness............. Education.............. Occupation...............
   Religion.................. Health................. Nationality...............
   *Type of speech defect, if any.......................................
   Type of physical defect, if any.......................................
   Nervous diseases...
   Marital history...
   Attitude toward child's defect.......................................

3. Other relatives (Write number of people having the following
   disorders)

	Physical Defect	Speech Defect	Other Important Information
*Brothers			
*Sisters			
Mat. Grandmother			
Mat. Grandfather			
Mat. Aunts			
Mat. Uncles			
Pat. Grandmother			
Pat. Grandfather			
Pat. Aunts			
Pat. Uncles			
Other persons living in home			

Birth History

Give age of the mother at the beginning of the pregnancy..................

Age of the father.............. Number of months of pregnancy..............

Weight of child at birth.............. Length of body at birth..............

Prenatal Conditions

Give the approximate weight and height of the mother at the beginning of this pregnancy.......................... ....

Was mother working during the pregnant period?..................
If so, what kind of work?.......................... How soon did she stop before the birth?..........................
How soon did she resume her activities after the birth?..........

What was the condition of the mother's health during pregnancy? Good, fair, poor. Was mother able to eat regularly and retain the food?..........................

Did mother have any severe shocks during pregnancy?..................
Injuries?..........................

Was mother examined by a physician before and during pregnancy?..........................
Was the pelvis measured?..........................
What comments did the doctor make?..........................
Will you furnish us with the name and address of the physician? Name..........................
Address..........................

　　　　　　　Street　　　　　City　　　　　State

Birth and Postnatal Conditions

Number of hours of labor, including the time from the first pains until the expulsion of the afterbirth..........................

*At birth was the baby delivered feet first, head first, breech (hip) first, or by Caesarean operation?..........................

*Did delivery necessitate the use of instruments?..................

*Were there any injuries?.............. If so, where?..............
.... Did baby have difficulty initiating breathing?.............. If so, how was breathing started?..........
.... How long was it before he started breathing normally?.............. Did he cry as soon as he was born?.......... Was it loud?.......... feeble?.......... Did he nurse as soon as he was placed at the breast or did he need to be coaxed?
.... How long did this condition last?..........................
Did he move around much the first two or three days or was he

still and quiet?.. Was his pulse strong, weak, slow, fast, normal?.. Was the soft spot on the top of the head soft and concave or hard and bulging?.. Did the baby have convulsions?........................... blueness of the body, lips, or feet?.. slow blood clotting time?.............................. slight bleeding about the nose and mouth?................................. twitchings of the muscles of the face?................ Was he one of a pair of twins?................ If so, was he the strong or weak one?............................... Did the head have an abnormal molding immediately after birth?............................. Was mother attended by a doctor, nurse, midwife, others?..

Developmental History

1. Was baby breast fed?................ For how long?....................
2. Why was he weaned?..
3. Was baby bottle fed?................ For how long?....................
4. Did the bottle milk agree with him?..................................
5. Were both fontanelles closed before child was 20 months old?

....
*6. Was the child's rate of growth seemingly normal?....................
If not, why not?..
*7. Give age in months at which the following took place:
First tooth................ Full set of teeth........................
Full set of second teeth.......................... Creeping on all fours................ Sitting alone................ Walking alone .... Feeding self................ Got voluntary control of bowels.......................... Got voluntary control of bladder................ Using spoon................ Using any object as tool...
Do you have any other information with regard to the child's development?...
*8. The following is a list of common childhood diseases. Please give age of child when disease occurred, whether it was serious or mild, whether the child had a high fever, and any noticeable effects which followed it:
Tonsillitis
Whooping cough
Pneumonia
Scarlet fever
Typhoid fever

Tuberculosis
Pleurisy
Chicken pox
Smallpox
Influenza
Diphtheria
Measles
Mumps
St. Vitus dance
Convulsions
Rickets
Enlarged glands
Heart trouble
Rheumatism
Thyroid disturbances
Nervous trouble
Infantile paralysis
Any others

9. Was child excessively spoiled and indulged because of his illness?

*10. Has child ever been seriously injured? State nature, age at injury, and effects

11. Was the child: very active?............; fairly active?............; very inactive?

12. Would you say that the child was slow, average, or rapid in his general development up to three years of age?

Present Physical Condition of Child

*1. What is the child's weight............ and height............ at present time?

*2. Does the child have any physical deformities?............ What are they?

3. Has the child had a physical examination lately?............ What were the main findings of his examination?............ Who was the physician?

4. Is there any abnormality in the following:
   a. Size of tongue
   b. Protrusion of upper or lower jaws
   c. Arrangement of teeth
   d. Palate

. e. Nasal passages..
5. Has he ever had tonsils and adenoids removed?........................
   Tongue-tie clipped?..
6. Does the child have any defect in hearing?...........................
   Seeing?..
7. Is the child usually in good health at the present time?............
   ....
*8. Is he: very energetic?..................; fairly energetic?..................;
   not very energetic?...

Co-ordination

Check the following items according to whether the child shows
   inferior, average, or superior skill:

Gracefulness	Dancing	Skipping	Jumping
Throwing	Catching	Kicking	Sewing
Cutting	Drawing	Writing	

Mental and Educational Development

1. Has the child ever had a mental or intelligence test?................
   What was the name of the test used?.......................................
2. What was the I.Q. obtained, or general ranking?.......................
*3. If the child is in school, in what grade is he at present?...........
*4. Are his marks above average, average, or below average?........
*5. Has the child ever failed a grade?.................... Has he ever
   skipped a grade?.................... Which one?...........................
*6. What are the highest marks the child has ever received?............
   .... In what subjects?.......................................
*7. What are the poorest marks the child has ever received?............
   .... In what subjects?.......................................
8. Is the child frequently tardy?.................... Why?....................
9. Does the child play truant?...
10. Has the child been absent from school very often?...................
    If so, for what reason?..
11. Has the child been punished by his teacher?...........................
    Why?..
*12. Does the child like school?.................... If not, why not?
    ....
13. Which of his teachers does the child like most?......................
    ....
14. Teacher's name.................... School...........................
15. What other schools has the child attended?...........................
    When?..

Handedness

1. Have the child's hands ever been bandaged, tied up, or restrained in any way?.............................. For what reason and how long?..............

2. At what age did he show a definite tendency to favor one hand while eating?.................... Which hand?........................ Up to that age, did the child use either or both hands indiscriminately?
....

*3. Did anyone ever try to influence his handedness in order to change him from left to right or vice versa?........................ How?..............

4. What is the attitude of the father toward left-handedness?......
....

5. What is the attitude of the mother toward left-handedness?
....

6. Did any injuries or illnesses ever change his handedness?........
....

*7. Has child ever written backward?..............

*8. Are there any activities which he can do better or as well with the usually nonpreferred hand?........................ What are they?..............

Play

1. Give names and ages of the three children with whom the child plays most often..............

*2. Is the child the follower or the leader?..............

3. Do they tease the child?..............

4. Do they fight with him?..............

5. Do they get along with him?.................... Do any of them have speech defects?..............

6. What games does he prefer to play?..............

7. What toys does he prefer?..............

*8. Does he play alone as well as he does with other children?......
....

9. Does he prefer to play alone?..............

*10. Which parent does the child prefer?........................ Why?
....

*11. Which playmate does the child prefer?........................ Why?
....

12. Who took care of the child when the mother was absent?........
....

Language Development

*1. How many months old was the child when he began to say single words?_____; simple sentences and phrases?_____

2. What were the first single words spoken?_____

3. Give any other examples of the child's early speech with the approximate dates for each_____

4. What method was used in teaching the child to talk?_____

 a. Who did most of it?_____

 *b. Do you feel that the child was overstimulated or understimulated with respect to speech?_____

 c. Did he understand what was said to him before he had learned to talk?_____

 *d. Did anyone talk baby talk to child?_____ Who?_____

 e. Did anyone use double-talking to child?_____ Who?_____ (Double-talking is like this: We-we-will-will-go-go.)

 f. Were the child's wants usually anticipated before he could communicate the need?_____

 g. Did the child gesture much in attempting to communicate?_____

 h. Do you think that the child's present vocabulary is superior, average, or inferior to other children his age?_____

 i. Did the child often surprise you by using large words?_____

 j. Did the child habitually mispronounce certain words?_____

 Give samples_____

5. Were there any sounds that he could not say?_____ Which?_____

*6. Did the child ever lisp?_____ Describe_____

*7. Was the child taught to speak pieces?_____ Was he often called upon to perform before strangers or friends of the family?_____ What was his usual attitude toward such demands?_____

8. Has there ever been any tongue-tie?................................. Cleft palate?........................... Hare-lip?..............................

9. Was there any marked articulatory defect?.....................

10. Describe the rate, intensity, and pitch of child's speech with respect to its being rapid-average-slow; loud-average-soft; high-average-low...........

*11. Did the child ever tend to say words backward ("got for" instead of "forgot," etc.)?............................... Give examples: ....

*12. Was the child generally retarded in speech development?........ ....

13. Was the child very talkative, average, or rather silent and quiet?...

14. Was any foreign language taught to the child or commonly spoken by his associates?...

Home

1. In what type of community is the home located: rural, town, city?...

2. Do the parents own or rent the home?.......................................

3. How many rooms in the house?...

4. Check the following items in possession of the family: car; piano; radio; 100 or more books; daily newspaper; gas, oil, or electric kitchen stove.

*5. Check word which most nearly describes economic condition of family: very poor; poor; comfortable circumstances; well-to-do.

6. Check phrase which most nearly describes father's attitude with an "F," and phrase which describes mother's attitude with an "M."

   a. Has no cultural interests (seems to live only to work and eat)...

   b. Has slight interest in other people's experiences, likes radio, likes magazine stores, does some social visiting....... ....

   c. Has a hobby in some creative field (music, pictures, cabinetmaking, gardening, reading, etc.)..............................

   d. Takes a specialized interest in one of the arts: reads widely; is aware of other places and times; discriminating taste...

7. Is there family friction with regard to money matters, religion, or anything else?..................... Is child aware of it?...................

8. Are both parents usually at home in the evening?.....................
9. Does the child have plenty of playthings or amusements?........

----

10. Are the neighbors congenial?..................... Do the parents like the neighbors?.................
11. Do the parents play with the children?.................................
12. Has the child ever lived in another town?.......................
*13. Of what things is the father proudest?............................
*14. Of what things is the mother proudest?.................:
*15. What things have made the father unhappy?.....................
*16. What things have made the mother unhappy?...................
*17. Of what things is the child proudest?............................
*18. What things have made the child unhappy?.......................

Childhood Problems

Following is a list of common childhood problems. Indicate how often these problems occurred in this child by encircling the letter which most clearly describes it. O indicates that it occurs often, S indicates seldom, and N indicates never.

1. Nervousness	O S N	16. Tongue sucking	O S N
2. Sleeplessness	O S N	17. Hurting pets	O S N
3. Nightmares	O S N	18. Setting fires	O S N
4. Bed wetting	O S N	19. Constipation	O S N
5. Playing with sex		20. Thumb sucking	O S N
organs	O S N	21. Face twitching	O S N
6. Walking in sleep	O S N	22. Fainting	O S N
7. Shyness	O S N	23. Strong fears	O S N
8. Showing off	O S N	24. Strong hates	O S N
9. Refusal to obey	O S N	25. Queer food habits	O S N
10. Rudeness	O S N	26. Temper tantrums	O S N
11. Fighting	O S N	27. Whining	O S N
12. Jealousy	O S N	28. Stealing	O S N
13. Selfishness	O S N	29. Running away	O S N
14. Lying	O S N	30. Destructiveness	O S N
15. Smoking	O S N		

31. How did the child's associates (parents, etc.) react to these problems?...
32. How is the child usually disciplined and who does it?..............

----

33. What types of discipline are most effective?................................ Least effective?.....................

*Adult Developmental History

Vocational
1. What opportunities did the case have for earning money as a child?...
2. Did he have an adequate allowance?..
3. What positions have been held? Give salary, working conditions, length of time employed, reason for leaving......................
....
....

Educational
1. Preferred subjects in secondary schools and college...................
....
2. Subjects disliked...
3. Attitudes toward instructors..
4. Extra-curricular activities...
5. Scholastic record...
6. Reasons for quitting school...
7. Conflicts with school authorities..
....

Sexual experiences (Indicate type, frequency, and attitudes toward activity)

Social
1. Favorite associates..
2. Disliked associates..
3. Recreational activities...
4. Arrests, probations, commitments to institutions......................
....

SPECIAL CASE HISTORIES

Articulation Cases
1. Has the child ever had any other speech defect?.......................
....
2. Was the child slow in learning to talk? In what way? Did he ever lose his speech entirely?...
....
3. With which sounds did he seem to have most trouble?...............
....
4. Did he ever have a mouth injury?..
....

5. Was he ever tongue-tied?_____

6. Has he had his tonsils and adenoids out? Did any speech defect result?_____

7. Has the child ever had any other mouth or throat operation?
_____

8. Did the child ever wear a brace on his teeth?_____

9. What dental work has been done?_____

10. Did the child have any accident to his first set of teeth?_____

11. Was his first set of teeth malformed?_____

12. Has the child's speech shown any improvement recently?_____

13. With what sounds or words does the child have trouble?_____

14. Does he have most trouble with these sounds at the beginning, middle, or end of words?_____

15. Do you think the child's speech disorder may be due in part to:
   a. Being stimulated by baby talk?_____

   b. Being stimulated by foreign or vulgar speech?_____

   c. Lack of proper training by parents?_____

   d. Negativism or refusal to conform to the speech standards of the parents?_____

16. What else may have caused it?_____

17. At what age did his speech difficulty begin?_____

18. Has it ever entirely disappeared?_____

19. What has been done to correct it?_____

20. Can you give us any other information about his speech?_____

21. How sensitive is the child about his defect?_____

22. Is he scolded or teased about it?..

23. Can the child carry a tune? Is his hearing normal?.....................

Voice Cases—General

1. Is the subject able to produce any voice at all? Has he ever lost his voice? Has he ever overstrained it?...

2. What differences appeared after puberty?.....................................

3. Can the subject carry a tune alone? In unison?.............................

4. What throat diseases or injuries has he had?.................................

5. Is his voice like that of any other member of the family or any habitual companion?..
6. What do you think caused the disorder?.......................................

7. Are there certain conditions or situations which make it worse? At what times is it most noticeable?...

8. Has the subject been under any prolonged emotional strain?

9. Is the child sensitive about his voice?...

10. What has been done to correct his voice defect?.......................

11. Has the child habitually spoken through clenched teeth or out of the side of his mouth for any length of time?.........................

12. Does the child do a lot of whining? Screeching?.......................

13. Does the child seem to be much more tense than the average child?..

14. Has the child ever talked in a monotone or used a peculiar pitch level?...

15. Does there seem to be any retardation in sexual development?

Nasality and Denasality

1. Has the child's voice always been nasal?.....................................

2. Are there times when he speaks without nasality? **When?**........

3. What vowels does he nasalize most?...............................

4. What consonants?...

5. Have his adenoids and tonsils been removed? When, and how bad were they?...

6. Has he ever had any injury to his nose or throat?...............

7. Do any others of the child's family or acquaintances speak in a nasal tone?..

8. Has the pitch of the child's voice always been about as high as it is now?...

9. Has the child been under any prolonged emotional tension or nervous strain? Is there anyone else in the family who shows such a condition?..

10. Is the child aware of his peculiar voice quality? Is he sensitive or ashamed about it?..

11. When he lowers his voice and relaxes, does he have as much nasality?...

12. Has the child suffered much from head colds or catarrh?........

13. Has the child ever had an operation on his nose?...............

14. Can the child gargle?..

15. Has the child ever had sinus trouble?...........................

Delayed-Speech Cases

1. Is the child superior, average, or inferior mentally?..........

2. Is the child hard-of-hearing?...................................

3. Has the child ever had any disease or trouble with his ears?

4. Are there any deaf people in the child's immediate family?....

5. Has the child ever shown short periods of speech?..............

6. Did the child ever have more speech than he does now?.........

7. Has the child ever uttered words under strong emotion which he has never said since?...

8. Has the child ever seemed to have periods when he could not understand other people's speech?....................................

9. Were there any injuries to the mouth?....................................

10. Were there any bad shocks during speech?....................................

11. Were there any serious illnesses during the first year?....................

12. Were two languages spoken in the home?....................................

13. Has the child ever been punished for speaking or during speech?

14. Is the child a twin?....................................
15. Did the parents overstimulate or understimulate the child?....

16. What people did the child dislike during the first two years?

17. Is the child ambidextrous?....................................
18. Was the child jealous of any other person?....................

19. Does the child use his silence as a way of getting more attention?....................................
20. Has the child ever had any sudden fainting spells? Paralysis?

21. Is the child isolated too much?....................................

22. How do the parents try to teach him to talk?....................

23. Are the child's wants usually anticipated and fulfilled before he expresses them?....................................

24. What sort of speech standard do the parents insist upon?........

25. What history of negativism is present?....................................

26. Check: threats; severe punishment; speech conflicts; competition for speech; impatience; attitudes of parents and other children....................................

Stuttering Cases

History of stuttering

1. Give approximate or exact date at which stuttering was first noticed......

2. Within the month immediately preceding the appearance of stuttering, did the child experience:
    a. A severe fright?......
    b. A severe shock of any kind?......
    c. Severe sickness with high fever?......
    d. Severe punishment?......
    e. A great deal of excitement or emotional upset?......
    f. A situation involving great need for immediate communication in which he was unable to say what he wanted to?......
    g. A situation involving communication but without sufficient vocabulary to enable him to continue?......
    h. A situation in which he tried but was unable to compete successfully for attention or speech?......
    i. A change in social environment?......
    j. Use of the nonpreferred hand?......
    k. Peculiarities in sexual behavior?......
    l. Thyroid disturbances?......
    m. Any other?......

3. Did any other defect occur at the same time that stuttering did?......

4. Who first noticed the stuttering?......

5. In what situation was it first noticed or commented upon? Under what circumstances did it occur?......

6. Were the first signs of stuttering repetitions of the whole word (boy-boy-boy); or repetitions of the first letter (b-b-boy); or repetitions of the first syllable (ca-ca-cat); or complete blocks on the first letter (b...oy); or prolongations of the vowel

(caaaaaaat)?

7. If repetitions, about how many times did they occur before the word came out?

    a. Were all signs of stuttering alike?

    b. Did the child stutter in several different ways?

    c. If so, in what ways did they differ from one another?

    d. Did the first blocks seem to be located in the tongue, lips, chest, diaphragm, or throat?

    e. About how long did each individual block (on one word) seem to last? (Imitate and time yourself.)

    f. Did the child stutter easily or exert some force, much force, or terrible forcing at the time when you first noticed his stuttering?

8. Were the words stuttered upon the words which began sentences, or were they scattered throughout the sentence?

9. Was the stuttering confined to one single word, or two or three words, or to no particular words?

10. Were there any particular sounds with which he seemed at first to have more trouble? If so, what were they?

11. When stuttering first began, did the child ever avoid a speech situation because of his stuttering? Give examples, if any

12. Did he pause noticeably before attempting a word?

13. Did he ever repeat a word until he had said it without stuttering?

14. Did he ever prolong a word preceding the word stuttered upon?

15. Did he ever repeat a phrase several times before attempting the word upon which he stuttered?

16. Having had trouble with a word in a sentence, did he ever repeat the whole sentence until it was said without any stuttering?...

17. Did he ever obviously substitute another word for one with which he was having trouble?...
....

18. Having stuttered upon a word, did he increase the rate, pitch, or intensity of the other words which followed it?....................
....

19. At the time when stuttering was first noticed, did the child seem to be aware of the fact that he was speaking in a different manner?...   ....

20. Did he seem to be indifferent to his blocks?..........................
....

21. Did he ever show surprise or bewilderment after he had had trouble on a word? If so, how did he show such reactions?......
....

22. Did the blocks at first seem to the stutterer to be unpleasant?
....

   a. Why do you think they were unpleasant, if they were?
....

   b. Do you think he felt irritated with himself? Frustrated?
....

   c. Did he ever show anger when anyone helped him with the word?..

   d. If not, what was his reaction?...
....

   e. Did he ever show any fear of stuttering?...........................
....

   f. If so, how did he show it?..
....

   g. Did he ever show any shame as a reaction to stuttering?
....

   h. If so, how did he show it?..
....

   i. Did he ever show any flushing? Paleness? Eye-bulging? Heart-pounding? Gasping? Sweating? Peculiar body movement as a reaction to his stuttering?........................
....

23. Did the child ever seem conscious of his stuttering in any way at first? If so, amplify your answer. After having a lot of trouble on a word, did he ever:

a. Suddenly stop trying?_____
b. Suddenly leave the speech situation?_____

c. Shout the word? Cry? Hit someone? Smash something? Spit upon somebody? Hide his face? Laugh? Do something else?_____

d. Seem to be a little more careful with his speech in attempting words on which he had difficulty? How? By lowering voice? By slowing down? By ceasing other bodily activity for the moment? By looking straight ahead of him for the moment? By shifting his gaze away from the listener? Any other way?_____

24. What attempts have been made to treat the child for his stuttering?_____

25. At the time when stuttering was first noticed, were there any situations in which he seemed to have more trouble? If so, what were they?_____

26. Were there any people to whom he stuttered more often? Who?

27. Were there any topics of conversation with which he had more trouble?_____

28. Did he seem to have more trouble when narrating something?

29. When asking questions?_____
30. When answering questions?_____
31. When interrupting?_____
32. Did he ever stutter when overheard talking to himself?_____

33. Did he talk to children with less trouble than to adults?_____

34. Did excitement seem to cause more stuttering?_____

35. Did he talk to strangers with less trouble than to people he knew well?_____

36. At the time when stuttering began, did fatigue, fear, illness, or pressing need for communication seem to cause more trouble?

37. Did he stutter more on words which were new to him and which he had not used or did not use often as yet?_____

38. Did he stutter more or stutter less on words which he had been using a long time—that is, "pet" words or stock phrases?........

39. Did the child speak any languages besides English? Which ones? Did he stutter more or less in these languages than in English?.................

40. When talking without stuttering, did he seem more active generally and more animated or lively—"more in the spirit of speaking"—than when stuttering?.................

41. When saying something on the spur of the moment—blurting it out as though he had given no thought to what he was going to say—did he stutter more or less than when he seemed to decide what he was going to say before speaking?.................

Development of stuttering

1. Since the stuttering first began, has there been any change in the stuttering symptoms?.................

2. Did you notice a gradual increase in the number of repetitions per word stuttered upon?.................

3. Did you notice a gradual increase in the number of times the stuttering occurred?.................

4. Were there any instances in which the number of troublesome words and number of repetitions suddenly increased?.................

5. Were there any periods (week or month) when this seemed to have occurred?.................

6. Can you give any explanation for these "bad" periods?.................

7. If possible, give their approximate dates and causes.................

8. Did there seem to be any period of change from repetitions as the usual form of stuttering to complete blocks (b-b-boy to b...oy)?.................

9. Was there ever a time in which repetitions began to end in complete (though temporary) blocks (b b b...oy)?.................

10. Was there ever any time when complete blocks were released in the form of repetitions (b.....b boy)?.................

11. Has there been an increase in the length of time the complete block lasts? (Was it "b..oy" at first, and "b........oy" now?)
....
....

12. When the complete blocks first appeared, upon what sounds or words were they noticed?...
....

13. Did the child force when the complete blocks were first experienced or was there a mere holding of the posture until release came?...

14. Did the amount of forcing increase as time passed?...................
....

15. Did it seem to be localized in any particular part of the speech organs, at first: lips, tongue, jaws, throat, chest, entire body?
....

16. Did there seem to be any spreading of the forcing from one of the above speech organs to others? Explain...................................
....

17. Did the stutterer ever force on the repetitions of sound or syllable?...

18. If the stutterer has any facial spasms or grimaces, give approximate date of their first occurrence, and describe their nature (how they look, what he does, etc.). Can you account for their appearance? Explain what you think caused them.......................
....

Index